A Square Deal All Round

The History Of Perkins Engines: 1932 - 2006

David Boulton

DEDICATION

This book is dedicated to the original pioneers, Frank Perkins and Charles Chapman, whose vision and persistence live on in the products of today.

A Square Deal All Round

The History Of Perkins Engines: 1932 - 2006

David Boulton

ISBN: 978-1-84306-349-0

First Edition

A catalogue record of this book is available from the British Library

Author: David Boulton

Printed and Bound by: Cromwell Press Limited.
Designed and Published by: Landmark Publishing Limited.
Edited by: Ian Howe

Photo Credits
All photographs used are taken from Perkins' Archives unless otherwise stated

Designed & Published for Perkins Engines
by Landmark Publishing

Landmark Publishing, Ashbourne Hall, Cokayne Ave, Ashbourne, Derbyshire, DE6 1EJ

Forewords & Acknowledgements

Frank Perkins, entrepreneurial genius, was a man of unusual vision and confidence. He was also quick to see the potential in others and formed a partnership with an extraordinary engineer, Charles Chapman.

The story is a classic tale of engineering triumph and the book opens with a candid account of two men starting an enterprise amidst the effects of a worldwide economic depression. Driven by a single vision of success they brought to the world a new concept in diesel power- the compact high-speed diesel.

Therein is our heritage. As you read the book you will enjoy, I'm sure, visiting all the facets of what has made us to be recognised today as 'The Industry Experts'. Explore what has guided us, and the risks taken along the way. Experience our relationship with suppliers, our distributors and those around us. And always, how from Frank's time to the present, Perkins has looked to surprise and delight customers. Along the way, you will also see many examples of integrity, excellence, commitment and certainly, teamwork. Assets that today we know as our values.

The diesel engine has certainly helped to change the world for the benefit of all; it remains at the heart of our future and that of the Perkins' brand. Undoubtedly, we take great pride in the work of all those that helped to make Frank's vision come true. Today as we celebrate that success, I am sure that we will be just as proud of all those that are now building a future for the Perkins' name - in tomorrow's world.

Hans Haefeli

President, Perkins Engines

The story of Perkins Engines is a story of survival – against all probability in the early years and in the face of considerable adversity later. The importance of Perkins in the development of the high-speed diesel engine and its acceptance throughout the world is undeniable. The availability of cheap, economic and reliable power sources has been a powerful influence on the development of many nations, especially in the years following the Second World War. Frank Perkins and Charles Chapman may have started with a clear vision but even they could not have anticipated the level of success the company has enjoyed after the troubled early years.

When I offered to write this history after a conversation with Michael Baunton in 2000, I had no idea just what I was taking on. It had been clear to me for some time that this was a job waiting to be done, and that I probably knew as much as any other long-serving employee. The task of deciding what should be included, just what was important and especially what would be of interest not just to other employees –whether retired of otherwise – but also to the general public, was daunting. I hope that my work has achieved a sensible balance.

On the basis of it being impossible to satisfy all of the people all of the time, I tender my apologies unreservedly for anything left out or in any way found wanting. Errors, mistakes and omissions are mine alone: any opinions expressed in this narrative are also mine and must not be taken as those of Perkins' management, past or present.

I have failed to mention in the text the reason for choosing the title I have given to the book: it is simply one of the several interpretations put upon the famous Perkins trademark of four circles and the square. There have been various attempts to explain its origin and meaning, as may be seen from the short description in the Appendices; which the reader chooses to believe is not critical since the most important fact is that the logotype has survived and is known worldwide.

I am indebted to many people without whose input, advice and criticism this work would have been impossible. Although there are too many to mention individually, I must single out several individuals whose help and encouragement were especially valuable.

The late Martin Vulliamy was a mentor, friend and guide over many years, and the late Gordon Dawson CBE provided help, criticism and wisdom throughout my efforts: I wish both had lived to see the publication.

The help of Gordon Dawson, Ken Galloway, Ken Wright, Dereck Lambe, Terry Sismore, Russell Bennett, Bert Saville, Paul Rogerson, Mike Hawkins and Roy Chowings has been crucial during the development of the narrative. The other members of the Perkins Heritage Group have also played a major role, in particular Ian Stuart, David Corkill and Maureen Fenn for their assistance in identifying relevant pictures from the huge archive of photographs.

The written histories produced by the late Charles Chapman and Laurie Hancock, plus the more recent work of David Porteous – and the successive editors of the Echo – have all formed an essential part of my research. I am especially grateful to Hazel Chapman for permission to use many extracts from her father's manuscript in the early chapters of this work. The information gathered by the late Chris Thompson has also been invaluable, and I am grateful to his family for passing his archive material to me.

I have been granted unfettered access to archives and personnel within Perkins; my thanks to Michael Baunton, Hans Haefeli and his management team for their support and encouragement.

The unsung endeavours of the many 'squirrels' who had kept and stored so many documents and artefacts from the earlier years must also be acknowledged; my thanks to you all for passing these on to the Heritage Group. In the current age of computers and electronic files with limited life I have serious concerns for any future historian, who may not receive such tremendous help.

Every author depends upon the unstinting support of his publisher in making the raw manuscript fit for purpose: my thanks to Lindsey Porter and the team at Landmark Publishing for their patience with an amateur.

Finally, I must express my heartfelt thanks and gratitude to my wife, Anne, who has put up with innumerable piles of documentation around the house for the past six years. In addition she has painstakingly read through the drafts to correct my slips and bad grammar, and given me encouragement throughout.

David Boulton

Author

CONTENTS

CONTENTS

Mid-1932 was not a propitious time to float a new company. The worldwide depression was still very much a fact of life, and survival was difficult enough for established concerns, without adding the problems of starting from scratch with a novel and untried product, in a world suffering from the worst economic conditions for many years. This was the challenge facing Frank Perkins when he created F. Perkins Limited in June 1932. The circumstances might indicate that this was an act of desperation, undertaken by a man gambling on the future since all else seemed to be failing around him: I prefer to believe that it was more of a calculated risk, taken by a man with unusual vision and confidence. The later adoption by Frank Perkins of a phrase from Proverbs (29:18) – 'Where there is no vision, the people perish' – inscribed above the main door of the original Eastfield offices in 1947, perhaps suggests that he was later aware of some special vision. But such thinking (with the benefit of hindsight) is getting ahead of the story. We need to go back some years to understand the events leading up to that day.

Following the end of the First World War in 1918 there were years of serious reinvestment on both sides of the Atlantic. This was not just a question of rebuilding the ex-combatant countries and their industries, but also of coming to terms with the loss of much of the cream of a whole generation's young men. There was an impact too from new technologies and ideologies as they developed. Through the 1920s times were hard and got harder. By 1929 the economic difficulties being experienced in the USA culminated in the Wall Street Crash on 24 October, with a subsequent impact on the London Stock Market a few days later. Within a month there were joint talks between the American and British governments on ways to tackle the depression. It is not my intention to dwell on, or attempt to interpret, the historical facts behind the slump and its recovery, but it is as well to recall some basic figures:

1. In Great Britain unemployment rose from 1 million in June 1929 to 2 million in August 1930, peaking at over 2.7 million in 1931 before a slow recovery.

2. In the USA the figures rose more slowly, but no less catastrophically, from 7 million in April 1931 to a peak of 11.6 million in August 1932.

3. Germany also suffered severely, with unemployment at almost 5 million in 1931, not recovering until after 1933. Hyperinflation was also a tremendous burden.

There were many measures taken in an attempt to stem the slide. The Bank of England lending rate was at 2.5% in May 1931, a 22-year low, with borrowing from Bank of France and the New York Federal Banks helping to prop up the fading economy. In September 1931 Great Britain abandoned the Gold Standard, with 30% devaluation against the US Dollar, and in the following month a landside victory saw a 'National Government' replace Labour. In the next few months, the austerity measures already introduced were further reinforced by import duties and tariffs, rising to 30% on many goods and 33.3% on steel.

The problems in Britain were widespread. In particular the motor and aircraft industries were suffering, not only from poor sales but also from the inefficiencies resulting from too many small manufacturers chasing that small market. Among other industries similar conditions prevailed: in particular the makers of heavy agricultural and road-making equipment were in the middle of a crisis that had started some years previously. Here the need for change was also critical, and none more so than in a company named Agricultural and General

Frank Perkins, the founder

Engineers Limited, commonly referred to as A.G.E. And this is where our story could be said to start.

Formation of a 'conglomerate'

A.G.E. had been formed in 1919 as the result of some forward thinking by Thomas Lake Aveling and Frank Garrett, two industrialists who visualised the need to bring together companies with similar agricultural machinery businesses into a more powerful body, allowing rationalisation and improved efficiency. This proposal had been enthusiastically supported and promoted by Archibald W. Maconochie, an industrialist who had risen to fame and fortune during the war selling provisions such as soups, jams and pickles to the Armed Forces. He had considerable standing in the City being a director of the Great Eastern Railway amongst other interests. Rationalisation was needed in part to combat the effects following the Great War, when increased competition from American manufacturers had seriously undermined the British sales position in Australasia and South America, as well as in the USA. There were also losses following the revolution in Russia and the repudiation of debts by that new government. A further reason was the need for modernisation, to accelerate the change to the internal combustion engine within an industry that had been founded upon steam power. Although some firms approached to join the new group had declined the invitation, on 4 June 1919 A.G.E. was formed from the following companies, some of the best-known names in the agricultural machinery industry:

Blackstone & Co. Ltd (Stamford)

Barford and Perkins Ltd (Peterborough)

Aveling and Porter Ltd (Rochester)

Peter Brotherhood Ltd (Peterborough)

E.H. Bentall & Co. Ltd (Maldon)

Bull Motors Ltd (Stowmarket)

Charles Burrell & Sons Ltd (Thetford)

Burrells Hiring Co. Ltd (Thetford)

Clarkes Crank and Forge Co. Ltd (Lincoln)

Davey Paxman Ltd (Colchester)

Richard Garrett & Sons Ltd (Leiston)

James and Frederick Howard Ltd (Bedford)

L.R. Knapp & Co. Ltd (Clanfield)

E.R. & F. Turner Ltd (Ipswich)

The new concern took over all the shares of these constituent companies (with the exception of Peter Brotherhood Ltd, where only 70% of the shares were taken) in return for A.G.E. shares, at an agreed valuation. Archibald Machonochie was elected the first Chairman of the new Board, the remaining directors taken from the boards of the member companies. It has to be noted that the original directors made money from the creation of the company, since there was a 5% commission, taken in shares by the promoters of A.G.E., on the purchase price of every firm persuaded to join! Although there was good business sense in combining these companies, one of the first actions taken was the construction of a new headquarters, Aldwych House, in London. This office building had a large showroom for their products on the ground floor. A perceived need for a prestigious address seems to have over-ridden a more cautious approach, and such expenditure early in the existence of the company now appears ill-advised. It is

perhaps indicative of the expectations of the founding board of directors that they would make an impact on the post-war market and enjoy lasting success.

An early attempt to introduce centralised purchasing and sales from the new premises failed, perhaps due to the reluctance of the member companies to give up their independence of action. As a consequence the envisaged advantages of combined operations failed to materialise so that A.G.E. limped along in a disjointed manner, with individual directors and their companies avoiding the issues that needed to be addressed. The appointment of Gwilym E. Rowland as Managing Director in succession to Machonochie did little to resolve this situation. He learned the foibles and weaknesses of the other directors, and (according to Edward Barford in his autobiography) applied the process of 'divide and rule' to ensure that he got what he wanted! It is worth noting that Rowland was a shrewd businessman who had apparently made money during and after the war as a company tax expert, whereas most of his fellow directors were essentially country gentlemen, thrown into industrial life through an accident of their birth and their fathers' aspirations. There seems little doubt that Rowland traded on their ignorance of business methods and laws to his own advantage.

The change from the 'steam age'

There were, however, some positive signs that individual companies understood the impact of the new technologies. Moves towards shared premises saw Barford and Perkins vacate their premises in Peterborough at the end of the 1920s and relocate to Rochester, sharing the works occupied by Aveling and Porter. With both companies already

Directors Alan Richardson and Charles Chapman

successful producers of road rollers there must have been some interesting discussions regarding product lines to be pursued, although the small petrol-engine-powered rollers made by Barford were complementary to the larger rollers from Aveling. These were still mainly steam-powered, although developments with diesel engines were moving ahead. Another sign of change was the development of diesel engines by Blackstone. Brotherhoods already made spark ignition petrol engines which were being used by Barford and Perkins in their small rollers.

Towards the end of 1931, the signs of severe financial problems in A.G.E. became public, mainly forced by Edward Barford who, from his position as PA to Rowland, had seen practices that were contrary to the interests of the Group and perhaps fraudulent to boot. The resulting furore, and threatened legal actions, culminated in the resignation of G.E. Rowland and other senior members of the board. Thomas Aveling took over as Chairman to attempt to salvage something from the wreckage and restore confidence in the Company. However, this was too late: at the Annual General Meeting convened in February 1932 it was declared that the company had reached the end of its financial resources and proceedings were set in motion to wind it up.

At this time, Frank Perkins (FAP) was Works Director of Aveling and Porter, with Charles Wallace Chapman (CWC) recently appointed as Secretary to the Company. The original collaboration of Perkins and Chapman had come about in 1929, when Perkins had recruited Chapman as Chief Engineer from the wreckage of Vickers-Petters Ltd at Ipswich, another company that had fallen victim to the slump. Chapman had previously worked at Beardmores in Coatbridge, Scotland where he became interested in the potential of the diesel engine for vehicles. Perkins and Chapman were engaged in converting the Aveling and Porter products from steam to diesel power, using Blackstone horizontal engines. At the same time they were developing a 'high-speed' diesel engine to fit into an agricultural tractor to be made by Garrett at Leiston. This engine had four cylinders, with a bore of 4.38 and 6.38 inches stroke, and an output of 42.4 brake horsepower (bhp) at 1,150 rev/min (rpm). It was known as the 'Invicta', and was being produced in competition with a similar-sized engine to be made by Blackstone in Stamford. In 1931 (28 August according to Chapman) a further proposal was made to develop a six-cylinder version of the Invicta engine to power a modified Garrett lorry, their first move away from steam power for such vehicles. This engine was designed and produced in only two months, based upon the tractor engine design. However, it never made it to the Commercial Vehicle Exhibition on 30 October 1931, as had been the intention, although as Chapman noted, '*the experience came in useful later*'! It is worth noting that the prototype tractor engines completed proving trials successfully, including a 1,000-hour field trial, but only a handful were produced.

Charles Chapman had already been present for the bankruptcy of both Beardmores and Petters, his first two employers; soon after his appointment as Secretary of Aveling and Porter he discovered what was entailed in being secretary of a subsidiary of a group on the verge of bankruptcy. In his words he 'became an expert at paying wages out of an overdraft we weren't allowed to have, and in persuading suppliers to let us have materials on three or six months credit, backed by Bills we hoped we could eventually meet'.

As the winding up of the Company progressed, Perkins and Chapman met from time to time and inevitably discussed their future. They recognised that jobs in the engineering industries were hard to come by, especially at senior level. At one point they even considered buying a laundry in Sevenoaks but Frank Perkins was convinced that there was potential in the small diesel engine for road vehicle use; he suggested that if they could not find a suitable company they should consider raising sufficient capital to start their own venture. Charles Chapman was equally enthusiastic about the future for the diesel and they

talked around the possibilities, even considering the purchase of the rights to the Invicta engine since both men considered it was capable of reaching production. Further reflection, however, convinced them that such a course was doomed to failure, since there were proven engines available already, competing for a limited volume in the depressed truck market.

The fateful decision is made

Chapman recalls that the birth pangs of Perkins diesels could be said to have started one evening in March 1932 at his house in Strood, Kent. Frank Perkins had travelled to visit him by train from Whitstable. Their discussions concluded that if they could design and develop a diesel engine small enough to fit into private cars, light vans and 30cwt trucks, not only were there no competitors but they would be tapping an enormous and expanding market. However, they recognised that the engine would have to be as small as the existing petrol engines, have similar power and an operating speed to take advantage of the existing transmission systems – a tall order given than at that time a 'high-speed' diesel engine probably ran no faster that 1,500rpm whereas a typical petrol engine in a car would run up to 4,000rpm. There were also questions regarding the fuel injection equipment and its ability to handle very small amounts of fuel at the rotational speeds envisaged, to say nothing of the control of costs, since the benefits of economy would be worthless if the engine proved too expensive to build and sell. At that time there was no diesel engine operating that approached the size and operating parameters they were considering: this was truly a moment of history, where more cautious men might have decided the risks were too great to proceed!

The evening's discussion continued, however, with Chapman making notes about the basic design of the combustion chamber and injection system on the back of an envelope; at this moment the concept which became the Perkins 'Aeroflow' combustion system was born. They decided that around 40 bhp would be a reasonable starting point, and believed that a four-cylinder engine of 3-inch bore should achieve this goal.

It was with the question of financing that their deliberations continued, and almost foundered. Frank Perkins was confident that he could raise around £10,000 for initial financing, this sum being envisaged as adequate to cover the first two years' work, at the end of which they were hopeful of having an engine promising enough to sell. Their optimism was sufficient to believe that having reached that point, raising further finance to cover production start-up costs would be easier! Sets of figures were worked out, pared down and further reworked, on the assumption that they would start with a full-sized four-cylinder prototype, avoiding the experimental stage of a single- cylinder engine to establish the initial performance parameters.

Eventually they had a set of figures that came to £10,000 and appeared to include enough time and labour to attain the initial objectives. This included the need for Frank Perkins to take out a provisional patent on the combustion system (as Chapman was still nominally Chief Engineer of the Aveling Diesel Department he could not legally do this) and to attempt to raise the necessary capital. They had set their own salaries at £750 and £540 per annum for FAP and CWC respectively. By this stage it was getting late, so Charles Chapman got out his car to drive Frank Perkins to the station, and almost ended the partnership before it began by having a heavy collision with a truck which was running on only one (nearside) headlight! Both men were very fortunate that they were only slightly injured, although the car was written off. This was to be but the first of many near disasters for the young company in its early years of existence.

The winding-up of the affairs of A.G.E. took time, the results being mixed for the constituent companies within the Group. Barford and Perkins combined with Aveling and Porter to form Aveling-Barford

17 Queen Street, where it all started

Limited, eventually relocating to Grantham. This was masterminded by Edward Barford, who also persuaded Ruston and Hornsby of Lincoln, Ransomes, Sims and Jefferies of Ipswich and R.A. Lister of Dursley to help finance the purchase of the two companies from the Official Receiver. Garretts, along with Burrells (who had already relocated to the Garrett works at Leiston), were sold off to Beyer, Peacock and Co. Ltd. Brotherhoods and Blackstones managed to survive through management actions which regained their autonomy. Thus by April 1932 Frank Perkins and Charles Chapman were in a position to free themselves for their new enterprise. They had the assistance of a number of key figures whose importance in the story of F. Perkins Ltd cannot be overestimated.

First amongst these was Mr George Dodds Perks, one-time Chairman of Aveling and Porter and a board member of A.G.E. A solicitor by profession, he had been a mentor to the younger FAP as he made his mark in the A.G.E. businesses. Whatever losses he suffered did not appear to have caused him any lasting financial embarrassment, and he was one of the first men to be approached by Frank Perkins.

The second key figure was Captain Alan Joseph MacDonald Richardson, a country landowner, farmer and brother-in-law of FAP. Alan had met and married Claudia Williams some time before Frank met and married her sister Gwyneth: their families remained in close touch, with Alan being godfather to the first Perkins child. Chapman relates that 'Captain Dick' (as he became known) had suggested to Frank that with the family business no longer in existence it would be a good idea to start some new combined business; when the diesel idea was mooted he offered to help finance it, provided that G.D. Perks (who knew FAP's business qualities) was also supportive.

The third key figure was Frank's father, J.E.S. Perkins, who knew the other supporters and whose connections in Peterborough proved instrumental in providing the first premises for the embryo business. John Edward Sharman Perkins had graduated from King's College London in 1884 and had joined his father, Thomas, in the family business, Barford and Perkins in Peterborough. He eventually succeeded his father as Joint Managing Director, alongside Edward Barford. That company, founded in 1840, occupied old and sprawling premises in Queen Street, in the centre of the city, which had been an ironworks for many years. They graduated from making general agricultural equipment and machinery to the manufacture of lawn mowers and road rollers, later pioneering the use of petrol engines in a new small roller using an engine design by Brotherhoods. With the move to Rochester the Queen Street premises had become disused and were in the hands of a local estate agent. It was proposed that the new company could make use of a small part of the rambling and antiquated works.

Formation of the new company

Frank Perkins typed out, on 10 April 1932, a document he titled 'Original Prospectus' for a new company to be called 'F. Perkins Ltd, Engineers'. The document is reproduced elsewhere in this book and is, like most such documents, optimistic in its outlook. On 7 June 1932 the Company was registered, with an authorised capital of £12,000 and offices at 17 Queen Street. The Ordinary Shares of £1 each were taken up as follows:

Mr G.D. Perks	£5,000
Captain A.J.M. Richardson	£2,500
Mr J.E.S. Perkins	£2,500
Mr F.A. Perkins	£1,000
Mr C.W. Chapman	£350

There were other reasons for using Peterborough as a base. The name of Perkins was well known in the district (not only for the Barford connection but also for the unrelated Baker Perkins), there was

a reasonable pool of engineering labour available due to the other industries, while the position of the city on the railway not far from London and the Midlands was also conveniently close to potential suppliers and customers.

While these arrangements were being decided, Charles Chapman had finally finished with Aveling and Barford, handing in his letter of resignation on 12 April 1932. He immediately started work on the design of the first engine. He was assisted by Mr W.F. Pailing who had been employed in charge of the diesel drawing office at Aveling. Bill Pailing had gone to work temporarily at Ford in Dagenham but was persuaded to join the new venture: while the office arrangements were being sorted at Peterborough he started doing sectional arrangements of the proposed engine, working with a drawing board on his dining table. The design grew, with lengthy arguments about the details, since CWC wanted to keep all dimensions to a minimum, with siamesed cylinder bores, minimal crankshaft webs, etc., aimed at keeping the diesel as small as possible to compete with the petrol engine's size and weight. As the design took shape, sketches of parts were sent out to prospective suppliers since they did not have printing facilities. During this early period, Bill Pailing's wife acted as secretary, typing up letters on the kitchen table using a typewriter belonging to Frank Perkins.

Chapman commented about the reception from two possible suppliers of pistons at this time. One did not deign to reply at all but the other made a personal call: Eric Dennis of Automotive Engineering of Twickenham not only accepted the embryo company as he found it, but also took the time to give advice on the design and offered to make samples when they were ready to start. It is no wonder that Automotive Engineering remained a supplier to Perkins for many years.

17 Queen Street

By June the basic design was completed, the Company was registered and the offices in Queen Street ready for occupation. Thus on a Saturday in June the staff of F. Perkins Ltd took up residence in Peterborough; by now they numbered seven, since along with the four directors there were three employees. Bill Pailing has already been introduced but alongside him were Ted Marvill and Denis Hughes, both recruited from Avelings. Edward Marvill was an apprentice draughtsman and the son of their ex-Chief Draughtsman, whilst Hughes was an ex-Navy artificer who had been in charge of the field testing of the Invicta engine in the Garrett tractor. Within a matter of weeks two local girls were engaged too, Muriel Andrews as typist and a Miss Elphee as a tracer, each being paid 30 shillings a week. It is interesting to note that Muriel had originally started work at Barford and Perkins as a typist at the tender age of 17, fresh from the Peterborough Commercial School.

The offices at 17 Queen Street were hardly palatial, consisting of two rooms downstairs, a staircase leading to a big room upstairs, with a lavatory on the landing. Initially they occupied just the downstairs, with the front room as the General Office housing all the staff under Bill Pailing, with the Managing Director (FAP) and Technical Director (CWC) plus secretary sharing the tiny back room.

The priority was to complete the detail designs, a task shared between Pailing, Marvill and Hughes (who soon learned how to draw the simpler parts). As each drawing was ready it was given a number and prints were made, using a very old and basic blueprint machine in the corner of the office; copies were then sent out for quotation. The requests were simple and bold, on the basis of having to be right first time. Prices were requested for quantities of six, one hundred and one thousand sets of parts, the unspoken hope being that they could finance at least the initial six! Where necessary, visits were made to discuss the design, the tooling and the possibility of continuity of later supply on the assumption of getting into production. From comments made by Chapman, and the recollection of the high unemployment of the time, it is clear that many plants were lying idle, or at very low production levels: small wonder that any new possibility was being viewed with optimism.

It appears that a considerable amount of the procurement and machining of parts was done using Peter Brotherhood, just up the road in Lincoln Road, another survivor of the A.G.E. collapse. Some limited recollections from their archives suggest that the business from Perkins was a godsend in the period when little new work was coming in. For those of us whose memories are limited to the occasional prob-lems of the 70s and 80s it is impossible to understand just how bad the economic conditions were. Even in an area of limited industrial employment such as Peterborough the impact of the depression was severe, whilst elsewhere an increased crime rate was identified with the high unemployment level. Later in the year there were hunger marches and rioting in London as desperation grew with the onset of winter. It was against this background of pessimism and despair, therefore, that the optimists Chapman and Perkins took the next steps to put their new venture on to the map.

y the autumn of 1932 the new company had grown further. Frank Perkins had negotiated a lease of a small part of the stores building across Queen Street in the old Barford and Perkins works to act as a workshop, at a cost of £75 per annum. The first works employees had been signed on. Norman Burney was the first, at 75 shillings for a 47-hour week: he too had been at Aveling and Barford, working on the assembly and testing of the experimental engines. Norman's first job was to prepare the workshop to receive the engine parts as they arrived and in due course to build the first unit. A bench was obtained, and a coke stove to heat the shop, followed by an adjustable test stand, along with a Heenan DPX4 hydraulic dynamometer. Norman Burney remained with Perkins for thirty years until his death in 1962. The second works employee appeared in November when Ted Sell was signed on as general assistant-cum-millwright at 30 shillings a week. By this time further tools were being procured, with measuring equipment too, to ensure that all parts could be accurately inspected when they arrived.

By Christmas 1932, Chapman recounts that the weekly wage bill had gone up to eleven pounds and fifteen shillings, whilst capital expenditure had already reached £3,254. However, by that time the first engine had been run!

The first engine is tested – and christened

The initial highlight had been the arrival of the first cylinder block from Beans, a specialist iron foundry in the Midlands, to admiration by the whole workforce. Then other components began to arrive, to the point where the first engine could be assembled carefully. Meanwhile the test bed was positioned and secured on girders bolted to the floor and aligned with dynamometer. An exhaust system was rigged, discharging into the yard (they had no access but merely knocked a hole through). A fuel tank was bolted to the wall nearby, allowing gravity feed to the engine. The exhaust system was arranged with a flap valve so that the colour of the exhaust could be assessed: the crude test was whether the plume was visible or not, the term 'JV' being coined for an acceptable, 'just visible' smoke. Came the day, almost exactly six months from the formation of the Company, when Norman Burney reported that all was ready to mount the engine to the bed: Charles Chapman's reminiscences recall that it was a Saturday, prob-

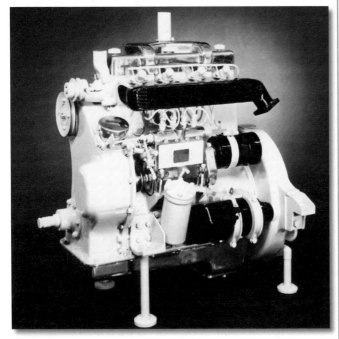

One of the early Wolf engines

ably 4 December 1932.

All hands set to work, coupling the engine and overchecking that all parts were tightened and aligned, the fuel tank filled, the engine topped up with lubricating oil and the water system primed. The fuel system was bled through progressively until no air was visible bubbling from the pump or injector pipes. The injectors were primed and 'pinged' as their needle valves opened and fuel sprayed into the combustion chambers. At last all was ready and Bill Pailing was elected, as the strongest, to turn the engine over, using the starting handle since electric starters were an optional extra! A string was attached to the fuel pump rack and held by Norman Burney so that once the engine started it could be stopped again quickly should the need arise. After a few careful turns to ensure everything was free Bill Pailing heaved on the handle, with a quick 'snap' over the compression – all waited for the 'woomph' as the engine fired. Nothing happened; the flywheel gave half a turn, oscillated and came to rest! He tried again, and again, stopping to remove his jacket, and then tried many more times. This continued for some hours without any sign of firing from the engine. Chapman reckoned that eventually the engine got called 'bitch' and soon after was christened 'Vixen' as a more acceptable name!

As daylight faded everybody had a turn and were getting tired enough to call it a day, Bill Pailing had a brainwave. The Vixen, in common with the later Perkins engines with the 'Aeroflow' combustion system, had detachable caps (or covers) on each combustion chamber in the cylinder head; he suggested that these be removed and really heated up to see if the problem was lack of heat to initiate combustion. The caps were duly removed and heated by suspending them on wires in the coke stove, which was stoked up to a fierce heat. Once the combustion caps were glowing they were removed from the stove and replaced in position. Just how this was done is not recorded - viewing the cylinder head on the early engine suggests that this was achievable only at great risk of burnt fingers! Once all were positioned Pailing tried again on the starting handle, the engine fired and picked up speed rapidly as all four cylinders came in. In their haste, or maybe fatigue, the water to the dynamometer had not been turned on so that the rev counter raced up beyond 2,000rpm before someone grabbed the string and pulled the fuel pump rack closed, stopping the engine. Thus the first Perkins engine completed its first run, and Frank Perkins suggested they call it a day and celebrate. With the time approaching 6pm the team cleaned themselves up and moved down Queen Street to the Bay's Wine Shop for a few drinks.

The following days were spent in getting to know the engine, and especially how to start it. Filling the water system with hot water, boiled up on the coke stove, appears to have been the preferred method so that performance runs could be made and the engine 'tuned' gradually to provide better output. This was done over a period, using short runs to measure the various parameters and check the effect of different adjustments. They finally reached 80 pounds/ square inch brake mean effective pressure (bmep) at 1,500rpm, seen as a fair figure for a small engine at that time (when 100lbs/sq.in. bmep from a larger engine could be achieved).

Problem solving

After this period of performance checking and adjustment, one day Chapman left Norman Burney to run for a period at 1,500rpm to check consistency of power and fuel consumption. After a time, Chapman returned to the shop to see how things were progressing. Norman told him that the engine was behaving oddly: every fifteen minutes or so the engine started knocking then the speed increased and the load on the brake showed the equivalent of 100lbs/sq.in.

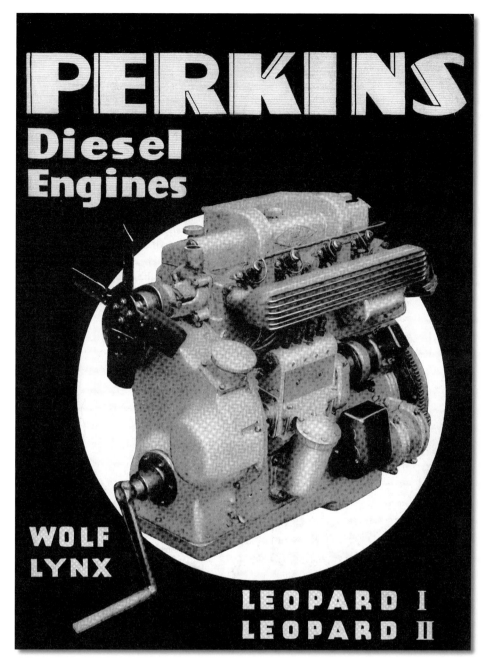

PERKINS
Diesel
Engines

WOLF
LYNX

LEOPARD I
LEOPARD II

An early brochure which gave
technical details and dimensions
for the first engines

An early brochure which gave
technical details and dimensions
for the first engines

Accordingly, a sketch was made and a set of injectors ordered. Once received, they were tried and found not only to give extra power, but also to ease the starting problems. Through such incidents are engineering developments and breakthroughs made, allowing for correct diagnosis and remedial actions of course! Thus early in 1933 they found themselves with an engine which could run at 3,000rpm or even up to 4,000rpm, gave competitive power for a diesel and had a reasonably low fuel consumption. Although starting was not always immediate, needing a judicious spray of paraffin into the air intake on occasion, it was relatively easy by hand cranking or by electric motor.

At a Board Meeting on 19 January 1933 the progress was reviewed and it was agreed to put in hand 24 engines, with orders placed for 100 sets of the smaller and less expensive parts. Against the optimistic tentative plans made in mid-1932, this was good progress and confirmed the confidence the two principals had in their abilities. A proportion of the parts, and their machining, was contracted from Peter Brotherhood Limited. Exactly what this work consisted of is not now clear, although as noted in Chapter 1 the Brotherhoods' records suggest that they were grateful for this business at the difficult time.

The first search for customers

While the engine development had been proceeding, Frank Perkins had been contacting potential customers to stimulate their interest in the new product. Among these were Colonel Cole, Chairman of Humber Cars, and Thomas Keep, Managing Director of Commer at Luton; both companies would later become members of the Rootes Group. As a direct result, Perkins purchased a Hillman car, minus engine, to install one of the prototype engines, and Mr Keep sent a 30cwt Commer chassis for a second trial installation. (Although the Perkins records refer to the car as a 'Wizard', this is disputed by Russell Bennett, who insists the vehicle was a 'Vortic'. I have been unable to trace a photograph of the latter but it is certain that both were in production in the early 30s.)

The car was completed first and was possibly the first true diesel-powered car in the world (although Daimler-Benz might contest such a claim). It is possible to imagine the pride and hope that accompanied that first vehicle when the engine was started and it first moved under its own power. Although visually indistinguishable from its petrol-powered counterpart, Chapman comments that the engine 'had a healthy diesel "knock" at idle and the front wings rather flapped about from the vibration'. These effects disappeared as the engine speed increased, however, and on the road the engine seemed smooth at any speed above 20mph in top gear. On the level the car would reach 50mph, with the engine turning over at slightly over 3,000rpm, and

bmep. After about half a minute it would drop back to the original speed and load. Chapman stayed to watch and sure enough after a few minutes it repeated the trick: a check on the exhaust showed clouds of grey smoke. They waited for a repeat and stopped the engine immediately, then removed the cylinder head cover – hot lubricating oil immediately gushed out over the engine. A close inspection of the engine parts eventually determined that the problem was due to lubricating oil being unable to drain quickly enough down the return passage drilled to the sump, but instead building up in the cylinder head. Eventually it was sucked down the two small holes drilled between the cylinder head cover and the intake ports for crankcase ventilation; the resulting small quantity of oil each stroke gave extra power. This discovery initiated a debate on the reason why this should generate power when extra fuel sprayed via the injector did not. The discussion concluded that there might be merit in trying an injector with two holes instead of one, with fuel directed not just into the passageway to the combustion chamber (as the original patented design) but also with a spray directed into the cylinder itself, mimicking the effect of oil being present there. The sense behind the proposal was that the air trapped between the piston and cylinder head in such a small engine was unavailable for combustion in the original design, this air amounting to perhaps one third of the effective compressed charge.

Pictured in Helsinki with the Hillman car with Wolf engine en route to Moscow in 1934 are Frank Perkins (right) and Charles Chapman (centre)

would cruise quite happily at that speed. Trials continued around Peterborough without mishap.

Chapman relates that some time later, maybe in early April, Frank Perkins asked him to join him on a business trip to Perth and suggested they use the Hillman. They set off early one morning sharing the driving. With stops for breakfast and lunch they arrived in Perth for a late tea, having run 360 miles uneventfully at the car's 50mph cruising speed and averaged around 40mph.

The following morning, after FAP had completed his business, he suggested they go and try a real hillclimb on the road from Amulree to Kenmore. (These days this is a narrow metalled road, but in the 1930s it was apparently little more than a mountain track.) With four aboard the car they set off, up a road which in places is steeper than 1 in 4, and before long the radiator was boiling furiously, there being no fan fitted to help cooling at low road speed. There was no option but to continue to the top, where they stopped to let the engine cool, eventually topping the radiator up before returning to Perth. With no apparent ill effects the next day, FAP decided to tour around a little instead of taking the direct route back to Peterborough. Accordingly they set off northwards, passing through Braemar, Balmoral and Tomintoul before swinging west to Grantown to pick up the main road south to Kingussie and Blair Atholl before returning to Perth. All of this was done with no spare parts being carried, nor anything other than the car's standard toolkit, over quite desolate country on poorly surfaced roads. CWC relates that this didn't seem to perturb FAP at all, although he himself had some misgivings at times:

'It was on the stretch from Blairgowrie to Braemar that I first began to feel perturbed. I was driving and the car had been running beautifully, but it gradually seemed to be labouring a little. I had never been on that road before but so far as I could tell we were on a level part running alongside a glen and should have been slipping along at 45 to

50 mph but the car didn't want to do more than 30. I suspected that the boiling the previous day had done something to the engine but said nothing to Frank and changed down to third, hoping the engine would pick up. It didn't. It slowed again and in desperation I changed down to second, which seemed a little easier. Then there seemed to be a slight rise in the road as it bent to the left and I hoped we would top it but the engine began to labour so I did a really quick change down to bottom. As we breasted the steep little stretch ahead I saw a notice – "Devil's Elbow, Danger". We had climbed the Devil's Elbow which was 1 in 5, without my even noticing until the last few yards that we were on a hill!'

The journey back to Peterborough was accomplished without any incident, and the pair were pleased with a successful outing for their prototype engine. Any lasting pleasure soon evaporated, however, when the second engine was installed in the Commer truck chassis and driven back to Luton for test: Chapman comments that 'I think it was in connection with this vehicle that the phrase "couldn't pull the skin off a rice pudding" was invented.' Commer didn't think much of the engine, which was really too small for the truck. It was replacing a six-cylinder petrol unit of about 50% greater capacity.

More power is needed

An emergency meeting was held, since if there was no way to satisfy their first truck customer it was unlikely they could go elsewhere. As the engine was already operating at 100lb/sq.in. bmep it seemed unlikely any uprating was possible. After some discussion somebody suggested a capacity increase by boring the cylinders out from 75mm to 80mm diameter, since theoretically the increased capacity should give an extra 14% torque. They decided that there was sufficient metal between the bores to allow this increase, so new pistons, rings and gasket were ordered for urgent delivery while a block was machined. With general manufacturing still in the doldrums the parts appeared

An early advertisement used a letter from Alan Richardson praising his 'Wolf' powered car

quickly and the engine was built. It was decided to rename this version the 'Fox' and it was swiftly installed in the Commer, where an improved performance was certainly achieved. The views of Mr Keep soon dashed their rekindled hopes, however. He commented that, although it might be just adequate for the thirty hundredweight, since Commer fitted the same petrol engine in a two-ton truck it was clear that the Fox would still not be capable of an acceptable performance.

A further conference ensued and in desperation the partners agreed to try a further increase of 5mm on the cylinder bore whilst keeping all other dimensions as the original Vixen (so that the 100 sets of parts already ordered could still be used). With the torque increased by almost 30% over the first engine, but with the overall length not changed, the engine would still fit the installation. However, there was little metal left between the cylinder bores and the head-securing studs, while the bearing loads would increase beyond what was considered 'safe'. At a Board Meeting on 12 April this course of action was agreed, with two engines to be built and the necessary new parts ordered to build a further batch of 24 units with 85mm bore.

The first engines of this size, now named 'Wolf', were rushed through build and test so that one could be fitted in the Commer truck before the end of June 1933. This time the Commer engineers agreed that the performance achieved was acceptable, and that the engine could be considered a commercial proposition. An agreement between Humber, the parent company, and F. Perkins Ltd., was sealed in October 1933. It was agreed to show a Perkins engine at the Commercial Vehicle Exhibition later that year, and to offer the engine as a more costly alternative to the petrol engine in Commer vehicles. Thus the first agreement with an original equipment manufacturer was gained, after much (often panic) action.

While this important business was being negotiated, FAP had engaged Captain G.R. Greenbergh as part-time Sales Manager. Greenbergh was associated with Pagefield Commercial Vehicles Ltd of Wigan, who manufactured refuse carriers; in conjunction with that enterprise an office was opened in Pall Mall, at Quadrant House. They rented a suite of three rooms at a rent of £135 per annum. The main job given to Greenbergh was to persuade motor dealers to become Perkins agents, and to sell the new diesel engine as a conversion to replace the petrol engines in existing trucks. At the end of June 1933 the Board agreed to fix the price of the Wolf to Main Agents at £172, with lower prices for fitment as original equipment. CWC comments that to his recollection the first conversion was for Mr T. Seymour Mead of Manchester, in a somewhat ancient van. With several dealers showing interest, in addition to the Commer agreement, a further batch of 25 engine sets of Wolf parts was ordered.

The first financial crisis

In July 1933 a review of the finances of the Company showed that of the original £10,000 there was only about £1,000 remaining. Since the engine parts cost about £80 per set, and they had already committed to some 100 sets of the small parts and 75 sets of the larger components such as blocks, heads, crankshafts and fuel injection equipment, there was an impending liability of around £8,000 which the company did not have: the few orders received did not begin to cover such expenditure. The manager of Barclays Bank in Peterborough soon dispelled any optimism they had about sitting on a goldmine, since Mr Grimwade reminded them that speculation was not their kind of business. Frank Perkins's suggestion that the bank could take a lien on the undertaking met with a certain amount of derision. 'What undertaking?' was the immediate question, and a valid one, since the company owned no premises or plant, or even equipment worth more than a few hundred pounds. Apart from some sympathy the only positive help forthcoming was the promise of an overdraft of £3,000 against personal guarantees from Messrs Perks and Richardson.

The offer was duly reported to the next Board Meeting, where the prospective guarantors dismissed such 'help' by advising that they would prefer to put up the money themselves. Thus the additional £5,000, which Chapman had estimated would see them through to the end of 1933, was covered by an unsecured loan (at 7.5% interest tax-free) from the directors – Mr Perks advancing £2,000, Alan Richardson £1,950 and Edward Perkins £650. It transpired that this was sufficient, with a struggle, since the Company finished the year with £188 in the bank and £14 5s in petty cash but 'with hope in our hearts', in Chapman's words.

It is interesting to review the first road test of the Commer Centaur 2-ton truck fitted with a Wolf engine: this appeared in the Commercial Motor of 6 October 1933. The headlines announce: 'Exacting Trials Reveal Excellent Road Performance. Flexibility a Marked Characteristic.' The article notes that this is the world exclusive announcement of the entry into production of the Commer/Perkins combination, regarding this as an epoch-marking event, since this was the first production release of a diesel-powered truck at 30cwt and 2-ton capacity. After a detailed description of the engine and the installation the road test results, around the Bedford area close to the Commer works, are described. It is clear that this was the first prototype, with less than 100 miles under its wheels at the time of test, yet hill-climbing, overall liveliness and fuel economy are praised. The lack of governing is commented upon, with the engine being noted as noisier 'above 3,000 revs/min'! The quoted figures of 24.9mpg at an average speed of 17.25mph over a hilly main road course may not be seen as impressive for a vehicle of just over 4 tons gross weight today, but clearly for the time it was a worthy achievement. This road test had been preceded by the announcement of the engine in the 6 May 1933 edition of the magazine; the closing paragraph is interesting if only because the author has found no other reference to the subject matter:

'We understand from F Perkins Ltd. that the American manufacturing rights of this engine for industrial purposes are already provisionally taken up, and that applications have been received from several European countries.'

Fact or journalistic licence? We will probably never know!

At the end of 1933 the total sales revenue totalled £6,701 for about 45 engines. Overall trading, however, was still well in the red, and the first balance sheet of the Company, following its first 18 months of existence, did not make optimistic reading.

The total loss of £7,500 was offset however by the creation of a 'Development Account' which credited some £3,900 against the future on the grounds of the engine development done during the period; the remaining loss of £3,600 was deemed 'disappointing' in the report to shareholders but with confidence that the next year would show a profit on the expected larger turnover.

The start of 1934 saw some more active trading, with engines for conversions being sold along with the occasional batch for Commer. Attempts to interest other truck manufacturers, such as Albion and Dennis, saw no orders placed since both felt that there was no real market at two tons: the greater opportunity was felt to be at three to four tons, for which the Wolf was really too small and lacked power. One bright spot, however, was found in Welwyn where a Mr Crawford created a new works to produce a diesel-powered truck called the 'Arran Dieselet', for which the standard engine was the Perkins Wolf. Although orders for this new truck soon equalled those of Commer, there was no rapid increase in engine sales.

As a result of the comments made by prospective customers it was soon decided that an increased capacity engine was needed. Since the bore increases that resulted in the change from Vixen to Fox and finally to Wolf had reached the limit of stretch within the existing cylinder block, the decision was to increase both bore and stroke in a

I-ВЫЙ ПРИЗ

(Легкий класс Дизельский)

При соревновании в СССР

ДВИГАТЕЛЬ ПЕРКИНСА „ВОЛК" в 1½-тонном ГРУЗОВИКЕ „ГАЗ."

Разные тресты покупают Дизельские Двигатели Перкинса (типа „ВОЛК"), из которых один (легкий Класс Дизельский) заручился Первым Призом на Дизельском Соревновании 1934 г. Двигатель этот был подвергнут испытаниям, в соревновании с двигателями со всего света, с пробегом свыше 12,000 километров от Москвы до Кавказских Гор, и в продолжении 100 часов на испытательном станке.

Тип „ВОЛК" (40 Б.Л.С.) может быть доставлен с арматурой для установки в автомобилях „ГАЗ" или автогрузовиках, а тип „ЛЕОПАРД" (60 Б.Л.С.) имеется для 3-тонных грузовиков „АМО."

ДИЗЕЛЬСКИЕ ДВИГАТЕЛИ ПЕРКИНСА, ПИТЕРБОРО, АНГЛИЯ

The exact origin of this advertisement, dated 1934, is a mystery, but it appears to have been published in the hope of generating business following the success in the Moscow competition

larger crankcase but to try to retain as many other components as possible, since commonality would keep their costs down as well as keeping pattern and tooling changes to the minimum. Accordingly the new design, with bore of 100mm and stroke increased to 127mm, was rushed through and components ordered. Tests showed that the power could be increased to 60bhp at 2,400rpm, compared to the 45bhp at 2,500rpm of the Wolf. Maximum torque also increased from 145 to 158 lbs.ft, and the specific fuel consumption reduced to 0.36 pints/bhp/hr (publicity figures).

The new engine, retaining the animal name tradition, became the 'Leopard' and was to find immediate greater appeal with truck manufacturers such as Bedford, Dodge and Albion. A de-rated version of the Leopard was also built, with the same cylinder dimensions but reduced power through adjustment of the fuel injection pump: this was known as the 'Lynx'. Later there were to be customers who felt that the Leopard did not offer the same pulling power as their petrol engines, so once again fingers were crossed and a bigger bore version was devised, boring out the cylinders to 105mm to create the Leopard II, the original engine becoming the Leopard I. This larger engine was rated at 75bhp at 2,400rpm and with 190lbs.ft torque seemed to offer sufficient power for the truck people.

Developing sales – and increasing product knowledge

While the engine developments were being pursued by CWC, there were changes on the sales side too, with agents appointed around the country from Devon to Scotland. Interest was also shown by Birmal Boats, a subsidiary of Birmingham Aluminium Co. Ltd, who wished

to take engines and convert them for marine use. A further 200 sets of Wolf parts were ordered, to be called up at 20 sets per month. An initial batch of 25 sets of Leopard parts was also ordered and, with some confidence, Captain Richardson agreed to loan a further £3,000 to assist cash flow until sales covered the outgoings. It was also agreed to spend £550 on advertising, and to arrange for a Wolf engine to be tuned for an attempt on record breaking for a diesel-powered car – this part of the story will be covered a little later.

As more Wolf engines came into service the Company began to get the feedback necessary to confirm the good and the bad features of the design. Not only was the engine a largely unknown quantity, but it was also operating in a new market whose expectations were uncertain. Road transport was a developing industry and featured both fleet operations and the owner/operator. While the fleets were generally well looked after, with regular good servicing and proper attention to avoid overloading, the same could not be said of the smaller operations, where some were working on a shoestring. People were buying and converting old trucks, fitting a new Perkins engine on hire purchase, then trying to cover repayments and running costs while somehow scraping a living. Such vehicles were often overloaded, then run for the maximum time at high speeds with minimal servicing, so that oil and filter changes were neglected and routine adjustments ignored. Horror stories have always been a part of any engine manufacturer's files, and CWC tells one typical tale:

'I remember inspecting one engine that was actually driven to the works where it arrived making horrible noises and with smoke pouring out of the bonnet louvres. When the cylinder head cover was lifted the whole interior was a gooey mass of sludge, which completely hid the valve-gear. On removal of the cylinder head itself it was found that half of the valve springs were broken, with one valve fallen into the cylinder and embedded in the piston crown, which had broken through. The oil sump was full of a black sludge with a pint or two of black viscous oil floating on top. The oil filter element had clearly never been cleaned since new; no oil could possibly pass through it so that the engine was relying on oil passing through the bypass to circulate round the system. Yet this truck had been in service until that day when the driver passing through Peterborough called in to say his engine wasn't pulling as well as it did!'

Other complaints were received, often comparing fuel consumptions against some other owner's achievements. In some such cases the works would receive visits from errant vehicles and have the opportunity to experience the driving techniques of their operators. Even on well-maintained vehicles they often found that lack of common sense (we might call it 'lack of mechanical sympathy') was the real cause of many such complaints. Driver education in those early days was unheard of, but definitely needed! Neglect of routine maintenance was also the cause of other failures.

Obviously not all problems were easily dismissed or excused. Experience confirmed that attention to details was needed to improve many aspects of the engine design to meet criticisms of its frailty when operated to its capability. For instance a change to replaceable bearings with white metal on a steel backing cured problems of early bearing failure, but had to be followed by hardening of the crankshaft bearing surfaces when these were found to wear too rapidly. This in turn showed the need for closer control on the hardening process when crankshaft breakage was experienced – shown to be due to the hardened bands running into the fillet radii between journal surface and webs.

Other components also gave trouble, with valve springs, injectors and connecting rods also receiving attention. CWC notes 'Almost everything that could go wrong with an engine went wrong with one or other of them, but fortunately not with all.' It's a comment that will be familiar to every development engineer, although he would hope to apply this to prototypes rather than production units!

It would appear that CWC and his staff spent quite a bit of time sorting out such problems, so that the appointment of service engineers – Cyril Kent and Joe Hinch – both eased the burden and ensured that more rapid attention was given in the field. A 25cwt Commer truck was purchased and fitted out to become the first Service vehicle. Gradually letters of appreciation began to arrive as the operators found that the engines did serve their purpose and problems were dealt with promptly.

One aspect noted, however, was the ability of the engine to operate well above its designed speed: drivers came to know that the engine was willing to run to 3,000 or even 4,000rpm given the right conditions, so that operation with the foot flat on the accelerator became normal practice! CWC tackled this potential for abuse by the addition of a governor and a seal on the fuel pump, thus preventing operators over-fuelling to gain a little more power at the expense of increased fuel consumption, to say nothing of smoke level and decreased reliability. By July 1934 the acceptance of the engine as an alternative to their own petrol engines by a number of truck manufacturers, plus growing sales for conversion of vehicles by the new network of agents, convinced the Perkins Board of the need to expand their premises. A further workshop, adjacent to the original in the old Barford and Perkins works, was rented for £175 a year and fitted with cranes and test bed equipment.

There was still close scrutiny of expenditure since income was well short of 'break-even'. Although orders were being received at a rate of about 140 engines a year, this was short of the calculated 200

needed. Further loans were made by Messrs Perks, Richardson and Edward Perkins to help out, but by August an estimate showed a further £9,000 to £10,000 would be needed up to mid-1935 where it was hoped self-financing from sales would be possible. An approach was made to the head office of Barclays Bank in London in an attempt to get an overdraft facility up to £15,000 against Directors' guarantees, but this was unsuccessful; the best that was forthcoming was a limit of £5,000 with joint guarantees from four directors. By the end of 1934 they were close to the limit, with the bank pressing for a reduction, but an agreement to extend was eventually negotiated.

The close of the year showed considerable progress made, with overseas involvement in both Russia and Hungary, plus an Albion order for export to India. The Russian interest was sparked off by a Wolf engine supplied to fit in a GAZ truck, which was then entered in an international competition: Frank Perkins and Alan Richardson took the Hillman car, fitted with the Wolf engine, from Helsinki to Moscow to observe this trial. The truck duly won its class and received the principal award, a cut glass rose bowl which is still a prized exhibit in the Perkins trophy display. Unfortunately, in spite of the interest generated by both the truck and the Hillman car, the net result in terms of orders was precisely nothing!

Progress, but not profit

At the end of 1934 the marine engine agreement with Birmal was also progressing, with an engine test witnessed by Commander Clover of the Admiralty. A total of 150 engines had been sold, for around £30,000 including spares, with firm orders in hand for another 45 units. The balance sheet for the year showed an overall loss of £4,024 but with the 'Development Account' now standing at £8,699, plus an overdraft at the bank of £1,377. Add to this the £7,000 of unsecured loans and the amount of £12,472 owed to suppliers and the status of the Company is very clear – they were living on borrowed time, whatever the potential for future business might be. The suppliers were effectively financing the business as the Company traded on their good faith, plus the fact that business in general was not brisk, so even trading with late payers was better than nothing. The tone of the Directors' report was optimistic, with the Development Fund described as favourable compared to the spending of other companies of a similar nature. (CWC comments that at Aveling and Porter they had spent over £30,000 on the development of a diesel engine under licence without getting a single engine to marketable status, suggesting that the Perkins achievement was not without merit.) However, the loans had been used up by the end of the year. Messrs Perks, Edward Perkins and Alan Richardson yet again rescued the struggling enterprise by providing a further unsecured loan of £2,000.

The directors and staff, hopeful that profitability would soon be forthcoming, greeted 1935 with considerable optimism. There were signs of a steady demand for the engines from both agents and manufacturers, and a further extension of the workshops had been necessary, with a dedicated test shop now in place, with three test brakes. The first workshop area had been assigned to assembly and engine erection, with the engines being built up on low wooden platforms, each one being in the charge of a fitter with an apprentice assisting. All parts were still brought in finished, with inspection and water test where necessary followed by the washing of major components in a paraffin tank, assisted with the modest pressure from a garden syringe to clean machining swarf from inaccessible corners. As each new cylinder block was mounted to its platform, the fitter would commence by line boring the main bearings to size, while the assistant prepared the crankshaft and connecting rods with their piston and rings assembled. The rest of the carcase of the engine was then built up with the cylinder head and the other standard parts, to be followed by the customising parts (sump, flywheel and housing, plus bracketry) to suit the requirements of the specific vehicle. This principle will be familiar to anybody who has worked in the Perkins of today, except that doing it all in one place is a far cry from the modern assembly line. By this time there were some 36 men and youths in the workshop, plus about a dozen in the offices, which by then included the top floor of 17 Queen Street.

The shop floor weekly wages bill had reached £61 15s 8d, an average wage of around 35 shillings a week (£1.75), although at that time there was one employee, D Lal Gupta, who was an Indian student and actually paid a premium of £50 for the privilege of working in such a modern and progressive company! The best paid men were Norman Burney, at £3 15s (£3.75) and Harry Beeton (erection shop charge hand) at £3 10s.

A breakthrough, then disaster!

In March 1935 a telephone call from Commers was received, with an order for eighty Wolf engines, and a request for urgent delivery. It transpired that one vehicle with the Wolf and a bus body had been exported to India, for the Gwalior and Northern India Transport Company. They had been pleased with the vehicle and were intending to standardise on Perkins for their fleet. This represented six months' production at the current rate, and suggested to the Company that success had really arrived. With steady demand from other customers and the agents, orders for parts were increased and yet more of the old Queen Street Works was rented, this time another 3,600 square feet at a cost of £80 per annum. CWC in his capacity as Company Secretary was at last able to say that they were now operating at a profit and could soon clear their overdraft and start repaying the loans.

Then came Budget Day on 1 April. Yet again Perkins was faced with a setback as the Chancellor announced an increase in the tax paid on fuel oil for road vehicles. The increasing popularity of diesel engines was not due purely to their better economy, but also to the fact that the tax on fuel oil was much lower than that on petrol. With the fuel oil price only about one third that of petrol, the running costs soon recouped the extra cost of the diesel engine, persuading operators that the change was worthwhile. (In fact, Perkins' advertising of the period majored on the economics as part of the sales pitch.) The Chancellor's announcement of a huge tax increase, from one penny to eight pence per gallon, effectively killed the market overnight. Cancellations came from all sides as the potential customers recalculated the costs and savings, and within a few days the order book was halved. It was fortunate that there were export orders, especially the 80 engines for India, otherwise bankruptcy would have been an inevitable and almost immediate result. As it was, the cash flow situation was grim, with material ordered arriving daily and payments to be made, but with sales much lower than expected. Deliveries were maintained to Commers, but it was clear that a major crisis point had been reached.

CWC recalled a visit from Captain Richardson who asked him if there was any hope. 'Without more money, none', was his blunt answer. Richardson then asked how much more was needed and when. CWC gave him a guess, based on his knowledge of the immediate commitments, of between £10,000 and £15,000. Bearing in mind

that the three subscribing shareholders had already paid £19,000 into the Company (in early twenty-first century terms around £850,000!), this was an enormous extra burden. Since none of the directors concerned had seen any return on their investment, with the two working directors paid a very low salary for their input, it would not have been surprising if at this point the company had collapsed. As will be seen, Captain Alan Richardson ultimately saved Perkins by risking a further large portion of his capital, with no security whatsoever. By staking his fortune, on the basis of his faith in the product and his personal trust in Frank Perkins and Charles Chapman, he undoubtedly saved Perkins from an early demise and thereby sowed the seeds for future success, which was ultimately to pay him back handsomely. The name of Alan Richardson is virtually forgotten in the Perkins of today, but every employee, past and present, owes a huge debt to this man.

Some Personal Glimpses

Russell Bennett can with justification call himself the first Perkins apprentice, although they were not thinking that way at the time. He went to enquire about a job in March 1934, was interviewed and offered a job 'starting Monday'. Thus on 21 March 1934 he presented himself at the door promptly at 8am, to find everything locked and nobody around. A neighbour commented that he was too early and when eventually Norman Burney arrived, his first question was 'who are you?'

Russell's recollections of the people and work of the time are still clear. His first job was to chip the cylinder block castings to clear the tappet area of casting flash, and he also learnt to squeeze the ends of the fuel injection pipes to form a conical shape using a Bosch fixture.

One day Russell was under a vehicle in the inspection pit, removing the pistons from the Wolf engine and getting very dirty in the process. Frank Perkins drove his Hillman Vortec into the shop to get the bearings checked and on seeing an apparition appear from the pit, asked 'Who's this darkie, then?' The name stuck and Russell became 'Darkie' within the Company for the rest of his working life!

Another memory comes from one Guy Fawkes Night, when Cyril Kent and Ted Sell put Russell onto the roof of the workshop to drop 'little demon' fireworks down the stove chimney, causing great consternation to Harry Beeton, who blamed the miners for leaving something in the coal. Russell also recalls that overtime was worked but was unpaid (Ted Marvill was something of a martinet, expecting everyone to continue working!). A ham sandwich and a cup of tea would be collected from the Norfolk Hotel for all those working through to 7pm.

The engine test procedure in those early days was rudimentary. Each engine would be motored for an hour to run it in before testing proper started. It was then run for about 12 hours before going on to full load, at which point power and fuel consumption would be measured and the timing adjusted to give an optimum reading. Charles Chapman would personally pass off each engine, using a string to the stop control while checking it would run two minutes at 3,000rpm! The 'finishing department' consisted of Russell and Guy Barker who would add the flywheel and other dress parts to the tested engine.

The overall situation was reviewed at the April 1935 Board Meeting: it was decided to reduce engine prices to manufacturers by 12% in an attempt to regain the ground lost with the fuel price increase. An attempt would be made to get conversion work into the factory, and offer a discount for the displaced petrol engine but hold the conversion price. A new salesman was engaged, at a low salary but on a commission basis, to renew efforts to attract conversion orders. However, at the end of May there was no real sign of extra business, with only about 30 engines on order compared to 92 at the end of March. CWC met with the Company's accountant, Mr Selby, for a review of all costs and overheads in an effort to match them against this heavy reduction in sales revenue.

Another financial crisis, and a daring solution

The projected income was estimated to cover only the wages and overheads, leaving a considerable shortfall on all the purchased material spread over a large number of small suppliers, in addition to the major accounts with CAV Ltd (fuel injection equipment, starter motors and dynamos), Ambrose Shardlow (crankshafts), Automotive Engineering (pistons) and the two major casting suppliers, Midland Motor Cylinder and Beans Foundry. They decided to pay the smaller accounts as they became due and delay the intermediate accounts for as long as possible. The major accounts, however, represented a much larger issue: if they were not paid within a reasonable time the suppliers would stop deliveries, Perkins could not then produce anything and that would really be the end! After further deliberations they concluded that although the economic slump was past the worst, no supplier would wish to lose business already in hand and might be amenable to a request to extend credit: their hope was that an honest statement of the problems inflicted on Perkins by the fuel tax change might sway the major creditors. They believed that a level of mutual trust and friendship had been built up, and this proved to be the case, with the major suppliers agreeing that they would assist Perkins to get over the immediate problems, with an undertaking that once this crisis was past they would be paid in full.

The case made by the Perkins management – that the diesel engine would prove its viability even at the new fuel cost – was accepted. CAV Ltd was especially supportive and took the longer term view; at this time they were committed to start manufacture of the pumps made under licence from Bosch. With the diesel industry in its infancy they needed all their customers to stay in business and eventually increase their production. It is interesting to remember that the extra fuel tax was initially applicable to ALL road vehicles using diesel engines: this was interpreted as applying to mobile machinery such as road rollers. Another ex-employee of A.G.E., Edward Barford, was incensed by the ruling and lobbied intensely to have it overturned, arguing that such a measure would kill the UK industry's switch to the diesel roller and revert it back to steam! The impact on the export market and the competitiveness of the British industry was a crucial part of the case. Barford succeeded in obtaining exemption for road-making equipment, thus saving Aveling and Barford Ltd from a serious, or even terminal, reversal in their fortunes.

Alan Richardson to the rescue

The savings made through the decisions and agreements were sufficient for a short period, but by 4 June Chapman advised the Board that a further £4,500 would be needed by the end of the month to clear the most pressing creditors. No immediate decision was reached, resulting in further pleading with suppliers for more time, but at the

July Board Meeting it was agreed to increase the share capital. The proposal was to increase to £38,000 in preference shares, £9,000 of this to be taken up by Mr Perks, Alan Richardson and Edward Perkins in lieu of the existing loans, trying to place the remainder outside. There was no real belief in this as a solution; the chance of finding backers with money to risk pouring down the drain seems to have been wildly optimistic. It was at this point Alan Richardson made his first offer, to lend another £5,000 without security pending any income arising from the preference shares. This bold offer gave some breathing space, allowing some time to work out strategies for the immediate future, aimed at regaining part of the home market as well as developing the export potentials where cheaper fuel added to the attraction of the diesel engine's economy and durability. The appointment of good dealers in the UK, was supported by the recruitment of L.W. Hancock as Sales Manager. His efforts, along with support from Alan Richardson, who had been appointed as Sales Director, were to promote the Perkins products and help convince the doubting buyers of the benefits. Laurie Hancock may not have been a trained engineer, but he proved to be a born publicist and was later to take such a role full time (and incidentally after his retirement to become the first person to produce a written history of the Company).

The overall review of prices and margins, plus an assessment of the most optimistic sales volumes that could be expected for 1935, resulted in the following:

▌ Total potential sales 500, excluding Commer but including 100 home conversions and 100 export sales.

▌ Leopard price to manufacturers set at £144 for the bare engine, and list price at £192. Conversion list price at £240 (exhauster extra).

▌ For the Wolf the manufacturing prime cost was estimated as £114, excluding fixed overheads, with price to Commer being set at £120 bare, and £140 dressed. List price was set at £177 10s, and conversion at £225 (exhauster extra).

Perkins also took considerable pains to identify vehicle running costs, the potential savings and time to amortise the actual increased purchase price, etc. Tabulations of running costs based on yearly mileage, servicing, wages, depreciation, etc., were made available. Publicity based on unsolicited testimonials from satisfied users, reprints of Commercial Motor road tests and articles were all used as evidence to sway the views of the hard-nosed operators, whose main concern seemed to be the unproven reliability of these small engines. When used in high-mileage operations, any off-road time became a major factor in computing profitability. In off-road applications, of course, where cheap fuel was still available, there were many untapped opportunities: it was agreed that more efforts would be made to push for sales in the industrial and agricultural markets where competition against the petrol and petrol–paraffin engines would be mainly on the basis of increased economy and reliability since cheap fuel was not a factor. A new department was set up under Geoffrey Guest to tackle this new initiative. Gradually sales were won, for stone crushers, welding sets, compressors and light railway applications. It was found that high speed and low weight were not significant factors in such markets; indeed they were seen as disadvantages by some potential customers against their established engine suppliers.

One application carried out at this time was the fitment of a Leopard engine to a Fordson tractor, needing a special cast-iron sump to take the front axle mounts plus a heavy flywheel and adaptor housing to mate with the clutch and gearbox. This work was done with a co-operative Peterborough Fordson dealer, who allowed parts to be measured by the Design staff. The first prototype was put to work lo-

At Brooklands: the world record-breaking Parry Thomas 'flat-iron' car driven by Reg Munday, 9 October 1935.

cally and ultimately was followed by a number of conversions, some of which went to New Zealand, some as Fordson tractors which were then used as the motive power for motor scrapers. (A contact during 2001 with a museum in New Zealand confirmed that at least one of these early conversions still exists and awaits restoration, having been rebuilt at some time as a tractor proper!)

Another interesting involvement for CWC had been a request from the London Passenger Transport Board for a trial of the Perkins 'Aero-flow' combustion system in an AEC engine in a bus. This was eventually designed and a trial made on a Route 11 bus, the first example of 'third party' engineering business for Perkins.

Publicity through record-breaking

Another publicity effort at this time was the already-mentioned attempt on speed records, using a modified Wolf engine in a Parry Thomas 'Flat-iron' racing car. In spite of adverse weather conditions at the Brooklands track on Wednesday 9 October the car, driven by Reg Munday (a well-known racing driver of the time) set a series of records for the new diesel 3-litre class. This car was one of three veteran cars designed and built by Parry Thomas, familiar to the racing fans of the time due to its shape and frequent appearances in races at Brooklands. The records set were:

Flying kilometre	94.70mph
Fifty kilometres	88.11mph
Fifty miles	88.44mph
Hundred kilometres	88.38mph
Hundred miles	88.13mph
One hour	88.25mph

The Wolf engine had been modified by Mr Leonard Vale-Onslow, a tuner better known for his work on motorcycles. There were no major changes to the structure of the engine, but all reciprocating parts were lightened and polished, porting polished to improve airflow and of course fuel injection changed to increase flow and therefore power. For the one kilometre record only the engine was fitted with a Zoller supercharger, all the other records being accomplished in naturally aspirated form. The peak power was increased from 45bhp at 2,800rpm to 62bhp at 3,000 rpm, with maximum bmep of 125lbs/sq.in. at 1,400rpm, using engine serial number 3085. There is little doubt that this achievement was most impressive to the specially invited audience, in spite of the cold and windy weather, and represented the first attempt on diesel car records since the governing body (A.I.R.A.C.) had agreed the category in 1934. Much credit was given to Reg Munday for his hard work in adapting the car and engine, plus his driving prowess, but it is interesting to read his autographed hand-written comment on the souvenir leaflet produced later: 'I have handled many of the best racing cars made, but for simplicity and consistent reliability, without constant tuning, the Perkins job is really outstanding. Give me a diesel every time.'

Looking back, it is difficult to know how much impact this performance had on the public, but certainly it would put the Perkins name in front of a new audience: the publicity material makes play of the advantages of the diesel, especially the economy and efficiency, low maintenance and overall simplicity. Easy starting and the almost complete absence of exhaust smoke are also identified as particular traits of the Perkins units.

While these efforts to attract new sales were progressing, the financial position was not improving. No new money had been forthcoming from the Preference Shares, the £5,000 lent by Alan Richardson had been used and once more survival became an issue. Once again 'Captain Dick' came to the rescue in September, with a further £5,000 loaned on the understanding that this was to be converted to Preference Shares as soon as possible. At an Extraordinary General Meeting

This shows one of the original Fordson tractor conversions exported to New Zealand in 1935. seen in the Geraldine Museum in February 2005, awaiting restoration. (Picture D Boulton)

on 3 October the share structure was changed: the existing 12,000 £1 Ordinary Shares were converted to 24,000 ten shillings shares, a further 20,000 Ordinary Shares were created and the total capital increased to £60,000 by the authorisation of 38,000 6% non-cumulative Participating Preference Shares of £1 each. These latter were to share equally any remaining distributable profit after 6% had been paid on the Ordinary, up to a limit of 10% on both classes, after which any balance would go to the Ordinaries. All this of course presupposed that profit would eventually come! On 21 November this new structure was enacted, bringing in two new shareholders – Mrs Annie Winifred Perks and Mrs Yda Emily Margaretha Richardson – the latter being Alan's stepmother who had taken over his last £5,000 loan. It will have been apparent to the reader, however, that this did not actually bring more capital into the Company, with the result that by the December Board Meeting CWC was once more reporting a gloomy situation: accounts dating back to August remained unpaid and suppliers were pressing for settlement. To stave off liquidation an immediate £6,000 was needed, with a further £9,000 as soon as possible.

What had started as a year of optimism had turned into a disaster, with only £22,000 of sales in the last six months, following the £44,000 of the first half-year. (Total sales for the year appear to have been about 180 engines, although an exact figure cannot be determined from the records.) Although there was an order for 23 Wolf engines following a tour by Cyril Kent to Argentina there was little else. Although Alan Richardson had rescued the Company during the year, he actually stood to make less than the other shareholders if success finally came: understandably he wanted someone else to carry some of the risks. After more deliberations FAP agreed to find £1,000 by 1 January 1936. Alan Richardson agreed to loan the additional £5,000 needed, followed by another £10,000 on a debenture, provided that Mr Perks could find £5,000 for Preference Shares to match Mrs Richardson's £5,000. Desperation had become the order of the day and the year closed on a glum note. In spite of this, the accounts showed a doubling of turnover to £62,570 and after the consigning of another £8,000 to the Development Account a paper profit of £3,386 was shown.

1936 opened with two Board Meetings to sanction the issue of £20,000 in 6% Debentures to cover the loans from Alan Richardson and Mr Perkins. Security against these was problematic since the tangible assets of £10,222 had to cover £4,610 owed to the Bank and £13,083 to creditors! On the positive side, orders were starting to come in slightly more quickly, partly as a result of overseas tours. Some of the Leopard engines had been in service for a year and were showing reasonable results; since they were over 40% more powerful than

the Wolf for a price only 8% higher whilst fitting under the bonnets of many popular trucks such as the Commer, Bedford and Albion, the selling process was easier. In fact during 1936 the actual sales showed an accelerating swing in favour of the Leopard, so that over the year about 610 of the more powerful engines were sold compared to only 150 Wolfs. During the year the Arran Dieselet went out of production, killed by the fuel tax, but this was more than replaced by the new Leopard business, both home and abroad. Sales started to improve from around 17 a month to over 35 a month by the end of March.

An interesting situation arose due to an arrangement made by FAP with Automotive Products, whose overseas representative had been given a brief to 'sell' Perkins engines during his regular tours on the European mainland. In early 1936 Daimler-Benz of Stuttgart became interested in taking an option for an exclusive licence for Germany. A car was sent to Peterborough for conversion to a Wolf and on its return it was accompanied by CWC who stayed for several weeks to observe the trials. Although the Wolf engine acquitted itself well on performance versus the small Daimler-Benz engine being developed for cars, it was eventually rejected because the exhaust emissions were slightly more visible than the competitor's. This was a great disappointment to Charles Chapman, but the cynics may prefer to believe that there was never any real intention in the DB camp to take a British engine, only to get a yardstick to monitor their own progress. Certainly the first appearance of the Daimler-Benz 260D diesel engine in a private car was at the Berlin Motor Show of February 1936, where it caused something of a sensation. It seems that intentions to produce a diesel-powered car at Daimler-Benz dated back to as early as September 1933, and their six-cylinder prototype was rated at 82bhp and 2,800rpm: thinking at least in parallel to the Perkins/ Chapman philosophy, plus some greater regard for the smoothness, and therefore customer acceptance, of the alternative power plant.

Closer to home a more satisfactory negotiation was concluded. In May Vauxhall at Luton began to offer the Leopard as an option in the Bedford truck chassis: as a result General Motors of Antwerp became interested. A visit by FAP and Laurie Hancock was made to persuade them to standardise on the engine for the Chevrolet trucks made in Belgium; since diesel fuel was very much cheaper in Holland and Belgium the benefits were potentially much greater for the customer. After tests General Motors agreed and were anxious to start this new venture properly, thus a special week-long course was arranged for their sales and service people, together with demonstrations at the plant. A group travelled from Perkins to support the process, with lectures on the technical aspects, and on the potential problems in service that might be new to personnel who were unfamiliar with the diesel engine. One small episode recounted by CWC points out the problems and dangers of language quite clearly: during the early liaisons with General Motors he got into the Perkins-powered truck with the local General Manager in Antwerp when that gentleman decided he wanted to try it himself. They noted that the fuel gauge was showing near empty so the manager instructed one of the truck drivers to 'take this along and fill the tank up with gas-oil'. After a short delay the truck was brought back and off they went with the GM man driving himself. A mile or so from the plant the engine started to misfire and splutter, then pick up, race, then die again. They opened the bonnet and CWC suggested they must have a fuel airlock, but on opening the bleed valve it was clear what had happened from the smell of the fluid dripping from the system. The driver had misinterpreted 'gas-oil' for 'gas', and filled the tank with petrol! Needless to say the Perkins team were at pains to emphasis in their lectures to the GM staff the dangers of using the wrong fuel.

The Perkins men had worked hard to build up good relations with the GM group, both work-wise and socially, often beyond the call of duty. They were rewarded by results. Orders picked up and they soon found it necessary to expand again, this time renting one of the larger shops in the old Barford and Perkins works: the 7,500 square feet cost about £200 per year. They also rented the old drawing office to accommodate the increasing office staff. Inevitably this meant once again that outgoings were exceeding income; in the September Board Meeting Charles Chapman was again facing his fellow directors with the news that a further £15,000 was needed to stave off the demands of their creditors. He countered this with the good news that orders were now coming in at the rate of two thousand engines a year, so that they would soon be on a profitable basis. The outcome was a further increase in authorised capital to £98,000: this took the form of 38,000 6% Preference shares and 1,200,000 Ordinary shares of one shilling each. It was agreed that existing holders of Preference shares could convert them at par into Ordinaries by 1 March 1937, new subscribers for the Preference would have the option of taking up ten one shilling Ordinaries in respect of each one pound Preference while Debenture holders could subscribe for Ordinary shares at par up to the value of the Debentures held. Once again to keep them going Alan Richardson made a further temporary loan of £5,000.

In order to attract new shareholders a dinner party was held in Peterborough, followed by a walk round the works and a sales pitch regarding the product and the prospects. Most of the guests were friends and family of Captain Richardson. The talks must have been persuasive; by the end of the year the existing Preference shares had been converted to Ordinaries and a total of £18,000 6% Debentures issued. These were split between Alan Richardson, his sister Mrs Firbank, Edward Perkins and two other friends of Alan's – Captain B.M. Wills and Colonel Gresson. This vote of confidence must have meant a great deal to the staff of the Company, even though it was a vote from a small number of close 'interested parties'.

Meanwhile on the technical front all was not well. While the export trade was expanding nicely the same could not be said of the home market. Although this was partly due to the lingering effects of the fuel tax hike, there was also the question of market sophistication. The existing engines were relatively crude and simple four-cylinder units and were replacing smoother-running petrol engines, usually six-cylinder of higher horsepower, which were much kinder to transmissions, chassis and occupants. The Board had suggested that 'A six cylinder version of the Leopard might be a good idea' at the end of 1935. As a result, Chapman had already schemed out, with his newly recruited technical assistant, Alec W. Gosling, the preliminary design of a six-cylinder diesel: by skimping everywhere he had arrived at a design which would fit into the existing truck chassis, such as Bedford and Commer, and which was in appearance much more like the contemporary petrol engines. His hope was that the power and speed would also prove similar, whilst the basic design was aimed at production using simple tooling; the goal of in-house production at Queen Street would remove much of the reliance on other machinists and cut many costs to the benefit of Perkins' profits. At a Board Meeting on 12 November 1936 the preliminary design was discussed and it was agreed to finalise the design and produce experimental engines. The combustion chamber proposed was an improvement over the original, with hopes for both easier production and better performance; it was agreed to apply for a further patent on this aspect too.

The end of the third full year of their existence came to a close with a familiar story of shortage of cash, but with much improved results and prospects. The sales of engines and spares during the year totalled £99,318, almost 60% up on the previous year. After the transfer of £3,450 to the ubiquitous Development Account they were left with a paper profit of £687. The Company was growing apace and achieving some recognition with a growing number of customers; during the year Perkins had become a full member of the Society of Motor Manufacturers and Traders, the body recognised as the 'voice' of the British motor industry. The growth of personnel had continued, with an office opened in Birmingham, several salesmen employed and a design department established at Queen Street and costing £2,000 per year in salaries. The total bill for salaries and wages was now almost £19,000 – at around £360 each week against the £220 at the end of the previous year Perkins was becoming a significant employer and contributor to the local economy. To end a more promising year the directors felt justified in inviting all employees to a sausage supper with free beer as a year-end celebration.

Some Personal Glimpses

Long-serving employee Jim Broughton recalled in 1982 some of his experiences with the various vehicles that arrived for conversion at Queen Street. One of the most unusual, and most elegant, was a Bentley. Another was the racing car referred to in this chapter: 'I was just a lad at the time of course, and was the only one small enough to fit behind the wheel of the car. I was allowed to sit and steer while it was pushed from one part of the factory to another. It was still a tight fit. They said the steering wheel had to be taken out to let Reg Munday get in, then it was refitted!' (So maybe the present-day Formula One cars are not so novel after all!)

Jim also recalled that the bulk of the business was with commercial vehicles. 'Many's the time I saw lorries drive into the yard with a car on the back. The car was lifted off and the driver drove off in it, leaving the lorry behind for the conversion. That would take two days or so.' One of the most significant contracts he recalled was that with Bedfords. New chassis would arrive, with petrol engine installed, at the rate of about twenty a fortnight. The petrol engines would be removed and Perkins diesels fitted, and the chassis, complete with unwanted petrol engine lashed on behind, would go back down the A1 to Bedford for completion. Ironically, although he was doing the conversions, Jim was under 18 and could not hold a driving licence, so he never test drove his own conversions.

Albert Chapman also recalled the early days of trouble-shooting before a team of service engineers had been developed. He first hit the road as a teenager when he had completed his apprenticeship, dealing with engines in places as diverse as a Cornish tin mine and defrosting fuel lines on a truck out on the Great North Road. On one occasion he had been sent up to Scotland to work on an engine running an emergency generator set in a hospital. He was working away by candlelight when he heard someone come up behind him, who asked 'How's it going?' He looked round and there was Frank Perkins himself, the last person he expected.

'How much are you getting paid?' he asked. Albert told him and FAP replied: 'Well, as you are doing a man's job it's time you got a man's pay.' And he remembered, because when he got back Albert was told he'd been given a seven shillings (35p) a week rise.

First prototype Panther (P6) running on the test bed at Queen Street in 1937. (Picture by courtesy of Russell Bennett)

The Company entered 1937 with an overall feeling of optimism once again, and with an order book showing steady growth. Although the London office had been closed with the departure of Mr Greenbergh, the sales function had been strengthened with the appointment of Laurie Hancock and the recruitment of some additional staff to sell engines for conversion purposes. New agents had been appointed in Australia – Queensbridge Motors in Melbourne and Reo Motors in Sydney – and February brought the news that General Motors Australia were hoping to order 100 engines each month for their Bedford truck production. (Unfortunately this never materialised but it was a further incentive for the ambitious plans for expansion already being developed).

Finding a new factory site

The Board had agreed during January that prospects were sufficiently certain to justify the construction of new premises; accordingly the Chairman was authorised to negotiate for the purchase of a suitable site. Meanwhile Bill Pailing, now the Works Manager, submitted a list of machine tools to start machining of the major engine components under their own roof: it was calculated that the savings made would cover the repayments necessary under a hire purchase agreement. The capital cost was kept down by specifying simple machines such as radial drills. Frank Perkins' search for a suitable site eventually identified a small farm at Newark village on the outskirts of Peterborough. With over 30 acres Walnut Farm was promising, could probably be purchased from the executors of the recently deceased owner and was reasonably close to the city with room for future expansion as and when justified.

Unfortunately. as these plans were being made the bright prospects diminished once more: the order book by the end of June showed only 300 engines, a rate about equal to the closing six months of 1936. The home vehicle and conversion business had failed to pick up and although exports and the new industrial sales were reasonable they did not match the earlier expectations. Since material orders had been increased, stocks were high and once again the cash position was worrying. Moves were made to reduce costs, with the new Birmingham office being closed and some salesmen put on to a commission basis. The cycle from euphoria to doom and gloom seemed to be a regular feature of their existence!

First test of the new six-cylinder

There was still one good reason for optimism: in April Chapman had reported to the Board that the first prototype of the new six-cylinder engine had run successfully on the test bed, and was up to expectations as far as performance was concerned. This engine was designed, detailed, parts procured and first run in five and a half months from the Board decision to go ahead. At the time nobody could foresee the eventual impact that this new engine would have, both on the market and the fortunes of F. Perkins Ltd. It was seen as the best hope for survival, as the Wolf was becoming unsaleable while the Leopard was facing stiff competition from other British manufacturers. The Board decided to take a gamble and order 500 sets of material on the basis of a few hours of test-bed running – not an action for the faint-hearted, and a vote of confidence in Chapman's ability to get it right first time! At the same meeting it was agreed to proceed with the design of four and three-cylinder versions of the engine, and to build prototypes with the objective of showing all three engines at the Commercial Motor Show in November, only seven months away. Chapman had of course been in a similar position before, at Aveling and Porter, but now he had other roles to play too in keeping an eye on the financial aspects of the Company as well as juggling the design and test side with a small and overworked staff. Bill Pailing was also stretched, keeping the works running while he reviewed drawings as they were produced, as well as ensuring that the necessary tooling and machinery were ordered. Chapman comments that Ted Marvill, by then Chief Draughtsman, used to protest as fractions were shaved off dimensions as the detail drawings were completed, always with an eye to keeping the engine size small enough to fit under existing truck bonnets. It was not only an internal concern: 'I recall that when we sent the drawing of the cylinder head to Midland Motor to quote for castings, they held up their hands in horror and said that the depth had been cut so fine there was no room for the cores, and it could never be successfully cast. But it was!'

Somehow they managed to get it all done, presumably with much burning of the midnight oil, so that all three engines were displayed attractively at the Commercial Show on their own stand. The fact that the three-cylinder was only a mock-up at that stage, and was destined to reach production only in 1952, was immaterial: the Company was showing a family of diesels that for the first time achieved the compactness and appearance of contemporary petrol engines. As the early literature shows, these engines were originally intended to have animal names, as had become the tradition, with Panther (6-cylinder), Puma (4) and Python (3) as the chosen designations. However, there were some polite remonstrations from Phelan & Moore, who were already marketing the 'Panther' motorcycle, so the original literature was hurriedly withdrawn and scrapped (although not totally, as the archives now prove!). Taking the first letter as the cue, the engines became the P6, P4 and P3, and were destined to become not only long-lived designs but also eventually legends in their own right, especially the P6. With a launch rating of 85bhp at 2,600rpm, it was an immediate sensation. The publicity brochure pulled no punches – 'THE P6: THE WORLD'S LIGHTEST DIESEL ENGINE' – going on to identify outstanding achievements in economy, weight, compactness, adaptability, cold starting, silence, etc.

It is noticeable too that the Company was already claiming 'hundreds of millions of vehicle road miles in the hands of satisfied users in all parts of the world . . .', then listing countries far flung across the globe! Just how much of this could be true is open to some conjecture, since the total number of engines built by the close of 1936 was only just over 1,100, but perhaps we can forgive some artistic licence at this stage.

The arrival of the P6 heralded the arrival of Perkins as a major po-

PERKINS
of Peterborough
produce a
"6"

THE "P.6"
SIX CYLINDER
DIESEL OF
"Record-breaking"
CHARACTERISTICS

A LIGHT-WEIGHT DIESEL ENGINE IDEAL FOR USE IN
OMNIBUSES-COACHES-LORRIES-PRIVATE CARS
AND ALL INDUSTRIAL APPLICATIONS

First sales brochure for the P Series engines. Note the 'Panther' designation on this document, pre-dating the change to plain 'P' Series

tential supplier; all the commercial vehicle makers took notice as well as the end-users. Demonstrators were available, probably a Commer truck and a Studebaker car, supporting the intention to sell not only for trucks but also for passenger cars; both vehicles were in great demand during the show and received considerable praise.

In the Commercial Motor of 8 October 1937 a four-page article began 'A milestone in the history of oil-engine progress is set up by the introduction by F Perkins Ltd of Peterborough of a six-cylindered oil engine rated at 29.4 HP [RAC rating!], which develops, with normal settings, 85 BHP and weighs (without flywheel) only 580 lbs.' The article goes on to describe the engine in detail, describing it as a triumph of design as the first proprietary light six-cylinder oil engine to

An example of the iconic P6, part of the Perkins Heritage collection

This 1944 longitudinal cross-section of the P6 marine engine shows its constructional details. Note the front-mounted flywheel

make its appearance in the country. The potential for greater output than 85bhp was remarked upon, as was the achievement of 4,000rpm on the test bed. The article concluded with their impressions after driving the Studebaker car fitted with the Panther engine: the ability to pull down to 9mph in top gear and then accelerate to 65mph with no sign of distress, and up a 1 in 10 gradient, clearly impressed the journalist!

Purchase of Walnut Farm

If the product had 'arrived', there was also good news regarding the future home. Negotiations had been concluded over the land at Newark village, the 33-acre farm being purchased for £2,780 with the farmhouse included. The money came from Barclays Bank, who held the deeds for security. At the same time plans were drawn up for the factory: with a floor area of 54,000 square feet it was roughly twice the size of the area currently rented at Queen Street. The cost of construction was estimated at £12,000 and did not proceed, however, since Chapman had to advise the Board that their purchase accounts were on average two months in arrears, the suppliers were once more getting difficult and a sum in the region of £15,000 to £20,000 was

needed to restore confidence! Meanwhile orders had been placed for machine tools to a total value of £13,300: the mills, six-spindle borers, lathes and drilling machines were to be sufficient to machine 50 sets per week of P6 cylinder blocks, heads and connecting rods. (In terms of today's prices, the equivalent of around £700,000 would not buy many modern tools.)

Inevitably the Board's enthusiasm for new factory premises waned, the plans were put away and arrangements made to rent a further section of the old Queen Street works for the machine shop. At about the same time, the need for attention to jig and tool design became apparent, resulting in the recruitment of Vic Burney who established the initial department. (A part of the new area was used for the conversion business, with vehicles being brought in for engine installation by Perkins' staff, including Frank Hart who was to become a well-known figure within the Company and with its customers.)

Once more Alan Richardson came to the rescue with a further £5,000 loan (which was repaid by 31 December – to be immediately followed by a further loan for a similar amount!). With confidence that 1938 would at last see an improvement in fortunes, Alan Richardson and some friends formed a syndicate to purchase the machine tools, which were then rented to the Company at 5% per annum. Eventually hire purchase was arranged, buying them from the syndicate over three years.

A review of the events of 1937 showed around 760 engines sold; the £135,000 sales figure allowed a paper profit of around £11,000 once a further £6,500 had been added to the Development Account. The cost of developing and preparing for P6 production had absorbed over £30,000: Barclays were approached once more for help. With assets around £20,000 and stocks of £45,000 there was a more tangible feel to the Company. The order book of 145 engines included around 40 of the new P series with enquiries still rolling in, although those for the older products were slowing. The Bank was amenable to overdraft facilities, allowing up to £27,500 at 1% above Bank Rate, with a general charge against the assets. Through some judicious juggling with the goodwill of the suppliers the overdraft was kept to under £11,000 at the end of 1937, a somewhat more healthy position than had been forecast.

The interest in the P6 at the London Commercial Show was enough to encourage the Company to attend both the Brussels and Amsterdam Automobile Shows. However, during the first half of 1938 orders were only about the same as 1937, although it was the P series that was attracting the attention, with several manufacturers testing engines. The Wolf engine showed some sales for portable compressors, generators and welding sets, while sales of the Leopard were mainly for Fordson tractor conversions abroad. As a further attempt to boost sales, Laurie Hancock introduced a new concept – the 'Perpetuity Plan'. This plan allowed the owner of any Perkins engine to exchange it for a fixed payment, when it was worn out or damaged, for a reconditioned engine. The replacement unit carried the same guarantee as a new engine and included any improvements incorporated in new engines of the same type. By allowing the owner to have the replacement before returning the old engine the time lost during the changeover was minimised and unproductive downtime much reduced. Since there was no limit on the number of times the engine could be replaced (subject each time to the same fixed charge) this was a really attractive scheme and gave rise to the expression 'Perkins engines never die!' The Perpetuity Scheme continued to run for many years, ensuring that the Queen Street plant continued producing rebuilt engines long after the new production plant opened at Eastfield. It is difficult to quantify the real impact of the Plan upon the attitudes of operators to the 'dieselisation' of their vehicles and machines; certainly by providing, in advance, a means of identifying likely replacement costs there must have been encouragement to customers to take the plunge.

Laurie Hancock was also active in putting forward plans and propositions to encourage new agencies around the country. A memo of March 1938 to the Directors puts forward proposals for the conditions under which motor dealers would be offered agency status. These included levels of spare parts and engine stocks to be held, training of service and conversion personnel, advertising and discounting. In return the level of exclusivity for the territory (excluding original equipment manufacturers) would be granted. He went on to offer facts and figures to assist in calculating rebates and discounts, and to calculate running costs to persuade prospective users of the benefits of conversion. The memo reveals a high level of professionalism and thought being applied to the business of selling, clear evidence of the approach used by Laurie in his long and successful career.

During the year sales showed revitalisation, the two halves of 1938 producing orders of:

First half: Wolf 60 Leopard 140 P6 150

Second half: Wolf 30 Leopard 65 P6 385

(These are Chapman's figures but do not correspond with the 1,109 total sales figure recorded elsewhere; this is one of the discrepancies in the early records that we have been unable to reconcile completely.)

It is interesting to reflect upon the improvement in profitability brought about by the switch to the P6 and the in-house machining processes. The six-cylinder sold for £250, about £50 more than the Leopard: of the major components only the crankshaft and camshaft were machined outside so that the profit on sixty P6s was in excess of that made on one hundred of the earlier engines. By the end of June 1938, barely six months after its introduction, the P6 was being offered as a standard power unit by Albion, Bedford, Commer, Dennis, Dodge, Guy and Thornycroft in their trucks.

First road test of the P6 published

A Commercial Motor road test of 8 July 1938 was the first test of the P6 to be published, in a Commer LN5 lorry running at a payload of 5 tons with a gross weight of just under $7\frac{3}{4}$ tons. The engine received praise for its performance, refinement and engineering. Although the test was short by current standards, being of only 43 miles between Luton and Bedford, the fuel economy of 21mpg at an average speed of 28mph gave a saving of 0.6 pence/mile for an extra capital cost of £264. The flexibility of the engine down to 700rpm in top gear was noted, as were the low smoke and noise levels. (Such comments draw some reaction from employees of the time, who recall the distinctive noise of the P6, audible from some distance, as well as the tell-tale smoke trail under hard acceleration – however, the Press must always be believed . . .) Once again the CM praised the design for its lightness and asked rhetorically how it was that a small company like Perkins could achieve what larger concerns, with greater resources, had failed to do!

A further accolade came from the Seddon brothers, who had been conversion agents for Perkins. They were convinced that with this new engine it was possible to design a really successful purely diesel truck. They produced their first vehicle, a 4/5 tonner, with the P6 as standard equipment: this first step saw the founding of a new manufacturer destined to be not only a customer of Perkins for many successful years but also a new power in the industry, later becoming 'Seddon Diesel Vehicles'. Their first design was launched at the Scottish Show in November 1938 and by mid-1939 there were 22 trucks in use. Another road test published by Commercial Motor on 9 June 1939 con-

A typical publicity picture of a Commer lorry fitted with the P6. Posed outside the Boston 'stump' church, this picture dates from 1946

firmed that the performance of the truck, loaded to a gross weight of 8¾ tons, was lively and compared favourably with petrol-engined trucks of the class.

Contact with the Admiralty

While the vehicle side was going well, things had also begun to move significantly for the marine engine business. A friend of Chapman's from their days in Kent was Commander W.G. Cowland (later to be Rear Admiral), who in 1938 was Superintendent of the Admiralty Engineering Laboratory in West Drayton. He arranged to put the P6 engine through the Admiralty Type Test to see whether it might prove suitable for use in light auxiliary craft, such as launches, pinnaces, etc. The test was successfully completed and Perkins were then approached by the marine section of the Air Ministry, who operated a considerable number of small craft acting in support roles as seaplane tenders, air-sea rescue, target towing and other similar operations. All of the craft in use at the time were powered by petrol engines, mainly Meadows engines of around 100bhp; most of the craft were on semi-planing hulls and had been built by Power Boats Limited of Southampton. These craft were known as 'hard-chine' type and were able to start planing at around 12 knots, the engines being sufficient to give a top speed of around 20 knots 'on the plane'. The engines used needed to be relatively light, otherwise the boat would not lift into the planing position but would plough through the water like a conventional round-hulled craft. With the threat of war looming ever larger, thoughts were turning to diesel power to reduce the chances of fuel fires, and also to take advantage of the better efficiency of the diesel to increase the boat's radius of operation. The claims that the P6 was as compact and light as a petrol engine gave the Air Ministry their first chance to use the diesel in their high-speed craft, as up to that time the engines on the market did not approach the same power to weight ratio. Unfortunately 100bhp was not enough for some purposes and the real need was for 120bhp at about 2,250rpm: Perkins were asked if they could design an engine to meet this requirement without losing the power to weight advantage. The engines would need to be designed primarily for marine use, and should be suitable for saltwater cooling. The Ministry suggested that Meadows could advise on the marinising aspects and provide gearboxes and water pumps, while Power Boats could arrange a trial installation in one of their craft.

Perkins agreed to take on the task: Chapman and his small design team set to work on marinising the P6 and to produce the design of a larger six-cylinder engine. This had a bore increased to 4.375 inches but retained the 5-inch stroke of the P series; many other parts were common to both engines. The new engine in full marine form with reverse gear and all accessories turned the scales at 1,300lbs and produced 130 shaft horsepower at 2,250rpm. 10 lbs/bhp was a very competitive power to weight ratio for a fully-equipped marine engine of the time. The engine was designated 'S6', with the 'S' denoting 'Service'. Once again Chapman demonstrated the speed at which he could turn out a viable design: although the proposal was only made in June 1938 the first P6(M) was running on the test bed by mid-October, to be followed by the S6(M) before the end of November! Both engines completed their sea trials to the satisfaction of all parties.

Diesel power for aircraft?

There was more to come with regard to 'Services' interest. The belated realisation of the dangers and possibilities of an air war had awakened interest in the potential for a diesel aircraft engine, once again for the reduction in fire risk and better economy, to say nothing of the utilisation of an alternative fuel type. Experimental engines had been produced previously by Bristol Aircraft in England and by the Packard Motor Company in the USA, but both proved too heavy and low-powered for the modern aircraft. Meanwhile in Germany the Junkers Jumo

diesel was in production and gave take-off power of 1,000bhp, about equivalent to the Rolls-Royce Merlin at that time. During 1938 the Air Ministry placed contracts with one or two companies, possibly including Rolls-Royce, to develop a diesel combustion system, which might assist in the development of a successful production aero-engine of comparable performance to petrol units.

Frank Perkins and Chapman met with a Mr Tweedie in the Engine Development Section at the Air Ministry and at the July Board Meeting advised that a development contract had been promised, to design and produce a single-cylinder test engine of around six-inch bore. This engine would have a combustion chamber similar to the P6 'Aero-flow' design and after initial trials and acceptance would then be supercharged to establish the potential power output from the cylinder size.

Without waiting for the contract, and in spite of the other workload on his drawing office team, Chapman started work on the engine design. Schemes and details were produced along with the ancillary equipment needed, so that the 'Air Ministry Single', as it was called, was on the test bed and passed its acceptance test in February of 1939! It is little wonder that Charles Chapman remarks: 'By now I was getting a little tired of working against time. In fact I was getting a little tired, period.'

Better financial prospects

The end of 1938 showed a total of 1,109 engines sold, including 279 P6s. More to the point, the Company now had a range of engines that the users wanted to buy. It seemed that the major setback caused by the fuel tax bombshell of 1935 had been passed, and that somehow – mostly due to the major financial contribution from Alan Richardson – survival had been assured. The 1938 balance sheet still showed tight finances, with a bank overdraft of £29,406 (including the loan to buy the land!) and creditors at £34,835. Debtors stood at £30,071 and the Development Account at over £30,000. On a turnover of £157,773 and an issued capital of £55,504 the paper profit of £11,711 meant that things looked brighter, although after six and a half years of operation there was still no dividend for the Ordinary Shareholders. Considering all the development work of the past year, and the setting up of the machine shop, the Directors could look back with some satisfaction upon a year of advancement. However, the war drums were beating louder and the outcome of 1939 was going to be dependent upon issues well outside the control of the Company.

Some Personal Glimpses

During the celebrations of the Golden Jubilee of Perkins' formation in 1982, a number of early employees provided comments about their memories of the company. Some are reproduced here to provide some insight into working conditions and people in the earliest days.

Ernie Morson joined as a fitting shop apprentice in 1938 at a time when all engines were literally hand-built and considerable individual skills were needed. The apprentices spent months learning the various facets of their craft, working alongside a skilled man at each sub-assembly station before going on to the final engine assembly area. Piston heads were filed to give correct compression height and bearings were scraped to give correct clearances by hand – it took skill and time. 'A set of four pistons could take all day, so if you made a mistake it could be a serious business,' said Ernie. He recalled that those who made mistakes were given much cause to make sure they did not forget, going on to recall how he narrowly escaped three days' suspension after he accidentally cracked a cylinder block. 'I was learning jig- and tool-making at the time and was asked to get a broken tap out of a block, but as I tried to get it out I managed to break the block itself. I was told I would be suspended for causing the damage and that was a real blow because I was only getting about five bob (25p) a week in those days. But my governor spoke up for me and I got away with it.'

Apprenticeships at that time were a long and hard four years' work but gave those that persevered a very comprehensive training in basic metalworking skills. Another person who discovered how hard it was to pick up a broken craft apprenticeship was Bill White: 'I'd been round to all the major companies like Brotherhoods and couldn't get anything,' said Bill. He came to the yard of F. Perkins Limited and happened to run into the legendary Harry Beeton. 'I asked him if there was any chance of a job to complete my apprenticeship. He looked me up and down and just said "Yes, you can start on Monday – but you'll have to do another five years!" It was as simple as that. It wasn't much of an interview and there was never anything on paper. I just started the following Monday.'

Joe Roberts also started in 1938 as an office boy. His job was to do the tea round, sort the post and light the fires. A fire nearly got him the sack almost before he started when the fire in FAP's office failed to draw and filled the office with smoke. Tempers flared and Joe was told he was sacked. However, Miss Andrews, Frank Perkins' secretary, waved him away and then sweet-talked him round to save Joe's job!

Fred Bedford, later to become Perkins' first 50-year employee, remembered the heady moment when production went beyond 100 engines per month for the first time. He believed the year was 1938 and remembered that the event sparked off much jubilation, plus a bonus payment at the instigation of FAP. At the time Fred was earning 11 shillings and seven pence (59p today) per 48-hour week. The bonus was 5 shillings – 25p – which was a lot of money then and gave good cause to go out and celebrate! Fred used to work in the 'Black Hole' in the Queen Street test shop: it was so-called because of the murky atmosphere arising from the practice of running every engine without the exhaust manifold fitted. 'Flames used to shoot out of the engine and

so did the soot! If you were working in there you just got covered in black.' He remembered, too, some of the practices which would send shivers down the spines of today's safety officers. Much of the rotating machinery was unguarded and exposed: he recalled how during one torsional vibration test one worker caught his tie in the machine. It ripped the shirt off his back but miraculously did him little harm – but taught them all a lesson about ties and testing!

Another story from the test shop was recalled by Bob Coltman of Public Affairs. He remembers the Friday night baths taken by tester Ron Ireland in the heat exchanger tank. The water from the engines was run into a 52-gallon tank which had cold water pipes running through it to act as a heat exchanger. Ron had the natty idea of turning off the cold taps and allowing the water in the tank to get really hot. Then, with the tank steaming nicely, he would strip off and plunge in with his bar of soap for his weekly scrub-up! 'We got so used to it we didn't really notice it,' said Bob, who joined the Company in 1936. 'You would just think, "Oh, there's Ron having his bath again."' It would seem that he was never caught, otherwise he might have been in very different hot water!

One of the earliest female employees was Joyce Bell, later to become one of the longest-serving employees. She recalled her first meeting with Frank Perkins when she knocked on his office door as a shy 14-year-old. 'He had a gruff voice and I must have looked terribly nervous, because he asked, "Are you frightened of me?" When I answered, "Yes, I am a little", he replied gruffly, "Well, you don't have to be."' Joyce never forgot the kind way he tried to put her at ease. 'Working for the company was very enjoyable. It really did have a family atmosphere. I knew everybody by their Christian names. They were happy days.' She recalled that there were rougher edges of factory life too: 'If you had to walk through the factory you dared not stop for long. They would paint your heels while you stood there unawares!'

Chapter 5: The War Years (1939 to 1945)

The order book, as the spring of 1939 approached, showed a not-unexpected picture. Orders for the Wolf and Leopard were dropping off as experience grew with the P6 and new customers expressed interest. By April orders were appearing at the rate of seventy engines per month, including Air Ministry orders for P6(M) engines for their boats. Other Ministry contacts were made regarding the possible use of twin S6 engines in the A12 tank, but beyond a mention in the Minutes of Board Meetings nothing further is known of this proposal. An interesting contact in March was from Vosper Marine, who were building Motor Torpedo Boats and Motor Gun Boats for the Navy: they asked if Perkins would consider building Isotta Franchini petrol engines under licence for these boats. After some discussion the Board declined on the grounds that this would interfere with their other business.

Not surprisingly there was continuing pressure on finances, with stocks increasing and a need to start paying instalments to the syndicate for the machine tools. Frank Perkins and Charles Chapman travelled to talk with Barclays Head Office in London. Their case must have impressed the bankers since they were allowed a further £20,000, with the proviso that the Directors signed a guarantee for £5,000 of it. Thus by June the position looked better, with further customers opting for the P6, including Nash Motors in the USA – FAP was running one of their cars and the P6 gave it a top speed of around 90mph in good road conditions. Perkins continued to try to treat business 'as usual', in spite of increasing threats of war.

First effects of the declaration of war

When war was declared in September 1939, Perkins was immediately in contact with government departments regarding possible assistance to the war efforts. According to L.W.J. Hancock in his history of the Company, they were offered two alternatives: either to provide vehicle diesels to the Ministry of Supply with capital, a new factory, and up to 20,000 engines a year, or to supply marine diesel engines to the Admiralty, RAF and the War Office for various applications. Hancock remarks 'for some inexplicable reason, they chose the latter.' No comments, however, can be found in the Minutes of Board Meetings of the time or elsewhere, so any possible explanation for the decision is lost.

Within days the order book was in tatters as vehicle engine orders worth £25,000 were cancelled. Fortunately this was eventually offset by increased Air Ministry orders for marine engines, including the new S6(M): poor availability of gearboxes, however, meant that deliveries could not be completed fast enough. Once again a cashflow crisis was

resolved by a further £10,000 loan from the Bank for a two-month period. It was also agreed to increase prices for all engines other than marine by 15%. Additional office space was urgently needed, and premises at 30 Priestgate were eventually taken over from Wyman Abbott, while successful renegotiation of rental for the Wood Street workshops was made with the owner. The accounts at the end of 1939 showed a profit of over £12,000 on a turnover of £206,000, but with an overdraft of £57,640 and stocks worth over £76,000. Sales during the year totalled 1,218 engines, with the P6 accounting for 543 of these. By the Annual General Meeting of June 1940 there were over 1,000 engines on order, with a value of around £438,000. For the first time the Directors felt justified in declaring a dividend of 10% for 1939, even if paid out of borrowed money.

War need for a really big engine – the T12 is proposed

During 1939, the work on the Air Ministry Single had continued, with promising results: after the early acceptance trials work had continued using a separately-driven supercharger. Additional interest was now being shown, this time for a marine engine to power Air Ministry air-sea rescue boats. The RAF were using a few craft of 60 feet, each powered by three Napier Lion petrol engines of 500bhp: there were also a few newer boats powered by twin Rolls-Royce Merlin engines rated at 1,000bhp each. Both these aero engines had been marinised to suit these large planing craft which were capable of very high speeds. The problem was of course that the aircraft industry had a desperate need for the Merlin to power fighter aircraft in these early days of the war. Production was not yet geared up to produce the volume needed, and in any case the use of petrol engines in lightweight naval craft was not ideal: with their unarmoured construction and relatively large fuel tanks any successful enemy attack was likely to have disastrous results.

The Ministry reached a belated conclusion that a lightweight high-speed diesel engine of around 1,000bhp was urgently required; unfortunately no such unit existed or had even been seriously considered by British industry. There had been some thought within Perkins, however, since Charles Chapman and his Technical Assistant, Alec Gosling, had considered the potential for further development of the Air Ministry Single. In late 1939 the possibilities were discussed at the Air Ministry and in December a development contract was placed with Perkins to design, develop and produce two twelve-cylinder engines, based upon the AMS cylinder size. The brief identified that the engine should produce around 1,000bhp and be of a size to fit in an engine room to replace the Merlin on the same bearers. It was also stipulated that twin diesel engines with fuel for the boat's effective range (500 miles?) must weigh no more than twin Merlins plus fuel for the same range. Not surprisingly, the urgency for the engines was 'yesterday' with high priority given for materials and all else required to produce them – although cash was not so plentiful since the whole job was to be done for £12,000! There was a further limitation on materials: in view of the shortage of light alloys the engines should be mainly of cast iron construction, utilising as little aluminium as possible. In accepting the contract the Board agreed that a third engine should be built for development purposes. A twin-cylinder engine, with the cylinders in a vee, was also built for performance work, although little reference to this engine can be traced beyond some photographs.

Here was a challenge for the skill and intuition of Charles Chapman as a designer and engineer: nothing to match the proposed engine had ever been produced in England; the idea of a six-inch bore engine running at over 2,000rpm and producing power in excess of 1,000bhp

One of the T12 engines fitted to the test bed, probably 1942

A typical S6 marine engine of the war years. Note here too the front-mounted flywheel

was extraordinary. With little background except their own experience in designing the existing small engines, plus what little could be gleaned from elsewhere in Germany and the USA, Chapman and Alec Gosling started work with their small team. The actual experience within Perkins was limited – Alec Gosling had joined in 1936 with no diesel knowledge at all, while John Mustart was an experienced design draughtsman but with limited diesel background. Other members of the team were Martin Vulliamy, a young Cambridge graduate appointed as Research Engineer, and Bill Spoor, whose expertise was in technical calculations.

The contract was for a 12-cylinder engine in vee form. Chapman decided to work with the basic dimensions of the AMS: using the six-inch bore and stroke gave a swept volume of 33.3 litres. The design took shape as a 55-degree vee, the two banks of six cylinders being treated as individual in-line engines with separate fuel, water and oil pumps – with interconnection where necessary using non-return valves. (Chapman's idea was to provide a measure of 'fail safe' in operation, so that in the event of a failure on one bank the engine might still operate sufficiently well to get the boat home.) The engine design incorporated a number of novel features, such as the bevel drive from the front end of the crankshaft to the camshafts, fuel pumps and oil pumps; this may have been inspired by the bevel drive on the Merlin, where a complex drive arrangement at the rear of the engine took the drive to the camshafts, fuel pumps, other auxiliaries and the supercharger. The individual fuel injection pumps were linked hydraulically to allow the use of single throttle and stop controls; another unique feature requiring a new design solution.

The centrifugal supercharger, made by British Thompson Houston at Rugby to a Napier design, was driven from the crankshaft nose through step-up gearing and fed air at a maximum boost pressure of 7.5 lb/sq.in. to the intake manifolds via twin charge coolers. The use of seawater as the cooling medium was also a novelty.

It remains unclear if there were other outside influences on the design: we know that there were several powerful engines seen during the war years at Queen Street. As well as captured German engines such as the Junkers Jumo and Daimler-Benz aircraft engines supplied by the RAF, a V-12 petrol engine was received from America. This engine apparently arrived in a large cabinet-made wooden case, fastened together with a myriad of brass screws. This was unpacked by Albert Hall, who recalls the occasion well. Exactly what the engine was remains something of a mystery – it could have been a 'Liberty' aircraft engine of First World War vintage. A version was modified for marine use by the American record breaker Gar Wood who had set a number of records and wrested the Harmsworth Trophy from the British using his 'Miss America' series of boats. Gar Wood was also a leading force behind the building of the American 'PT' boats used in the Second World War with great success. (Possibly the interest here

was in the marinising arrangement, rather than other design features, since this engine design was already over 20 years old. Some 'Liberty' engines are believed to have been fitted into RAF boats, but with poor results.)

Production increases

As 1940 ran its course the Company was getting busier, and making money. In April 112 engines were delivered and there were 663 on order. By August the order book stood at over 1,000 and engine deliveries were not keeping pace although running at twice the rate of 1939: material bottlenecks on camshafts, cylinder block and head castings, were largely responsible for the delays. We have in the archives one 'stray' memo dated 20 August 1940 concerning engine order and delivery status: from 1 to 19 August thirty-five engines had been ordered by non-Ministry sources, and 41 engines delivered. These were a mixture of vehicle, industrial and marine units, mainly P6s and S6s.

An additional complication of the Ministry contract was the requirement for engines to be rebuilt possibly at a rate of 2 to 5 engines per week, for which premises and equipment were needed. By October the orders outstanding had reached 1,110, including 500 marine units for delivery up to June 1941; by now premises were being proposed at Newark on the new land, sanction being sought from the Ministry of Aircraft Production. Subsequently this idea was dropped and space found in an existing factory to the north of the City at Werrington, known later as 'the bulb factory'. This was requisitioned to become the 'rebuild' factory for the Ministry.

At the end of the year the order book was still increasing, with over £500,000 of firm orders and a further £250,000 expected. As a result increases of staff for both production and engineering were being proposed, and an additional truck purchased in view of the burgeoning business. The production for the year was approximately 1,170 engines, although the exact figure cannot be confirmed – P6s account for almost half of the figure. A sausage supper was organised for all employees, both male and female, and a bonus paid to staff. From the Board Minutes it is noticeable that service agreements were being renewed and the directors' salaries increased substantially after the lean years. Confidence in the future also increased, with Board discussions on expansion considering not just the wartime needs but also the likely post-war picture.

1941

In February 1941 the T12 engine was running in naturally aspirated form, with no problems reported – only 14 months from start of design. Once again the speed with which this engine had been designed, procured, built and the first unit run is amazing, considering the prevailing conditions, the complexity of the engine and the small team working on it. The Board recognised the contributions of Alec Gosling and John Mustart with salary increases and a cash bonus. The Minutes also record that interest in the T12 was being shown in the USA; some preliminary proposals were noted regarding the possible licensing charge that would be made, the extent of territorial coverage and reciprocal technical information flow.

At the end of March, Charles Chapman had tendered his resignation as Company Secretary, due to the pressure of work on the technical side. Mr Gerald McKeown, a chartered accountant and Chapman's brother-in-law, was appointed as his successor. Later in the year further appointments were made, of Mr A.G. Smith as Chief of Rate Fixing and Planning and of Mr A.J. Dillingham, who was elected to the Board in the position of Finance Director 'for the duration of the war'. At about this time, Alan Richardson took over responsibility for Sales and Service, spending much more of his time at Peterborough or on Perkins' business, although he was still primarily a farmer. His perfectionist approach and attention to detail, plus insistence upon the elimination of problem areas in the engine design, was recognised by Chapman as a major factor in the success of the P6 in particular.

The Board also debated the problems being experienced with continued production of the Leopard engine and it was decided that this engine would no longer be offered. The establishment of the re-build factory at Walton was noted, with reimbursement of costs for fixtures and fittings being sought from the Ministry. Agreement had also been reached with the Ministry for pricing up to March 1942, and an edict had been received regarding the setting up of a 'workmen's canteen', run by an outside contractor. Orders had been placed by Messrs Maudslay and Company for S6 vehicle engines, to be supplied from early 1942 on a cash-on-delivery basis: this business would take second priority to military orders. The initial requirement was for two engines each week, to rise later to five a week. The sales price was set at £495 for the first 24 engines. Large orders were also expected from Commer Cars, and it was noted that there were outstanding orders for 1,000 crankshafts for the P6 engine and that production parts orders stood at £107,000, around 1,000 engine sets! A small but interesting item in the Minutes records the establishment of a new Company Seal – this for the first time shows the four circles around the diamond, with a 'P' in the centre – the logotype which was to become an integral part of Perkins' identity in future years. (There had been a competi-tion for a new logo prior to the war, but the winning idea, with a six-pointed emblem surrounding a 'P' was quickly dropped due to the possibility of confusion with the Star of David and potential Jewish connotations. Laurie Hancock claimed credit for the new design, al-though there have been a number of other, and conflicting, claims regarding its origin and meaning.)

Freed from his Secretarial duties, Chapman was able to concen-trate on the development of the T12 engine, which had just entered the supercharged phase of its development; very soon this showed a problem when the crankshaft broke. This aspect of the design was acknowledged by Charles Chapman to be risky – in order to keep weight and dimensions to a minimum the bearing size was consider-ably less than established standards dictated. It was fortunate that no other components were damaged, so that a new crankshaft was fitted (taken from the kit held awaiting build of a second engine) and the testing continued. Since a repeat failure was seen as extremely likely, a design revision was put in hand immediately to provide a stronger crankshaft: an idea was 'borrowed' from the Junkers Jumo engine to strengthen the crankshaft in the vulnerable fillet radii region and the resulting process became known as 'junkerising'! In addition, a part of the problem was attributed to torsional vibration, and expert help was sought, resulting in the design of a damper fitted on the crankshaft.

1942

At the end of 1941, a final dividend for 1940 of 6% was paid on Prefer-ence Shares, and 10% on Ordinary Shares. The final payment for the hire purchase of the machines was paid to the Syndicate and it was noted that the Bank had now deleted the Directors' liability clause 'in view of the war footing'! The total engine production in 1941 was 1,485 engines, of which the P6 (606 engines) and S6 (474) made up the bulk. A bonus was paid to staff in view of the high level of effort through the year. The total sales amounted to £673,758, an increase of more than 50% over 1940, although the profit at £16,700 was down and the Bank overdraft up, at £98,000. The labour force was substan-tially increased, with the presence of women on the factory floor com-monplace, and necessary, to increase productivity.

Rescued air crew members visited Queen Street to thank Perkins employees for their support. Seen here with one of the many fe-male machinists employed during the war period

A typical RAF air-sea rescue launch, powered by P6 or S6 engines. Believed to have been taken in the mid-1940s

Disagreements over the S6 for Maudslay

Although production had increased considerably over the two years since war had been declared, it was still nowhere near meeting demand. The Ministry of Aircraft Production carried out an investigation of the Company's order book and its abilities, appointing a consultant to assist in reorganising to increase production. Marine requirements took first priority, of course, and other needs were subservient to military requirements. This meant that the Maudslay order was treated as a low priority, a situation that pleased Chapman since he had a considerable argument with FAP, and the Board, regarding this application. His views were quite clear. Deliveries were behind on the marine engines, and the existing facilities were unable to cope with increased vehicle engines production too. There was also the undeniable fact that the S6 was not designed for vehicle use, nor was it suitable! The main reason for Maudslay's interest apparently stemmed from their inability to obtain engines from Gardner, and was possibly also influenced by the presence of Bill Pailing, the erstwhile early Perkins employee, at Maudslay. Chapman's strong view, supported by his colleagues in the Engineering area, was that provision of an unproven engine could only result in damage to Perkins' good reputation in the vehicle market. In Chapman's manuscript he comments that 'although the order was later accepted, it was never executed or even started' – this is certainly not the case, since some of the old hands assure me that some engines were indeed shipped to Maudslay. They were a disaster and had to be withdrawn. The fact that some advertising literature for the vehicle version of the S6 has survived suggests that events did go further than Chapman recalls.

The Minutes record that in March 1942 Charles Chapman tendered his resignation due to the situation, and that this was not accepted by the Board. Alan Richardson suggested instead that he should take three months' holiday and reconsider his position. At this same meeting it was recorded that the T12 was to proceed with Acceptance and Type Tests for the Ministry.

According to Chapman there was considerable confusion a few days later regarding the future of the project: a meeting had been arranged at Queen Street with Ministry personnel to inspect the second engine, completed as a mock-up, to agree installation arrangements and timing for sea trials. The meeting was joined by only one of the expected Ministry personnel, Squadron Leader Jinman; after a wait for the others he called the Ministry, only to be told that 'all work on the T12 contract had been stopped on the previous Friday'. This was a total surprise to Chapman, who travelled down to meet Major Bulman (then Deputy Director of Engine Developments) the next day. He ascertained that cancellation papers were being prepared but would take about six weeks to go the rounds. Major Bulman promised that if the engine could complete its Type Test by 31 May he would exert all possible pressure and influence to get the stop order rescinded. Chapman and his team in the test area, including Harry Lane, the Shop Foreman and Norman Burney, in charge of the engine, worked round the clock to complete the test. They succeeded, after a problem with valve springs, and managed ratings up to 850bhp at 2,300rpm Emergency rating, rather less than had been hoped for. The 'stop order' was rescinded so that work could continue. A meeting at the Ministry of Supply looked at production but this never proceeded. Chapman's manuscript implies that this was the end of the T12 (and blames it upon the interference by Frank Perkins), but in fact this was not quite the case, as may be seen a little later in this narrative.

At the May Board meeting Frank Perkins reviewed the past history of the products – in Chapman's absence – and suggested that now was the time to improve quality and to market a product 'in which the customer has more pride than hitherto.' He went on to ask the Technical Department to submit plans for an engine suitable for a maximum load vehicle, which could also be used industrially, and for a redesign of the P6 to make it suitable for a Seddon-type truck at a gross weight of 7–8 tons. While Chapman records nothing regarding this demand, he notes that FAP felt that he had spent too much time playing around with the T12 and that the delays with the S6 and its production were Chapman's fault (reputedly a statement relayed to him by Major Bulman of the Ministry.) It is certain that there were major problems with the S6, an outbreak of cylinder scuffing on test eventually being traced to production management trying to speed the liner finishing by increasing the honing pressure too much.

Charles Chapman resigns

At the Board Meeting of 11 June, Frank Perkins referred to the Ministry wish to restrict S6 production to marine use, but noted that with a target of 100 engines per month and a current Ministry demand of only 55 a month there was still the potential to supply Maudslay.

The following month progress on the T12 was reviewed: Frank Perkins commented that sea trials were essential and would be carried out. The T12 performance versus the Hall Scott petrol engine was compared. By October 1942 Chapman was recorded as absent due to sickness and FAP reviewed proposed reorganisation charts for Production, Technical and Service Departments with the Board members, showing a proposed Products Department reporting directly to the Managing Director instead of to the Technical Director – subject to agreement with Charles Chapman. The outcome of these discussions is not recorded but by the end of the year Chapman had resigned from the Board and severed all connections with the Company. It can be concluded that the quarrel between the two men had reached a point of no return. Chapman took up a commission in the Naval Reserve and worked on couplings during the remainder of the war years. His subsequent career as author and consultant brought him back into contact with Perkins after some years, as will be related later. The departure of Charles Chapman had a very serious effect upon both the morale and overall effectiveness of the Engineering area: he was the

most experienced designer and the principal architect behind the success of the P series and S6 engines. The vacuum left by his departure was an important factor in the immediate post-war period: without detracting from the work carried out by Messrs Gosling, Mustart, Condie and Vulliamy in developing the existing products, the absence of the original designer and especially a manager with organisational ability and 'clout' in the Boardroom proved a key factor in later events.

A 'hush-hush' application

During the early 1940s another, very secret, marine application was also originated which involved Perkins in the early stages. A Royal Navy initiative was proposed with a primary objective of attacking the German capital ships secreted in the Norwegian fjords. These heavily armed ships, including the Tirpitz, were a major threat to Allied shipping convoys as well as to the Royal Navy fleet, yet they were invulnerable to the existing sea and air forces while they continued to lurk menacingly in the narrow Norwegian waters. Vice Admiral Sir Max Horton, in command of the submarine force since January 1940, initiated the development of a prototype miniature submarine, based on a sketch made by Commander C.H. Varley. The latter worked with Vickers-Armstrong, Admiralty and Portsmouth Dockyard specialists to complete the design and produce two prototypes, named as X3 and X4. The first of these was laid down in September 1941 and launched on 15 March 1942 by Varley Marine at Hamble. X3 was fitted with a Perkins P4, rated at 32bhp, which gave a surface speed of 6 knots unladen, with an electric motor and batteries for submerged running; the diesel being used of course to recharge the batteries too. The craft was designed around a crew of three and was intended to have a range of up to 1,400 nautical miles.

The X3 was 43.5ft long and had a beam of 5.5ft unladen, increasing to 8ft when fitted with the two 'pannier' charges (each containing 4,000lbs of 'Amatol' high explosive) which were her sole armament: the method of operation was intended to be by a stealthy submerged approach to the enemy ship riding at anchor, then to lay the charges

The Perkins fire brigade on parade outside the Queen Street works, showing the uniforms and equipment of the 1940s

beneath the ship and arm them with a delay mechanism before making an escape. The submarine was fitted with a 'wet and dry' compartment, which would allow a trained diver to exit the submerged craft to cut anti-submarine netting and overcome other harbour defences where necessary. The craft displaced 22 tons unladen on the surface and 30 tons with the charges attached: with a freeboard of only a foot or so, the craft was fitted with a six-foot air mast to allow the engine to be run safely with the main hatch closed. The commanding officer was strapped to the mast during surface running to avoid his being washed overboard!

The X4 was launched later in 1942 and was virtually identical but slightly longer at 45 feet. Needless to say, these craft were very primitive, with little comfort for the crew in the very cramped interior, having barely 4ft headroom and very basic navigation and other equipment. The range of the craft was limited by the crew's endurance rather than by fuel, trials proving that the use of a second crew for transit (towed behind a larger submarine) was an essential consideration for operational use. During the trials X3 sank in 114 feet of water when the induction mast valve was left open when the craft submerged; fortunately all three crew escaped and the craft was salvaged and refitted. Both craft were used for basic training of crews at Port Bannatyne on the Isle of Bute from May 1942: the performance of the craft was sufficient for the Admiralty to order quantity production of an improved and slightly larger operational craft, which had a crew of four.

These definitive 'X' craft were numbered X5 to X10, to be followed later by X20 to 25. They were built in 1942/3, initially by Vickers-Armstrongs and later by a consortium of Broadbent in Huddersfield, Markham in Chesterfield and Marshalls of Gainsborough. They also built later craft, known as XT (training) and XE class, which were larger and more sophisticated. For some unrecorded reason all these production craft were fitted with 42bhp Gardner engines – as used in the London buses of the time – although there were apparently no problems with the P4 that have been identified. (If they had needed more power, why not use the P6?) Both X3 and X4 remained in service for training until 1945, when they were scrapped. Thus the Perkins association with the submarine service was essentially non-operational until the post-war craft, know as the X51 or 'Shrimp' class, were commissioned.

History records, however, that the Gardner-powered craft were successfully used in attacks on the Tirpitz, an exploit recorded in books such as Above Us The Waves. A total of 32 craft were completed up to 1944, of which six were lost in action and two others in collisions. Twenty-six men lost their lives in X craft. For the successful operations there were two VCs, three DSOs, one DSC, two DSMs and two CGMs awarded. Quite a record for a branch of the Senior Service that was small in all respects except courage.

Success of the P6 and S6 in wartime applications

It is unfortunate that very few records survive regarding the use of the P6 and S6 engines in the many boat applications powered during the war years. There is no doubt that these engines assisted in part with the rescue of many aircrew forced to ditch in the seas around the British Isles; indeed some of these crews were entertained at Queen Street by Perkins as part of the war effort to boost morale. Unfortunately, although there are some photographs of these events, there

This picture dates from about 1950 and illustrates the rambling nature of the Queen Street works and its proximity to Peterborough City centre

Captured in this 1950 photograph are three of the original staff taken on by Frank Perkins in 1932. From left to right they are Bill Paling, Norman Burney and Edward Marvill

is no written evidence supporting them, so we may only guess at the tales that might have been told! Earlier historical reviews suggest that Perkins engines assisted in the rescue of over 14,000 aircrew during the course of the war, a substantial number and evidence of their 'unsung hero' role during the conflict. Records at the RAF Museum, Hendon, and in the hands of Philip Simons, the Coastal Forces Historian with the British Military Powerboat Trust at Southampton, suggest that Perkins engines were used in the following categories of craft:

Royal Navy

60-foot Admiralty Fast Seagoing Motor Boats (3 x S6)

25-foot Fast Motor Boats (later versions) (1 x P6)

35-foot Fast Motor Boats (later versions) (2 x P6)

45-foot Fast Motor Boats (3 x P6)

Royal Air Force

38-foot Seaplane Tenders (2 x S6)

40-foot Seaplane Tenders (2 x S6)

41.5-foot Seaplane Tenders (2 x S6)

60-foot General Service Pinnaces (3 x S6)

Royal Army Service Corps

44.5-foot 'River' class Fast Launches (2 x S6)

48-foot 'Derby Winners' Class Fast Launches (3 x S6)

A number of these craft still survive, although not now with the original engines. One of the best known is the Hyperion ('Derby Winners' Class), built by Samuel White on the Isle of Wight as part of a batch of ten ordered in 1940. She was delivered on 8 February 1943 and saw service including the mock invasion exercises leading up to the D-Day invasion in June 1944 where she, along with other boats of the Class, saw action in support of the invasion. Hyperion flew the flag of the Rear Admiral, operating on beach clearance along Gold, Sword and Juno beaches. Her total service record is not known, but in June 1945 she was used, with sister vessels Grand Parade and Humorist, in the Channel Islands following the German surrender; later she was

used for range clearance duties. Hyperion remained in service up to 1971 and upon disposal went through a number of hands before her current owner Bob Cake took her restoration in hand.

According to Philip Simons there were some 2,500 wartime craft still surviving in 2002, not all Perkins-powered of course but a tribute to the way these boats were built even at time of war.

There were of course applications other than marine propulsion that used Perkins engines in the war years. Alongside the obvious industrial uses – such as compressor plant, generator sets, cranes, excavators and welding sets, all of which were essential to maintain services, clear bomb damage, etc. – there were special on-board generator sets used on naval craft. The need for electrical power to 'degauss' naval craft was a little-known but essential application. For craft engaged in minesweeping, or operating where German mines could have been laid, regular degaussing of the metal hulls was necessary to reduce electrical field built up during voyages and thus reduce the attraction of magnetic mines. Perkins generator sets were used for this purpose, for instance the S6 rated at 54kW, as well as providing emergency power and standby power for many buildings. With an 'automatic' set, using a system covered by British patent 541496, provision of full power could be obtained within eight seconds of power interruption. Other unsung but essential duties included providing dockside power for recharging of submarine batteries, emergency power for military communication centres, ordnance factories, etc.

Wartime growth and production

The war years saw production from the Queen Street works rise steadily, from 1,218 in 1939 and 1,170 in 1940, to successive figures of 1,485, 1,869, 1,746, 1,695 and to 2,278 in 1945. These do not include the many engines reworked and rebuilt for both Ministry and civilian use. The Wolf and Leopard engines had been phased out of production by 1943, so that later figures were for S6, P4 and P6 products only. The 1945 output comprised 1,388 P6s, 342 P4s and 548 S6s. The total wartime production of around 12,000 engines also included a number of vehicle engines, permitted by the Ministry for urgent applications, and industrial engines sold for essential purposes not directly connected with the war effort.

The growth of manpower was also considerable: from around 275 people at the end of 1939 the total workforce at the end of 1945 was about 1,000, spread around the 100,000 square feet of factory and office space and able to produce up to 200 engines a month, material permitting. Active support from the Ministry had also assisted in ensuring that additional space was found around the Queen Street premises, the upgrading of the heating system and other improvements.

Throughout the period of the war Perkins, and indeed the City of Peterborough itself, seems to have led a charmed life as far as air raids were concerned. Very few bombs were dropped around the city centre, and there was little work for the Perkins volunteers who formed both their own fire brigade and the Home Guard 'fire watch' detail. Photographs of the time show many familiar faces amongst these volunteers – Bill Baxter and Martin Vulliamy among them. There are inevitably stories of activities on the nightly watches, equipped with the ubiquitous stirrup pump and buckets of sand to extinguish incendiary bombs. By 1945 Perkins had taken over most of the premises around Queen Street which had previously been a part of the old Barford and Perkins site. In addition other offices nearby had been rented or requisitioned, including those already mentioned in Priestgate, as well as the New Bedford Hotel in Queen Street.

As part of their efforts to maintain morale, Perkins workers donated to the 'Wings for Victory' campaign (£35,000 raised in 1941 alone), and took part in National Savings and other drives. Weekly collections made by the workforce resulted in ten-shilling postal orders being sent regularly to the ex-employees who had been drafted into the forces 'during hostilities' – an addition to their pay which was gratefully received by the men concerned. (Terry Sismore was one grateful recipient and recalls that on his return to the Company after demob he would be gently reminded of his workmates' generosity by their cadging of cigarettes in 'repayment'!)

A small but significant morale-booster was the regular appearance of the 'Perkins Reminder' – a monthly diary format that always included an appropriate cover (often in cartoon form) as well as quotations and sayings, advertisements and technical data on the products. This appeared throughout the war years, in spite of paper restrictions, and was edited by Laurie Hancock. Used as a sales aid around the distributor and customer network, it continued to be produced until the 1970s and is still a well-remembered offering.

Plans for post-war production

As the war came to a close, efforts were made to revise the proposed plan for the new factory at Newark. An important player in this project was a newcomer to the Company named Norman Collins: he had come to the attention of Frank Perkins in his role within the Ministry of Supply and had been seconded part-time to Perkins to assist in reorganising the plant for greater productivity. W.N. Collins had been instrumental in reorganising the servicing operations for the military workshops looking after vehicles on a countrywide basis, and his planning abilities were recognised by FAP, who lost no time in offering him a role, as Service and Sales Director, in the ambitious plans being formulated for the post-war development of the company.

Little has been said in this chapter about the finances of the Company, which had moved into profitability – as did many others – through their successful supply of articles essential to the prosecution of the war. Turnover during the period from 1942 to 1945 had topped one million pounds each year, but the profits were not high and varied somewhat, with heavy taxation ensuring that success did not come easy. Chapman commented in his unpublished history: 'The total profits earned by the Company over the seven years from 1939 to 1945 were roughly £270,000. Of this some £46,000 (before tax) was paid as dividends on the Preference and Ordinary shares, leaving around £224,000. From this taxation took over £200,000, reducing the net retentions of the Company to barely £24,000 out of its seven years efforts.'

He goes on to note that if income tax had remained at the pre-war level of around five shillings in the pound, and there had been no 'excess profits tax' to contend with, the Company might have been left with nearer £168,000 instead of a paltry £24,000. On this basis, the financing of the required factory expansion would have been possible from its own resources – and thus it could be concluded that the war hit Perkins badly! This assumes of course that Perkins would have been equally successful in selling every engine it could produce, but for peaceful use instead. This must be left as an unanswerable question, for looking back even with the benefit of over fifty years of hindsight it is impossible to make a valid judgement. Whether profitable or not, the position in which Perkins entered the post-war period was very much one of strength and promise.

Some Wartime Recollections

Stan Reedshaw, an employee who worked on maintenance in the Engineering Department, recalled how during the war period they could be working all day on the factory floor and then spend all night on fire watch or Home Guard duties. In the early period Perkins had the Home Guard unit but did not have its own air raid shelter. He recalled the technique for taking cover during an air raid: 'First came the siren and then the red alert. The theory was that the Germans would go for mass bombing of the town centre so that it was thought likely that the Queen Street factory could be hit, particularly if they were going for the railway. Everyone had bicycles in those days, so when we got the alert we had to rush out of the factory, jump on our bikes and pedal away from the town centre. Mind you, back at the factory they knew how long it should take you to get back when the all-clear sounded – so you were in trouble if you were late.' (During 2005 the author obtained a copy of a Luftwaffe aerial photograph of Peterborough, clearly identifying the Baker Perkins works, the railway yards and the Westwood airfield as well as the city centre. No mention appeared of Perkins!)

Ernie Harrold was another employee who remembers working on a number of wartime Navy projects, including the X-craft prototypes. He recalled that it was so secret that he was effectively locked up in Hull, doing the work on the installation in an air-raid shelter, actually during air raids on the city. Ernie of course had to sign the Official Secrets Act before working on this job! He was effectively kept under armed guard on another occasion while working on an engine, being warned that the corvette was under a 'red alert' to sail at any moment due to the German invasion threat. Once the job was complete and tested, he was allowed to go. Another service visit with Albert Chapman to attend to a pair of 54kW generators used on a minesweeper found them being plied with too much navy rum, which ultimately stopped the work for a time!

At the end of the war the Company was in a good position for building upon its wartime success as far as the products were concerned. Charles Chapman cites a number of factors which were in its favour:

1. Perkins was the only diesel manufacturer in the world with engines in its class fully developed and in production.

2. There was already some eight years of operational experience with the P series engines: early faults had been eliminated and the engines had a good reputation.

3. After six years of concentration on wartime needs and very little 'normal production', and with a large part of the developed world either devastated or disorganised, there was an enormous potential demand for the products.

4. No other European country, and especially Germany, was in a position to compete.

Chapman summarised the development of Perkins over the war years by reviewing the balance sheets for 1939 and 1945:

	31.12.39	1.12.45
Number of employees	275	1,000
Total wages	£27,286	£188,185
Total salaries	£17,786	£76,621
Average wage/salary (per week)	£3. 3. 0	£5. 2. 0
Turnover	£206,320	£1,304,484
Turnover per employee	£750	£1,305
Turnover per £1 of wages/salaries	£4.55	£4.90
Total Profit	£12,162	£64,266
Profit as % of turnover	5.9 %	4.9 %
Total Tax	£4,000	£53,750
Tax as % of turnover	2.0 %	4.1 %
Tax as % of profit	33.0 %	83.5 %
Fixed assets	£46,998	£77,084
Stock	£76,641	£100,298
Debtors	£40,462	£177,976
Cash	£194	£295
Development account (including patents)	£36,302	£18,479
Issued Capital	£55,654	£81,504
Comprising (a) Preference Shares	£20,450	£30,700
(b) Ordinary Shares	£35,204	£50,804
Turnover per £1 capital	£3.70	£16.00
20. Bank Overdraft	£57,846	£50,938
Creditors (excluding tax)	£57,640	£119,402
Tax (a) Due	£3,532	£84,793
(b) Future	£3,920	£14,750
Profit and loss account	£138	£1,017
Gross Dividends paid for the year	£4,747	£6,922
Dividends as % of turnover	2.3%	0.53%
General Reserve	£15,000	£15,000
Liquidity (debtors + cash, less bank/creditors/tax)	-£83,282	-£91,612

However, the Company was not in good shape financially, thanks largely to the effects of high taxation. Furthermore it was operating in rented premises, a good proportion of which had been requisitioned under Government orders, and within which there was no room for expansion. The constraints imposed by the layout of the Queen Street buildings were also very serious, since the series of small workshops prevented efficient operations. The separation of offices in what was really a rabbit warren of old-fashioned and dilapidated buildings also did nothing to encourage good communication and working practices. Just to add to the pressure, it was known that the City Council was anxious to remove all industry from the centre of Peterborough as part of its post-war redevelopment. The Directors therefore had an interesting dilemma, faced with a seemingly limitless potential for immediate and future sales whilst boxed into a situation where they had neither space nor cash to take advantage of the opportunity!

Planning for post-war expansion

It was fortunate that they still owned the land at Newark, which FAP had continued to operate as a farm during the war. Starting in early 1945 more land was purchased adjoining the farm, all in relatively small parcels and from a series of owners. Estimates had been made during the closing months of the war to establish the size of new factory required and the likely expenditure: a sum of around £250,000 had been determined, covering building, services and plant. None of the current shareholders could fund this venture. In view of the past record, with negligible assets and poor profitability, it seemed unlikely that a public share issue would prove successful. All was not lost, however, since the Government had established the 'Finance Corporation for Industry Limited' (FCI), a new body whose principal objective was to assist the financing of manufacturing industries where ability to fund expansion needs through normal sources was not equal to the potential viability. F. Perkins Limited was clearly one such company. One of the body's representatives was Mr G.S. Nelson, who became a staunch supporter of Perkins and ultimately became General Manager of FCI in the 1960s.

A detailed plan was drawn up for the new factory; on 20 June 1945 this was ready for submission to the appropriate authorities, naming the five directors of the time:
F.A. Perkins, Chairman and Managing Director
A.J.M. Richardson, Marketing Director
A.W. Dillingham, Finance Director
V.R. Wilkinson-Allen, Works and Production Director
W.N. Collins, Service Director
(Mr Wilkinson-Allen later changed his name to Ferguson for personal reasons).

The factory planning envisaged the production of 3,000 new engines each year, with space available for conversion of base engines for vehicle, industrial and marine customers. There would be capacity for rebuild of 200 engines per month as well as production and supply of spare parts. The declared intention was to purchase the latest specialised production machinery, and to introduce flow line manufacture. The plan defines as its objective: 'To build up and maintain a reputation for quality engines that will give trouble-free service in operation at a minimum maintenance and running cost.' A total factory space of 161,000 sq ft was specified with a building project cost of £127,016, excluding land.

The submission noted that the order book included 21 different applications of the three base engines, with a further 51 projects under consideration and technical evaluation. (The 3,000 engines a year already looked very low considering that the marketing projection in-

This view of a part of the machine shop at Queen Street dates from 1945 and gives some idea of the working conditions of the period

dicated a demand of 7,500 units in 1947.) Perkins also emphasised the importance of exports to Great Britain's recovery and the Government's own warning that demand would soon increase substantially beyond the pre-war figures, adding that Perkins had an important part to play in this drive, based upon its own pre-war evaluations and identified potential. In setting a figure of 40% of production for exports the Company expressed confidence that this could be exceeded once output bottlenecks were overcome and Ministry demands satisfied.

Getting a decision from Government

During the summer and autumn of 1945 contacts were made with the complex Government departmental structures involved. Initial Ministry of Supply reaction to Perkins' requests for action had been to offer a delay in the de-requisitioning of the premises taken over during the war years: Perkins did not favour this, since it only delayed the eventual move. In a letter to Mr W.A. Tookey at the Ministry of Supply on 9 July Frank Perkins refers to a meeting held at Melbourne House the previous week at which the question of Perkins' moving away from Peterborough was obviously raised, along with the concern over the position of the Perkins factory in the centre of the city. FAP highlighted the declared intentions of British Thomson-Houston to retain their factory barely two miles from the centre of the city for the manufacture of consumer goods (later this became the Hotpoint factory at Fletton) with a considerable number of additional employees, yet objections were being made regarding an established company such as Perkins. He went on to say 'It would seem unreasonable to raise objections to our Company remaining in the town where they have been for so many years and where practically all the employees have

permanent homes, when a new firm having no previous connection with the town will remain in operation as a result of their war-time activities.' He then suggested that the continued insistence on the migration of the Company to a distressed area would probably result in difficulty in continuing the business successfully. 'The production of our engines within this city is not a transitory one, and through no fault of our own, we are faced with extinction unless approval of our

Engine test in 1945

application is given. We feel very strongly that such approval should not be denied, varied or withheld from us.'

Whether it was this forthright approach that finally swayed the argument is not known. Consent was finally obtained on 11 September 1945 for the new factory building at what was to become known as the Eastfield site at Newark village. By November discussions opened with the FCI and after more negotiations an agreement was signed in July 1946. Under this agreement the FCI subscribed in cash at par for a series of shares:

$4^1/2$% Redeemable Cumulative Preference Shares of 10s each = £95,917
Ordinary Shares of 1s each = £27,534
4% Debentures of £1,000 each = £213,000

In addition some of the existing shareholders subscribed for a further:

$4^1/2$% Redeemable Cumulative Preference Shares of 10s each = £4,083
Ordinary Shares of 1s each = £9,466

Thus the new capital received by the Company between late 1946 and early 1947 amounted to a total of £350,000, a significant vote of confidence in the future. There were of course some strings attached to the FCI investment, especially control of overdraft facilities at the Bank and the payment of dividends and unappropriated profits.

The final Building Proposals were given to Peterborough City Council on 5 October 1945, showing a factory consisting of 12 bays, each 200 feet by 60 feet, giving an area of 144,000 square feet. The City Council had already designated the Newark area as a potential industrial site (fortunate in view of the length of time Perkins had owned the land!) and was prepared to support the development by improving the services to the area, including roads, water, drains and electricity supply. The plans for the redevelopment of the Queen Street area were already in being, showing a shopping centre and other amenities (it was no fault of Perkins that this plan should remain unfulfilled until the late 1970s).

Eastfield construction started

The process of clearing the site and commencing building began, but not without its difficulties. In the post-war environment there were shortages and allocations, not just of the basic materials such as steel and concrete but also labour. At the end of 1945 Perkins had around 600 production personnel and a total workforce of about 1,000. The indications given to the Ministry were that this number would not increase, although in the new factory the more efficient conditions would allow a considerable increase in engine production. Due to the high demand for engines it was noted that company labour could not be released to assist in the factory construction.

Along with the building plans, within a few weeks the requirements had been identified for the plant and equipment to upgrade the production facilities. The development of facilities included machining of the main components, covering cylinder blocks, cylinder heads, main bearing caps and connecting rods. The assembly and test areas would also be upgraded although the cost was modest in comparison with machining. For blocks a budget of £44,000 covered purchase of milling machines, radial and multi-spindle drills, boring and tapping machines. These dedicated machines would not only increase output but also reduce reliance upon operator skill, in the critical areas of cylinder, cam and crank centre boring. The cylinder head budget of £15,500 was primarily for milling machines and multi-drilling machines, and the bearing cap allocation of £7,000 mainly on milling. An expenditure of £16,000 for connecting rod machining covered a total line comprising milling, boring, drilling and grinding machines whilst the £17,000 spent on assembly and test included major expenditure

The P4 engine was used in many roles from the 40s onwards: this is a typical industrial engine of the period

on test dynamometers. The total budget of around £125,000 included consumable tooling and maintenance areas and was considered a 'Priority A' requirement. By modern standards this capital expenditure seems modest indeed, even allowing for the tremendous inflation over the intervening years. Added to this essential budget, there was an additional 'Priority B' list, covering £24,000 for tool room and general purpose component machining. This was noted as 'not essential but very desirable from a cost reduction aspect'.

Just to put these costs into perspective, around £150,000 for equipment and £125,000 for the building meant a commitment of around 25% of the yearly turnover for their new factory. An ambitious project, even given the 'bullish' views of the new markets and customer demand as seen by the Directors.

Much opportunity but frustratingly slow progress

While the new site was being prepared the business of the company continued at Queen Street. Production was maintained at the best pace possible taking into account the supply difficulties in the aftermath of the war. Rationing continued of course, with some items remaining in short supply until the early 50s. The effects of this, on a population coming to terms with the negative impacts of the final victory, are well documented elsewhere and have no place in this history. The Company struggled to 'make do' in the dilapidated and overcrowded Queen Street works, determined to continue production of the P6 and P4 engines as the spearhead of the sales efforts both at home and abroad. It was clear that many opportunities existed, not just for new vehicles but also to convert existing machinery to take advantage of diesel engine economy and durability. Appendices to the Ministry submission showed not only outstanding orders of 2,420 engines for approved Ministry of Supply applications, but also a further potential 1,800 sales for home and export markets. The projected monthly requirements for 1946 were shown as 491 engines, covering purely the new truck and truck conversion sector: to this a further 95 engines a month were projected for industrial sales and a further 38 engines a month for marine applications. The submission suggested that the total of around 7,500 engines for 1946 was if anything an underestimate of the likely demand. In fact the volume of new engines produced in 1945 was 2,278 and for 1946 only 3,625, due to the lack of capacity and the inability of suppliers to meet the increased call for their parts. Moves were made to increase production by subcontracting some assembly to Beans Industries, who never achieved the targets set. Other possible assemblers were sought but without good results. Problems with fuel pump supply from CAV meant that an alternative source was urgently needed, and Simms Motor Units were selected as the most likely, with development costs partially covered by Perkins. (In March 1946 a report by the industry body, the British Internal Combustion Engine Manufacturers Association, suggested that around £750,000 of engine orders were held up due to fuel injection equipment shortages.)

To ease the overcrowding in the Queen Street offices a drawing office was set up at Southampton in conjunction with Sparshatt and Sons; John Condie was seconded from the Technical Department to take charge of the venture, intended to handle the growing design needs of the applications business. After discussions with government a number of the requisitioned premises in Peterborough were retained for a further period to ease the pressure on space for the growing workforce.

S6 production fell from 548 in 1945 to only 52 in 1946 as the military orders dried up, while P6 volume rose from 1,388 to 3,073 in the same period. The P4 demand increased too, from 342 to 500. The majority of these engines was for vehicle use. A limited amount of design work started on new products, with an engine identified as the 'D9' being proposed to extend the power range upwards for larger trucks. Captain Richardson requested a power and speed uprating for the P6; as a result two engines were run on field trials at Wimpey Construction.

Publicity moves ahead

Campaigns for engine sales to all sectors started, targeting not only the home market but also looking at export potential. Appointment of dealers, distributors and 'sign holders' to support the engines in the field was a further priority, while the 'Perpetuity' scheme assisted the conversion market by reducing the depreciation factor as well as offering fast availability of replacement engines. Conversions of tractors and combine harvesters became significant, with support from Ford and Massey Harris.

Freed from the strictures of wartime, Laurie Hancock and his publicity staff were given their head, advertising through trade journals as well as the relaunch of the Perkins News as a sales promotion aid.

The end of 1946 brought a considerable change in the financial position, not least with the share structure where the issued capital consisted of 200,000 Redeemable Preference Shares of 10s each and 1,819,400 Ordinary Shares of 1s each. The total of £190,970 was about two and a half times that of a year before. The Bank overdraft had vanished, being replaced by £163,000 of the 4% Debentures – secured against the assets of the Company. The creditors at £218,540 exceeded the debtors of £183,952 and stocks had risen by about £185,000, all good and saleable material.

1947 – a cold start

The early months of 1947 are well remembered as 'The Great Freeze' which gripped the country for many weeks. Closure of the works for several weeks was necessary as power cuts and supply failures affected everyone since the power industry proved incapable of providing sufficient electricity to cope with the unprecedented demand. It was suggested that this crisis of power supply might continue for some years, with the need for staggered shifts being seriously debated. The intended powerhouse installation at the new factory was reconsidered, with the installation of up to five T12s in place of the planned two becoming a serious possibility, provided that the engines could be reacquired from the Admiralty. (This proposal was eventually dropped after a Ministry of Supply directive that power generation had to be continuous, not just standby.)

The weather exacerbated the difficulties faced by the Company as it struggled to keep production rolling at Queen Street while the new factory was being fitted out and gradually occupied as new machines were installed and others transferred. The construction of the new building included an east wall constructed from corrugated iron

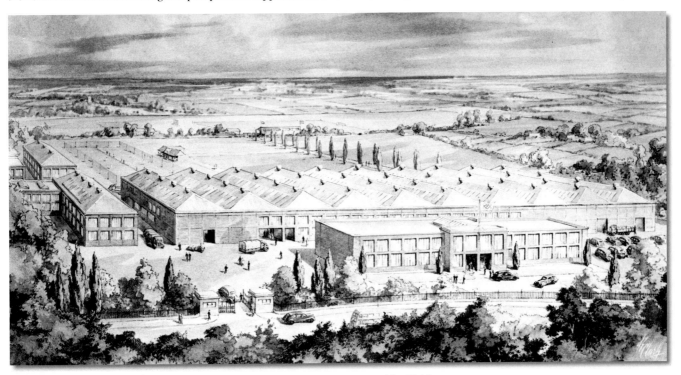

This artist's impression shows the new Eastfield factory layout as proposed in 1946

This view from 1952 shows the factory with its first extension and also the unspoilt farming countryside around Newark Road at the time

rather than brick, allowing for expansion in that direction. Unfortunately this thin wall, added to the severe weather conditions, made the building incredibly cold; extraordinary measures provided more heat to the workforce, including borrowed steam engines. Inevitably there were delays in the completion of the buildings too; at one point a request was made to the Ministry of Supply for 30 German Prisoners of War to assist in the work.

Difficulties with component supply and raw materials increased as total demands on outside suppliers rose. The financial position soon showed a familiar story, with the new FCI capital proving insufficient to meet the total needs. Further negotiations resulted in the authorisation of a further £487,000 of 4% Debenture Stock to a round figure of

An Austin 'Loadstar' lorry fitted with a P6(V) conversion. Typical of the many adaptations available to the market during the late 40s and early 50s

Fordson E27N tractor fitted with the P6 (TA) engine, pictured working in the early 1950s

£700,000. At the end of 1947 only £400,000 of this had been issued, leaving a reserve for future requirements, plus cash of around £45,000 in the Bank. To maintain a closer control on their committed capital FCI appointed Mr J.C. Welch, FCA, to the Board as their representative. Turnover at the end of 1947 was £1,398,623 and profit £62,761, compared to the 1946 figures of £1,249,795 and £16,000 respectively.

Progress through the year had also been positive, with sales of 3,895 engines to a total of almost 100 manufacturers covering vehicle, industrial and agricultural use. Issued parts lists for engines and applications totalled 870 in support of these customers. The service network covered 92 countries and in India negotiations were proceeding to allow building of Perkins engines overseas for the first time. Extensive overseas service tours by Joe Hinch and Cyril Kent spread the diesel gospel and trained local personnel.

In England, Ford Motor Company were seeking engines for their Thames 7V truck chassis, with a proposal that the truck conversions would be done by Perkins at Peterborough, thereby creating another problem of available space. The conversion of the Fordson 27N tractor to take a P6 eventually resulted in a tractor being shipped to Ford for their assessment. To satisfy the need for diesel power in lighter vehicles, and to increase payloads, the possibility of using a light alloy cylinder block was suggested for the P6. Samples were produced by Renfrew Foundry in RR50 alloy and machined. Some trials up to 4,000 miles were carried out but this exercise eventually came to nothing.

The new factory starts working

The new Eastfield factory began operations gradually, starting with machining and sub-assembly areas. It was widely publicised as an example of modern factory planning at its best, attracting attention worldwide. The layout was interesting and worth describing in some detail.

At the north end of the site two single bay blocks housed (1) casting preparation and welding, together with the power and compressor house, and (2) the fuel injection department with canteen facilities above. The goods entrance passed between these buildings to the goods inwards and stores area at the north end of the ten-bay factory. From there material flowed to parallel machining lines for blocks, heads, connecting rods, aluminium section, rocker assemblies, automatic lathes and general purpose machining. The flow continued southwards to finished parts stores, sub-assembly, engine assembly and test. Beyond test came the engine finishing and despatch areas, with tool room and maintenance at the southernmost end. Additional machining areas were here too, since the S6 and P4 parts were not handled in the main factory, which was laid out for the P6 as the volume product. Single flow direction through the plant resulted in massive efficiency increases: the mixing of machining and assembly processes, with the resulting cleanliness problems, does not appear to have been an issue considered then! The works offices were housed on the west wall, with administration offices in a separate block to the west, fronting a lawned and landscaped area. Car parking and cycle sheds were situated to the north of the office block.

Although the initial target was for 25 engines per day, this grew to 100 a day by the end of 1948, with two shifts being run from July. Queen Street remained busy too, with rebuild of engines reaching 8,000 units. With the expansion of the plant came changes in management and in the workforce. The total of employees rose from 1,170 in 1947 to 1,580 by the end of the following year. A new Director and General Manager was recruited, Mr Arthur Griffiths having had considerable mass production experience at Ford: his predecessor, Mr Reginald Ferguson, had been the major driver in getting the new factory completed but was sidelined to a special projects role as 'Consultant Director'. Edward Marvill, the 'boy' of the original workforce of 1932, became the Works Superintendent with responsibility for the day-to-day running of the new plant. Another appointment was that of Richard Perkins, son of the founder, as Assistant to the General Manager, taking responsibility for the Company Programme. Another change of organisation put Sales and Service under the control of W.N. Collins as Commercial Director, with Captain Richardson relegated to the role of Director of Publicity. There were other changes as the Company settled into manufacturing operations on the new site. Queen Street continued however, and an opportunity was taken to buy the premises, for £45,000, securing tenure until the City Council plans for redevelopment came to fruition.

The end of 1948 saw a total of 6,865 engines produced, an increase of nearly 3,000 over the previous year: of these over 6,000 were P6s. Truck manufacturers included Austin, Chrysler, Dodge, Ford, Jensen, Dennis, Rootes, Seddon, Vauxhall and Vulcan figured in the customer list, while Fordson and Massey Harris tractors with the P6 were becoming popular too. In spite of the undoubted success, the capital employed was once more insufficient and FCI came to the rescue with more Debenture issues bringing the total authorised to £1,450,000. In his Chairman's Statement to the shareholders accompanying the Accounts for 1948, Frank Perkins covered the year's highlights:

Build of the 25,000th engine in 1948. Watching the fitter are Messrs Griffiths, Perkins and Marvill

The country home at Thornhaugh village purchased by Perkins in 1950 appears old but in fact dates from the 20th century. This bargain investment served as the managing director's home and visitors' guest house until the 1990s

'The year 1948 was one of great expansion in your Company's business, and the results attained were in close agreement with the forecasts made and the plans laid in 1947 and in the early part of 1948. The turnover reached the record figure of £2,370,000, an increase of 66.4% over the previous year, and this figure was achieved in spite of the fact that the new factory did not come into full operation until the later part of the year. The net profit earned was £87,619 after charging all working expenses and depreciation. On a normal capitalisation it would have been £118,025 as £30,406 has been charged for Debenture Interest before arriving at the profit . . .' He went on to cover the other changes in funding, the purchase of the Queen Street premises and the new factory operation. 'We cannot help feeling a sense of pride in the Company's achievement in getting this magnificent factory in full working order, and we are encouraged by the complimentary remarks of knowledgeable visitors from home and abroad, to the effect that it has no superior anywhere.'

He noted the steady increase in demand for engines for agricultural purposes and the Government recognition of the benefits to the economy of the fuel savings possible by moving to diesel. Comments on the Government drive for 'hard currency' sales and standardisation followed, with clear evidence that Perkins was well positioned to produce engines for world markets at a price that was low enough to ensure customers did not start manufacture themselves, even though component prices had not reduced as expected. He could also have mentioned the S6, where a decision to phase it out had met with opposition from Government circles who saw this engine as the only feasible diesel for new boats planned for the early 1950s. Alan Richardson strove to get the phase-out decision reversed, and also to develop engines with more power to suit trucks with increasing payload and a need for greater performance.

1949

The turn of the year brought completion of the new offices at Eastfield, with the Drawing Office being occupied in mid-January. Financing needs drew another £150,000 from the FCI loan, taking the total used to £500,000 of the £750,000 made available. A decision regarding customer terms put major OEMs onto one month's credit, with all others having to pay cash once notification of engine delivery had been made. Potential export markets in South Africa and the North American continent were addressed by visits, with a proposal to form a local sales company in South Africa being actively pursued. The situation in Canada was less clear-cut, with some British Government concern expressed at Perkins' proposals: it was agreed to devote attention to Chrysler and Massey Harris. Research suggested that there was little market in the USA or Canada for small diesels. However, in India an approach by Simpsons of Madras for P4(V) engines became the first phase of a long and successful partnership in that subcontinent.

As the year rolled on a series of improvements for the workforce were made, with the introduction of a works shutdown for two weeks, and the increase of senior staff holiday entitlement to three weeks instead of two. From the beginning of 1949 a pension scheme was introduced, using Midland Employers Mutual Assurance Ltd, with employee contributions starting at salaries above £600.

Through 1949 progress continued to be made, production volume again increasing massively to 15,093 engines, 14,292 of these being P6s! The Company hosted 'At Home' days in May to show off the new plant to both employees and the local population with the attendance topping 5,000. Efforts continued to hold prices down and indeed to make cost savings: one serious consideration was the introduction of in-house fuel injector manufacture. An agreement was signed with Air-

Above: A special dinner was arranged on 9 June 1950 to celebrate the first 18 years with personnel from the first years. Alan Richardson addresses the group

Right: The menu was autographed by all present and was retained as a memento by Muriel Andrews, Frank Perkins's first secretary

craft Steel Structures Limited for this: it was calculated the capital cost of £85,000 would be recovered over one year's production. Another possible venture was proposed by Chrysler, who were looking for a manufacturer for petrol engines to substitute for those previously purchased from the USA, and which had been made less attractive as the pound was devalued from $4.00 to $2.80. After careful consideration of the project it was turned down, even though there would have been potential for supply to customers other than Chrysler/Dodge in Great Britain. Within the Boardroom discussion continued regarding a larger engine – a project code-named PRO 14 was designed to provide a larger truck engine, better suited than the S6 (once again being considered for vehicle use!). The three-cylinder P-series engine design was dusted off and an approach made to Harry Ferguson Ltd regarding possible interest for their new tractor: this resulted in an invitation to visit the new factory in early 1950. Prototype P3s were put in hand and a tractor requested for conversion.

Another innovation was the setting up of a small film unit to make training and sales promotional films, while attendance at shows adver-

tised engines to suit many applications covering agricultural, industrial, marine and on-road uses. Among the many new customers was the Metropolitan River Police, a partnership to stand for many years: they had purchased a number of P6- and S6-powered craft made surplus by the Services. At the Lord Mayor's Banquet on 9 November 1949, Prime Minister Clement Attlee mentioned a number of examples of companies whose efforts to increase output were worthy of commendation – 'In Peterborough a firm making diesel engines for export had considerably increased output, and this was a firm in which output per man has been doubled during the past two years and exports increased at the same rate.' Exports for the year represented 72% of output, and the total workforce increased to 2,050 by the end of December.

1950

In opening months of 1950 expansion was very much in the air again. Further land to the south of the site was purchased and planning was in hand for a doubling in size of the main factory building. Early discussions with the Board of Trade were less than encouraging, since Mr Daniel proposed the relocation of the whole plant to Merseyside instead! A suitable reply was drafted and eventually the BoT agreed to the proposal as submitted, to be funded by Perkins. The plans were eventually authorised in July at an estimated cost of £186,628.

It seems that the Company was at last realising that they could not depend upon the P6 to provide the bulk of production for much longer. At the June Board Meeting Frank Perkins reported on a new design for a 4-cylinder engine designed primarily for tractor use. This, along with the larger vehicle engine (still designated as PRO 14A) and the P3 engine, showed that the product range was at last expanding to both higher and lower powers. With demand exceeding supply there was concern about engine allocation on a fair basis, keeping customers reasonably happy at home while meeting the overall Government demands for increased exports too.

On 13 June Frank Perkins addressed the local and national Press at the Eastfield factory where they gathered to view the plant. His speech from that day has survived. After some remarks about the early days

of the venture and the personnel involved, FAP commented on the honour recently bestowed upon Ted Marvill, one of those earliest employees, who had been awarded the MBE by King George VI. He went on to review the fundamental principles that guided the operation of the Company, noting that, although many industrialists claimed it was impossible for them to be philanthropists, he believed that in the true meaning of the word Perkins claimed to be a 'friend of man', rather than someone who merely gave away money! He then enumerated those bodies of men the Company had made into friends: this started with the financiers – the uninterrupted succession of dividends suggested that duty had been done by them – followed by the most important group, that of the customers, whose support paid wages and salaries and allowed the enterprise to continue. Success here was evidenced by the increasing output of engines from Peterborough, currently surpassing that of the entire American diesel industry in the power range produced, although Perkins could still not keep pace with the demands of end-users around the world.

After stating his ambition to offer those customers an unsurpassed service support worldwide he turned to the question of 'labour', and the oft-stated complaint that today's employees did not match the industry of their grandfathers. The Perkins philosophy was 'to pay fair but not extravagant wages and to try to make conditions as happy and productive as possible. We work a forty-hour week because we find that increases our productivity, and take the view that it is not the hours you work but the work you do in the hours that counts. We try to make this factory a pleasant place to work in, as far as possible removed form William Blake's "dark satanic mills".' Frank Perkins continued by criticising the modern tendency to use incentive schemes,

Rebuilding of engines for the 'Perpetuity Scheme' at Queen Street in 1950 was an important activity supporting engines in the field

rejecting them as an expedient and an escape from the responsibilities of good management! Joint Production Committees with Trades Union participation were seen as largely unnecessary, since joint consultation was an ongoing process with no reason for a more 'formalised' approach for labour relations. His closing statements covered the drive being made for exports, and especially the opportunities for the English manufacturer in the export markets. 'Until the sterling area currencies can look the dollar in the face, American engineering products are virtually excluded from sterling markets and no other country is today in a position to manufacture and export engineering products in volume . . . here is the opportunity to establish our goodwill in these markets – let us seize it!' He closed by reviewing the position regarding the factory expansion and Government approval.

Considerable attention was also being paid to the end user, with expenditure on a series of mobile schools aimed at ensuring the training of personnel wherever engines might be in service. At home too there was emphasis on the future with a manager being sought to take charge of the Apprentice Training Scheme.

At about this time an offer was made for Thornhaugh Hall, five cottages and about 170 acres of land, to the west of Peterborough. The sum of £20,000 secured the property, originally built by Stanley Brotherhood, the son of the founder of Peter Brotherhood Limited, in 1913. This magnificent house became the home for a director and a guest house for distinguished visitors, while the estate provided good game shooting. Another property purchased in 1950 was Park House, on the corner of Princes Gate and Broadway in Peterborough, which was converted into flats and also became the home of the Sports Association Bowls Club.

The end of 1950 showed production totalling 25,216 engines – an increase of over 10,000 units from the previous year – but with the vast majority still P6s. The forward production plan, however, showed the intentions to diversify as the extended plant became available: along with 200 P6s a day, the plans showed 60 P3s and 40 P4s per day, 130 'Leopard 4s' (as the tractor engine had become known) per shift, and batch build of S6 and PRO 14A of around 50/100 per month of each type. Demand for the larger 6-cylinder from Vauxhall and Dodge was expected to commence in 1952. The total turnover of the Company was continuing to grow at an increasing pace, from under £2.5million in 1948 to nearly £4.5 million in 1949 and about £6.7 million in 1950; profits had moved correspondingly from £87,619 to £290,000 and over £600,000 in 1950. This success was shown by the continual growth in employees too: at the end of the year the figure was around 3,000 and growing weekly. The opening of subsidiary companies in South Africa and Australia also marked a change in the Company's direction: the rapid expansion meant that reconsideration of both the Company's status and structure was urgently needed.

At the end of 1950 Frank Perkins and Alan Richardson, must have looked back on their achievements since the end of the war with a great deal of satisfaction. They had seen their small and struggling company grow to an enterprise of both stature and national recognition: in local terms to an employer of considerable importance and influence. From 'two men and a boy' they now gave employment to nearly 3,000 people, were producing over 25,000 engines a year (of which over 70% were exported) and providing motive power for an ever-increasing range of customers on the worldwide market. That a private company had achieved such success and expansion was all the more laudable, even if aided by the backing of the Financial Corporation for Industry Limited in the last few years.

During the 'Works At Home' for local industry and the Press on Thursday 15 June 1950 Frank Perkins spoke about the Company's achievements and the people involved. He went on to confess that any success he had personally achieved was due to his policy of always trying to choose associates who were more intelligent than he! His speech touched upon many other aspects of the principles on which F. Perkins Ltd had been founded, the people and attitudes, opportunities and successes. He then introduced the Chairman of the FCI, the Rt Hon. Viscount Bruce of Melbourne, as Guest of Honour.

In his reply for the guests, Viscount Bruce referred to the achievements of the Company and the contributions made to post-war recovery. He noted that the answer to the current economic problems was the creation of real wealth, and that money was not the wealth desired, but production was: a need that Perkins was helping to meet. His closing words were: 'Mr Perkins must be a happy man today. What he has achieved has benefited all associated with him and at the same time he has the satisfaction of knowing that in doing this he has not only helped his own country but has done something to help the solution of the economic problems that confront the world.'

The need for refinancing

In the cold light of mid-1951 the plaudits and success had to be tempered by some hard facts. Although the support from the FCI had been a key factor in achieving so much so quickly, their role was now over. Repayment of the loans — made so readily to finance the initial expansion – was now essential so that FCI could continue its role of promoting other industries. Permanent working capital would have to be found from another source, and repayment of the loans amounting to £1,237,000 was about half of the total sum needed to continue and expand the business. The repayment was due on 31 December 1951.

Alongside the FCI involvement the existing shareholders held around £4,000 in ten-shilling Preference Shares and about £91,000 in one-shilling Ordinary Shares. The decision of the Board to raise about £3,500,000 of fresh capital was communicated to the existing shareholders by a circular letter on 26 June 1951, together with notice of an Extraordinary General Meeting to be held on 19 July.

There were considerable complications in the share dealing associated with the original FCI financing and options. One of the conditions was that FCI would have the option of subscribing to Ordinary Shares to the nominal value of £50,000 at par. If this option was exercised then the other shareholders could, between them, take up a similar amount at par.

Thus a complex proposal was made to reorganise the Company's capital structure:

a. The one shilling ordinary shares were increased by two million, these being split evenly between FCI and the other existing shareholders.

b. Preference shareholders were given the option of accepting ordinary shares in exchange or a cash sum.

c. All the one shilling shares were then converted to ten shilling ordinary shares, and the authorised share capital increased to £1,300,000 in ten shilling shares.

The Nuffield Universal tractor produced by Morris Motors was a popular conversion to use the P4(TA) and L4(TA) engines. Seen here is an L4-powered tractor ploughing in the Fens

At the end of the process there should remain about 1,500,000 ordinary shares unissued: rather than apply for a Stock Exchange quotation these would be placed with outside investors at a price expected to exceed £1 per share. If these proposals were accepted about £1.5 million would be realised, sufficient to clear the FCI loan capital.

The necessary resolutions were duly passed at the EGM and at a Board Meeting on the same day £1,500,000 of $4^1/2$% First Mortgage Debenture Stock was created in 10s. shares. Through Baring Brothers and Co. this Debenture Stock was advertised in the Financial Times of 23 July 1951, applications opening and closing on 26 July with the issue fully subscribed. The FCI loan was repaid and their representative, Mr Welch, resigned from the Board, having fulfilled his purpose and assisted the Company through some critical years. During 1951 two new directors were appointed to the Board, one being Richard Perkins, son of the founder, and the other Sir Richard Yeabsley CBE, as a non-executive director assisting mainly on the financial side. In a further realignment Arthur Griffiths was appointed General Manager and Production Director.

The reorganisation of the capital as detailed above was duly completed. With all 1,528,732 shares placed privately at 20s. per share, a sum approaching £1.6 million was available after repaying the loans and covering the issue expenses. At last the Company was on a good footing and able to concentrate on expansion to support the burgeoning market for its products. During 1951 the volume of engines produced reached 34,961, an increase of 38% over the previous year and 900% over the 1947 figure. In financial terms the turnover reached £9.35 million and profits were up to £926,872, or 9.9%, with a dividend of 20% paid on the Ordinary capital.

In his report to the twentieth Annual General Meeting Frank Perkins stated: 'I think it will be agreed that the financial position as shown in the balance sheet is very satisfactory. Our Company is now the biggest producer in the world of diesel engines from 50 to 70 horsepower as regards the amount of horsepower produced in one factory. . . The Company's success has been built up on the basis of a very high degree of standardisation, 95% of the efforts of our 3,500 employees being engaged on one size of engine.'

Charles Chapman claimed that the price of the P6 in 1951 was only 35% higher than in 1939, while the price of coal and of the average manufactured article was around three times that of pre-war. The benefits of using modern machinery and methods were largely responsible for the competitive edge achieved by F. Perkins Ltd. at this time. Chapman also recorded that at the end of 1951 Perkins engines were being supplied for use in some 230 different applications, with over 70% being exported to 116 different countries. The competitive advantage was increased by the service support available worldwide from the Company's service representatives. The need to instruct and train both end-users and the distribution network – including the use of the purpose-built mobile schools touring the territories – had been identified and made a priority by the Perkins' management. This was an example to all manufacturing concerns. Chapman did not make any more than a passing comment that the instrument of success was his own design of the P6, conceived and brought to production so quickly.

The Festival of Britain

A small but important piece of publicity that came Perkins' way during 1951 was associated with the Festival of Britain, a celebration that took place in London on the south bank of the Thames and commemorated the 100th anniversary of the Victorian 'Great Exhibition'. In the 'Minerals of the Island' Pavilion a P6 tractor engine took pride of place, being used to show the various materials used for component parts. Recognition of the important efforts being made by Perkins to assist post-war recovery and expand exports came in many ways, one

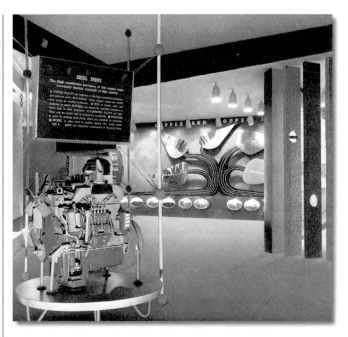

The P6 engine was used in the Festival of Britain in 1951 to demonstrate the use of various metals in industry

being an award for best 'House Journal', the first of a series of trophies recognising the hard work of Laurie Hancock and his publicity team.

Expanding export business was clearly of prime importance to both Perkins and the country as a part of the drive to clear the stagnation and debts following the war. Among the countries taking Perkins engines in ever-increasing numbers was newly-independent India, the destination of the first major export order back in the 30s and the base of Simpson and Co of Madras, who were already operating an engine reconditioning service and showing interest in producing engines under licence. Perkins' presence at exhibitions around the world was another factor influencing customer choice, and testimonials from delighted customers continued to generate good publicity.

Not all good news

Alongside the continued good fortune, growth and profit, there were some warning signs. It was becoming clear that reliance on one successful product for too long can prove to be a mixed blessing, and unfortunately the P6 fell into this category. Although there was a move away from Frank Perkins' 'standardisation' approach towards a more modern and diversified product range, this had started too late. Another factor of the apparent complacency was the advantage Perkins had enjoyed with a suitable engine available at a time when new vehicles were in short supply and there was a need to re-engine some of the existing machinery to prolong its life. The size of this potential conversion business was now shrinking, at least in the home market, where more modern competitors' engines were appearing on the scene. The rush in Peterborough to develop new engines and get them into production resulted in service problems as faults became apparent and were not corrected fast enough. There were other underlying factors too, such as the small capital reserves held by the new public company and the lack of a 'captive' market. (Since an engine is not an end-product in itself, merely becoming a part of another machine, the producer has to rely upon its acceptance by sufficient customers and in sufficient volume to ensure profitability.)

New products at last

The first 'new' product was of course the P3, the emergence of the design originated in the late 1930s for a three-cylinder version of the 'P' series. This drew heavily upon the components already in volume production for the P6 and P4, with only the block, head, crankshaft

The self-build cooperative of Perkins workers produced high-quality housing for their families on the new estates in Peterborough at a time of national shortage. Here a pair of houses on the Dogsthorpe estate is being readied for the roof structure

and camshaft as the major new items to be procured, plus a handful of other parts unique to the shortest engine in the range. Starting from a handful of prototypes in 1951, production reached 2,238 in 1952 and this modest product embarked upon a lifespan that was to exceed 50 years, ensuring the P3 design a place in Perkins history as its longest-living product of all. Not a bad record for an engine that started with the distinct disadvantage of having only three cylinders. The inherent 'nodding' motion from the 1,2,3 firing order needed careful attention to the installation to avoid customer complaints! Its simplicity and low price, however, plus the extension of diesel economy and durability to a lower power range, found favour for many new applications and a new set of customers.

The second new product was a large four-cylinder engine, which was designated L4.

The design team, led by Chapman's assistant Alec Gosling, produced a simple and rugged engine with bore and stroke of 4.25 and 4.75 inches respectively, giving a swept volume of 4.42 litres (269.5 cubic inches). The design centred around a massive crankshaft running on three main bearings, and featured the proven Perkins 'Aeroflow' combustion system. It seems likely that the design was influenced by an American 'Hercules' engine, already in production for tractors and which had been closely examined by the engineers in Peterborough. The engine rating was limited to 62bhp at 2000rpm but with high torque from 1,000rpm providing ideal 'lugging' power for agricultural use and industrial applications. A marine version was to follow quickly and proved popular for workboats in particular.

It was claimed that the L4 was the cheapest diesel in the world of its power class, and it quickly found favour with both existing and new manufacturing customers, as well as with the users since conversions were produced for existing tractors such as the Fordson Major

and Nuffield Universal. Volume production started in 1953 with 2,895 engines made, growing steadily to around 15,000 per year by the end of the 1950s.

The third new product was the long-awaited bigger six-cylinder engine intended for the larger trucks being produced by all major commercial vehicle makers. Introduced as the R6, this engine was rated at 108bhp at 2,700rpm and followed the general design of the P6, including the combustion system, but with bore and stroke of 4 inches and 4.5 inches respectively. With considerable testing already carried out, there was increasing urgency to get this engine into production to ensure that the truck manufacturers continued to use a Perkins engine. The Engineering team, under the guidance of Alec Gosling, were concerned about the timing drive of this engine, where a triple roller chain was specified. A preference was expressed for an all-gear timing train as on the L4, but this was rejected on cost grounds and the engine was to proceed with the chain arrangement, a decision that was to prove crucial. The R6 was announced in 1952 and entered quantity production in 1953, with Bedford and Dodge trucks specifying the engine. It is interesting to note that there had been some in-house resistance to the production of an engine as large as the R6, with the Sales Department pressing for an updated version of the P6, with more power and perhaps slightly increased capacity.

1952: substantial progress

Taking stock at the end of 1952, the first full year as a public company, the directors could take some satisfaction in the continued progress. Perkins engines were being used in 534 different applications, with the Company trading in 116 countries and attending exhibitions in 21. At the autumn Commercial Vehicle Exhibition in London there were 123 Perkins engines on show, appearing on 44 different stands.

The payroll now showed a movement from 3,300 employees at the end of the previous year to 4,300. During the year 38,154 engines had been produced, an increase of 9% over 1951. The sales turnover now exceeded £11.3 million, although profits were only £710,433 compared to the previous £926,875. (An explanation of this was that heavy duties paid on parts purchased abroad, due to inadequate availability in Britain, had added £256,249 to costs.)

The year had seen the expansion of the Eastfield plant by almost 50%, with the main factory building stretched by adding a further ten bays alongside the originals. The layout of the plant was changed radically, with a central roadway running the length of the plant, allowing movement of production material closer to the point of usage. The machining and assembly lines were re-aligned too, introducing a 'flow line' layout with raw materials entering at the north end and finished engines being despatched from the south end. The work entailed in such a fundamental rearrangement lasted into 1953, resulting ultimately in a plant with P series production concentrated in the new east bays, with new machinery for R6, S6 and L4 production arranged in the west side. Engine test was positioned at the south-east corner, with finishing and despatch at the south-west.

There were a number of lesser but notable local achievements. To help ease the housing shortage in Peterborough, Perkins pioneered a self-build programme by setting up an employees' company to build a group of houses on the new Dogsthorpe estate. This company ran on a co-operative basis, with each group member contracted to put in a minimum of 18 hours each week in their free time. The project was expected to take 2 years to complete, with the brickwork being completed by a local builder but the members doing most other jobs. The Sports Association was also going from strength to strength, with various teams competing successfully in local leagues, and other social activities included a pantomime at Christmas.

In support of the overseas activities, there were now 29 personnel seconded to various operations abroad. They assisted sales, service and administration in offices sited in Canada, France, Turkey, Rhodesia, South Africa, the Belgian Congo, India and Australia. Subsidiary companies were operating in Australia, South Africa, France and Canada. Richard Perkins had toured the world during the year, visiting countries in the Far East, Australia and Canada. A notable success was an order worth 1.25 million dollars from Canada for engines to power the Ford trucks to be supplied to India as part of the Colombo Aid Plan.

Along with the rest of the nation, Perkins people had mourned the death of King George VI in February 1952, with special memorial services being held in the plants at Eastfield and Queen Street. As the year drew to a close, it was apparent that the next twelve months were destined to be busy, with participation in the nationwide Coronation celebrations for Queen Elizabeth II being added to the local celebration of the Company's 'coming of age'.

1953: Celebrating the first 21 years

A week of celebrations in July 1953 included visits by customers, dealers, suppliers and of course employees and their families. There was a special celebratory 'Service of Thanksgiving' at St John's church in the Peterborough Market Place, attended by 1,000 people. The solemn service included the reading of lessons by Frank Perkins and Ted Marvill, special prayers for Brotherhood, for the Good Name of British industry and for the Homes and Fellow Workers. It was fitting that the phrase 'where there is no vision the people perish' should have a place too, unremarked, in the order of prayers.

During the review of the past 21 years by the News, it was noted that in 1932 there had been 12 employees occupying 5,505 square feet of space. By January 1953 this had grown to 4,256 employees occupying 565,042 square feet on sites totalling 120 acres. The special 21st Birthday and Coronation issue of the Perkins News carried

An early diesel conversion of the 'little grey Fergie' model TE-20 to use the new P3(TA) engine

many special features including remembrances by some of the earliest employees of those days. A special dinner was arranged for thirty-one employees with unbroken service since the Company started: during this dinner special presentations were made to Frank Perkins and Captain Richardson by those longest-serving employees to commemorate the Company's success.

A number of other significant events were recorded. A link to the Royal family was forged when Perkins engines were specified for the various small boats carried aboard the new royal yacht Britannia. In the Honours List Director and General Manager Arthur Griffiths was awarded the OBE for Services to Industry. A further event to prove very significant was the recruitment of Mr M.I. Prichard from the R.A. Lister Group, initially to the position of Personal Assistant to the Chairman and Managing Director.

Sales efforts continued apace, with engines to suit passenger cars being shown at the Earls Court Motor Show. One of the first users of the P6 in a Humber 'Super Snipe' was Harmar Nicholls, the MP

for Peterborough, who became something of an ambassador for the Company as he extolled the virtues of the local products. Customers recorded their appreciation of the P6 engine in many applications, one of the most impressive being the 31,303 hours achieved by a P6 in a Thames River Police launch.

During the year production of the P3 rose to 5,224, with the L4 and R6 showing first year sales of 2,895 and 2,467 respectively. The R6 was being specified by an increasing number of truck manufacturers as first equipment, and the L4 by Massey Harris in combine harvesters. The P3, as well as finding favour for tractor conversions such as the 'little grey Fergie', was offered in the Trojan light delivery van, with fuel consumption claimed in excess of 45mpg. Overall production rose to 47,168 engines, an increase of 26.4% on the 1952 figure, while export coverage was claimed to encompass over 138 countries. The rearrangements within the Eastfield factory had been completed, with plans already being made for further expansion.

1954

Financially, the Company saw some overall improvements, with turnover increasing to £13.216 million and profits to £778,645. In spite of the 16% increased turnover, the factory stockholding had been reduced by £1.1 million compared to the previous year, while the overdraft of £296,682 of 1952 changed to a credit of £129,578 at the end of 1953. Overall results merited a 20% dividend to shareholders, increased from the 15% of the previous year. The financial health of the company gave confidence to the Stock Exchange, so that when a market quotation was obtained in April 1954 the share price rose from 35 to around 43 shillings in August, peaking during the year at over 50 shillings.

The address made by Frank Perkins to the shareholders' meeting in May 1954 included the expected optimism: 'For twenty years our Company has been a pioneer of the lightweight high-speed Diesel Engine. The time has now come when one of the Vehicle Manufacturers has begun to follow our lead and to manufacture Diesel engines for their own vehicles. Nevertheless new uses for our engines are arising every day. You will be pleased to hear that we expect to increase our output for 1954 by a similar percentage to last year, and we look forward to this growth continuing through 1955.'

The manufacturer referred to was the Ford Motor Company in Essex, whose own diesel truck engines had started production. FAP went on to report that over 14,000 Perkins engines were already operating in India, with the agreement now made with the Indian Government for Simpsons & Co. local assembly and eventually at least partial local manufacture. He also noted that in Australia a reconditioning plant had been set up, since there were 17,000 engines working there. In his statement he commented upon the need for increased working capital as a consequence of the increased turnover, stating that the Board were actively considering the need for a further share issue. Business through the remainder of 1954 continued positively, another strengthening of the European position coming with the inauguration of a new French company, 'Société Francais des Moteurs Perkins', set up to manufacture the P series engines at Courbevoie, using premises owned by Ateliers GSP. The new company was to be 50% owned by French interests, and would initially assemble engines from parts machined in Peterborough. Progressive introduction of locally procured parts, all fully interchangeable with their British counterparts, would follow.

'Peterscourt': part of further expansion

There was an interesting change in Peterborough too. Shortage of offices forced Perkins to look around the city for additional space, to house commercial operations and also the product instruction school. A building close by the Cathedral and standing at the junction of City Road and New Road was finally selected. It had been constructed in about 1864 as a college to train Church of England schoolmasters for

Heralded at the time as the new bigger engine to carry on the tradition of the P6, the R6 unfortunately did not gain the same reputation. This early publicity photograph of a vehicle version was taken in 1953'

the dioceses of Peterborough, Ely and Lincoln and was known as St Peter's College. During World War II it was used as a club for American forces and after the war became a teachers' training college again before falling vacant. In 1952 Perkins purchased the building and carried out extensive works to provide offices, product school accommodation and also a new Social Club. This later facility was housed in what was known, erroneously, as the 'chapel', which was separated from the main building. It was converted to provide a large lounge complete with stage and able to take an audience of 200 people. Adjacent rooms housed the bar, a further lounge area and a games room. The complex was renamed 'Peterscourt' and quickly became established as the headquarters for the Sales, Service and Publicity sections of the Commercial Division. Behind the main three-storey building

The P6(C) was a popular conversion for fleets using large passenger cars such as the Humber Super Snipe. This group of five such cars was used by Thomas Estates in the 1950s

– something of a rabbit warren – there were prefabricated buildings put up for the American servicemen as sleeping quarters. These also became office accommodation and housed the Product School. The whole site of about 3.3 acres had extensive gardens, which were also resuscitated as part of the rebuilding process. A new feature added during the work was an imposing entrance: this incorporated a 17th-century oak door, found stored in the London Guildhall after the blitz, with new ironwork made by the Company that featured the Perkins motif of a square and four circles.

At the end of 1954 Frank Perkins' forecast was proved correct. The turnover had increased to over £16.8 million, with profits exceeding £1 million for the first time at £1,169,340. With a healthy bank balance of £701,122 and tax reserves of £350,000 the Board once again declared a dividend of 20%. Engine production reached 61,956 with L4 and R6 volumes increasing to 8,953 and 8,567 respectively, although the P6 with 28,208 units remained the highest-selling product.

1955: An error of judgement?

In his statement covering the accounts for the year, the Chairman stated that, since their cash position was healthy the intention, previously declared, to raise more capital through the issue of further shares for cash was postponed. Instead it was proposed to capitalise the Share Premium Account, and a part of the General Reserve, and make a one-for-one share 'scrip' issue.

In his 1964 account of the Company's history Charles Chapman examines this decision very critically and in considerable detail, commenting that the overall financial position hardly justified this action, although he admits that his comments were made with the benefit of hindsight. However, it does appear that the young public company need not have taken such an action, which effectively halved the value of each share and benefited the shareholders not at all in the following year, since the dividend was itself halved. Chapman's contention is that with the shareholders' perception of the Company's worth, and a general public view that Perkins was a successful 'growth' company, a 'Rights' issue might have been made instead. This would have brought benefit to the Company, in the form of increased capitalisation, as well as to the individual shareholders who could have either exercised their rights to buy additional shares or sold on those rights in the Stock Market. The Company would have received more money to fund further expansion and placed itself in a more secure financial position. The overall perception of the Company at the time would have meant that there would have been an enthusiastic response, and the dividends for the following couple of years at least might have been secured. However, the opportunity was lost and the eventual outcome was to put the fortunes of Perkins in jeopardy.

The record results of the previous year ensured the year opened well, with existing customers taking engines in increasing numbers, and new customers were appearing regularly. Demand for the new engine types was promising; the R6 was being specified in new truck models by a number of manufacturers. The L4 was generating new business on the agricultural side, one major potential volume user being Cockshutt Farm Equipment of Brantford, Ontario. They signed an order for engines for their combine harvesters and farm tractors during a January visit by Richard Perkins to the Toronto offices of F. Perkins (Canada) Limited, the new subsidiary company. Visits were also paid to major American OEMs Studebaker Corporation, International Harvester and Oliver Corporation, all showing interest in the potential of diesel engines for their products. (The conversion of large American cars to diesel for taxicab operation was already a significant niche market in Europe where fuel savings were a significant factor in operating costs. There had also been some Checker cabs converted in New York City.) Closer to home there were fleet sales for the P3(V) engine, notably to the Marley Tile Company for use in their Trojan delivery vans.

Growing importance of Perkins to Peterborough

The total Perkins payroll in Peterborough continued to increase, with over 5,300 employed. Peterborough was a small market town but had other significant manufacturers such as Baker Perkins, Brotherhoods, the Mitchell Group, Newalls and Hotpoint – to say nothing of established employers such as the railways, the brickyards and the sugar beet factory – so Perkins was already a major economic factor. The employment catchment area had widened into the fens, with bus services bringing people from considerable distances. During the period 1953–5 further factory extensions were taking place, with extra bays added to the south end of the main plant giving about 50% more floor area. This additional space allowed further component machining, a new engine test shop plus revised engine finishing and despatch. Separate buildings for the tool room and field test workshops brought the new building area to 150,000 square feet.

With the increasing size of plant and workforce came other changes. In November 1954 a company newspaper was launched: initially known as the Peterborough Diesel Echo, this venture was destined to become an essential part of the Perkins image. The opening editorial dedicated the paper's existence to the task of spreading information to its readers and to promoting the interests of the employees. By enlisting the cooperation of many voluntary contributors around all departments, as well as the many sections and clubs within the Sports Association, the Echo was assured a flow of interesting features and news for years to come. It also provided the means for communicating Company plans and successes, with its monthly publication giving a faster update than the Perkins News. This latter magazine continued to flourish, the quarterly issues providing readers with a well-organised mixture of news and views, together with advertising, on a worldwide basis. Laurie Hancock and his staff achieved success in 1954 as 'Best House Journal' in a nationwide competition. (The survival of many copies of the News to this day demonstrates the readers' appreciation. Many articles remain a source of interest, information and amusement, although the magazine style and lack of 'political correctness', especially with its scantily-clad pin-ups and sexist jokes, may not suit some of the changed outlooks of today!)

A further source of pride and success was the work of the Perkins Film Unit. In 1954/5 a number of new films were produced, including 'You Can't Be Too Careful' (highlighting industrial safety issues) and 'Thames Division', tracing the story of the Metropolitan River Police and their craft – where Perkins marine engines were giving sterling service to the policing of the world's busiest waterway. Another film success was the latest version of 'The Peterborough Diesel Story'; this first revision in colour brought the history of Perkins up to date as well as providing opportunities for publicity. In those days the free loan of 16mm films to clubs and societies, as well as their use in trade shows and exhibitions, meant that a wide audience would see the Perkins films during any year.

Labour relations and overseas potential

Within the context of what today would be called 'corporate responsibility', Perkins worked in conjunction with the Amalgamated Engineering Union to produce a booklet called 'Wage Structure for Hourly Paid Employees', a copy being given to every shop floor worker. The recognition of the need to work with the trade unions was typical of Frank Perkins' commonsense grasp of the working environment. In the foreword to the booklet he was quoted: 'We have tried to make conditions in this Company as harmonious as possible, and feel sure that those who are, or will be, employees of this Company will complete that harmonious unity which is so vital in an organisation such as ours.'

The approach taken with the AEU was to stand Perkins in good stead over the next few years. By making an agreement on representation with one powerful body, Frank Perkins established a period of industrial peace while other companies went through continual problems of labour unrest. His ability to get on with people at all levels inside and outside the Company and his sincere but confident approach surely deserved better recognition and reward on a National scale, but this was never to be. However, in May Frank Perkins was

Monty Prichard joined in 1953 as PA to the Managing Director.

Although diesel cars were never popular in the 1950s, Perkins provided conversion kits using the little 4.99(C) for many popular British cars. This Vauxhall Victor installation is a typical example

honoured by being elected Vice-President of the Society of Motor Manufacturers and Traders, recognition of his association with the SMMT since 1936.

Reference has already been made to the content of the Twenty-Third Annual Report and Accounts of F. Perkins Ltd in the previous chapter. This report was presented at the Annual General Meeting held at the Mayfair Hotel in May 1955 and covered the progress made through 1954. While recognising the continuing success and ever-increasing sales, Frank Perkins noted the difficulties experienced with obtaining some components due to a shortage of supplier capacity. He believed that as the British motor industry expanded this problem would increase until suppliers recognised the burgeoning demand for their products. Added to this was the problem of labour shortage: with national unemployment running at around 1% (a situation unprecedented in peacetime since the Industrial Revolution!) all industry was experiencing recruitment difficulties. During the year Perkins had started engine production in France, with negotiations with Yugoslavia likely to result in production there too. He suggested that there was a changing picture with regard to exports, with many countries wanting their own indigenous industries rather than spending precious foreign currency on imported finished goods. He recommended that British Industry had to move pragmatically with these changing conditions. He concluded that Perkins could look forward optimistically, continuing to provide quality products at reducing prices to meet customer demands.

New appointments

During the year a number of organisational appointments and changes took place in the Company. Mr M.I. Prichard was appointed a director, along with Mr K.E. Woollatt. Monty Prichard was given responsibility for Engineering, welcome if belated recognition of the importance of a strong and well-directed technical department to the future of the enterprise. After a period of 'hands-on' involvement with the existing personnel and some reorganisation of the departments he concluded that the appointment of a manager for the Experimental Department was essential and searched for a possible candidate outside the company. MIP had been in discussions with the Shell Research Centre at Thornton in connection with some technical problems and among his contacts had been Mr J.G. Dawson, their Chief Engineer, who he believed could be an ideal man for the job he had in mind.

James Gordon Dawson had joined Rolls-Royce in October 1938 as an engineering pupil, moving on during the war to become their

Gordon Dawson was appointed as Engineering Director by M.I. Prichard in 1955

youngest manager when he was put in charge of a new Experimental Test Department in 1941. His work included the running of all new engines from the Griffin through to the first RR gas turbines. After the war he had moved to Shell, rising to his current position at Thornton. The approach by Prichard turned out to be timely; Dawson was unhappy with changes at Shell which would move him to the London offices heading the Product Application Department, handling technical contacts with customers. He did not want to uproot his young family to the big city. Following MIP's approach, Gordon Dawson found himself commuting instead to Peterborough within a matter of weeks, having accepted the job although he had no previous experience of diesel engines. His recollections of his arrival at Peterborough are an interesting insight into the situation he found and the problems being faced during this period.

Dawson was installed in the original Queen Street office used by Frank Perkins when he set up the company in 1932. He found an Engineering Department split into two geographically, with the Experimental Department based in the rambling old buildings at Queen Street, handling engine development and research (including a range of engine test beds), while the Design and Field Test departments were housed at the Eastfield plant. The challenge of the new job, in an industry with which his previous contacts had been as a supplier, was tempered by an expectation of major changes in personnel and organisation to address the problems detailed by Prichard. As he settled into the role, however, he found that many concerns were unfounded, although the technical problems were real enough. He quickly determined that the existing personnel were competent, while his lack of diesel engine experience allowed him to question the staff from first principles to determine why things were approached in a certain way.

Solving the R6 problems

JGD found that the product problems were largely a result of Board pressure to get the R6 into production too quickly. Part of the difficul-

The P4(C) engine conversion found popularity for taxi work in European markets. This group of Chrysler cars in Belgium is typical of the use in the early 1950s

A further six bays were added to the Eastfield factory in 1955, along with extensions to the office block

ties arose from inadequate testing of changes forced by production demands and cost reasons: as a result warranty costs had escalated to a totally unacceptable level, causing a major deterioration in the Company's profitability. Poor decisions had resulted in problems with the oil pump, bearings and especially the chain drive for engine timing. Resolution of these issues took time. The chain drive took the longest time to fix, with innovative use of high-speed photography finally identifying a problem of resonance and excessive 'flap' under certain speed conditions on the longest stretch of chain. Careful placing of damper pads, plus a revision by Renolds of their chain design at Dawson's insistence, provided a solution.

Unfortunately it took six months to reach this stage, by which time the engine's reputation had gone. Vauxhall stopped using it and overall the production volume decreased sharply, in spite of concerted and successful attempts to confirm the reliability of the revised engine, renamed R6 Mark 2. There were attempts to sell the engine into the USA, to produce a turbocharged version with more power and even to rename it again as the 6.340. The writing was on the wall, however, and production fell from a peak of around 9,000 engines in 1955 to 5,346 in 1956. The engine was phased out in 1959, and production plant shipped out to Brazil for the new licensee operation Motores Perkins. Ironically the engine found a new lease of life in South America, as related in Chapter 19.

While this was going on, the other design activities were more successful, the first being the L4 of course. In Gordon Dawson's words: 'The main production engines had been designed in the thirties and, although they had been well-developed over the years, had been caught up by the competition. Amongst a number of drawbacks, one major one was that they still had the original indirect injection combustion system and new direct injection combustion systems were being introduced [by other manufacturers] which gave a substantial improvement in fuel economy. The whole range needed reassessing and updating and this was urgent if Perkins was to keep its place in the market much less achieve any further expansion. There was much discussion amongst the higher echelons and finally it was a matter for a Board decision.'

It was tragic that the first effort to address the new product needs should have resulted in a loss of reputation and sales that was to cripple the Company in a very short period. Perhaps the 'right first time' achievements of the P6 (and Charles Chapman) had clouded the judgement of the Board? (Along, of course, with their tendency to support decisions based on cost considerations rather than on technical judgement!) It is noteworthy that the research work in Perkins on direct injection systems was aimed at engine speeds well above 2,200rpm, whereas those rivals already in production with DI engines (such as AEC, Leyland and continental manufacturers) tended to peak at around this speed.

Let us now return to the events and successes celebrated in the latter half of the year. On 8 September there was a ceremony attracting both local interest and the BBC when the last of the 28 'self build' houses was completed on the Dogsthorpe estate. This event triggered the creation of a new group, known as the Secundus Self-Help Building Society, and a further 25 employees set forth on their arduous but rewarding task, on a site at Walton.

Growing Applications workload

The reputation of Perkins diesels was growing in many applications, and this showed in the increasing amount of design work carried out in the Eastfield Design Office to support the increasing number of new parts lists. Over the years a major part of Perkins' success as an independent engine supplier stemmed from individual attention to customers' needs, including trial installation and back-up which ensured satisfaction and adequate installation quality. Whilst major companies

such as Ford might look upon this as interference, small customers appreciated the complete service and as a result came back for more.

There was a growing interest in conversion of motor cars and light goods vehicles as many operators came to recognise the advantages of diesel economy and reliability. This was supported and fostered by Perkins, who established a new Drivers' Club, to cater for the interests of industrial, marine and vehicle sectors alongside the established Agricultural Drivers' Club. Although membership was free, renewal was annual with the package of benefits including free insurance up to £100, a club badge and access to courses and advice. The club officials included Frank Perkins, Alan Richardson and Norman Collins with Mr T.R. St John Browne administering the Club from the new Sales offices at Peterscourt, in the centre of Peterborough.

Original equipment manufacturers introduced many new machines. Marshalls of Gainsborough announced a new crawler tractor (L4 power), while the Hyster Company of Portland, Oregon, advertised Perkins engines as the diesel option on their RC-SC range of fork lift trucks (the relationship continued for 50 years). By the end of the year there was news of a repeat engine order for Yugoslavia worth nearly £1 million, to be fitted in Massey Harris Ferguson tractors. Engine production for 1955 amounted to 68,867 units, with P6s accounting for 46% but with P3 and L4 volumes showing significant growth. In spite of the R6 problems, growth of 11% over the previous year showed that momentum being maintained.

Miniature Submarines

There are two stories of engine applications that made a lasting impression and created excellent publicity at that time. The first concerned the P6 in the hands of the Royal Navy. As recounted in Chapter 4, the P4 engine in the wartime X-craft miniature submarine prototypes had been replaced by Gardner engines for production craft. At the end of the war these craft, and others on the stocks, were scrapped. A reawakening of interest in small submarines within the Admiralty in the mid-1950s resulted in the design of a revised 'X-craft' to serve a number of roles. The X-51 Class was designed, and four craft built by Vickers Armstrong Shipbuilders Limited at Barrow-in-Furness. These craft were launched as HMS Stickleback (X-51), Shrimp (X-52), Sprat (X-53) and Minnow (X-54). They were designed for a crew of four or five and could carry delayed action mines or limpet mines. Motive power was provided by the venerable P6 (M) engine, already well known to the Navy and appreciated for its reliability.

After the formation of the flotilla based at Portland, Perkins interest resulted in the craft and their crews being 'adopted'. There were visits by crew members to Peterborough, including membership of the Drivers' Club, and in November 1957 HMS Sprat journeyed up the Nene from the Wash to pay a visit to the city, tying up at the customs house by the Town Bridge. The flotilla saw service in various locations, including a visit to the USA, before being disbanded in the late 50s. HMS Stickleback was sold to the Swedish Navy on 15 July 1958 and was renamed Spiggen. She was operated for anti-submarine training of naval personnel and harbour defences for some years before being donated to the Imperial War Museum in 1976. The craft is on permanent display at Duxford, where visitors can walk through the partially sectioned hull with the P6 clearly visible. (Also at Duxford are the remains of one of the original X-craft, sunk during the attack on Tirpitz.) It seems likely that one of the X-51 class submarines was used during the making of the film Above Us the Waves in 1955, which covered the wartime exploits.

An Australian adventure

The second story concerned a new application for the L4 engine in Australia. Chamberlain Industries Pty Ltd of Perth was already mar-

The Chamberlain prototype tractor, with the L4(TA) engine and used for the Redex 'Round Australia' rallies during the 1950s, is preserved in a museum in Perth and paraded on special occasions

keting large tractors using their own engines. They conducted some research on the possible market for a medium-sized tractor for the outback farms and discovered that there were special needs to be met. The farmers wanted a tractor with a comfortable driving environment and large fuel capacity, able to serve as basic transport in situations where a passenger car could not be used. Design work proceeded and the L4 was identified as the most suitable engine.

With the prototype ready for test an opportunity arose which proved to be the most arduous trial imaginable for a farm tractor. The Australian Sporting Car Club were organising the 'Round-Australia Redex Trial'. This was a production-car rally over 3,000 miles across poor roads and tracks in the outback. Originally Chamberlain intended to enter a tractor to compete in the Trial itself, but this was outside the rules. Undaunted, the company offered the services of a tractor for the roughest part of the rally and the organisers seized on the idea, suggesting that useful back-up could be provided on the stretch between Darwin and Perth. Accordingly a prototype was prepared with covered cab, front axle shock absorbers and headlights, together with high gearing giving a top speed of 50mph at the rated engine speed of 2,000rpm. Naturally the engineers tuned the engine to some degree, with higher governed speed allowing 60mph maximum and 55mph cruising where conditions permitted. Thus equipped, and with a support car in attendance, the crew set out from Perth and reached Port Hedland (1,277 miles) in two days at an average speed of around 40mph. At Darwin they awaited the arrival of the rally cars for the return journey.

Once underway the tractor acted as 'tail end Charlie' to the competitors, assisting breakdowns, towing vehicles out of boggy areas, straightening bent chassis and assisting cars to the service stops. They helped 30 vehicles – one VW was carried on the drawbar for 140 miles at up to 45mph. At the conclusion of the rally the tractor had averaged 33mph and 20mpg over the distance, used no lubricating oil or cooling water, and won the respect of competitors and organisers. Their only problem was one puncture soon after they left Perth. The performance was praised in the Australian press and in England Motor magazine ran an article on 11 January 1956. Perkins seized upon the interest generated, reprinting an article from Sport and Country magazine with the headline 'The greatest drive . . . by a FARM tractor', together with the slogan '(Perkins) tractor engines cover the ground . . . they also cover every requirement'.

The year closed with growing concern over the reliability of the R6 engine, with some complete engines being replaced under war-

ranty. Even the L4 was not immune to faults, with a spate of cylinder block cracking problems adding more woe. The publication, in May 1956, of the F. Perkins Limited Annual Report for 1955 showed that while the turnover reached almost £20 million (an 18% increase), the profit before taxation had dropped to 4.2% from the 6.9% of the previous year. After the bullish stance adopted by the Chairman and the scrip issue of shares in 1954, the latest statement was uncomfortable: 'During the year the Company spent £666,708 on Fixed Assets and with further calls on the cash resources to finance an increase in stocks and trade debtors our cash in hand at the end of the year was £574,103 less than a year ago. It is now clear that with Capital Commitments of £729,000 it will be necessary to raise additional finance in the near future, and your Board is giving thought to this problem. It is worthy of note that no new capital has been raised since 1951 and in the meantime the turnover had been doubled.'

One has to recall the lost opportunity of the previous year to generate working capital when share prices and shareholder confidence were high. In his statement Frank Perkins noted the difficulties of material shortage as well as the problems of the R6. On the positive side he saw the continuing impact of diesel power across all market sectors worldwide, citing the successful growth of export markets. Total payroll passed 6,000 personnel at the end of 1955, and the launch of a Works retirement scheme continuing his policy of being in the forefront of labour issues. In commenting upon the continuing development of new diesel designs for the future, he noted that the Company was '. . . at the same time studying other new forms of power which may have an application in the very long term future'. This was an interesting and prescient comment on the path to be taken in the Engineering Department in the future.

1956

Events in the spring of 1956 demonstrated the increasing usage of diesel engines in many applications. At the Brussels Auto Show, Chrysler exhibited the P4 (V) as an option for the Plymouth saloon, while Dodge, Studebaker and International Harvester trucks were on show with P6 engines. Perkins was also beginning to achieve a significant penetration of the municipal vehicle market: historically there had been resistance to the use of diesel engines where long periods of idling and low annual mileages were reckoned to make them uneconomic. A paper presented by L.W. Bugg of Perkins in December 1955 to a meeting of municipal engineers in the Midlands contradicted this view, demonstrating that even with 5,000 miles' annual usage there were savings to be made versus petrol engines. A review in 1956

The earliest connection with Massey Harris was the fitment of P6 engines in the 744 tractor. Many were exported and this restored example was photographed by the author in February 2005 in the Geraldine museum in New Zealand

The Thames river police were enthusiastic users of Perkins marine engines, initially in ex-services launches. Here a patrol passes Tower Bridge at speed in 1953.

showed sales growing from 29 authorities in 1952 to 297 in June 1955, out of the 2,056 local authorities. This trend was to continue, with Perkins becoming the preferred engine. There were special actions taken to provide additional reliability; amongst these was the fitment of chromium-plated cylinder liners to combat corrosion of the cast iron liners due to low operating temperatures. (There were occasional problems of oil consumption seen in municipal operation, usually due to lack of proper running-in of the engine. In such cases an immediate cure was sometimes found by borrowing the vehicle overnight for a fast run to Peterborough and back, the on-road 'thrashing' being sufficient to bed the piston rings to the liners!)

The presentation of papers to various bodies was a feature of the Company's public affairs during the year: Arthur Griffiths spoke on the subject of production automation and modern methods, while Norman Collins produced an article for Motor Industry on the increasing use of diesel engines at home and abroad. Whenever possible, company executives were extolling product virtues and benefits for the end-user. (This approach was employed by Gordon Dawson, whose many technical papers to bodies in the USA, London, Paris, Amsterdam, Moscow and Rio de Janeiro during the 1960s were often awarded prizes and brought much credit to both author and Company.)

There were occasionally national news items that allowed the Publicity Department to benefit. One such was the use of a Seddon low loader with a P6 (V) to transport Donald Campbell's Bluebird jet boat to Lake Coniston, and also to display it in the Lord Mayor's Show in London. Marine applications often made good press too, including the use of three P6 (M) engines in the royal barge for Britannia, and the Perkins-powered fleet of 38 boats used by the London River Police.

An unusual piece of work for the Perkins film unit was the production of 'The Red Poll Story', a film made on behalf of the Red Poll Cattle Society. In recent years a copy of this film could not be found within Perkins but one was obtained through the help of the East Anglian Film Library. (Copies of all surviving Perkins Film Unit productions have now been given to EAFL to ensure their preservation and survival.)

Alan Richardson leaves Perkins

Early summer brought changes to the Board when Captain Richardson resigned as Deputy Chairman, having served since 1944. He 'retired' to look after his other family interests in Gloucestershire. His successor was Sir Richard Yeabsley, a Board member since 1951, and Monty Prichard became Deputy Managing Director at the age of 40. At about the same time, Frank Perkins became President of the SMMT for 1956/7, after his term as Vice-President – an honour which necessitated the purchase of an Austin Sheerline limousine, since FAP had always used American saloons for his personal transport!

Monty Prichard announced organisational changes on 26 June with the formation of new divisions. Ken Woollatt was made General Manager of the Administrative Division, R.F. Mead of the Accounts Division, Bernard Lynn of the Purchase Division and Gordon Dawson of the Engineering Division. The changes were calculated to improve the efficiency of the company; the total manpower had now passed 6,000 and complexity of both production output and customer base had increased. The post of Company Secretary later passed from Ken Woollatt to Mr T.A. Read, who had joined the Legal Department in July.

Further changes followed in the autumn with Edward Marvill becoming General Manager of the Manufacturing Division and R. Albon of the Personnel Division. All divisional heads became members of the new 'General Managers' Conference' – a weekly meeting under the chairmanship of Monty Prichard co-ordinating the administration of the Company. A resignation at director level followed soon after when Arthur Griffith left the Company, apparently as a result of some disagreement. (He took a job at Alvis Motors, working on military vehicles, perhaps fitting their 'small batch' environment better than the increasing high-volume production of the Perkins plant.) Richard Perkins took over as Manufacturing Director on a temporary basis until a replacement could be recruited.

Early July saw the annual Sports and Family Day, attended by around 15,000 people. The sun shone on a successful day, with performances by the Dagenham Girl Pipers among other attractions. The full programme of activities and sports ensured all attendees were kept entertained, with the Fire Brigade giving a demonstration and the Perkins Footlights Club providing a stage show.

Insight into Site Strategy

During the author's researches for this history a number of 'forgotten' items came to light. Amongst these was a copy of the 'Four Year Plan' developed by Monty Prichard and presented to the Board on 31 August 1956. This proposed capital expenditure through to 1960 and made a number of interesting points, based on a perceptive view of the Company's immediate prospects and future needs. The engine strategy proposed that a new 'big bore' six-cylinder engine should replace and overlap the R6, along with redesign of the P4 and P6. In addition the C99 would go into production along with V8 and V6 engines aimed at the American market.

The site strategy also recommended that engineering activity should be concentrated at Eastfield, in new workshops and offices at the south end of the factory. Service and engine reconditioning would remain at Queen Street although engine testing would be shifted to Eastfield, eliminating one of the prime objections to the continued city centre presence of the factory. All training activity would be concentrated at Peterscourt, including the Trade School, with sales moved to Eastfield, occupying the old drawing office area. There were also plans to extend the main factory area to the east of the existing plant, including a new canteen to service the personnel at the south end of the site. Plant and machinery for the production of the new engine types added major investments to the not inconsiderable cost of buildings. New facilities for casting preparation and painting at the north end were also planned, and some expenditure at Queen Street would improve the handling of 'Perpetuity' returned engines.

The timescales and costs for this quite massive series of changes were identified, all to be completed by the end of 1960 at a total cost approaching £2.7 million. Although the proposals appear to have been well received by the Board, only part of these came to fruition in the envisaged timescale. (In fact most proposed changes eventually came to pass, with considerable layout changes and of course vastly increased cost.)

On 23 September Frank Perkins saw the first results of the launch, in the previous year, of an appeal to provide Boys' Clubs in Peterborough. The foundation stone for the first club, on the Grange playing field in West Ward, was laid by FAP in front of a large gathering of civic leaders. He paid tribute to the fund-raising achievements of the Supporters' Association and the members of the Peterborough Council of Boys' Clubs, of which he was president.

As autumn approached, the activities on exhibitions and shows increased. At the Earls Court Commercial Motor Transport Exhibition in September, Perkins launched the R6 Mark 2 engine, claiming many detail modifications to improve the engine life and efficiency. The Company had stands too at the Earls Court International Motor Show, the Public Works and Municipal Services Exhibition at Olympia, the Smithfield Show and the Boat Show to round off the year. In addition to the presence of engines on their own stands, Perkins people were delighted by the increasing presence of Perkins-powered machinery,

vehicles and boats. As well as the R6 Mark 2, the marine version of the P3 was presented at the Boat Show, complete with an optional hand-starting system to reduce the reliance on electrical systems for some markets.

Frank Perkins at the SMMT

In his role as President of the SMMT, Frank Perkins made a speech to welcome many guests, including government ministers, to their annual dinner the evening before the London Motor Show opened. He noted that the guests that night, who included the presidents of General Motors, Ford and Renault, controlled between them the output of 70% of the world's motor industry. He took the opportunity to compare the record of past government high investment in nationalised industries, with poor results, to the attitude of the Chancellor of the Exchequer towards private enterprise. The insistence on reduction of investment was damaging the ability of industry both to expand and to export; yet the motor industry as a whole had still increased their exports by £19 million in the first eight months of the year. He addressed his remarks in particular to the Chancellor of the Exchequer, the Rt Hon. Harold Macmillan, in making a case for more capital investment in the industries for which exports were essential.

After noting the policy of the Socialists in making the common man better off, he asked if the leaders of either party really understood the necessity for more capital. He commented: 'We must all preach the potentialities of an enlightened capitalism which attacks poverty by insisting on production rather than concentrating on spreading the jam thinner.' He then turned to the idea from Mr Macmillan for the European Economic Union: 'Speaking as a private individual it does seem to me that from the political point of view an integrated Europe is the only possibility for survival. We have fought all our wars in Europe in the past to prevent the mastery of Europe by one power.' After referring to the threat from Russia, he argued that Europe must build its strength through the arts of peace, to ensure their resources were superior to those of Russia. He forecast the eventual ebbing of the Russian tide and the future need for free trade with Germany. His closing words were measured and set the seal on a contentious speech: 'Most of you here are directors of public companies, and the most important function of directors is to be planning future policy. The politicians in power are the Board of Directors for our country, and it is very refreshing to find that they are planning a policy for economic success in Europe coupled with the continued development of the Commonwealth.'

Harold Macmillan gave a sparkling speech in reply and both press and guests the next day were unanimous in their view that the Banquet speeches were 'the best and most scintillating in living memory'. Certainly Frank Perkins proved to be prophetic in his view of the future, although some aspects may have taken longer to reach fruition than he probably expected.

A week prior to this speech, Monty Prichard had given a vigorous and practical reply to the question, 'Can better management overcome the evils of inflation?' while addressing a joint meeting of the Incorporated Sales Managers' Association and the British Institute of Management held at the Royal Festival Hall in London. After noting the damage being done by those who did not appreciate the need to change methods to weather the competitive storms, and the fact that Britain was facing true world competition for the first time in its industrial history, he advocated the proper use of the best men available to encourage management to better itself and compete.

He offered the opinion that top management failed because it could not, or would not, delegate responsibility and authority.

He asserted that 'There is nothing about an organisation more important than its future. One can be as proud and "cocky" as one

HMS Stickleback was one of four P6 (M)-powered midget submarines of the Royal Navy flotilla adopted by Perkins in the mid-1950s, and was later operated by the Swedish Navy before being presented to the Imperial War Museum at Duxford, Cambridgeshire

wishes about the past, but it is where it is going that matters, and top management's paramount responsibility is for visualising, initiating and achieving future objectives.' Lord Woolton, who followed him on the dais, remarked that for a man who had declared his extreme nervousness before the meeting, it had been a remarkable 'maiden' speech!

Sales progress

While directors were making their presence felt in politically orientated areas, sales efforts were showing continued good results, in spite of the poor acceptance of the R6. More municipal authorities had turned to diesel power, a total of 441 now using Perkins in their fleets. There were 23 different chassis manufacturers offering Perkins as optional first equipment for a wide variety of vehicles. Many machine manufacturers were also specifying diesels, in a multitude of industrial equipment such as earthmovers, compressor sets, paving machines, dumpers, concrete mixers and excavators. Perkins had pioneered conversions and persuaded manufacturers and was now reaping the benefits. Success was not confined to the home market either, as a visit by a party of Czechoslovakian industrialists had resulted in tentative arrangements being put in hand for Czech students to attend the School; a pleasing result since trade relations between the two countries had only just been re-established.

Elsewhere in the world, however, events were not so happy. The Hungarian uprising, and the subsequent rapid Russian retaliation, resulted in an appeal within the Perkins factories for clothing and money. In quick time over two tons of items were collected and despatched, together with over £1,000 in donations.

A further major issue at this time was the closure of the Suez Canal, and the resulting delays as shipping was forced to take the longer route round the Cape. The impact on fuel supplies meant that fuel rationing was imposed on industry. Worse was to follow and the impact of the fuel crisis was to become yet another factor in the difficulties faced by F. Perkins Limited in the coming year.

Apprentice Association launched

The formation of the Perkins Apprentice Association in late 1956 marked the growing importance being placed upon the training and education of youngsters entering the Company. There had been apprentices since the early days (Russell Bennett claiming to be the first such in 1932!) but their training had not been focused and formalised. Under the new Training Manager, John Talbot, a team of instructors was formed and a dedicated facility with machine shop, drawing office and classroom installed in the northernmost factory block below the canteen. The Apprentice Association not only drew the boys together socially but also promoted other aspects of technical training through less formal routes. The team spirit engendered in the group also helped foster the right spirit of goodwill across all contact within the Company, as well as helping promote Perkins' name through external contacts.

The new apprentice scheme, embracing craft, student and graduate streams of candidates catering for future recruitment across the whole range of activities, was promoted nationally. The good publicity and competitive salaries while training attracted many school leavers and graduates, with a fair number destined to spend most of their working lives within the Perkins family – including the author!

The year closed with production at a record 74,846 engines. This was in spite of a reduction in the R6 volume to only 5,346 and of the P4 to 6,913. The L4 volume increased to 11,802 and P3 to 11,167. The big surprise was the P6, which sold its highest ever volume of

39,322 units – a product in its nineteenth year of production still accounting for over 50% of total output.

1957

The twenty-fifth Annual Report and Accounts for the year ended 31 December 1956 show turnover at a record £21,502,582, but with profits before taxation down to only £768,934. Thus, after the heady days of the early 50s, profit had reduced to only 3.6% of turnover, which itself had grown by 8% from the previous year. In spite of the obvious problems a dividend of 10% was paid to Ordinary shareholders. The Chairman, in his statement published at the AGM on 13 May 1957, remained optimistic about the future. He reported that there had not been a propitious moment to raise additional finance, but noted that careful stock control had limited the bank overdraft to a reasonable figure. In reviewing the changes made to the structure of the Company and its facilities Frank Perkins covered the expansion of the factory and the work in progress to improve administrative and drawing office facilities which had remained unchanged since 1951. The loss of Vauxhall as a customer, as a result of the R6 debacle, had been offset by new contracts from two large customers that more than replaced the lost business. The growth in exports, both direct and indirect, was significant – at 74% of the total production – due largely to the efforts of the Export Sales Department in following up leads. The adverse effects of the Suez crisis – fuel rationing, embargoes and serious shipping delays – had impacted on the last two months of the year and carried over into early 1957. (During this period engines scheduled for Egypt were apparently shipped to Turkey and Syria, reaching their intended destination circuitously.)

The impact had proved severe, with short time working necessary in some areas of the plant in January when a four-day working week had to be introduced, lasting until early April. Such problems did not appear in the Perkins News, where good news was a vital factor in keeping the market informed. Success in export business continued to be a source of satisfaction, with the increasing use of engines in all manner of applications brought to the readers' attention. Alongside the announcement of the new apprentice scheme was news that Perkins was giving some financial support to the Technical College in Peterborough, seen as having a vital local role in developing future engineers.

Development of a new small diesel

While the serious day-to-day business of making and selling engines was proceeding, within the Engineering Division the plans for new products were reaching a critical stage. After bringing the R6 in its revised form up to the required Perkins standards, Gordon Dawson's team turned their thoughts to its successor. More immediately, however, they had another new product in its last stages of development before production, the new and revolutionary small engine initially called the C99, but which was destined for launch in late 1957 as the Four 99.

The need for a small engine suitable for modern passenger cars had been recognised some years previously and the initial prototype work had been carried out using minimal resources. To avoid the expense of casting a cylinder block for the first engine the first action had been to produce an all-welded prototype. This block was built into a complete 1.5-litre engine, designated Q4, using a Morris Oxford petrol engine crankshaft plus other prototype components fabricated to suit. The initial tests used an in-line CAV fuel pump and the engine was installed in a Vauxhall car. The engine ran, although not for long, and was sufficient to persuade the Board that such a small engine would be saleable for both small vehicles and in other sectors. Thus design work proceeded and the C99 was created. Considerable development tests and trials were necessary to evolve the final version, since this engine

had to run at 4,000rpm rated speed and develop around 50bhp. The potential for this small engine running at rotational speeds similar to the contemporary petrol engines was apparent, allowing similar road performance with no need to change the overall gearing, while the size and weight were also similar. The diesel engine would have an inherent torque advantage and fuel economy was expected to show a massive advantage.

Among the changes to design made during this period was the incorporation of the 'Howard' combustion chamber. This was unique to Perkins, who purchased the patent rights from the inventor, Mr Howard of 'Rotavator' fame. It gave cleaner combustion and was more suited to higher speed than the original 'Aeroflow' design and also superior to the Ricardo 'Comet' chamber of the period, which was tested in parallel at the insistence of Frank Perkins.

A significant new fuel pump design

Another innovation was the fitment of the new CAV DPA distributor-type fuel injection pump. This was being made by CAV under licence from a design by Vincent Roosa, initially developed by the Hartford Machine Screw Company in the USA. The pump was cost-effective due to its smaller number of parts compared to the standard in-line fuel pump although its performance depended upon extreme accuracy of machining and close tolerances. The pump went into production for the Standard tractor engine in Coventry in 1956. There had been concerns about the practicality of the pump for high production volumes but initial experiences proved that the design was viable, so that Perkins chose to go for the pump for the new product. The pump was named 'distributor-type' since it relied upon one pumping element feeding discharge ports for each cylinder in turn, in a manner similar to the spark ignition system of a petrol engine, rather than the single pumping element per cylinder of the conventional diesel 'in-line' pumps. The Engineering Department were soon testing DPA pumps for the existing engine range, to take advantage of the possible cost savings. One other aspect of the DPA was the incorporation of a hydraulic speed governor, essential to ensure drivers did not seek to exceed the mechanical limits of the engine: while the governor allowed about 10% overspeed, any attempt to continue with foot on the floor resulted in swift reduction of fuel delivery; the effect to the driver was akin to running into a brick wall and became a well-known limitation to over-enthusiastic 'pressing-on'!

Replacing the R6

While this new product activity was proceeding there remained the major problem of the R6 engine, which was still seen by the Board as the right choice for their large engine. Fortunately Gordon Dawson did not share this view and he had already initiated some design investigations into possible alternatives. During a visit to the Detroit annual meeting of the Society of Automotive Engineers (SAE) in early 1957 he had the opportunity to discuss the requirements for diesel engines with Harry Bolensky, then Chief Engineer of Ford Overseas at Willow Run, Detroit. The conversation confirmed that although the R6 was now seen as reliable, it was too small and of an outdated design. Dawson proposed that, if Ford were agreeable, he would undertake to provide a 120bhp engine in about two years: this suited the Ford programme requirements and the proposition was accepted, subject to proving.

Armed with the possibility of this major interest, in a market where Perkins sales efforts had so far proved fruitless, Dawson returned to Peterborough to convince the Board of the need for a change in strategy. Evaluation of the various schemes produced by the designers suggested that an engine of about 350 cubic inch swept volume, retaining six cylinders, represented the best compromise. By squeezing various parameters it seemed possible to attain this capacity within an overall length close to that of the R6. It required a more optimistic view of safety factors and the achievement of thin water passages between adjacent cylinders to avoid the potential problems of siamesed cylinder parent bores.

One layout proposed by the design team led by Russell Bennett and Bill Westwell was seen as potentially very attractive, although it had untried features. It introduced a short jackshaft driven at engine speed from the timing gears to a wormwheel giving half-engine-speed drive to a vertically-mounted DPA fuel injection pump. This drive was also taken downwards to drive the lubricating oil pump whilst the jackshaft could extend horizontally backwards to drive engine-speed accessories such as compressor, exhauster or hydraulic pumps. The benefits of such an arrangement were seen in an overall length reduction of about two inches, a simple timing gear arrangement and a significant reduction in engine cost. The potential problems were quite daunting, since the design relied upon the DPA pump being successful in six-cylinder form and upon a successful design solution for the wormwheel and pinion drive. After much debate, including detailed discussions with CAV over the production difficulties they were experiencing with the DPA pump, Gordon Dawson was sufficiently convinced to sign off the drive arrangement for prototype build. He also convinced CAV to base engineers at Queen Street so that much of the DPA development was carried out on Perkins' premises.

There were other risks of course, not least the crankshaft design, which had a factor of safety well below conventional standards. That the engine should prove so successful, and capable of considerable stretch in power terms as well as its use for a multitude of applications, is a testament to the design team and the foresight of the Director of Engineering.

The other significant change on the engine was of course a change to direct injection instead of the Aeroflow system. This entailed a bowl-in-piston combustion chamber, with angled injectors. Thus was born the Six 354 engine, destined to become the best-known product of the period and a worthy successor to the P6.

Another important detail change introduced by Gordon Dawson was the circulation of new drawings to the production areas. Sight of drawings, well ahead of eventual release for production, ensured feedback on acceptability as well as suggestions for changes to improve components from viewpoints other than purely design.

It is perhaps opportune to note the change of nomenclature for the engines that was introduced at about this time. The original policy of giving engines names had of course been discontinued with the 'P' series, and the use of letter designators for family, plus a number identifying the number of cylinders, had continued for some time. It was decided to change this system to identify the number of cylinders and the engine swept volume in cubic inches, rather than litres. Thus the R6 became the Six 340, the C99 became the Four 99 (and eventually the 4.99), while the new big six became the Six 354.

It is worthy of note that the stroke of the new engine was 5 inches, or 127 millimetres, the same as the 'P' series, but with a bore of 3.875 inches to give an increased swept volume. The 5-inch stroke appears to be lucky for Perkins, or perhaps it is one of those strange coincidences that occur from time to time. Martin Vulliamy claimed that the reason was quite mundane, and resulted from the need to limit piston speed to around 2,000 feet per minute – an empirical design limit. Whatever the explanation, this dimension has been a common factor across all the most successful engines from Leopard and P Series to the present high volume products.

A satellite office in Coventry

While the Engineering Division was working on the 4.99 and 6.354, further work was being carried out in a small design office at Coven-

This Dennis refuse collection vehicle pictured in 1955 is typical of the many conversions sold by Perkins in the 1950s, and which pioneered a revolution in the municipal vehicle sector

The R6(V) became the diesel option on many British-built trucks, including this 1950s Dodge, which is similar to those used in the film Hell Drivers

try. This was initially under the control of Russell Bennett, who had moved back to Perkins after a period with the Rootes Group after the war. The shortage of experienced draughtsmen in the Peterborough area forced Perkins to consider alternative ways to address the problem: the opening of an office in the heart of the motor industry's home territory was a pragmatic solution.

The Coventry team initially addressed the production of a 'standardised' industrial product, known as 'stage-by-stage', and was later responsible for redesigning the cylinder head on the L4 to convert the engine into a direct injection derivative, to be designated in the new style as Four 270D (the 'D' being used to designate the direct injection derivative for engines where the original had been with the Aeroflow combustion system). This engine used the CAV DPA fuel pump and became the first Perkins engine to enter production with a direct injection combustion system. The Coventry office was relatively short-lived, but the recruitment of design staff locally producing valuable work for Perkins without moving them away from their homes, was a key factor at the time. Eventually relocation to Peterborough brought Russell Bennett, Ralph Reaves and Gordon Ryan, among others, into the main design office.

Returning to the events of 1957, there were organisational changes as further 'Divisions' were created. Richard Perkins became Director and General Manager of the Sales Division, while Norman Collins was named similarly for the Service and Spares Division. Publicity efforts were augmented by the publication of a new occasional newspaper entitled On Show, which appeared for each of the major exhibitions focusing attention of attendees on new products and Company achievements. Another publication – The Perkins Driver – was produced to keep in touch with the growing membership of the Perkins Drivers' Club.

Another innovation in early 1957 was the launch of the Suggestion Scheme. This allowed any employee to suggest possible improvements to the product, the way in which the company operated, safety im-provements, etc. The only stipulation was that the suggestion should not be something that the proposer should have put forward as a part of his usual job. All the suggestions were considered by a committee composed of representatives drawn from across the Divisions. They decided on the action to be taken and the reward to be made, based on the likely saving to be seen by the Company. The employees welcomed the new scheme enthusiastically: 283 ideas were put forward in the first month of operation.

The summer edition of the Perkins News noted that the Silver Jubilee of the Company went unmarked by any special celebration. However, the event did not pass unnoticed by others, who sent many congratulatory messages to mark the occasion. The same issue carried many stories about the customers and applications around the world, underlining the progress made in the 25 years. From taxis in Brussels to the crossing of the Atlantic by a 23-foot lifeboat powered by an L4, and even a Daily Mirror bathing raft (powered by twin L4s) on the south coast, Perkins engines were making their presence felt and attracting good publicity. This applied equally to the R6(V) where good reports of performance, fuel consumption and long life were printed, even from owners whose previous bad experiences with the early engines did not stop them persevering with the relaunched product.

Hell Drivers

The R6 generated some further publicity of its own during the year with the release of the new J. Arthur Rank film 'Hell Drivers'. The stars included Stanley Baker and Patrick McGoohan, plus a fleet of 15 Dodge seven-ton tipper trucks, powered by the R6 (V). The driving sequences were, for the time, quite spectacular and the stars themselves did some of the driving. Even today the film is still shown on TV occasionally, although the road sequences nowadays appear unrealistic and speeded-up as the trucks tear round corners 'on rails' at frightening speeds! At its release Perkins garnered local publicity with an engine in the foyer of the Odeon cinema on Broadway, Peterborough, plus accompanying posters and technical data.

The relaunched R6 Mk 2 received positive responses, including coverage from John Moon in the Commercial Motor of 30 August 1957. A road test of the revised engine fitted in a Dodge articulated truck and run at over 18 tons gross weight returned excellent fuel economy and one of the highest time-load-mileage factors ever recorded on their tests up to that time. Although Moon admitted that longevity could not be established during a two-day trial he added '. . . I have enough faith in the engine manufacturers to believe that the modifications that have been effected will give trouble-free running'. In the months to come, faithful users who had switched to the new engine affirmed their acceptance of the revisions.

The year closed on a positive note at the Smithfield Show, with the launch of the new 4.99 engine, initially for agricultural use. It was displayed not just on the Perkins stand but also in a small combine harvester exhibited by Fahr of Germany. Other equipment manufacturers were said to be keenly interested. At the same venue the second launch was that of the Massey Ferguson 65 powered by a new variant of the P4, designated 4.192Y. This tractor was an important announcement for MF, taking the Ferguson hydraulic system originated on the 'little grey Fergie' into a higher power range with the new machine. Although the P3 had been available for the Ferguson early in the 1950s, and had been used for many conversions, Harry Ferguson had an aversion to diesels so it was only in later years that the Standard 4-cylinder diesel engine had been used alongside the petrol and paraffin versions in preference to the P3. The 'merger' of Ferguson and Massey Harris in 1953 (read A Global Corporation by E.P. Neufeld for some fascinating details!) meant that there was wider interest in the use of Perkins engines, building on the success of the P6 in the Massey Harris 744 in Britain. The new MF65 was to be of major importance to both companies.

Yet another launch at Smithfield was that of the Fordson 'Dexta' tractor, powered by a P3 engine derivative called the F3: this engine was built and tested at Peterborough, using major castings supplied by Ford and a Simms in-line fuel pump to differentiate it from the standard Perkins product. The publicity was at some pains to avoid indicating the major role of Perkins in this new Fordson. (The engine was to provide significant and valuable additional volume for the Eastfield factory over several years, although only marginally profitable due to the hard bargain driven by the Ford buyers. Unsubstantiated folklore of the time suggested a profit margin of only £4 10s. per engine!)

Another new customer was announced at the same time, with Allis Chalmers fitting the P3.144 (TA) in their D272 tractor and the P6 in the new 'Gleaner' combine harvester. This provided further evidence that the pioneering work in selling diesel engines to the agricultural market had made a mark in another North American organisation.

Another feat for the Chamberlain tractor in Australia claimed attention as the same prototype 'Champion' tractor with L4 engine completed the 1957 Mobilgas round-Australia Rally during September. It covered the full rally distance of 11,140 miles in 19 days, averaging 586 miles a day and 18.5mpg. The tractor was again an unofficial 'entry', acting as tail end Charlie to the rally and assisting other entrants where needed. The tractor managed to maintain average speeds close to those required by the actual competitors over all manner of poor surfaces.

In spite of all this apparent success, 1957 closed with production volumes down to 56,386 engines, a drop of almost 25% on the previous year and actually the first fall in output since the war years. The major culprits were the P6, whose volume was less than half that of the record previous year, and of course the R6 where the drop in demand of the previous year had continued. That some blame could be attached to the difficult trading conditions was indisputable, but

the product problems were a major factor, as was the need for a more modern range of engines to compete with the new products of erstwhile customers. From the record results of 1956, the latest figures showed a drop in turnover to £14 million, almost one third less than 1956, with the first trading loss since the Company went public (£318,751 after tax, compared with the profit after tax of £348,075 in the previous year – itself a poor result on the record turnover).

According to E.P. Neufeld in A Global Corporation, Frank Perkins asked Monty Prichard in August 1957 to take a hypothetical position as Administrator of the Company and assess the changes necessary to ensure that shareholders obtained a fair return on their investment. This request led to a memorandum entitled 'The Future of F. Perkins Limited', presumably produced in late 1957 although no copy can be found. This document pulled no punches in identifying a series of factors fundamental to the current health of the enterprise. Decline of profits in spite of rising sales, greater importance of spare parts sales due to deteriorating product quality, loss of three vehicle customers and increasing competition were all identified as contributors. The need to maintain and preferably increase expenditure on research and development was apparent in order to combat competition and introduce new engines. The conclusion reached was:

'To exist, the Company needs new products, technologically and commercially competitive. To introduce these it needs a substantial addition of capital during 1959 and 1960. This is unlikely to be available from normal sources. Amalgamation with a complementary organisation with cash available would appear to be the only real solution.'

In the next chapter the events subsequent to this conclusion will unfold.

Some Personal Glimpses

The late Dennis Hall had a lovely story about one of the numerous claims arising from the R6 problems. A letter was received from the Mother Superior of a Leicestershire convent whose party of 30 nuns had set out in a hired Bedford coach to visit a sister convent in Norfolk. The coach broke down and the nuns telephoned for help. While waiting for the replacement coach they sought refreshments in the local café: thus the claim was for around £12 to cover an assortment of sandwiches, cakes and minerals! Sad to relate, the claim was refused very politely on the grounds that it might set a precedent!

The author started work as an apprentice in 1957 and retains clear memories of life at that time. The transition from a small Suffolk town to the bustling life of Peterborough and the Perkins factory was striking enough, but some thoughts on differences between then and the late 20th century are perhaps of interest. Most of the workforce arrived on bicycles or in buses – the Company had its own bus station in Oxney Road. There were some cars and quite a lot of motorcycles but the main area of parking at Eastfield was the rows of cycle sheds! The bus journey on the Eastern Counties 301 was sixpence (2.5p) into the City Centre, and lunch in the canteen was around one shilling and sixpence (7.5p). On a starting wage at seventeen of £4 14 shillings and a penny, and after giving £2 10s for board and lodging, it was possible to live – just!

First impressions of the factory were the smells – of diesel oil, machining coolant ('white water'), exhaust fumes and cigarette smoke – and the overall untidiness, with lots of swarf in the machining areas and bins of material all around. There was camaraderie between the apprentices and friendliness elsewhere, and certainly an overall feeling of purpose around the works. There are, of course, many stories about the Apprentice School, the instructors and the antics of my fellow apprentices. Perhaps a suitable outlet for these stories will appear one day!

n his Christmas message in the Echo for December 1957, Frank Perkins declared the past year to have been the most difficult of the Company's existence and promised that the New Year of 1958 would see improvements. Certainly there was something positive in the opening months as Perkins was featured on a BBC Panorama programme covering the successful resettlement of ex-service personnel into industry. The Perkins safety film 'You Can't Be Too Careful' also received praise for addressing the reduction of industrial accidents, with over 50 copies sold to various concerns while a further 350 companies hired the film to instruct their employees. There were successes to report at the annual Boat Show, where the largest and the fastest boats on show were Perkins-powered.

In January, Edward Marvill attended the apprentices' dinner dance, presenting certificates to the first group who had completed their five years' training. In his speech proposing a toast to the Association, he looked back on his own time as an apprentice and declared himself honoured to be making awards to the new group.

A further indicator of success for personnel within the Company was the publication of the results from the first year of operation of the Suggestion Scheme. From more than 2,000 ideas put forward, awards had been made to over 300, with considerable benefits to the Company as well as to the financial and personal satisfaction of the contributors. The Sports Association proudly opened the modernised bar at the new Peterscourt Social Club – called the best in the City – while the workers at Queen Street were promised better parking arrangements as the number owning cars increased.

In March Frank Perkins decided to relinquish some of his executive responsibilities. He became Chairman and Joint Managing Director, with Monty Prichard as the other Joint Managing Director with responsibility for the day-to-day running of the Company. A new director was also announced, Mr George P. Ritchie joining the Board to replace A.J. Dillingham following his resignation on account of age.

Launch of the Four 99

The successful launch of the Four 99 in its agricultural guise at the Smithfield Show was followed by its release as a vehicle engine in April. Many employees attended a special showing at the old Polebrook airfield, leased by Perkins for storage and proving ground purposes. There they were able to drive various vehicles fitted with the Four 99 around the perimeter track – these ranged from Morris Oxford and Vauxhall Velox cars to small towing tractors and vans. The launch of the engine to the press and public was accompanied by a road test, under strict RAC certification, in which an engine fitted to a Velox achieved 56.6mpg over a 218-mile cross-country course at an average speed of 34.8mph. The engine, rated at 43bhp at 4,000rpm, had taken over five years to develop and involved road testing all over the world as well as specific performance testing at the Motor Industry Research Association proving grounds near Nuneaton. (It is interesting to note that the experience of many Perkins employees who later owned cars with the 4.99 fitted as a conversion showed similar performance was possible in everyday motoring: Mike Halse, ex-apprentice and later an outboard motor service engineer, recalls that he and his family in

The launch of the 6.354 engine was an important step in rebuilding the reputation of Perkins. This is an early vehicle version from 1960

The first move for product diversification was into outboard motors. Appearances at boat shows were important, with the boat builders helping publicity with displays such as this

an ex-Perkins fleet Vauxhall Wyvern regularly obtained 56/57mpg fully laden on holiday trips down to Devon.)

A royal visit

In April there was an informal royal visit to Perkins, when the Duke and Duchess of Gloucester toured the plant with their sons. During the visit the Princes and their parents met many senior personnel, as well as having the opportunity to talk with employees during the tour. As well as touring the main factory, where various sections and machinery were demonstrated, the party visited the Ambulance Room and the main office block. They also paid a visit to one of the first 'self-build' houses of the second group to be completed: at No. 1 Corfe Avenue, Walton they met the proud owners along with other members of the Secundus Self-Help Building Society.

Annual General Meeting of F Perkins Limited

On 9 June the twenty-sixth AGM of F. Perkins Limited was held at the Angel Hotel in Bridge Street, Peterborough. As noted at the close of the previous chapter, the results for 1957 did not make good reading. Frank Perkins was forthright in his assessment of the causes of the loss in turnover and profits. He noted that the pioneering work of the Company in proving the benefits of the diesel engine had been so successful that several large vehicle customers, notably Ford, had been convinced to produce their own engines. The Suez crisis had then served to adversely impact both the UK market and the overseas market. The closure of the Middle East market due to financial restrictions had interrupted sales to an important and developing area. Although some new customers had been gained to help offset the losses in sales, the new launches had been delayed and thus seriously affected the end-of-year figures. He identified the recent new product launches as well as the intention to diversify into products other than

diesel engines, although with some activities it was as yet too early to announce details. Good progress was reported in overseas subsidiaries, including Canada, France and Australia, with other developments in hand.

The comments of the Chairman were reinforced by an interview given by Monty Prichard to the Echo in May. He gave details of the substantial recovery already achieved in the first few months of the year, stating that in April the production despatches of new engines was a record at 8,248. After identifying the launch of the Four 99 as a significant event, he also noted the appearance of the updated and more cost-effective P4 and P3 derivatives, the P4/192 and the P3/144, as equally significant in providing competitive engines with wider application.

Reference had been made by MIP to the adoption of the P6 and R6 by Chrysler Corporation in the USA as an option for their Dodge 'De Soto' range of trucks. This was followed in July with the news that Ford of America were to offer the R6 in their new F600 truck for markets around the world. The evidence was growing that the message of diesel engine durability and economy had finally found receptive ears on the other side of the Atlantic. (In fact the use of Perkins engines in North American truck designs at this time proved to be limited to their export markets, so the success was less than had been hoped.)

Developments at Eastfield

It might be useful at this point to review the activities on the Eastfield site and the way in which Perkins had developed through the 1950s. As has been described previously, the factory had been extended several times to accommodate additional plant for machining not just the major components but also many other smaller components. The direction taken was to source castings, both ferrous and non-ferrous, from foundries around the country and then to install general-purpose

The launch of the Mars gas turbine was low-key, as were the production facilities shown here

including water pump assemblies, rocker levers and brackets, pipes and brackets, etc. This represented a significant departure from the earliest days when machining was all done by suppliers, with Perkins carrying out assembly, test and finish only.

It is interesting to note that continuity of aluminium casting supply was helped by a Perkins initiative to buy aluminium scrap and to process it in a facility housed within a rented hanger at the disused airfield at Polebrook near Oundle, mentioned earlier as the venue for the Four 99 launch. The resulting ingots were supplied to the various light alloy foundries producing castings for Perkins.

This airfield was also considered in the late 50s as a site for a plant to handle the strip and rebuild of 'Perpetuity' engines when cessation of operations at Queen Street was being actively pursued. The Ministry of Defence was not supportive, however, and shortly afterwards the site was reactivated as a 'Titan' rocket base during the 'Cold War' period. (This also meant that the Gliding Club, a very active part of the Sports Association, had to find a new home – relocating from Polebrook for a time to the Peterborough Westwood airfield.) Another possible rebuild factory site at Huntingdon, with local council approval and backing, had previously been blocked by the Government, who favoured, instead, a move to Corby New Town. Perkins did not view this enthusiastically: rebuild operations were destined to remain at Queen Street for several more years.

Within the main factory the major components were produced on flow line systems, referred to later as 'link lines' since they were built up from individual machines linked by conveyor tracks, turnover fixtures and buffer areas. The machines used were composed of special purpose multi-head drilling and milling machines, plus the occasional radial drill equipped with purpose-built fixtures, quick-change drill holders, etc. This arrangement allowed high production rates with a certain amount of flexibility, but with relatively high manning levels

equipment to produce finished parts in-house. This policy change was considered necessary to control component output and availability, to say nothing of tighter control of engine costs. Consequently by the end of the 1950s factory contained machining sections producing the heavy parts such as flywheels, flywheel housings and sumps, as well as aluminium components such as timing cases and covers and rocker covers. In addition, there was a myriad of smaller parts

The development of the new factory provided vastly increased space for machining. This 1950s picture shows part of the large section machining miscellaneous components

The Eastfield factory allowed assembly areas, such as this for the P6 engine, to be well planned with good working space for the operatives

and manual handling compared to the highly sophisticated and automated transfer equipment that was to come in the 1960s. The smaller components were machined on 'general purpose' areas, where many machines were flexible and capable of being reset, using dedicated fixtures as necessary, to handle different components. Skilled operators, known as setters, assisted this changeover process for batch production to suit weekly or monthly requirements.

As a result of the 'bespoke engineering' approach to applications design – where Perkins designed and procured parts to allow the engine to be dropped into the customer's machine or vehicle as a complete unit ready to be coupled up to transmission, radiator etc. and driven away – there were many special parts with relatively low volume to be sourced to suit these individual needs. Some of these parts were made in-works, while others were brought from specialist suppliers or the many small jobbing machinists around the East Midlands, or indeed elsewhere. In these pre-computer days the resulting listing, sourcing, programming and physically bringing the parts together for build at the right time was a major process, requiring a substantial workforce to control the necessary stages. Little wonder that the total workforce had grown to around 7,000 people, and that inventory levels on many of the slow-moving, batch-produced, parts tended to be high.

There were many other departments supporting production directly too, from the maintenance, tool room, jig and fixtures, work study, inspection and methods departments through the essential logistics controls to the service areas such as personnel, medical and canteen. Stores took up a considerable space, having to handle and house rough castings, the material machined in-works awaiting buffering and supply to the assembly tracks, the bought-in-finished parts and the consumable items from oil and fuel to hand tools, cleaning

rags and overalls. Many components at this time were delivered by truck via the central roadway through the main factory, dropping off at points adjacent to the area of use.

The complexity of production, with four major assembly tracks covering the P3/P4, P6, L4/R6 and Four 99, together with Engine Finishing and Loose Parts, necessitated a sophisticated Production Control process. The Company Programme identified production requirements on a rolling-year basis, with detailed breakdown for month and week ahead, actual daily build being controlled by the 'firm programme'. This was a dynamic document, varied to take account of shortages and newly identified customer priorities.

All engines were tested, to a variety of test plans depending on duty and rating, before being finished and painted for despatch. Engines were marked with their delivery week to assist tracking and priority handling.

With no computer available at this time, the Company used a Hollerith punch card system to break down the Company Programme into component part numbers to assist the purchasing and control process. With manual control this was a manpower-intensive operation.

My purpose in diverting to a consideration of the company structure at this time is to give some idea of the complexity of routine operations necessary whatever the current production volume. The functions were all needed and staffing levels could not be changed quickly to suit fluctuations in customer demand. There was a continuous review of costs, obviously, and attempts were made to reduce costs and complexity wherever possible – limited of course by the need to give the customer what he demanded! Concern over 'non-productive' costs and indirect labour costs was, is, and always will be, a major headache for those running any complex manufacturing enterprise. While the engine volumes were low in 1957 the Company continued to add to the losses since the overhead costs could not be avoided. The better days of 1958 helped, but not quickly enough.

Even while the apparent recovery was starting, the financial health of the Company therefore remained a concern, and not just internally. Since the Company went public in 1951 the shares were quoted and available through the London Stock Exchange. In the early days the share price had risen quickly to over 45 shillings, against the nominal value of 10 shillings, before being halved by the scrip issue. Since that point in 1955, the share value had fluctuated but never again reached such a high level. With the difficulties and adverse trading climate in the late 50s the share price fell gradually, and it seemed that whatever was being done, and whatever successes were publicised, recovery of shareholder confidence was unlikely. With shares quoted at about one third of their peak value it was apparent that F. Perkins Ltd was undervalued and 'ripe for takeover'.

Diversification Plans

The reader will recall the words of Frank Perkins at the Annual General Meeting regarding the investigation of alternative products in case the diesel engine business failed to continue to prosper. There were a number of possible diversifications considered, of which two were to proceed to fruition, namely the excursions into the production of outboard motors and gas turbines. The first of these resulted from a chance remark passed on by the Perkins North American office regarding the outboard motor business of the Oliver Corporation. Oliver was an agricultural equipment manufacturer (later to be a major and exacting diesel customer of Perkins) who had decided to branch out into the leisure market and had gone into production with an outboard engine design. Oliver had purchased the design and rights from Chris Craft in the USA, a company better known for boats but who had seen some potential in producing their own engines. Although there was a

The Massey Ferguson takeover signalled the retirement of Frank Perkins from active management. His farewell to the workers in February 1959 was emotional. Frank is accompanied here by the MF President, Albert Thornbrough

large and increasing market in the USA, as well as in other parts of the world, it was rumoured that Oliver wished to sell the business. Monty Prichard became enthusiastic about the chances for such a product, especially in Europe where the market was less developed than in the USA, and decided to visit Oliver for discussions. To the considerable surprise of his fellow directors, he returned to England having signed an agreement to take over the entire Oliver outboard motor division! Clearly space would be needed to handle this product, which was in many ways different to their diesel products. After a short search a suitable plant was found in the north-west of Peterborough at Sages Lane, Walton. Space for the commercial departments was found in the offices at Peterscourt and Eastfield.

A team was put together to handle the various aspects of the new venture, for which a new company was set up – Perkins Outboard Marine Limited. Gordon Dawson quickly realised that a separate engineering entity would be needed to control the technical side, and Horace Rainbow was recruited as Chief Engineer. The team started to test and evaluate the products, soon determining that there were design and quality shortcomings in the three sizes of motor – 6, 16 and 35hp nominal ratings. These engines were all twin-cylinder two-stroke petrol engines, running on a petrol/oil mixture, and with much light alloy in their construction. A concentrated period of activity produced a more satisfactory design standard, whilst the application of Perkins manufacturing methods made major improvements to the quality of build. Proving tests were conducted in tanks at the Walton Factory, in a flooded disused brick pit at Fletton and on the River Nene at Sutton Bridge. Publicity and Sales efforts were geared up to start marketing the engines for 1959.

The second new product diversification was into small gas turbines. Again, instead of opting for design and manufacture from scratch, the Perkins Board decided to look for a partnership with an existing company with a proven record and leadership in gas turbines approxi-

mating to the horsepower range of the current products. A search quickly showed the best option to be the Solar Aircraft Company of San Diego, USA.

A fact-finding visit by Gordon Dawson soon confirmed both the suitability of the product and the willingness of Solar to enter into a licence agreement. (In fact there was an existing UK licensee, Sugg-Solar Ltd., who were eventually bought out by Perkins.) A second new company was formed – Perkins Gas Turbines Limited – to handle all aspects of the venture. The licence gave exclusivity for sales into Europe, Africa and the British Commonwealth, excluding Canada, to manufacture and sell all gas turbines developed by Solar.

The products already in place at Solar ranged from 50 to 1,250hp, all being named after planets, including Mars, Saturn and Jupiter. The initial Perkins interest was in the smallest unit, the Mars, which at 50hp was suitable for a variety of applications. The most interesting use appeared to be as a portable emergency water pump, compact enough to be hand-carried by two men, complete with fuel supply, and able to pump 500 gallons a minute. The unit was hand-started via a crank mechanism, needing vigorous turning until sufficient speed was obtained for ignition to be self-sustaining, whereupon the gas turbine would accelerate to a speed approaching 100,000rpm – quite a difference from the diesels – accompanied by a high-pitched whistle and blast of exhaust gas. The potential for sale to fire brigades and for use by the Services ensured that this would be the first priority marketing direction. The initial space needed for production was small and was satisfied by the conversion of an old Nissen hut behind the Eastfield factory, with office space on the ground floor of the main factory close to the main office block. Compared to the money spent on the outboard side, this was engineering on a shoestring with a small number of staff and workshop personnel handling a product that was even more alien to a diesel company – its only tenuous connection was the preferred 'gas oil' fuel!

New diesel products

While this business was being developed, new diesel engines were also under development. The most advanced was the Six 354, although some of the more unusual features were causing problems. The DPA fuel pump in its six-cylinder form was proving difficult to get right: it took major efforts at Perkins and CAV to resolve a situation that at one point threatened serious production delay. Another problem on the Six 354 was the wormwheel drive arrangement, where premature wear was occurring. This was eventually cured after the recruitment of an engineer from Austin named Marcus Jacobson, who had solved similar gear problems there. The solution was to increase the gear centres, which forced changes to the cylinder block water passages to maintain clearance for the fuel pump.

The Commercial Motor Show in September 1958 saw the launch of the Six 340 (the latest reincarnation of the R6) and the C.305. This latter engine was a stretched capacity version of the venerable P6, having a cylinder bore of 3.6 inches instead of 3.5 inches, and featured the DPA fuel injection pump. The P6 was also upgraded to become the 6.288, also featuring the DPA pump. These engines were launched in a number of new vehicles from Commer, Dennis, Guy, Seddon, Scammell and Karrier. For Karrier the C.305 was a special version angled 24 degrees to the horizontal (right side down), thus enabling the engine to fit under the cab floor. The power increase was marginal, at 87bhp and 2,400rpm, but with a useful torque increase to 210 lbs ft.

There were other sales successes to report, with the Four 99 being specified in the Beardmore taxi and the Trojan 'mechanical horse'. By the close of the year the Four 99 marine engine for light craft and yacht auxiliary power had been announced, and there was more marine publicity when comedian George Formby's cruiser Lady Beryl II with twin P6(M)s was launched at Wroxham on the Norfolk Broads.

Production for 1958 reached a new record of 77,017 engines, up by 36% over the previous year, and over 2,000 engines above the previous record of 1956. The major contributors were the P3 and P4, thanks to the increasing tractor business with Massey Ferguson and Ford. The R6 continued its decline, as did the P6, but the little 4.99 contributed 1,500 sales in its first full year.

1959: Talk of takeover and Massey Ferguson

In the New Year the Perkins name appeared in the business pages of the national press as the price of the shares continued at a low level and talk of takeover was rife. Eventually the rumours became fact as Massey Ferguson announced their interest and intentions to buy all the Ordinary shares of F. Perkins Ltd. Through headline news in the February 1959 Peterborough Diesel Echo the employees were advised of the situation and their apprehensions were eased by the content of the announcement.

Mr A.A. Thornbrough, President of Massey Ferguson, was quoted: 'I look upon the acquisition of Perkins as the corner stone of the general reorganisation of Massey Ferguson facilities in Europe.' He went on to make it clear that Perkins would continue to supply existing custom-

Although an open test shop, the new facilities at Eastfield were spacious and tidy, a model for their time. (Although the noise level from so many engines running in the space would not be tolerated today)

ers. The interest of Massey Ferguson in Perkins appears to have been sparked by a visit made by Monty Prichard to the MF Headquarters in Toronto on his way back from the negotiations with Oliver Corporation for the outboard motor business. The financial difficulties Perkins were experiencing had been a topic of conversation but apparently not treated with any urgency by the Canadian company at the time. However, protracted and difficult negotiations with their major supplier, Standard Motor Company, over future engine supply made MF executives consider Perkins, already an established supplier, as a potentially better source.

While Prichard was in Brazil in late November 1958 a message was sent from Al Thornbrough asking him to call at Toronto on his way back. This he did, and on 6 December learnt that MF wished to buy Perkins. There seems to have been some added urgency in view of rumours of other companies interested in a takeover, according to E.P. Neufeld in his history of Massey Ferguson, A Global Corporation. MIP talked on the phone to Frank Perkins and by 8 December the issue was really completed.

However, the announcement was held back until 23 January 1959, when the MF offer to buy all 5,200,000 issued shares for 17 shillings and 3 pence each, cash, was made. This offer was recommended for acceptance by the Board and made unconditional by Massey Ferguson in early February: the majority of shareholders accepted with great relief after seeing their investment fall to a low of around 7 shillings and 10 pence per share during the preceding period. (The total cost to MF was reckoned to be about US$12.5 million.)

During February mass meetings within the plants were addressed by Frank Perkins and by Al Thornbrough. FAP spoke of his retirement from active management after nearly 37 years, accepting a position of Chairman of the Board of Directors. Thornbrough gave a reassuring message about the future: 'It is our intention and desire and commitment', he said, 'to transfer to Peterborough and the Perkins Company as rapidly as we can the requirements for engines in Massey Ferguson products.' The confirmation that Perkins was to retain its name under the new ownership was also seen as important to both employees and existing customers, as was the appointment of Monty Prichard as Managing Director of the new subsidiary of Massey Ferguson Holdings Limited. There was a moving scene at Eastfield when the shop floor employees gave FAP a rousing send-off by singing 'For He's a Jolly Good Fellow'. There were tributes from long-serving employees including Ted Marvill, while the Works Convenor Mr R. Waterston also added a brief and touching comment. Frank Perkins left a final message to all employees: 'I look forward to the continued growth of the Company, which we now serve, and I am sure with the added momentum received from Massey Ferguson, Perkins will far exceed present expecta-

tions. May I wish you all, every man, woman and boy, all happiness and success in the future.'

In reporting the events and publishing photographs of the historic occasion the Diesel Echo covered the history and growth of the Massey Ferguson organisation, identifying the takeover as the beginning of a new chapter in the life of Perkins as it became part of a worldwide operation with immense potential.

On the Monday morning after the takeover was announced, there was an attempted 'raid' by trades union shop stewards from the MF plant at Coventry who appeared at the main gates of the Eastfield plant. They apparently felt they had the right to walk in to talk to the Perkins workers! They were soon advised to the contrary and sent away, but of course the question of 'pay parity' across MF plants in the UK was an ongoing bargaining issue in years to come.

An interesting fact related by Neufeld was that the purchase of the outboard business from Oliver Corporation was originally to be financed by the transfer of 650,000 ordinary shares in Perkins to Oliver. Rather than have a competitor as a minority shareholder, MF offered Oliver 1,183,000 dollars in lieu of the shares and this was accepted.

In closing this important chapter in the history it is perhaps right to consider what might have happened if Massey Ferguson had not come along as a buyer and, probably, saviour. Neufeld has suggested that there were other potential suitors, but nothing in the author's research has put a name to these possible buyers. In view of the increasing swing to diesel in the automotive and agricultural sectors at the time, could Ford, Chrysler or General Motors have been interested through their British subsidiaries? There was reputed to be interest from Cummins Engines at some point in the 1960s, so might they have been another possible buyer looking to gain a foothold in Europe? This is all conjecture, although such an alternative would have changed subsequent history considerably! The other option might have been better Perkins management of the share issue in the early 50s: if more capital had been generated at that time, would the development of the Company have changed, the crisis averted and independence assured? Or would this have merely put off an eventual takeover for a brief period?

The writer views the MF purchase as being the best solution at the time. Continuing independence without the benefits of a 'captive' market would have been doomed to eventual failure – then a 'fire sale' purchase by one of the automotive 'giants' would probably have seen the Perkins name disappear forever. The importance of allowing Perkins to maintain independence of supply to other customers – and maintain the necessary client confidentiality – must not be underestimated either, since it allowed continued growth in other sectors and shielded the company from some of the vagaries of the agricultural market.

Chapter 10: Expansion (1959 to 1961)

pring 1959 saw Perkins planning for the future under new leadership and with renewed vigour. In April came the announcement of a new subsidiary of F. Perkins Ltd, to be known as Perkins Engines Ltd, under the guidance of Richard Perkins as Managing Director. The incorporation of the new company was designed to address the continued support of its traditional business with all existing customers other than Massey Ferguson. (It is interesting to note that Monty Prichard in his announcement of the new subsidiary referred very carefully to the 'merger' with MF rather than the more emotive 'takeover').

The announcement concentrated on the need to convince customers, and especially those in competition with MF, that Perkins still maintained independence and confidentiality when dealing with their needs. Through the formation of a separate company organisation, based at Peterscourt, and comprising sales personnel and the necessary support functions such as installation draughtsmen and service personnel, the necessary level of confidentiality and independence was assured. In effect, the formation of Perkins Engines Ltd created a situation where F. Perkins Ltd, the parent, had three customers in Massey Ferguson, Perkins Outboard Motors and Perkins Engines Ltd. All had their own sales and service operations but used the remainder of the 'group' facilities, covering areas such as Accounts, Publicity, Personnel, Security, etc. Even areas such as the Service School and Apprentice Trade School were identified as group facilities, providing services as appropriate to the sales operations as well as the manufacturing parent. The operations at Queen Street, comprising mainly Engine Rebuild and Engineering, would also remain as a part of the parent company.

Massey Ferguson as a 'hands-off' owner

It is perhaps important to note at this point that the MF policy of letting Perkins run their own business as far as other customers were concerned – almost certainly a position demanded by Monty Prichard – proved very successful. MF certainly acted as a 'careful banker' as far as capital expenditure was concerned, and over the years maintained close control over the financial aspects of the business. However, there was never a concerted move to place Toronto-trained senior personnel in Peterborough to control other aspects: in fact over the years there was a reverse 'migration' of Perkins-trained individuals into Toronto, where their influence grew. The freedom allowed Perkins to develop customers on a worldwide basis, even where they were in competition with MF products. This allowed production volumes to increase – contributing to the reduction and control of component, and therefore engine, pricing to MF advantage; the more so since the process of 'transfer pricing' gave MF an edge on profit margin compared to any competitor using an equivalent engine from Perkins Engines Ltd.

As the new operations settled down there were announcements of new Board appointments. J.G. Dawson was named Director of Engineering and G.E. Smith as Director of Production. While Gordon Dawson had already made his mark in the Engineering Department, Geoffrey Smith had been recruited from the Brush Group to become Personal Assistant to M.I. Prichard in 1957.

There were also changes in the outboard motors management. A small change was made in the name of the Company, from Perkins Outboard Marine Ltd to Perkins Outboard Motors Ltd as a result of a friendly request from an American Company with a similar name. The structure of the company was strengthened by the appointment of Alastair Denholm as General Sales Manager and G.W. Bailey as Home Sales Manager.

Creation of a Brazilian subsidiary

An announcement in May heralded the formation of a new subsidiary company in Brazil – Motores Perkins S.A. This was a joint venture between Perkins and Murray Simonsen S.A., a well-established Brazilian organisation. The issued capital of about £2 million was partly taken up by F. Perkins Ltd in the form of the transfer of the full machining line for the 6.340 engine, which was to be made in Brazil as the Six B340 engine. Transfer of this machining line, with a total weight of over 1,000 tons, represented a major operation as it was dismantled within the Eastfield plant, packed and then shipped the 6,000 miles to São Bernardo, a small town on the outskirts of São Paulo. (A later chapter traces the history of Motores Perkins S.A., which played an important part in Perkins overseas manufacturing operations through the remainder of the 20th century.) The space freed within the Eastfield plant was refurbished and readied for the machinery needed to manufacture the new 6.354 engine, scheduled to start production in late 1960.

Gas Turbines and Outboard Motors

Another event in the same month was the formal announcement of the manufacture of gas turbines at Peterborough, with the establishment of Perkins Gas Turbines Limited. The assembly of the 50bhp 'Mars' water pumping set had already commenced, with first deliveries scheduled before the end of the year.

July saw the new outboard motor plant at Walton featured in the leading article in the Diesel Echo. The personnel involved in the preparation of the new plant were identified, emphasis being placed on the experience that was being applied to the layout and operation of the plant, drawing upon the considerable expertise developed during the successive expansions and revisions within the main plant at Eastfield. The flow-line principles applied ensured the best use was made of the 43,000 square feet of floor area, while the complexity and unfamiliarity of some of the equipment meant a steep learning curve for the staff previously used to diesel production. Concerns among the staff transferred to Walton that they would be split from the 'family' atmosphere were allayed as a new local team spirit developed to ensure the end of July production deadline start-up was met.

The apprentices were also in the news with their first 'At Home' in the Trade School.

Around 400 parents, relatives and friends were able to see the school – and apprentices – in action and were able to tour the factory as well. Tea was offered in the canteen, where Gordon Dawson and Malcolm Sayers, the Training Manager, welcomed the visitors.

Massey Ferguson was in the news again in August when the purchase of the Banner Lane tractor plant in Coventry from the Standard Motor Company Ltd was announced. Monty Prichard emphasised the growing importance of the MF Group as a worldwide enterprise, with over 40,000 employees occupying over 15 million square feet of factory space around the world. He noted that the use of Perkins engines in tractors built at Coventry would start with the P3.144 in the FE 35 tractor in October, with other products being phased in at an increasing rate. After expressing satisfaction and the additional job security for Perkins people he added: 'I want to emphasise most strongly that this does not mean that our interest in the many hundreds of our customers diminishes in any way whatsoever. In fact the management and staff of Perkins Engines Ltd have been expressly charged with the duty of seeking out and securing business for Perkins engines wherever possible throughout the world.'

At the end of August the Company celebrated its most successful

Sports and Family Day with over 13,000 people attending. Invited guests included a number of MF directors and managers, as well as civic representatives from Peterborough City Council. As well as the customary display of Perkins products the visitors were able to inspect farm machinery and equipment fitted with various Perkins engines.

Further extensions to the main factory we announced in October, with an additional three bays planned at a cost of around £285,000. The extra space at the south end of the plant was intended to improve efficiency and provide space to carry out further changes in layout, including reduction in the outside storage of castings. In addition the plan reduced the main roadway through the factory, cutting truck through traffic and provided separate goods inwards and despatch bays at the south end.

Opening of the Walton factory

In October the Walton factory was formally opened and commenced production. Monty Prichard addressed representatives of the Press and Main Dealers at the opening ceremony and claimed that Perkins Outboard Motors Ltd would play an important part in the future of the Perkins organisation. 'We have formed this new subsidiary company and have spent a large sum on the best possible plant,' he said. 'This enterprise is not just something that is with us for this year and gone the next: we are in this outboard market for good. We are now ready to challenge the position of all competitors, including those in America. This new outboard manufacturing plant, the largest of its kind in the country, is an effective start.' The range of engines comprised 6,16 and 35hp models, with the option of remote control operation. With the wide variety of boats needing power and potential for usage worldwide, the future looked promising.

By the end of 1959 the overall picture indeed looked bright for the whole Group. Along with the new outboards and gas turbines, there were further models of the Four 99, Six 305 and Six 288 released for marine and industrial use, while the Four 99 was establishing a market for conversions in passenger cars and vans. The little Four 99(M) had achieved several new water speed records in France, and a 15ft boat had won the tourist class in the gruelling Paris Six Hour Race on the Seine. It was surprising therefore to see that the overall production volume for the year, at only 73,347 engines, was down by 3,600 engines compared to the previous year. There was a drop in P6, R6 and P3 production partly offset by volume increases for L4, P4 and 4.99. However, the plant was gearing up to meet the increasing needs of MF so the new decade was viewed with eager anticipation. An SMMT 'Motor Industry Bulletin' published in December 1959 included optimistic paragraphs about MF and Perkins, their performance and expectations. The same document carried interesting views about the future of the Motor Industry in the UK as well as its export performance, comparing this to other countries and especially France and West Germany where car production through the 1950s had outstripped the British achievements.

1960

The New Year started with good news from the National Boat Show, where diesel and outboard engines were exhibited and received with enthusiasm. The Show was held at Earls Court for the first time, more Perkins products were on view in boats and orders were placed for all sizes. Even the Mars gas turbine was on show, creating such interest that the sales literature ran out early in the exhibition run! It is interesting to note, however, from the minutes of the Directors' weekly meetings, that there were serious delivery delays on both outboards and diesels following the abundance of new orders. There were rumblings from Oliver Corporation, who were buying outboard motors for distribution in the USA, of delay in meeting their outstanding orders. There were serious problems with some suppliers, notably on

The early design of the 4.236 tractor engine shown here, with pressed steel inspection plate on the offside, was made in small numbers only in 1962/3

the production of outboard crankshafts, and fuel injection equipment for the diesels.

While the marine Four 99 was generating firm interest and orders, Perkins were able to announce that the vehicle version was to be offered as a standard option in the new Commer range of light commercial vehicles which featured a 'forward-control' cab arrangement. The range offered included small buses, pick-ups, and vans – with customising to suit specialist uses such as ambulances, mobile shops and caravans. This was the first time a British manufacturer had offered buyers a diesel option in such a new small vehicle and it was fitting that Commer, with their Perkins association dating back to 1933, should be the pioneer.

The February 1960 Perkins Echo (the name had been changed during 1959 to reflect the increased diversity of products) reported on a new management group within the Production Division tasked with increasing productivity and efficiency through a better understanding and communication between the 115 members of the management team. By changing the chairman and committee members each year the Production Director, Geoffrey Smith, and his assistant Albert Markham were looking to broaden the experience of every team member.

Apprentice Training

In the same issue the award of certificates to each of sixteen apprentices who had completed their training was featured with Norman Collins, Assistant Managing Director, making the presentations. In his address Mr Collins noted that in the old days it was the custom to get rid of apprentices when they had served their time. He added: 'But those days have gone. We hope that you will decide to stay with us and continue your careers in whatever field you have chosen to specialise.' (It is perhaps interesting to record that eight of those sixteen spent over 30 further years doing exactly that).

Another article at the same time was devoted to the Careers Committee, formed by the Company to give guidance to apprentices and to follow their progress for three years after their final placement. This indication of care extending well beyond the formative period shows the forward thinking of Perkins' management of the time regarding staff suitability and career development.

While progress on the extensions of the Eastfield factory was regularly updated via the Echo, it was at Queen Street that featured on

Above: The activities of the Sports Association were varied. Here the 1961 rugby XV is about to play a match against Ford Motor Company

Left: The annual Christmas parties for employees' children were well attended and supported – here Miss Perkins Diesel helps to entertain employees' children

long-serving employees than anywhere else in the Company.

The first anniversary of the formation of Perkins Engines Limited was marked with a review of progress. Although this sales and service operation employed only four per cent of the total Peterborough workforce, their importance in selling to all customers other than MF was obvious. On all fronts increased sales were reported. Of particular note was the comment from Leslie Bugg on 'Trade Sales', which covered conversion sales to vehicle, tractor and agricultural sectors. He highlighted the special impact on the public cleansing and refuse-collection activities where Perkins engines were now in use by almost 900 local authorities employing some 4,000 vehicles. This market breakthrough was further emphasised by an article in Motor Transport in June, where the author, Mr D.W. Jackson of Sunderland Corporation, stated that: 'unless the Chancellor introduces some really penal taxation on DERV, the purchase of a petrol-engined vehicle for public cleansing work is not likely to receive serious consideration in the future.' With operators claiming typical fuel savings in excess of £80 per vehicle per year, even when running mainly on low mileage stop/start work, the change in thinking instigated by Perkins in 1952 was clearly a major success for the Company. There were other savings too, on vehicle life, engine life and total maintenance costs, adding to the incentives to 'think diesel'.

New Product Activity

The 1960s were to be a period of intense pressure on the Engineering Department's resources, as new products were demanded. (See Chapter 12 for more details.) Already in the spring of 1960 there were demands for the direct injection version of the P4, initially designated Four A.203 D for MF, scheduled to be unveiled at the Smithfield Show at the end of the year. Along with the development of the new Six

the front of the March edition. The Engine Rebuild section at Queen Street handled around 10,000 engines each year as part of the 'Perpetuity' Scheme started in 1938, when factory reconditioning of engines, at controlled prices, was proposed as a cost-effective way to support customers. The receipt of a worn-out engine started a sequence of strip, inspection, updating and rebuild, with the refurbished engine ultimately becoming available for a further period of service. The same department was responsible for supply of non-current assemblies for spares purposes, as well as the production of sectioned and show-finished engines for display all over the world. The article commented that a higher proportion of the 900 workers at Queen Street were

354 there was the design and development of the four-cylinder version, to be known as the Four 236. This was planned as a vehicle engine for Commer Cars Ltd and for use by MF too. To add even more workload, there was a stretched, and dry-linered, version of the Four 270D, designated Four A.300, also mainly for MF: this engine featured a Lanchester-type balancer, to reduce the inherent second-order vibrations from this very large four-cylinder unit with considerable reciprocating masses. There was also the need to support the new Brazilian plant on the Six 340 and a version of the Four 203 for Ford tractors to be made in Brazil. Other new engine projects included the design of a large V8 engine.

It was clear too that the Company was facing considerable problems as production increased. The weekly Managing Director's meetings reported constant concerns over arrears of engine deliveries, mainly due to supply shortfall. Along with difficulties at CAV in producing sufficient DPA pumps for the growing number of applications, there were serious under-deliveries of cylinder liners from Laystall Engineering. Within the Eastfield plant there were machine breakdowns, delays in approving new fuel pump specifications, late design changes, etc. A typical report for the end of March showed the total arrears to be 2,243 engines against the despatch programme, and that over the previous three weeks there had been sufficient track stoppages to lose 1,700 engines alone!

In the middle of such traumas there was progress to be made on reducing the working week for staff, the finalising of the handling of spare parts from Queen Street to the new combined MF/Perkins Central Parts Operation at Urmston, Manchester, plus completion of the factory extensions to target. In April the Oliver Corporation terminated the agreement on their distribution of outboard motors within the USA, citing poor engine delivery – a new distributor was needed and discussions started with the Chrysler Corporation.

Looking back now, the sheer volume of work being undertaken seems immense but somehow it was being kept moving and – more or less – under control.

Out-of-work activities

Items reported during the summer showed that employees had time to play as well as work. The Sports Association highlighted extra endeavours as new clubs for go-karting, volleyball and motoring were started. The Gliding Club members spent a week of their holidays on a concentrated programme of flying from their base at Westwood Airfield. There was an organised outing for 490 club members and their families to Great Yarmouth, in addition to the activities of all the other sections: all for a membership fee of just three (old) pence per week! To show that outside-work activities were not confined to England, there was news of the formation of a football team in Brazil, with matches scheduled against teams from other companies in the embryo Brazilian motor industry as the Motores Perkins operation got under way.

In September the Sports and Family Day was marred by wet weather, but over 10,000 people still attended, enjoying a full programme of events including a display of cars ranging from a 1902 De Dion Bouton to the current BRM Formula 1 racing car. Exhibits of Massey Ferguson tractors, combine harvesters and other implements complemented the displays of all the Perkins products. The traditional sports, hobbies, Footlights Club show and other sideshows and refreshments made sure the attendees were well entertained.

As the year drew to a close the highlights included the introduction of the Six 354 at the Commercial Motor Show at Earls Court, to an enthusiastic reception by the Press, vehicle manufacturers and operators. 'Now in production at Peterborough' was the claim, and indeed the records show 91 engines produced during 1960! There was excellent coverage by the trade press, with John Moon of the Commercial Motor being a particular enthusiast for the new engine. His report on the road test of a Seddon 7-tonner noted: 'The main objective of the test was to assess the merits of the new engine. Manufacturers who install Perkins engines as initial equipment will find that the Six 354 will prove a "winner". The engine should also have a rosy future as a conversion unit . . .' He noted a fuel consumption improvement of around 10 per cent compared to the indirect injection P6, and claimed excellent cold

The Massey Ferguson model MF 35 tractor fitted with the A3.152 engine was popular in the 1960s, seen here as part of an outboard motor publicity shoot at Milton Ferry near Peterborough

starting as well as 'remarkable transmission and engine smoothness from as low as 8 MPH in top gear'. The new product seemed to be off to a good start, and was exhibited in its agricultural tractor form at the Smithfield Show too, with interest from a number of manufacturers.

There was another £1 million order from Claas in Germany, fast becoming a valuable major customer, with the new Six 354 being added to further orders for Four 99 and Four 270D engines.

Further reorganisation within Massey Ferguson in December created a series of operating units, of which Perkins Group of Companies was one. Indeed it was the only one with worldwide responsibilities, with M.I. Prichard as Managing Director. The other Operating Units covered the MF plants in the United States, the United Kingdom, France, Germany and Australia. A.A. Thornbrough presided over the Corporate Staff based in Toronto, maintaining overall control of a rapidly expanding Corporation.

Total production for the year was 136,588 engines, a truly staggering increase of 86 per cent over the previous year and was – by nearly 60,000 units – the highest yearly volume produced to that date. The major increases were in the P3 and P4-derived products – especially the 3-cylinder where Ford and MF requirements took the total to 70,895 compared to the 26,796 of the year before. The Four 99 output rose to 11,123 while the new versions of the P6 (Six 288 and Six 305) boosted the six-cylinder total to 11,521.

The results showed a total turnover of over £25,540,000, of which £19,710,000 (77%) was exported. Within this total £3.23 million were sales to the Commonwealth other than India and Canada, £2.13 million to India, £1.75 million to Canada and the USA, £2.4 million to Germany, £3.17 million to the rest of the Common Market and the remainder to the rest of the world.

As a demonstration of what could be done, and a foretaste of what was to come, 1960 had been a good year, with many problems overcome along the way.

1961

The start of the New Year saw a familiar pattern of reports in the Echo as the 1961 Boat Show opened in Earls Court and the Apprentices held their fifth Dinner Dance. A new organisation was announced in January with the formation of the 'Quarter Century Club' with Frank Perkins as the first President. The club was open to all employees with more than twenty-five years of continuous service, and was affiliated to the Massey Ferguson Quarter Century Club. The total number of employees eligible at the formation of the club was 40, including one husband and wife team. A first Annual Dinner was held at The Gordon Arms in Orton Waterville on 12 May, being well attended by the long-serving employees and partners who enjoyed a six-course meal and a programme of entertainment for the princely sum of twenty-five shillings a head.

Spring brought recognition of the growing importance of the licensee operations, with the appointment of Russell Bennett to the role of Chief Engineer, Overseas Manufacturing Operations, reporting to the Director in charge, Ken Woollatt. In addition to the established operations in India (Simpsons), Yugoslavia (IMR) and Brazil (Motores Perkins), there was growing interest in Argentina and Turkey too. In May there was a presentation to another long-serving stalwart, Ernie Harrold, who left Peterborough to spend time assisting the licensees in Brazil and Argentina.

In the Directors' Meeting minutes for January a small note covered a discussion around 'Possible Use of a Computer', following a review by Mr R.H. Williams of Computer Consultants Limited. Further discussions and visits to existing installations were organised as Perkins started a significant move away from their Hollerith punch card system to the development of computer systems. Perkins was in the forefront of this new technology, later to prove crucial to future development.

Throughout the year new successes were publicised as Perkins engines found increasing favour with customers. It was claimed that over 250,000 Perkins engines were being manufactured worldwide each year, with 814 different manufacturers using them, spread across every continent and covering every sort of equipment from vehicles to industrial plant, agricultural machinery and marine craft. Added to this, of course, were the new outboard motor and gas turbine ventures.

Ford Motor Company started to fit the Four 99 in their British 'Thames' range of vans, pick-ups and small buses, after considerable battles over pricing as Ford tried to drive Perkins' profit margin lower. Ford was also looking for larger high-speed diesels of around 2.2 and 2.6 litres and this was discussed with Perkins. They also confirmed that the F3 would be needed at least until December 1962, but wanted to switch to the 3.6-inch-bore version as soon as possible in 1961. Vauxhall confirmed their intention of fitting the Four 99 in their new Bedford CA van, so suddenly Perkins had most of the British light van manufacturers seriously interested in their small diesels. For larger vehicles more business was generated as new conversion packs were offered. One such kit was to adapt the Six 354 for the Bedford TK truck, following many requests from operators.

At the Royal Show at Cambridge a bigger bore version of the Four 99, designated Four 107, was announced to suit light agricultural machinery, and a special version of the Six 354 was exhibited in the new Track Marshall TM70 crawler tractor. The Perkins News carried many stories and pictures of new equipment, plus news of customers' experiences and comments – always good, of course!

The outboard motor production side was struggling to produce enough engines, even though orders were not meeting the sales forecast. There were still problems with both supply of parts and field failures. Competitive engines were purchased for analysis, especially for product quality comparison, as work continued to resolve complaints from home and abroad. A breakthrough was achieved with sales to the military, a special 'unbranded' 35hp motor being specified, and there were hopes that this would lead to further sales within the NATO alliance.

Gas turbines were selling slowly, a batch of water pumps were supplied to the Dutch Navy but the chance of meeting projected sales of 84 sets in 1961 looked slim. One development showing promise, however, was the 'Instructional Set', the first of these being supplied to Peterborough Technical College during the spring. Other colleges and universities showed interest in this innovative way to teach jet engine technology and thermodynamics 'in miniature'.

More new products

As the year progressed problems with component supply were never far away, with fuel pump supply a continual concern as Four 270D and Four 99 output was affected.

The new version of the larger engine, known as A4.300 for MF, was delayed by late revisions to the balancer assembly but initial production engines were programmed for Detroit tractor assembly in September and October. Agreement was received from the MF Corporate Headquarters to proceed with an interim manufacturing facility for the Four 236, the four-cylinder derivation of the Six 354. No agreement had been reached, however, about the possible use of this engine by Massey Ferguson in tractors at this time! (Most interest was being shown by vehicle manufacturers keen to have a larger and more modern direct injection engine to replace the ageing P4(V).) There had been some ongoing confusion around engine nomenclature. This was resolved in April when it was agreed to use all numeric designations – such as 4.99, D4.270 and 6.354. The addition of the 'D' was agreed to denote the direct injection version of an originally indirect injection model,

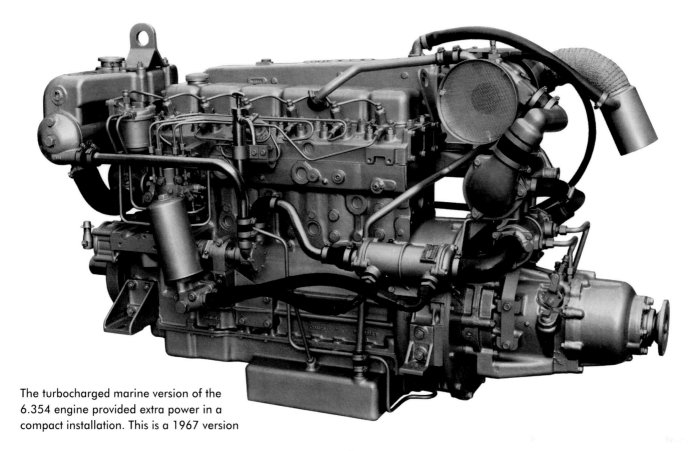

The turbocharged marine version of the 6.354 engine provided extra power in a compact installation. This is a 1967 version

while the use of an 'A' prefix was agreed to identify variants for Massey Ferguson. Apart from a slight trauma with Peugeot – who objected to '203' in France since they had registered this for a car model – the new nomenclature was to remain in use for many years.

Saturday 8 July saw the traditional Open Day take place in dull and threatening conditions. This did nothing to deter around 15,000 people who turned out to enjoy another action-packed programme, in spite of competition from the ladies' final at Wimbledon and the Third Test Match. The total workforce in Peterborough had risen to about 7,000 employees, a point noted by Monty Prichard as he welcomed the visitors as representative of 'the many thousands who depend upon us'.

Frank Perkins also noted the growth over the years in his address, adding: 'It may be of some interest to you to know that the production of diesel engines has now risen to 1,000 per day – making this by far the biggest diesel engine producing company in the world.' The enthusiasm and interest shown by the visitors in everything about them repaid the efforts of the many volunteers who had organised so much to make the day possible. Not only was the Eastfield works on display, visitors were also welcomed at Queen Street and Walton.

Retirement of Norman Collins

There were changes in the organisation during the late summer starting with Norman Collins, who decided to resign his post as Deputy Managing Director on reaching retirement age. The influence of Norman Collins during the critical period from the end of the war to the years immediately following the MF takeover is difficult to estimate accurately. He is remembered as a 'manager of the old school', and it is possible that during his later years in the Company he found himself out of tune with the younger element and the required rate of progress. It is clear, however, that he had considerable influence over Frank Perkins and was largely responsible for the thinking behind many of the organisational changes as the company grew and its influence spread. We are fortunate that Norman Collins kept much documentation after his retirement and that this has found its way into the Heritage archives. His interests extended beyond the diesel business too. Some of the

documents and memos retained concern gas turbines and the Wankel engine, for instance, and pre-date the attention eventually given to these by the Company. During his retirement years Norman Collins maintained an active interest in the engineering societies in Peterborough, and in the fortunes of Perkins in particular. That he lived to be 100 years old is of particular note: he had been wounded twice and was buried alive by a shell burst while serving in the First World War, being saved by the quick thinking of his comrades. His survival, where many of his contemporaries in the Seaforth Highlanders did not, is recalled poignantly in his memoirs published posthumously in 2000.

When Geoffrey Smith had left Perkins at the end of 1960 to take up a role at Hamworthy Ltd, Mr Frank Collis joined the Company from a London-based consultancy as Director of Manufacturing. He became responsible for overseeing much of the expansion work within the Eastfield plant, and was also a key partner in bringing Manufacturing and Engineering closer together: with Gordon Dawson he developed a sign-off procedure for new drawings, ensuring that manufacturing capability was taken into account in the design process.

Meanwhile Richard Perkins became Deputy Managing Director of Perkins Engines Ltd. Other changes saw Mr J.M. Collins appointed Director and General Manager of the Sales Division, while Douglas McNair became Deputy Director of Marketing. The Company also confirmed the intention to manufacture in Argentina, with more Peterborough personnel leaving to take up posts in the new plant in Cordoba, about 400 miles north-west of Buenos Aires. Those joining Ernie Harrold were Colin Smith, Derek Jackson and Peter Goodacre – together with their families.

New truck business for the 6.354

The new 6.354 attracted a customer in the USA when White Motors signed a deal to fit the engine as optional first equipment in their new range of 'White Compact' trucks, specifically designed for city and suburban haulage use. The agreement was hailed as a breakthrough both for Perkins and for diesel usage in such trucks, a sector hitherto the exclusive domain of the petrol engine. The importance of North America as a future market was emphasised as the sales office was moved from Toronto to Detroit, initially finding quarters in the Kercheval Avenue offices belonging to MF.

The autumn saw the new products chalk up a success when a 14-foot boat with a single 35bhp outboard won a trophy for first all-British craft in the Paris six-hour race. The new range of motors for 1962 was announced, ranging from 40bhp down to 4.5bhp, with sales prices from £233 down to as little as £64.

The Gas Turbine Division also gained publicity by selling a special 'Mars' pump set application for use at Waddesdon Manor in Buckinghamshire, providing an emergency water supply for fire fighting in this important National Trust property. A further gas turbine success hit the headlines in December after a pump set in service at South Shields assisted the salvage of a Polish trawler, Syruisz, keeping the vessel afloat over a 24-hour period.

The end of the year brought the announcement of the first turbocharged version of the 6.354, for marine use. Rated at 125bhp, the engine was claimed to be another 'first' in being the smallest 'blown' four-stroke engine in production anywhere in the world. It claimed advantages of improved power-to-weight ratio, fuel consumption and cost. This extended the power range of the engine usefully, if conservatively, and heralded the gradual application of turbocharging to small engines.

The year-end statistics showed yet another record as 161,863 engines was produced. Volumes of P3, P4 and L4 engines, and their derivatives, again rose while the 4.99 achieved 17,004 units and the 6.354, in its first year, 4,496. Although the high volume of P3 engines was in part attributable to the F3 for the highly successful Ford Dexta tractor, the impact of MF requirements was visible to all. Starting from the 15,392 engines delivered to the plants in Coventry and Detroit in the ten months of the 1959 financial year, the volume in 1960 rose to 64,821, and in the first seven months alone of 1961 to 54,521. Most of these engines were 3.152 and 4.192s, plus some 4.270D content.

With substantial production in the overseas locations, the Company's fortunes continued to rise. Alongside the promised 'explosion' of Massey Ferguson business, the growth in all sectors was promising and augured well for the coming years.

A New Year interview by M.I. Prichard in the Echo set the tone of confidence for the whole Company. 'With politicians and others exhorting industry to export more, we can tell them very bluntly and proudly that over 80 per cent of the engines produced at Peterborough during 1961 found their way into foreign markets,' he said. He reviewed the problems facing the Company with customers other than Massey Ferguson. They might be tempted to start producing their own engines – as had happened with Ford and Bedford – after the P6 (and the R6 to a lesser extent) had achieved market success and proved that the diesel was here to stay. He noted that the Company's position could only be defended if the products were world leaders and were offered at a competitive price. This had to be not only in comparison with other engine manufacturers but also with the cost of manufacture for the giants of industry who comprised much of the potential market. It was also essential to provide efficient delivery to match the customers' production programmes, and an after-sales service to match the technical superiority of the product.

Monty Prichard highlighted the good performance of 1961, and made special mention of the £3.3 million exports to Germany – no mean feat in view of their own industrial prowess, technical ability and determination to succeed. He reviewed the success of the 6.354 in North America, and directed special thanks to MF, without whose support at all levels Perkins could not have made such a bold push into the markets. He thanked all employees for their efforts through the year, and looked forward to a happy and prosperous 1962.

Good publicity was received for the new products as they became more widely known and appreciated. In the Commercial Motor of 2 February the Bedford CA 15cwt van was tested in both the petrol and diesel versions. Even though it was tested in less than ideal conditions, with snow on the ground, the 4.99 returned a fuel consumption some 20 to 25 percent better than the petrol version, while giving away little in performance. Another article, this time in Motor Transport for 23 February, compared the 6.354 and the Gardner 5LW engine in an 18-ton GVW Atkinson truck. This showed that the smaller Perkins engine provided better on-the-road performance although it could not match the Gardner on fuel economy. Under motorway conditions the 6.354 provided much better productivity due to its higher cruising speed, albeit with more noise transmitted to the cab. The lighter engine also allowed a greater payload than the older Gardner product. With Perkins engines appearing as original equipment in many vehicles, tractors, combine harvesters, boats and industrial equipment of all types there were many stories in the Company's trade papers

Frank Perkins was honoured by the County when he was elected High Sheriff in recognition of his contribution to the industrial development of Peterborough

and advertisements. One important article announced the acceptance of the 6.354 engine by International Harvester in the USA, for use in their new 'Loadstar' truck range as the diesel option, heralding a long association with one of the best-known names in the American transport industry.

In March Frank Perkins was honoured by Peterborough when he was made an honorary Freeman of the City by the City Council. This accolade, the highest honour which could be conferred locally, was received with typical modesty by FAP, who said that he looked upon it as recognition of the importance of the Perkins Companies in the life and prosperity of the City.

In May and June the Echo carried tributes following the deaths of three long-serving employees. Bill Spoor had joined Engineering at the outbreak of the war to work on the T12 engine, and had later been responsible for engineering administration before taking charge of the new Technical Office. Leslie Bugg had been a member of the sales staff since 1944 and was well known nationwide. He had been very largely responsible for the overwhelming success achieved in promoting sales to municipal authorities for their vehicles. Leslie had been taken ill shortly after attending a conference at Scarborough and died shortly afterwards at the age of 59. The other loss was that of Norman Burney, who died on 8 June, the day before he reached retirement age. He had been one of the original team in 1932, and just failed to achieve his ambition of 30 years' unbroken service – including a period as the first field service engineer before many years at Queen Street, where he was the General Foreman in the Experimental engine fitting workshop.

Good publicity on TV and film

In the June issue of the Echo another achievement in Brazil was recorded, where three hundred employees of Motores Perkins took part in a Labour Day parade in São Paulo, winning an award for best tableau. Some visitors from Peterborough also took part in the festivities. This Echo also carried stories about a national campaign on safety afloat, where Perkins had assisted the Transport Minister, Ernest Marples, and RoSPA to promote good safety practice for all boat users.

There was TV coverage in July when Anglia TV spent two days making a film about the Outboard Motors Division, including coverage of the Walton manufacturing facilities, engine testing at the Fletton brickpits, and interviews with several managers on various facets of the operations. A further feature followed, covering the Perkins boat-testing centre at Gosfield Lake in Essex. At the time this was a unique facility intended to assist the design and application of boats for outboard power, and their safe use.

Another well-known Anglia TV programme, About Anglia, devoted a ten-minute sequence to the leisure activities of the Perkins Gliding Club at Westwood airfield. Presenter Bob Wellings fronted the programme and was the first of the Anglia crew to be given a joyride in the club's two-seat glider after filming had been completed. The Perkins personnel featured included Stan Hickson, Terry Sismore, Shirley Bradshaw, Ian Smith and John Bowles.

Perkins was also featured in a Board of Trade film. 'South American Prospect' featured scenes of the Motores Perkins SA factory in Cordoba, Argentina, during the visit by the Duke of Edinburgh in March 1962: this film was later shown at the MF World Manufacturing Conference held in Peterborough. The royal visit was covered in a special feature by the Echo, taking the opportunity to give details of the new plant, which was intended to produce up to 12,000 engines each year, for use in locally produced equipment.

The major event organised to celebrate the one millionth export engine in September 1962. Frederick Erroll joins Frank Perkins and Monty Prichard in admiring the gold-painted 6.354

A number of retirements were highlighted in the Echo during the summer. The most important was that of Frank Perkins, who decided not to offer himself for re-election at the Annual General Meeting as a Director or as Chairman of the Company having reached the age of 73. He was, however, elected Honorary President of the Perkins Group of Companies, with many tributes being paid to him from the Directors and employees of the Company. One special tribute was made at a reunion of the staff members who had joined between 1940 to 1952: they presented him with a replica 'Armada Dish' a party at the Gordon Arms.

The One Millionth Export Engine Celebration

On Wednesday 5 September the Company celebrated the production of the one-millionth engine for export. Part of the commemoration was the production of a 'Roll of Honour', a document carrying the signatures of most of the 7,000 current employees, collected by a team of 32 apprentices visiting every corner of the plants over a week of days and nights. There were many other facets to the celebrations, with a display of engines and equipment all along the front of the East-field offices, with marquees to house the festivities and lunch for 300 special guests, some of whom arrived by special train from London. These included Mr Frederick Erroll, President of the Board of Trade, who signed the Roll of Honour and assisted at the ceremony when the one-millionth engine – a 6.354 specially painted gold – was unveiled. The avenue of engines on display featured the flags of every individual country and territory to which exports were made, 166 in total. It was

probably the most spectacular Company event up to that date and commemorated a unique occasion. The gold-painted engine went on to the Earls Court Motor Show later in the year, occupying a place of honour on the Perkins stand.

The same month the traditional Sports and Family Day was held in what had become traditional changeable weather! The many events were enjoyed by over 15,000 people, and included the usual parades and exhibits, plus some more unusual offerings such as the Apprentice Association's piano-breaking competition. The National Press, TV and radio gave additional widespread publicity to Perkins at a time when its achievements were the object of much pride to every employee, and covered the day's events.

More expansion plans

During these September celebrations Monty Prichard announced that further factory expansions were planned, with a major extension of the main Eastfield plant being augmented by the construction of a new component-machining plant at Spennymoor in County Durham. The decision to open a plant in the North-East was driven by a Government plan to increase work opportunities in areas of declining industry and high unemployment. There was some incentive involved in agreeing this move in order to continue factory expansion in Peterborough; the Perkins Board were reluctant to have a key supply plant so far from the main factory. Together these expansions would add 400,000 square feet to the facilities at a cost of over 4 million pounds, and would add around 1,250 jobs for male workers. With Peterborough engine production up to 1,000 engines a day, plus the support to overseas operations through component and CKD pack supply Pri-

Above & Below: The T6.354(M) found favour for offshore powerboat racing. Shown here is the triple engine installation in Ron Watts's boat Giovanna, with the boat itself seen competing in the Miami to Nassau race in April 1964

chard said '. . . the expansion is needed to keep pace with the intent to introduce new power units with design features in advance of anything in the same field anywhere else in the world'. He commented that over the previous fifteen years the Company's sales turnover had increased from £1,400,000 to £30,000,000. Exports accounted for an increasing proportion of these sales, up to the current level of 80%.

In November it was announced that the outboard motors would be handled by a new Division within Perkins Engines Ltd, with Harry Lymath appointed General Manager reporting to the Managing Director. This structure replaced the previous separate company and brought with it a series of other personnel changes. At a Main Dealer Conference to introduce the 1963 range of motors, Mr Lymath declared that the future looked bright, with advance orders for the new range already in excess of £50,000. Ahead of the International Boat Show in January, Perkins announced the availability of a new 'transom drive' unit. Known as the Perkins Z-drive, this device combined the virtues of diesel economy with some outboard motor advantages for boats ranging from 15ft runabouts to 30ft cruisers and workboats. Designed to be coupled to the 4.107(M), the new unit extended the application of the already popular 'baby' diesel to a new range of applications: it combined a conventional inboard engine mounting with a tilting and steerable propulsion unit. Thus it effectively combined the characteristics of an outboard motor by allowing the boat to be grounded in estuaries with the unit tilted as well as adding manoeuvrability. The 4.99(M) featured again in the news when a 15ft boat fitted with the engine won its class in the Paris six-hour race, a fourth consecutive success for Perkins power.

'National Productivity Year' was officially launched on 14 November 1962, an initiative designed to maintain and improve Britain's status in world markets. Monty Prichard had been appointed chairman of a Federation of British Industry Committee charged with preparing a Marketing presentation for the 1963 Productivity Conference. In a message to all employees MIP emphasised the importance of this initiative, in which Perkins would play an important role and make a substantial contribution to improving export effectiveness in an increasingly competitive world.

He quoted the words of Mr Harry Douglass – Chairman, Productivity Year and General Secretary of the Iron and Steel Trades Federation – regarding the importance of increased productivity to all companies, trade unions and employees: [to meet the needs] 'there must be a rise in productivity of at least 3.3 per cent. That means an end to the complacency, the "I'm all right Jack" attitude, which a comparatively easy home market has induced until recently'.

The year closed with good news from North America where Chrysler announced the availability of the 6.354 as an option in their Dodge truck range at the Detroit Auto Show. Elsewhere Perkins Hispania S.A. exhibited in Madrid, while at the Public Works Exhibition in Olympia various Perkins engines featured on the stands of many vehicle manufacturers, including Dennis, Shelvoke and Drury, Karrier, Marshall and Fowler.

A story in the December Echo told of the re-commissioning of many old American school buses, with 6.305(V) engines replacing the uneconomical petrol engines to provide additional years of service plus a 50% saving in fuel cost.

Elsewhere, Manufacturing Director Frank Collis gave more news on the new factory extensions. Eastfield would have a further seven bays added to the south end, to house a production facility for a new four-cylinder engine (this was the 4.236 but was not identified at that time). The Spennymoor plant was to be equipped to produce items such as connecting rods, gears, rocker levers and pulleys. Both plants were scheduled to be up and running in 1964. He noted that with the new engine adding around 65,000 engines a year to output there would be more jobs in Peterborough although retraining would be needed to take account of the switch of component production to County Durham.

The 1962 production statistics made good reading. The total of 188,256 diesel engines was again a record, with volumes of the P4- and P3-derived engines reaching levels of 31,744 and 90,387 respectively, going to the MF plants in Coventry and Detroit. The 6.354 gathered momentum with 24,337 units produced, and the 4.99 notched another increase to 21,513 engines. On the older products both the S6 and R6 were phased out during the year, while sales of the old stalwart P6, and its derivative 6.288s and 6.305s, continued to decline. Unfortunately accurate figures for the engine CKD kits shipped to the overseas plants are not available for this period: probably over 50,000 kits were exported as production increased within the licensee and associate companies.

1963

New Year 1963 was memorable, but for a good British reason – the weather. From early January to late March the conditions were the worst for many years, with snow lying on the ground for weeks and temperatures remaining at or below freezing for most of the time. The impact on life and work was severe across the whole country; even Peterborough was badly affected and there were problems within the plants with heating – and of course the maintenance of on-time deliveries of materials and parts, to say nothing of getting engine despatches away on schedule.

The year opened with the International Boat Show, where Perkins introduced new versions of the 6.354 and T6.354, these being the so-called 'horizontal' engines, laid almost flat to allow fitment under the floors of cockpits and allow more compact engine compartments to be used. The export offensive on the American market continued, with Monty Prichard addressing the press in New York and sales success being claimed as White Motors, International Harvester, Chrysler and Reo Motor Division offered the 6.354 as optional equipment for pick-up and delivery use. Amongst the first users were New York brewery fleets, and the United Parcel delivery operation.

At home 'National Productivity Year' attracted considerable advertising and stories of success. Later in the Year Monty Prichard addressed the NPY Conference at Eastbourne.

Early Powerboat racing successes

There was further marine publicity when a considerable number of Perkins-powered craft took part in the annual Cowes–Torquay Offshore Powerboat Race. The T6.354 acquitted itself well, with Ron Watts and Giovanna winning the diesel class and the first all-British prize. This laid the foundations for successes that were to continue for several years, generating good publicity, and sales, in the process. Later in the year the Company held its first Marine Diesel Conference at Brighton, attracting attendees from around the world.

The Perkins Film Unit made the news again with another new film, entitled 'A Rocket for Charlie', given wide release to spread the word about good safety practices.

Further local news saw another successful Sports and Family Day, attended by over 12,000 employees and their families. They were able to see the progress being made on the latest factory extensions – the additional six bays at the south end of the factory destined to become known as 'Factory 2' and to be occupied by the new 4.236 engine production area.

By the end of 1963 the Company was able to report yet another new record for production at Peterborough, with a total of 194,761 engines produced. For the 6.354, P4 and P3 derivatives new peak figures were declared, with L4 and 4.99 volumes slightly reduced from the previous year, while the P6 versions continued to slide gently towards oblivion. A customer milestone was set during the year when the 50,000th engine was delivered to Gebr Claas in Germany: at the Smithfield Show in January 1964 the same company placed orders for 6.354, 4.99 and 4.270D totalling £750,000 to get the New Year off to a splendid start.

If there was some growing complacency in the workforce this was dispelled to some extent by an article in the Echo in January

The 4.236 engine entered full production in 1964 and proved to be the highest volume product. This is a typical tractor version for Massey Ferguson

1964. The New Year message from Richard Perkins considered the success achieved, including the capital spend of over £4.8 million since 1959 and the factory expansion to over 1 million square feet. However, he went on to remind everyone that competition was increasing both at home and abroad. Perkins was continuing to move forward, with major support from Massey Ferguson, but must exploit every market and product to the full.

Other notable news concerned the release of a new film, 'The Royal of England', made by the Film Unit for the Royal Agricultural Society, whilst another sales story concerned a new fleet of vans purchased by the Post Office with 4.99 power. Once again the International Boat Show brought further success for the 6.354 range, and also saw the full launch of the 4.107(M) with the 'Z-drive'.

Spennymoor – an aborted move

In March, fourteen key employees visited the new 100,000 sq ft plant at Spennymoor in County Durham, looking also at the housing, countryside and amenities as well as being welcomed by local officials. This visit went very well, with enthusiasm on both sides, but the intentions were to be dashed later in the year when a failure to agree with the trade unions on wage rates and conditions between the two locations caused the whole project to be killed at the eleventh hour. The unions were looking for parity with Peterborough rates, and the negotiations ended in deadlock. As a result, the machining of small parts was absorbed within the Peterborough plants and the idea of satellite support factories within the UK was quietly forgotten. The space problem at Peterborough for machining was resolved when the Walton factory, originally wholly taken up with outboard motor manufacture, became vacant as the result of the sale of the whole outboard business to British Anzani. This came as the result of continued poor sales performance worldwide, plus increasing Massey Ferguson pressure to divest the operation of peripheral business in order to concentrate on the core products.

Personnel changes during the spring included the appointment of Mr T.A. Read to the Board, along with Mr V.F. Frayling. Horace Rainbow took on a new role as Chief Engineer, Advanced Projects and was joined by Albert Fiegel to look after the new Wankel engine project (See Chapter 12).

There was sadness in the Engineering area when Chief Applications Engineer Gordon Wingate was killed during a truck testing accident, which also injured other Engineering personnel. Another death in service was that of Sydney 'Johnny' Johnson, who served over 25 years in Sales and was well known to agricultural sales customers. In May another link to the earliest days was lost when the death was announced of Mr S. Anantharamakrishnan in India: his period in control of Simpson & Company Ltd had seen their production of Perkins engines grow to 12,000 engines in 1964. He was mourned in India too as an important industry leader.

In April the Company confirmed that full production of the 4.236 engine would commence in September, with the seven-bay extension – Factory Two – covering 185,000 square feet. Along with a new pedestal-type assembly track, there was a test facility with 54 test beds in an open shop, plus additional stores and finishing sections. The machining area was separated by a wall from assembly and test and contained dedicated transfer machinery for the cylinder block and head. This featured the latest design standards and was capable of exceptionally high volume output: the downside was that the nature of the lines reduced flexibility.

A further success came when Moteurs Perkins SA were awarded the 'Prestige de la France' by the French Economic and Social Council: since 1951 the Company had grown to 700 employees in Saint Denis, with a production to date of over 150,000 engines, serving 63 customers. Slightly further afield, Perkins was honoured by being asked to exhibit in Moscow, where both the Russian leaders, Khrushchev and Kosygin, visited the stand.

The powerboats were in the news again when Ron Watts took Giovanna across the Atlantic to compete in the Miami/Nassau Race, eventually finishing ninth overall and second in the diesel class after straying off-course. The three HT6.354 marine engines ran flat out for seven trouble-free hours during this race. A more off-beat achievement was the completion of a Land's End to John o'Groats marathon by a Yale fork-lift truck powered by a 4.203 engine: a 12-day trial of machine and engine.

There were two issues of the Echo in August. The regular version recorded the retirement of Laurie Hancock after 29 years' service; he had been responsible for many innovations in the marketing of the Company's products over the years, along with the publicity literature and house magazine. In the months after his departure he wrote the first history of the company at the request of Monty Prichard – a document of great value to subsequent writers, including of course the present author! Among the other items was news of high awards in the revised Suggestion Scheme, with a maximum of £400 and others of £250, £225 and £200.

The other Echo 'Special Edition' was of great interest, since within its pages were details of the new Factory 2 for the 4.236 and the expansion of the Walton plant to manufacture gears and rocker assemblies. In a leading article Richard Perkins expanded on the development of the Company to meet the challenge of the 1960s, including the threat from the new Cummins plant being built in County Durham. He also announced plans to build a new restaurant block at Eastfield and improve car parking. Details of the company's profits for 1963, of £2,108,000, were also published, together with the news that both Brazilian and French subsidiaries were now in the black.

In the annual Cowes to Torquay powerboat race on 15 August Perkins-powered boats filled the first seven places in the restricted diesel class, with Ron Hicks in Giovanna as the winner, best placed at 18th overall out of the 46 starters.

Factory 2 production starts

The first finished 4.236 came out of the new Factory on 14 August, although there had been limited pilot production on a makeshift facility ahead of this milestone. At that time nobody could envisage the impact that this engine was to make over the following thirty years. Neither was it obvious how far-seeing the decision to build such a different plant was to prove: the move to full transfer machine lines for cylinder block and cylinder head machining allowed for extremely high volume in comparison with the previous 'link line' concept. There was a trade-off, of course, in terms of the relative inflexibility for upgrades and design changes but the engineers responsible for major changes in future years became adept at meeting the challenge and minimising capital impact.

Other developments included the introduction of a new non-contributory Sick Pay Scheme for hourly-paid workers, providing 62/6 per week for men over 21, and 41/6 for women (equivalent to £3.125 and £2.075 in metric – not much now perhaps, but a step forward at the time).

During the final months of the year news of a new honour for Monty Prichard when he shared the Institute of Marketing's annual award with Lord Rubens of the Coal Board. In his acceptance speech he dedicated this as 'a tribute to the Perkins Team, across all areas'. He went on to emphasise the importance of marketing for future prosperity, citing Frank Perkins and Harry Ferguson as pioneers with the genius to see a future for their products.

Gordon Dawson was invited to address the annual conference of the Institute of Road Transport Engineers, and was also present at the successful launch of the DDE concept at the Commercial Vehicle Exhibition. The Perkins presence and importance in the vehicle sector was evident, with engines appearing on 40 stands in vehicles. In the USA the 6.354 was proving a success, with International Harvester and White Motors truck sales ahead of Mack: 13.6% of US truck sales featured imported diesels, the majority being Perkins. The Perkins Inc. President, Rudi Jansa, predicted a diesel breakthrough in light vehicles up to 5 tons as American customers accepted the engine on both economy and durability.

On the marine side Perkins announced an improved 'Mark 2'version of the Z-drive, and Fairey Marine standardised on Perkins 4.107 and 6.354 for their range of products. To round the year off with another good story, from the Island of Guernsey came news of a fleet of P6-powered buses that had an average life of 281,000 miles and were returning 14mpg versus the 8mpg of their petrol-fuelled competitors!

The usual end-of-the-year statistics saw over 200,000 engines produced in England for the first time, the actual figure being 209,265 units. The P4 and L4 posted 'highest ever' production levels, and, with the 6.354 output growing over 44% and the 4.236 confirming its potential with 2,554 sales, the scene looked set for continuing success on all fronts. The only significant reduction came on the P3 range, where the impending phase-out of the F3.152 by Ford produced a small volume decrease for the year.

1965

In early 1965 the new 4.236 factory was in full production, with a forecast that the output would reach 70,000 engines per year by the end of 1966. The plant was 'on show' to the Press to demonstrate how the £4 million investment was already contributing to the export drive. (This amount of money represented a large spend to Perkins, but was small beer indeed when compared to the huge sums spent by the motor industry when retooling for new models!) Along with this story came news of an offer from the Perkins marketing experts to use their knowledge to assist smaller British companies wishing to break into export markets. Monty Prichard was very active in the search for new overseas conquests, addressing conferences in Cincinnati and Johannesburg during the year, as well as hosting a conference in Peterborough on 'Trading with Canada' for the British National Export Council. In the Queen's Birthday Honours his activities were recognised by the award of the CBE. Another recognition earlier in the year was the presentation of the Gresham Cooke Award from the Institution of Mechanical Engineers to Gordon Dawson and Bill Hayward for their paper on the Differential Diesel Engine.

There was considerable activity on the domestic front as another successful Sports and Family Day was celebrated. This was in spite of the worst summer weather for 50 years, causing serious delays to the harvest and spoiling many holiday plans. The Quarter Century Club reported that there were now 118 members, whose total service exceeded 3,000 years. Another organisation in the news was the '200 Club', which held its first annual dinner: this club was exclusively for those employees whose suggestions had been awarded at least £200 by the Company. Community Service to the whole of Peterborough was not neglected with the installation of an employee, Gordon Tyers, as Mayor of Peterborough.

Opening of the new restaurant

The new restaurant block was opened, able to feed 3,000 employees and featuring the latest kitchen facilities. There were separate areas for shop floor and office staff, as well as rooms catering for directors, senior management and visitors. The old canteen area at the north end of the site was later converted into training facilities to support the increasing needs of the expanding company.

There was one business 'failure' reported in September when the Gas Turbine operation produced and sold its last unit: from July 1960 to September 1965 the total production had only been 167 units – 96 of these being water pump sets. A total of 44 instructional sets were built for technical colleges and universities, with a handful of other engines being fitted into ground starting and service units for BEA and other aircraft operators. Although a number of foreign navies had purchased sets for emergency fire-pumping use, there was no British interest beyond the one pump set sold to the South Shields Fire Brigade. The kiss of death appeared to have been the rejection of the engine by the UK authorities, including the Home Office, as 'too noisy', although the lack of support from MF for this non-diesel business could not have helped. Perkins maintained service support until 1973, when a final sell-off of the remaining parts was conducted. There are a few units still in existence, as museum pieces, although Solar Gas Turbines as an entity remains in existence and production to this day, as part of Caterpillar.

On the product front there was considerable publicity for the 4.236 and 6.354 – the vehicle customers offering these engines as first equipment included many well-known domestic, European and American companies. The new V8.510 engine was announced and exhibited at the Tokyo Fair, taking the Peterborough products into a new range with 170bhp at 2,800rpm from the 510-cubic inch (8.36-litre) engine. There was further news from overseas as Perkins announced an agreement with the Toyo Kogyo Company to manufacture Perkins engines in Japan for the first time. As the year drew to a close there was a further demonstration of Perkins' commitment to British Industry as the Company became a major sponsor for the Productivity Council's 'Quality and Reliability' Campaign.

There were some interesting stories in the Perkins Driver newspaper during the year.

One such concerned Hugh Cole from Lincolnshire, who claimed to have been the driver of one of the first Leopards in service. He took charge of a Bedford articulated truck in June 1935 and in four years ran 140,000 miles between Lincolnshire and South Wales carrying potatoes. The reliability was apparently exemplary, and it was 'More power than anything I'd driven before – like having a lion under the bonnet!' A more modern story concerned the sea tractor operated between Bigbury-on-Sea and Burgh Island. This unique vehicle must have been seen and ridden by many readers: it comprises a passenger-carrying compartment on stilts above the two axles, with power provided by a P6. The contrivance operates across the causeway and is able to carry passengers to and from the hotel on the island whatever the state of the tide. From its introduction in 1950 the machine had operated 'untouched' for 15 years, exhibiting first-time starting and using less than 15 gallons a week for the half-mile crossing every 20 minutes when the tide was in.

For once the year-end statistics did not show a new record of production. In spite of the undoubted success of the new products – 44,010 6.354s and 16,029 4.236s were produced – the total count of 183,019 engines in 1965 was lower than during the three previous years, mainly due to the loss of the Ford F3 business. These figures take no account of the considerable export business of CKD (completely knocked down) engine kits for the associate and licensee operations, where business was increasing.

1966

The export record was indeed something special, with 61.9% of production exported directly: overall exports reached 85% when the engines fitted into complete equipment were taken into account. There

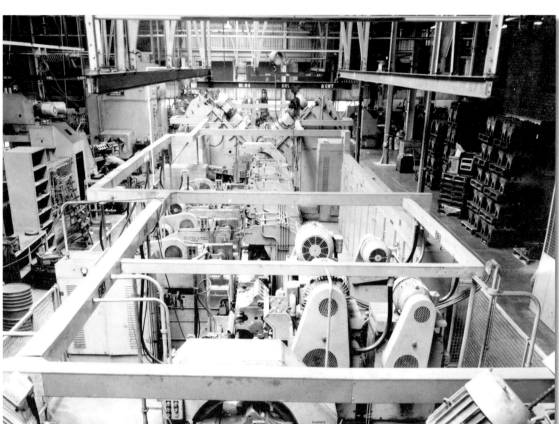

The investment in the new Fletton factory for the V8.510 engine was considerable. The cylinder block machining line seen here was a state-of-the-art installation for the time

were new records for individual areas, with exports to the USA increased by 47% (to £6.75 million) while West Germany and Australia saw gains of 124.8% and 118.6% respectively. Sales had increased from £42.2 million in 1963 to £48.8 million in 1965 – and from 1961 to 1965 the increase was 63.3%, or 12.6% per year. While a large part of the expansion continued to be generated by Massey Ferguson market growth, there were many new customers across all application sectors as the advantages of diesel power gained recognition.

At the International Boat Show in January 1966 there were 78 Perkins engines on display, including 42 fitted in various boats. In a special vintage display two T12 engines were on display, the first time these wartime prototypes had been seen publicly.

The Fletton V8 factory plans are announced

In March the plans for V8.510 engine production were made public. A new plant of 130,000 square feet was acquired from the Hotpoint Company, close by their main Fletton factory to the south of Peterborough. Scheduled to be in production by the end of the year, this new plant was to be self-contained, with machining lines for the major components plus assembly, test, finish and despatch facilities.

Further statistics were quoted when Jim Winstanley, the new Director and General Manager for UK Operations, gave his forecast for the coming year in the Echo. He noted that over the past two years more than 200 Perkins people had visited 76 countries and travelled 3.5 mil-

The new facility for producing the 4.236 engine included many new features, including the pedestal engine build system pictured here

lion miles on business. Perkins products were working in every corner of the world. In predicting a further increase in production for the year, Winstanley emphasised the constant need to improve product quality, in order to meet growing customer expectations.

Monty Prichard announced a pioneering initiative in April, when he gave details of a 'Modern Marketing Techniques' scheme being sponsored by the Board of Trade and the British National Export Council. This would take fifty key men to the Harvard Business School for six weeks, followed by a four-week study tour of American industries to see latest practices in action.

In May the new 'Queen's Awards to Industry' were announced. Perkins was granted the award for production and export achievements in 1965, with over 85% of production exported (62% directly) out of the total £38.3 million sales. Although this was a new award, it required the submission of a 'Statement of Case' document on behalf of the Company. This brochure makes for interesting reading as it gives – in simple and straightforward terms – the philosophy, intentions and achievements over the previous period. The award carried a special emblem, which could be used for the next five years on flags, stationery etc., adding further recognition to the Company's image.

A few days later, on 20 May, Monty Prichard opened the British Institute of Management conference in the Connaught Rooms in London, accompanied by a number of Perkins speakers who presented the Company's management practices in a remarkably frank manner. In his introductory remarks, Prichard traced the history of Perkins and its problems, the factors involved in the Massey Ferguson takeover and the overall attitudes now prevailing. The succeeding speakers, addressing an audience representing many leaders of British industry, built on these opening comments to paint a picture of the methods applied in managing the expanding operations. A copy of the brochure produced at the time has survived in the archives and contains much of interest regarding the ethos of the time.

The market in the USA was the subject of particular attention during the year. After the opening of a new Product Training School at the Wixom offices, and a successful stand at the Miami Boat Show earlier in the year, there was a concerted drive for vehicle sales. A Ford F750 truck was converted to the V8.510 for demonstrations, while a small fleet of United Parcel Service Ford F600s was converted to the 6.354, replacing worn-out petrol engines. In the British market too there was a novel event when JCB, in announcing their latest excavators with Perkins 4.236 and 6.354, arranged the 'kidnapping' of journalists to transport them to the secret 'hideout' where the machines were demonstrated.

Expansion at Eastfield

Within Peterborough there was more expansion in progress, with a start made on the new Engineering offices and workshops at Eastfield. The £1.375 million development encompassed 63,000 sq ft of workshops plus a single storey office of 45,000 sq ft and a five-storey block with 56,000 sq ft of office space. All were scheduled for completion by the end of 1967. The intention to close the Queen Street premises within two years was announced, although the engine rebuild operation had yet to be relocated.

In June Richard Perkins presented the latest production of the film unit at a World Premiere in London. Entitled 'Lifeboat', the nineteen-minute film told the story of British lifeboats, life-saving methods and the Royal National Lifeboat Institute from 1771. The first copy was presented to the RNLI.

Later in the summer, Perkins announced the formation of another licensee company, this time in Mexico. Motores Perkins S.A. was a venture with the Chrysler offshoot in Mexico, named Fabricas Automex S.A., and was to be based at a plant in Toluca, about 40 miles from Mexico City. The plant would produce 4.236 and 6.354 engines for local manufacturers, including Chrysler and Massey Ferguson.

Further successes were recorded again in the Cowes to Torquay powerboat race, when a Fairey Huntsman 28ft boat, Seven Dials, was placed fifth overall in a very arduous race, beating much bigger and more powerful rivals. Driven by Jane and Peter Hicks, the twin-T6.354-powered craft averaged almost 30mph over the course to win a series of prizes. Another Fairey Huntress won the diesel economy prize and came eleventh overall. With a single T6.354 and only 135bhp, this boat won the £500 prize for the lowest-powered finisher, and used only 42 gallons of fuel for the 200-mile race, at a cost of only £3.50!

During the year there were some significant retirements and organisational changes. Mr H.B. Harris, BEM, retired in April after 27 years and in May Eileen Kent, the first woman quarter-centurion and wife of Cyril Kent, went after 29 years' service. The Engineering Director, Gordon Dawson, resigned from the Company during the summer and was replaced by Geoffrey Smith, initially in an acting capacity. There were other directorial appointments, with Jim Winstanley becoming General Manager of International Marketing, Joe Hind appointed Staff Director of Product Quality and Reliability and Bernard Dyer as Staff Director, Manufacturing. There were also changes in the North American Company, where W.D. Winemaster became VP Marketing and R.C. Schmidt VP Engineering. At the end of the year Massey Ferguson announced a new Corporate structure, in which Monty Prichard was appointed Group Vice President, responsible for Perkins Group.

As the year drew to a close there were increasing concerns on the wages front as the Labour Government introduced a wage freeze and price freeze under their new Prices and Incomes Act. From September through to November unemployment had increased to 531,585 – up almost 200,000 on the figure of the late summer.

Peterborough production for 1966 reached 192,322 engines, with significant increases in both the 4.236 and 6.354 volumes. The V8.510 sold 136 units, built through the pilot production area at Eastfield, while the venerable P6 moved towards final phase-out with less than 1,000 engines produced.

The main drawing office at Eastfield was responsible for all production drawings. This view shows a small section of the office in 1962

The appointment of Gordon Dawson, after the belated recognition of the Board that major efforts were needed to rejuvenate the product range, became the catalyst for change. Although there had always been some activity to keep the products up-to-date and look to the future, the huge success of the existing products in the early 50s had allowed such efforts to take a back seat. The needs to reduce product costs and to keep customers happy became higher priorities than expenditure of scarce cash on research and development. As a result, the percentage of sales turnover spent on R&D was modest, a familiar story with most of British industry at the time and a failing remarked upon by American companies as potentially fatal. Complacency in the face of an apparently limitless market has afflicted many other enterprises in the past, to their ultimate detriment.

The design and production introduction of the 4.270D, 4.99 and 6.354 have already been described to some degree. The facilities in which this activity had taken place are perhaps worth describing in some detail.

Geography of the Engineering facilities of the time

The Design Drawing Office was situated in the north end of the main office block at Eastfield. It covered most aspects of basic engine design, adaptation for applications for existing and new customers, production of parts lists, control of design change and the essential activities associated with reproduction of drawings, etc. A further small design office, situated in a relatively remote first-floor location at Queen Street, looked after experimental design requirements.

Research and Development remained based at the ancient and rambling Queen Street works, in a set of crowded and very basic offices spread over two floors at the north side of the works. At this time much of the factory floor area at Queen Street was occupied by the Engine Rebuild Department (a source of considerable revenue since the 'Perpetuity' scheme was handling thousands of rebuilt engines each year), while other offices were occupied by the Service Department. The Experimental machine shop, fitting shop and some support offices were located on the main factory floor, plus the rig test and engine test facilities. The test beds were housed in a range of sheds and were draughty, noisy and dirty – and being situated only a stone's throw from the city centre were hardly ideal neighbours, especially when testing ran through the night and weekends! The whole site was plagued by leaky roofs, and flooding on occasion too, so conditions were often uncomfortable.

Other important sections of the Engineering Department included a well-equipped materials laboratory, fuel injection laboratory and stores areas. There were some other bright spots. For instance Perkins had been an early pioneer in the use of electronics at a time when the word was barely understood, much of the work being led by Sid Scott with enthusiastic managerial support from Martin Vulliamy. As a result, the use of cathode ray oscilloscopes for display of engine parameters such as torsional vibrations, engine indicator diagrams, injector needle lift, etc., was ahead of most other parts of the industry, who admired and envied the tools Perkins could apply to problems. The Materials Laboratory was also a pioneer in many respects and the Chief Metallurgist, Tom Wilshaw, became a nationally respected authority in his field.

A major disadvantage of the Engineering set-up was purely geographical – separation of design and development personnel by three miles did little to promote teamwork, and the links via telephone and written memo compare very poorly today when computers and video links make communication so much easier. The job of management in controlling activities, smoothing difficulties and ensuring progress cannot be underestimated. However, in spite of the many problems, miracles were accomplished and a great deal of work done.

A small department was located 'across the road' in an old warehouse known as 'Gibson's Yard'. Although actually a part of the Service Department, this group covered 'defect investigation' on engines returned from the field and was instrumental in pinpointing service problems of the time. Close liaison with the other sections ensured that prompt notice was taken of shortcomings, with lessons learnt fed back into the system for correction.

Applications Engineering

A large part of the effort in the Drawing Office in the 1950s was used to satisfy the needs of customer applications, providing the special parts needed to tailor engine installations to the individual machine or vehicle. Alongside this was the considerable 'conversion' workload, where the products were tailored to fit existing products. Adaption kits were marketed to end-users so they could quickly reap the benefits of diesel power. The design staff worked closely with the Field Test department, also based at Eastfield in a workshop and garage behind the main factory, to carry out the initial conversion work. The changes might include major parts such as a new oil sump or flywheel and housing, and would almost always involve new brackets, pipes, etc. Perkins owed much of its success to a willingness to provide exactly what the customer needed, but for the smaller users and the distributor network there was a move to satisfy their needs from a limited offering of 'pre-engineered' parts and base engines, thus cutting both the parts-listing time and the delivery. This range of components became known as the Standard Option Scheme, or SOS, splitting the engine into 'core', 'base options' and 'dress options'. From a special brochure the salesman could assist the smaller customer to draw up an engine specification to suit his particular needs without requiring special parts or the delay associated with producing an individual parts list every time. The factory could build the engine to the pre-engineered specification and allocate a code which allowed the service and spares personnel to support the engine in the field.

Getting the basics right

One essential change made in the late 1950s was the introduction of a new part numbering and classification system. This was based on a 'library' approach, with parts being classified by shape within allocated groups, so that like components would carry similar production part numbers (with a coding being allocated when the part was first designed and given a prototype number). The work was carried out using Brisch Berne as the consultants: the resulting system became known as the 'Brisch System' and provided a very powerful tool.

At the same time Perkins was switching from the old BSW/BSF range of hardware to use the American Unified system for nuts and bolts, in line with the changes going through the British Motor Industry. The implications and effects of these changes were of course reflected downstream to the suppliers and the production floor, causing considerable confusion until the benefits became apparent. Part of the change on hardware items was the creation of a series of 'Brisch' standards books defining the preferred range of nuts, bolts, washers, etc., by size of thread, length, material and other parameters. These fell in line with British Standards, and other standards where appropriate, helping to kill off the previous practice where a designer could invent a special length of bolt, say, without any real control being exerted – the implications for variety control had been horrible and had resulted in a very large 'Stock List'. The new system covering all parts gave the 'Standards Group' within Perkins considerable powers and allowed close control of part proliferation. They were able to see duplication, or near duplication, and as a result increased standardisation was possible – and not just on hardware. For example they found there were 56 different dipsticks in use; this was reduced to only six through the application of their standardisation criteria. Similar savings were made elsewhere, and the process ensured the inventory of part numbers was held within reasonable bounds.

Powerful controls were also introduced on drawing standards (using BS 308 as the major driving source), with extension to cover also reprographics, design change, parts listing and microfilming processes. The resulting improvements gave the Company an invaluable set of tools, which found their place not just for domestic production but also in the increasingly important licensee operations. The controls put in place for change control, on both drawings and parts lists, were also essential for a company becoming more 'global' in its activities. Introduction of procedures across many activities ensured that the Engineering Division was tightly controlled and that its standards were transferable and comprehensible.

Research

'Research' in Perkins terminology of the time covered the work on combustion and fuel injection equipment, plus the newer disciplines involved with engine turbocharging – this used a turbine powered by the exhaust gases to drive a small centrifugal compressor feeding compressed air to the cylinders, rather than the mechanically-driven superchargers more familiar on racing cars. Turbocharging had become a recognised means for increasing the performance of larger diesels but was only made possible on engines of around one litre per cylinder by the development of small and relatively cheap turbochargers. Perkins developed in-house turbocharging expertise using initially a unit designed and developed by John Binding, who owned a small business near Clevedon, Bristol. A small group at Queen Street, under the leadership of Doug Martin, gradually developed applications for the 6.354, after some initial trials on the R6/6.340 (with early field testing in Mexico).

Another in-house expertise developed during this period was in engine breathing, using single-cylinder research engines with bore and stroke identical to the P Series, and later the 6.354, 4.236 and V8. This work was supported by an airflow and swirl rig which allowed comparison to be made between port designs, often with very small differences in dimensions. This rig, in conjunction with the single-cylinder engines, allowed induction and exhaust port shapes to be evaluated and compared swiftly and cheaply, resulting initially in the cast port shapes used on the 6.354, and then the machined induction ports introduced on the 4.236. The team working on this, plus the associated fuel injection matching to optimise the engine performance, fuel economy and smoke characteristics, was plundered by the Cummins Engine Company in the late 1960s. Cummins had been very successful in larger engine sizes, and had even competed in the Indianapolis 500 Race before World War II. They were extending their engine range down to the one-litre cylinder size in what were to become famous as the 'B' series. Several key personnel were eventually attracted to Cummins, with Philip Jones, Eric Kemp and Ralph Ritchens moving across the Atlantic to join a company which became a major competitor in the Perkins size range. While this was a tribute to the respect the American company held for Perkins' engineering abilities, it did leave a gap in expertise for a short period. The Research team forged close working partnerships with the staff of CAV, the principal fuel injection equipment supplier, with full-time on-site technical representation forming an essential part of the teamwork. There were regular monthly meetings up to Director level from both companies, covering policy ('A' Panel), development ('B') and service matters ('C'): for a period Ricardo were included in tripartite meetings too. At the time Perkins represented the largest part of CAV's business on fuel injection equipment, so the level of cooperation was both understandable and necessary. As other fuel injection systems were considered, with Simms and Bosch being the major alternatives, close liaisons was developed with their engineering staff.

Mechanical Development

'Development' in Perkins terminology covered the mechanical side of engine development, with separate teams working on four main groups of parts – namely 'A' for accessories, 'B' for bearings, 'C' for cylinder and 'D' for drives. Location in the same office, liaising closely with a further group controlling engine build and test, ensured that each area was given sufficient testing time, and that the major problem areas were given priority.

Perkins also sought to use new technologies as they came along. Some reference has already been made to the use of high-speed photography for the problems of the R6 engine: another example was in the photo-elasticity laboratory, where Alf Blum was responsible for pioneering work. The technique involved the optical evaluation of the stresses in components using araldite models and polarised light, with scale loads being applied under laboratory conditions. An early success of this process was in the development of the connecting rod for the V8 engine, which had an innovative 'dog-tooth' profile for the split-line.

The shop floor areas – covering machine shop, fitting shop, test shop and rig test shop – were essential and were staffed by experienced and time-served operatives. Many still working in the 60s had been with the Company since the early days. The key supervisory personnel included Harry Lane, Les Toyne, Bill Bradley and Eric Phillips. They used their wealth of practical experience to interpret, support and progress the ideas, however outlandish, coming from the engineering offices. The machine shop was capable of making most prototype parts, but support from the Engineering Material Control team, an off-shoot of the Purchase function and based at Queen Street immediately adjacent to the machine shop, ensured that good service was obtained from other specialist suppliers as necessary.

The fitting shop was simple in concept, with each experienced fitter responsible for the complete build, strip or modification of an engine, including the taking of measurements as specified, aided by the inspector for the section. Each fitter tended to specialise in a particular engine type for the sake of continuity and efficiency, but would turn their hands to whatever was needed. Close liaison with the development engineers ensured that snags, defects and modifications were identified and reported.

The main test shop contained 26 test beds in an open shop area, except for two small cells dedicated to the DDE project, and ran mechanical development and endurance tests. This test area also performed pass-off tests on some of the project engines destined for customers as prototypes. A series of cells in a separate area (including the original 'black hole' used for all experimental work during the early and war years) catered for the Research activities. Occasionally special tests were conducted on engine stands outside in the yard, or even on field test vehicles brought in for the occasion.

Across this yard was the Rig Test Shop, under foreman 'Slim' Howard and staffed by a small band of fitter testers. The rigs were used to endurance and performance test items such as filters, pumps and fan belts – the rigs concerned were designed and built by the department and kept in an extraordinary state of cleanliness, with polished copper pipes and paintwork more akin to a ship's engine-room than a test house! Here too special tests were carried out on valve gear behaviour, water flow visualisation and similar investigations, often with complex (for the time) instrumentation, Perspex covers on cutaway castings, etc.

Solving some of the problems

The engineers also worked closely with suppliers, consultants and customers as appropriate, ensuring that the best use was made of available expertise. A good example of this during the late 50s and 60s concerned the development of better lubricating oils. As engine specific performance improved, and operators demanded longer servicing intervals, Perkins found increasing problems of oil deterioration being shown up in the field. On the indirect injection engines, notably the R6 and the 4.99, the amount of soot from combustion carried into the lube oil caused a phenomenon known as 'sludging'. This increased the viscosity of the oil so that in extreme cases the oil pump was unable to pick up oil from the sump and force it through the engine: bearing seizures resulted where owners and operators had stretched their oil change intervals too far. Close liaison with the oil companies ensured that their lubricating oil developments kept pace with the need for increased acceptance of high levels of contamination – the 'high detergency' oil was born. This close industrial cooperation continued as even greater demands were made as turbocharging and higher specific engine performance became the norm. (There were other needs for additives too, to overcome wear at highly-loaded areas such as cam/tappet interfaces for instance, and of course the development of multigrade oils to suit extremes of temperature. All were influenced to some extent by Perkins representation on motor industry committees.)

The problems being tackled during this time were many and various. On the existing engine types weaknesses shown up by field experience needed to be resolved. One such was the occurrence of water leaks from the 'wet' liners used on the 4.99 engine: use of a heavy pre-finished liner, sealed into the cylinder block at top and bottom, was common practice and had the virtue of simplifying cylinder block casting. Prolonged investigation pinpointed the cause as being a phenomenon termed 'crevice corrosion', due to high frequency vibration between liner and cylinder block. Various changes to the geometry were tried, and coating techniques were evaluated. However, such water leaks were a nuisance and expensive to fix in the field: the 4.99 suffered in certain applications and eventually the decision was made to produce a dry-linered version. The larger bore version of the 4.99, designated 4.107, was the first upgraded. To differentiate the change of liner it was identified as the 4.108 and went on to become a very successful small engine for vehicle, tractor, marine and industrial use, superseding the 4.99 and 4.107.

One particularly difficult application for the 4.107 was in the North American mobile refrigeration units, or 'Reefers'. Engines used for this purpose, on either road or rail containers, were expected to run continuously for hundreds of hours at relatively low speed and load but with minimum attention. Perkins competed with Mercedes-Benz for this business and found success with the Transicold Corporation.

The Engineering Department occupied a collection of offices on the Queen Street site. This is a section of the Mechanical Development office in 1964

Considerable detail changes to the engine were made in the light of running experience, notably with the introduction of the dry cylinder liner, a sump of huge oil capacity, and a special piston ring pack. The incorporation of a large 'by-pass' filter, able to remove tiny soot particles from the oil gradually without hindering engine oil flow and pressure, helped to extend oil change periods to an acceptable length.

Turbocharging the 6.354

While the 6.354 found immediate success in naturally aspirated form at 112bhp and then 120bhp for vehicle use, the attempts to introduce turbocharged variants were dogged by problems. This is not unexpected in any development programme and, in view of the calculated risks taken on the design of the 6.354, the need for design adjustments in the light of running experience was perhaps inevitable. The higher loading imposed on the engine at the proposed 150bhp rating for truck use uncovered shortcomings in several components. Major upgrades were needed for cylinder block, crankshaft, piston and ring-pack, cylinder head gasket and cylinder head.

As the engine became more popular in the USA for truck use on 'pick up and delivery' use especially another problem was found, possibly unique to North American operations at that time. Truck drivers inevitably applied the same driving techniques they used with the gasoline V8s and this included using engine braking as they left the freeway system via the 'clover-leaf' junctions rather than rely solely on the vehicle brakes. As a result the engines were subjected to a considerable amount of abrupt over-revving – the gasoline V8s would tolerate this with their relatively light and stiff valve gear and perhaps hydraulic tappets, but the 6.354 would not. British practice had decreed that a 30% overspeed allowance was satisfactory but a greater margin was clearly necessary for American conditions. After considerable evaluation a modified valve train was designed and proved, using shorter stiff valve springs, modular iron rocker levers and a 'polydyne' camshaft profile. This gave total valve control to well above 4,200rpm, or 50% overspeed, eliminating this failure as a concern although considerable warranty claims had to be settled on early engines.

Thorough testing proved the turbocharged engine for the less arduous duties in marine, industrial and agricultural applications, but under vehicle conditions the engine showed a serious lack of durability. One of the major means of testing at this time was via the Field Test Department, based at Eastfield: test engines were installed in various trucks and run round the clock under fully-loaded conditions over a variety of roads (this was of course well before most of the motorway network had been built).

The DDE

Added to the work on the 6.354 engine was a novel concept known as the 'differential diesel engine', or DDE for short, aimed at achieving a closer match of a diesel engine to the 'ideal' torque characteristics of the series-wound DC electric motor, where torque increases as speed decreases. Perkins had become aware of this concept through a paper published by Dr P.W. Glamann in 1955 when he was working for Berliet in France. A meeting was arranged over a weekend in Monte Carlo, when Gordon Dawson flew down to meet him. He found that Dr Glamann was pessimistic about Berliet funding his work further, and it was thus not difficult to persuade him to become a consultant to Perkins. A first attempt was made, paralleling the latest level reached by Glamann with Berliet: the base 6.354 was coupled to a conventional five-speed transmission through a simple epicyclic differential. The

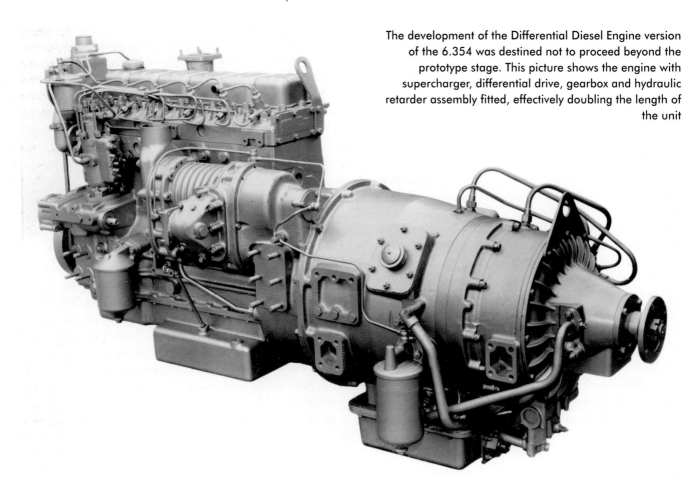

The development of the Differential Diesel Engine version of the 6.354 was destined not to proceed beyond the prototype stage. This picture shows the engine with supercharger, differential drive, gearbox and hydraulic retarder assembly fitted, effectively doubling the length of the unit

differential drove a BICERA compressor arranged as a supercharger feeding the engine intake. The drive arrangement provided increased supercharging as engine speed decreased, so that the boost level at low speed augmented the engine power and gave a characteristic approaching that of a 'constant horsepower' engine. Although the initial trial was promising, the actual power output was restricted by the fuel pumping capacity of the standard DPA fuel pump. With some enthusiasm a development programme was put in place, with the first moves being to procure a torque converter from KSB in Germany to replace the gearbox and to challenge CAV to develop a more suitable fuel pump with higher, fuel delivery. In addition a more suitable supercharger was needed to replace the prototype BICERA unit: a twin-screw compressor from Godfrey was obtained which was developed and reliable. To provide better induction conditions an air-to-air heat exchanger was added to give full charge cooling. The basic engine used initially was to the latest turbocharged specification.

Initial evaluation showed that, although it did not yet meet target performance, the engine system had potential. Changes were made to provide better torque converter and fuel pump matching, more compact charge-cooling to suit a vehicle installation, and upgrades for the base engine. The latter began to reflect the significantly higher loads imposed by the changes in operating characteristics. The higher cylinder pressures required better cylinder head gasket design, more substantial piston, ring and connecting rod design and also attention to valves to prevent accelerated wear due to flexure of the valve heads and lack of seat lubrication. All represented a challenge at that time, stretching supplier knowledge and materials to their limits. There were also problems with crankshaft and bearings, resulting in the specification of higher duty materials. The vehicle testing showed that additional braking was needed since the fundamental design reduced the available engine braking under overrun conditions; a hydraulic retarder was designed and fitted, tests proving that this could provide excellent braking under normal operation and reduced the need

to use the standard service braking system. (There was one instance, however, when the efficiency of an early version of the retarder fitted to a T6.354 in a Field Test articulated truck almost caused a disaster. The truck was exiting the A1 at Wansford on the way back to Eastfield in damp conditions; the driver applied the retarder on the slip road only to jackknife the truck and block the road – fortunately without any serious injury!)

Road experience showed that, compared to a turbocharged engine of similar maximum power output, the DDE unit always had the ability to handle truck weights up to 40% extra. Although the engine showed only small benefits in journey time over 'motorway' type driving, there were substantial benefits on hilly courses – as might be expected with a reduced need for gear changes. Fuel consumption was invariably better, especially under high speed/high load. One of the strange characteristics of the vehicle on the road was the decreasing noise level as the truck accelerated from rest - since the whistle of the supercharger reduced as engine speed increased. There appeared to be potential benefits of engine life, due to reduced average rotational speed, plus benefits in matching the output curve to suit other applications, such as earthmovers, instead of road vehicles.

Unfortunately the DDE project, after several years of relatively low-key development, was cancelled. A paper was published in 1964 and was presented to both the Institution of Mechanical Engineers in England and to the Society of Automotive Engineers in the USA. The Automobile Division of the I.Mech.E. presented the authors with the Gresham Cooke Award. Considerable interest in both countries, resulted in discussions with major manufacturers of vehicles after the presentations. The engine was formally announced and tested by various industry journalists, notably from the Commercial Motor. It is interesting to note that the Perkins team – consisting of Gordon Dawson and Bill Hayward, plus Dr Glamann – managed to avoid much discussion on the mechanical problems of the base engine. However, the project did not attract the commercial interest hoped for, since the increasing availability of larger engines and multi-speed/range change transmissions provided a more affordable, less complex solution to road transport needs. No DDE units survived, even as museum pieces, and the principles have become of academic interest only.

Why did it fail? The principal, and oft-quoted, reason was related to cost. The base engine was special and higher-priced than an equivalent turbocharged specification.

The package of supercharger, torque-converter and retarder system then added considerably to vehicle price and to the overall length of the total unit, and when a simple two-speed plus reverse transmission was added (since the torque multiplication of the original unit proved insufficient) there is little doubt that, when compared to the cost of the alternative transmissions being marketed, there was going to be a penalty. The author's own view is that the many mechanical problems experienced during development might at that time have proved insurmountable – but with today's much improved materials and techniques these might be overcome. It would need considerable expenditure to realise the potential of what could have been the most effective prime mover since the steam engine!

Duplex research

There was another 'novel' engine concept investigated during the 1960s by the Research Department under the management of Philip Jones. Along with his advocacy of new techniques on engine breathing, Philip promoted the idea of investigation through small cross-discipline teams of designs outside Perkins' normal scope. One of these teams began to examine the use of two-stroke engines rather than the traditional four-stroke, influenced by his former experience with larger engines. The unit considered became known as the 'Duplex', the design being based around a twin-cylinder unit with split-single-cylinder layout, using a Roots-type blower for cylinder scavenging. There had been successful petrol engines of this type, notably Trojan, Ehlich and Jawa, although the nearest diesel design had been the war-time Junkers Jumo aero engine, which had an opposed piston layout. The perceived advantage was that inlet and exhaust events could be controlled by simple cylinder wall ports but with the benefit of as-symetrical port timing. Some degree of supercharging was possible through careful scavenge timing. The small Experimental Design Office at Queen Street under Frank Morton produced detailed designs, enabling a fabricated prototype to be produced and run. The design incorporated a curved connecting rod, produced after work in the new Stress Analysis Laboratory, and a special DPA fuel pump modified to provide fuel injection twice per revolution. Although the engine ran smoothly and quietly, the team found that there were many conflicting requirements for air transfer and compact combustion space. Since scavenge air was also throttled the engine suffered from poor fuel economy and unacceptable exhaust smoke. However, it was a useful learning experience!

The 4.236 Engine

The development of the four-cylinder version of the 6.354, designated 4.236, was commenced in the late 50s. The engine was intended to be the successor to the P4 and was originally designed to be adaptable for many different applications, as was the Perkins custom. With the takeover by MF however, specific consideration was given to the needs of tractor applications – with the move towards a 'frameless' design with the engine forming an integral part of the tractor backbone. Thus a special version of the engine was developed, having an integral flywheel housing and starter motor pocket cast into the rear of the cylinder block. The front end of the block was also specific to tractor use, with the mounting face intended to match with the front face of the cast iron sump to pick up the front axle mounting attachment. The other addition was the incorporation of a 'Lanchester-type'

second order balancer, bolted to the block bottom face and driven from the crankshaft pulley at twice engine speed. The balancer incorporated the lubricating oil pump and featured two counter-rotating balance shafts, phased to the crankshaft rotation to damp out a large proportion of the vertical out-of-balance forces and thus provide smoother engine operation. This was important in farm tractor applications where there was no isolation through rubber mounts between engine and chassis.

The 'tractor' and 'vehicle' cylinder blocks were designed to be as common as possible to be machined down a common transfer line. Most other components for the engine variants were identical, with the exception of the crankshaft, where the tractor version did not have balancing webs while the vehicle version did. The cylinder head was identical. As experience grew, and the costing experts came to grips with the economics of engine pricing on very high volumes, there were cost reductions on many parts for the lower-rated tractor engines.

One of the changes made in the design of the 4.236 compared to the 6.354 was the induction porting design, mentioned earlier in this chapter. Airflow and combustion research with a variety of port shapes on a single-cylinder engine proved very fruitful when a fully machined port design was developed. This gave improved efficiency, performance and smoke characteristics while offering tighter control for machining in-works when compared to the production variations seen on the cast port designs (where foundry ability to maintain accurate shape and consistency proved a special concern).

The 4.236 engine proved a very successful and enduring product. It was developed into a family of great versatility, providing a range of capacities from 203 to 248 cubic inches, with turbocharged and spark-ignition versions, and with rated speeds up to 3,200rpm. Both cylinder bore and stroke were varied to suit the capacity and characteristics needed. The engine became the mainstay of production at Eastfield from the 60s into the new millennium, and was also the major product used by the overseas licensees and associate companies. As well as being the most successful engine for the range of MF products around the world, the 4.236 family powered products for many other major customers, including Caterpillar and JCB. Along with the 6.354, the 4.236 became the progenitor of later products such as the 1000 Series, Phaser and 1100 Series.

The 4.236 shared many design features and components with its six-cylinder brother, and also some of the problems! Early in their production lives both engines suffered problems of high oil consumption, the major reason being the tendency of the cylinder block to change shape in the cylinder bore area as running hours were accumulated. Since the introduction of stress-relieving for the 6.354 cylinder block proved an expensive and ultimately inconsistent palliative, the alternative was to develop piston and ring packs which would accommodate ovality of the bores up to 0.006 inches. The end-users eventually accepted that the engines would use rather more oil than might be preferred, but the engines' dependability seemed to make up for this shortcoming! A large part of the development effort in the 1960s was expended in sorting out the teething problems of the mainstream four- and six-cylinder engines, and providing units that met production needs for ease of assembly and test while maintaining low costs to satisfy the accountants and maintain a competitive edge over the opposition products.

Scuffing

One of the production requirements, which proved a major problem for some years, was the introduction of diamond honing stones in place of the more traditional carborundum grinding stones. This change was pioneered by the Perkins production engineers as they sought a means to increase the honing stone life as production rates increased – the use of diamond-impregnated material dramatically increased the number of blocks machined before a change of stones was necessary, an important consideration in keeping production costs down. However, the cutting action of the diamonds was not as clean as the more traditional abrasives, so that the cast iron of the cylinder liners tended to be smeared and folded rather than cut. As a result the ability of the bore surfaces to hold lubricating oil was reduced and there was a tendency for the oil film to break down during early life, resulting in a phenomenon known as 'scuffing'. This can best be described as an instantaneous welding of the piston ring and liner surfaces, which of course immediately broke down as the surfaces moved apart. The resultant high wear rate could cause engines to wear or even seize very quickly, and a considerable loss of productivity resulted as suspect engines had to be checked internally with special bore 'intrascopes' during the test cycle before engines could be passed for finishing and despatch.

During the late 60s and early 70s outbreaks of scuffing plagued Perkins on various higher-rated engines: the development of a 'double diamond', or 'plateau' honing process along with complex measuring and control processes helped to contain the failures, but it took the introduction of silicon carbide honing and more sophisticated honing machines in the 1980s to cure the problem permanently. Much development time was spent in evaluating increasingly expensive piston ring packs in an attempt to overcome a problem caused by the production demands for throughput at the cheapest cost.

Quality Control

It is relevant at this point to mention the importance of the Quality Control Department as an interface between the Engineering and Production functions. Perkins' management had introduced the QC function as an extension of the normal inspection processes, for instance the checking of incoming material batches, checks on production maintenance of tolerances, etc. The 'Quality Engineering' team oversaw test shop pass-off standards, including statistical approaches which became more sophisticated and allowed fuel injection pumps to be pre-set for fuel delivery, etc. On the mechanical side, QE carried out trials to shorten run-in tests on all engine types while still meeting the criterion of maximum load running immediately on installation without failure. It was a tightrope act balancing the expectations of Engineering without causing unnecessary delay and expense to the Production processes. In the 1960s John Fish was Quality Control Manager and established authority over the quality of all products via a small team of engineers, with the strength of personality (and support from the Boardroom) to stop production if he saw the need.

It is worth recording the lengths to which Quality Engineering had to go in order to satisfy some customers. Oliver Corporation in the USA produced farm tractors at their plant in Charles City, Iowa and selected the 6.354 engine for a new model. One of their pass-off criteria was a 'Power Take Off' horsepower figure, recorded on all tractors, which had to be above a minimum figure. There were soon problems on the 6.354 and Perkins had to record and advise all pass-off results to Charles City where the eventual tractor build would be noted and failures highlighted. This led to considerable work on statistical probability, the secondment of a Quality Resident Engineer to the wilds of Iowa, and continual bickering over variations. The implications of climatic variations, fuel differences and the effect of variable tractor transmission losses all added to a state of acrimony over a long period!

Developing the V8 Engine

A brief mention was made earlier of the development of a V8 engine. This was started in 1960 when it was realised that an engine giving more than 120bhp would be needed for the heavier trucks and agricultural machinery being developed by the industry. An early design was produced as a prototype, with a capacity of over 400 cubic inches and featuring indirect injection, using the same 'Howard' combustion chamber design as the 4.99. Little progress was made with this engine, however, and an improved design was ordered, initially of 452 cubic inches, but quickly expanded to 510 in order to increase the power to 170 rather than 150bhp (the latter could be achieved by a turbocharger version of the 6.354). The reasoning behind the choice of a vee engine rather than a larger straight-six was probably due to two factors – the potential use in the American market and the European truck designs of the time. The American petrol engines were predominantly V8s, and thus familiar to and accepted by the average operator: in addition the engine compartments of the medium trucks suited this configuration. In Europe the tendency was for trucks to move towards the 'cab-over' design, while the axle-load regulations of the time favoured a short engine rather than a larger six-cylinder protruding beyond the back of the cab, forcing the pivot point for articulated trailers further towards the rear axle. The Perkins solution of a vee design was not unique, since Cummins, General Motors and Caterpillar also developed V6 and V8 diesel designs in the USA, while Dorman made a larger V8 in the UK at about the same time.

The settled Perkins design incorporated direct injection, with two cross-flow cylinder heads and a Simms in-line fuel pump located in the vee between the banks of cylinders, set at 90 degrees. Design of this engine had been mainly completed at the home of Charles Chapman in Sussex, where Bill Hayward was seconded by John Condie to carry out the basic work under Chapman's supervision. (Chapman was back in touch with Perkins through Monty Prichard and he produced his own account of the early days of Perkins at about this time – much of the early part of this book has drawn heavily on his unpublished narrative.)

It is interesting to note that the design of the V8 incorporated a number of features that corrected some acknowledged shortcomings of the 6.354 design: notably in the crankshaft and the cylinder head to block fixings. The six-cylinder crankshaft was relatively flimsy, and proved to be of inadequate strength for the turbocharged and DDE versions without resorting to hardening measures – processes such as nitriding and tufftriding being introduced in production after fillet-rolling proved difficult in production volumes. In comparison the V8 crankshaft was massive, and featured bolted-on counterweights to provide the necessary dynamic and static balance. (The balance-weight fixings were to prove a considerable challenge, however, with several development engines failing spectacularly before aircraft quality fixings and close attention to squareness of mating faces and nut tightening procedures provided an answer.)

The cylinder head fixings on the 6.354 were not evenly spaced, so that clamping loads were uneven and required considerable detail development of the gasket design – and a change from 7/16 to 1/2-inch studs soon after production started. The V8 design provided a symmetrical fixing pattern, but even this proved an uneasy compromise since the inclined gasket faces trapped air in a pocket between the stud bosses – such problems were everyday challenges to the Engineering teams as they strove to develop a reliable engine for the market.

Many other challenges

The relatively small engineering team at Queen Street was considerably stretched by the amount of work in hand, and space could not accommodate many additional engineers, although several were recruited from BMC, as well as from the in-house apprenticeship scheme. Alongside the new products described above, there were upgrades of the P4, which became the D4.203, as well as the P3 (D3.152). Only the P6 and S6 were excluded from further development as the decision was made to cease production of these worthy but obsolete products.

There were further derivatives of the 3.152, 4.203 and 4.236 to follow, mainly at the instigation of Massey Ferguson to suit a niche market for gasoline-fuelled tractors in the USA. A small team, under the leadership of Bill Youde and with the help of outside consultants such as ERA, set about adapting the engines to take spark ignition and carburettors so that the same basic engine frame could offer the alternative of gasoline, and later LPG/LNG, fuels. This approach found favour not just with MF for their tractors but also with forklift truck manufacturers who needed such alternative fuels for operating areas where diesel was non-preferred, and where an engine with identical physical size, mountings, simplified installations.

The successes of the T6.354 marine engine in the offshore powerboat races in the 60s and 70s are mentioned in the chronological history. There was of course considerable support for this programme to develop the engine output gradually to higher power, and during the close season the race engines from some boats were returned to Queen Street for examination, updating and testing before despatch back to the owners. Quite a competition developed in later years as Ford got into racing too with their 'Tornado' turbocharged truck engine. This was developed by Sabre Marine for maritime use and also gradually increased in output: the power race culminated when they reached the point where nitrous oxide injection was needed to boost the power to allow the boat to 'get on the step' (i.e. for the hull to start planing), at which point the engine power required became less. Perkins did not go to this extreme, but engine development did achieve 290bhp and beyond, although strictly for limited-life racing use.

Another development on the marine engines was the introduction of 'reverse rotation' engines to allow twin engine installations to operate with propellers running in opposite directions, thus counteracting the torque effect which could make the boat more difficult to handle. The design changes needed were not numerous, although there were red faces when the first engine was ready to run and it was realised that a camshaft with reversed profiles had not been procured!

Working with a Japanese partner

Yet more work came from the agreement signed with Toyo Kogyo (later better known as Mazda) in the late 60s. This venture was two-fold. The first part of the agreement was the development of a TK engine design into the 4.154 engine, to be built in Peterborough from carcase engines shipped from Japan to supply the Perkins markets around the world. The availability of this engine filled a gap between the 4.108 and the 4.236 for a 2.5- to 3-litre diesel suitable for passenger cars, vans and small trucks. Later a six-cylinder derivative, the 6.231, was made available but this never achieved the expected volume. There were further versions of the 4.154 to follow, with swept volumes of 135, 165 and 182 cubic inches.

The second part of the agreement with TK concerned the development of high-speed derivatives of the 4.236 and 6.354 specifically for the Japanese market. A redesign was carried out in the early 1970s to provide a short-stroke version of each engine, becoming the 4.224 and 6.335, with an indirect-injection combustion system allowing ratings up to 3,200rpm. There were some challenges in meeting the requirement, with lessons learnt regarding cylinder block and head design, as well as breathing and fuel system requirements. It is interesting to recall the impressions left with Bill Westwell and Bill Stewart, who attended many meetings in Japan: invariably the small Perkins team would be faced by a large number of Japanese engineers, most saying little in deference to their senior personnel, but all taking pages of notes throughout long meetings.

Field Test

One of the most important sections of Engineering was the Applica-

tions and Field Test operation, already mentioned. This group looked after the installation of engines into customer prototype vehicles, as well as carrying out the testing of prototype engines in a variety of vehicles. The specialist designers were experts in determining the changes needed to accommodate the engine, and in providing drawings quickly for the new components needed. The engineers became experts in every aspect of engine installation, being able to advise customers on the best means of mounting the engines in any type of machine, the limitations for fuel, air, exhaust and auxiliary systems – and to assist in predicting the performance of the combination. Many customers became reliant upon the help available, although others insisted on going their own way! There were often specific challenges, for example in the case of the first Ford Transit truck. Ford had designed their engine compartment around the V4 petrol engine parameters, so that when Perkins offered to fit the 4.108 engine the Ford engineers were adamant that it would not go in. True, there was a limitation on length, but the Perkins team redesigned the sheet metal of the cowl and was able to demonstrate a viable conversion that was soon adopted (with some placatory Ford-inspired modifications!) for production.

The test fleet consisted of a variety of trucks owned by the Company and operated on a day-and-night basis, always fully laden, to accumulate mileage quickly. Such testing under true road conditions invariably threw up design weaknesses that conventional endurance testing on test beds failed to show. The advent of the motorway system helped the Perkins trucks to achieve greater mileages at higher average speeds (in line of course with the abilities of the average truck drivers too). The test driving was not without incident, on one occasion a truck overturned on the M1, blocking the carriageway with concrete blocks and featuring on the national news!

Higher gross vehicle weights, greater daily mileages and closer attention to running costs all increased the pressure on truck and engine manufacturers for better equipment with enhanced durability, reliability and extended servicing intervals.

Perkins also worked with farmers and the agricultural equipment makers to field-test their equipment, placing prototypes with operators known to work their machinery hard. The increased sophistication of the marketplace was starting to become evident in the 60s: no longer were people willing to accept the products purely because diesels were cheaper to run and had increased life – competition was becoming keen so that a more professional and responsive attitude was increasingly essential.

Cost reduction activity

It would be wrong to close this chapter without reference to one of the minor but essential developments on the design side, the introduction of 'Value Analysis' as an aid to cost reduction and product improvement. There had always been pressures on the cost of the products, since competitive pricing was essential to make inroads into the conversion market initially, and later to fend off the increasing competition from other diesel manufacturers. 'VA' was a new approach to the continual search for better and cheaper components, and under the management of David Raven the disciplines became a powerful tool. Innovation in design, materials and processes were very much to the fore: some of the now-accepted approaches, such as shell-moulding, sintering and fabrication, first came into consideration as the VA team challenged the conventional methods and asked the simple question: 'is there a better and cheaper way?' True, some schemes were quickly dropped as testing showed no benefit, but others became production reality with proven and lasting benefits. David Raven left the company quite quickly, but he had sown the seeds of a new approach to component design and evaluation; a succession of new ideas challenging conventional thinking. Supported by other initiatives such as the 'Suggestion Scheme', cost-reduction and value-analysis approaches became a part of the Perkins armoury in the continual struggle to curb costs and maintain a competitive edge through a 'value-for-money' philosophy.

Trials with the Wankel engine

In the previous chapter there was reference to the Wankel engine. This rotary unit was seen as a unique and potentially important alternative to the conventional reciprocating engine when first publicised by NSU/Wankel. In line with their policy of investigating possible alternative power sources, Perkins quickly acquired a licence and undertook research into the new design, rapidly determining its potential advantages and problems. Principal amongst the latter was the difficulty in sealing the seals on the epi-trochoidal rotor both on the circumference and sides of the housing. Under the shrewd guidance of Horace Rainbow the team looked for low-friction routes and were successful in making improvements: he also designed a water-cooled rotor which proved advantageous. From the work carried out, the solutions proposed were ultimately fed back to NSU. This work was carried out at Queen Street by a small group designated 'Advanced Engineering' with Albert Fiegel as manager.

The main advantage of the Wankel engine was its power density – the design offered greater power from a given package size and weight than any other engine of the time; in fact it was the size of accessories such as alternator and starter motor that made the package much larger than it could have been. As a result Perkins looked at producing a Wankel outboard motor, and the first version was being tested when the outboard business was sold. The potential for a diesel version of the engine was discounted quite quickly when it became apparent that there were insurmountable problems with compression ratio and 'quench' area. Some work was carried out at Shrewsbury by the Rolls-Royce Diesel Engine Division with their twin-chamber 'Cottage Loaf' design, but they apparently also decided the problems were insurmountable, although for a period the use of the engine as a compressor was considered. Perkins dropped further consideration,

and overall the engine design has never caught on – only Mazda have really persevered with the engine into the 21st century. It was a clever invention that has never achieved its apparent potential.

The concept of an Advanced Engineering Group was fundamental to the Perkins policy of looking at other options for power plants. This carried on over a number of years and examined in considerable detail the merits of fuel cells and the Stirling cycle engine, plus a plethora of devices generated by inventors, most of which proved impractical but which were nevertheless given due consideration. Alan Sparrow, an experienced engineer and inventor in his own right, was the principal evaluator of ideas right through to his retirement in the 1980s.

Another aspect of Engineering's work was the consideration of the competition, in the shape of other diesel engine designs on a worldwide basis. This ranged from a planned exchange of products with Ford to the purchase or loan of others' products. During the late 60s, for instance, vee engines from General Motors, Cummins and Caterpillar were tested, stripped and reported. A range of small engines made by Italian company Lombardini was also tested and examined during the mid-60s, with a view to extending the range of products offered: however, the recommendations made by the Queen Street team resulted in the idea being dropped. Although ideas were found which impressed the Perkins engineers and designers, it was evident that competitors at the time were unable to achieve the 'value engineering' and product adaptability that kept Peterborough products so price-competitive and flexible.

Towards the end of the 60s it became obvious that increased space and staffing was necessary for the Engineering Division. There was also renewed pressure from the City Council to vacate the Queen Street premises, thus allowing redevelopment of the city centre to be started. There had been several attempts to produce plans for the resiting of the remaining occupants of the old premises, but by 1967 the construction was well under way, as will be seen in the following chapter.

Above & Left: Francis Chichester and Gipsy Moth III pictured before they set sail on his epic round-the-world solo voyage in August 1966

The beginning of 1967 brought some sad news. Edward Marvill, the 'boy' of the original group of employees who accompanied Frank Perkins from AGE to Peterborough in 1932, had died at his home in Dogsthorpe Road on 27 December at the age of 57, having been in poor health for some time. During his years at Peterborough he had undertaken various roles, including being first works manager at Eastfield. At the time of his death he was area manager of the engine rebuild shop at Queen Street. There were tributes from many colleagues, who recognised that 'Uncle Ted' had contributed greatly to the Company's success and supported many activities outside work.

A report in the January Echo gave news of an endeavour, destined to win global coverage later in the year, as Francis Chichester talked to Perkins after arriving in Australia on the first long leg of his historic round-the-world solo voyage in Gipsy Moth. His craft had been fitted with a 4.107(M) as the auxiliary engine, mainly to power the lighting and radio equipment. He declared the engine 'perfect' after the 14,000 mile journey, commenting that: 'Preliminary sea trials had shown how reliable it is – and this is one thing over which I have no worries at all.' Nevertheless the engine was given a thorough check by the service engineers before he left on the return voyage. During the journey home there was an announcement from Buckingham Palace to say that he had been awarded a knighthood.

There were celebrations at Peterscourt as the Service School celebrated its 21st Birthday. After starting in two rooms in Geneva Street in 1945 with Tom Parrish as the sole instructor, and 187 students in that first year, the school had grown to ten instructors and an annual attendance of over 4,000. With trainees drawn from all over the world the servicing of Perkins engines was in good hands.

At the International Boat Show at Earls Court Perkins-powered craft featured prominently again: boats worth over £100,000 were sold 'off the stands' with one – Jolina IV built by Souter and Sons of Cowes and powered by twin HT6.354s – named Boat of the Show. Richard Perkins was presented with three awards by Sir Max Aitken of the Daily Express for successes in the 1966 Cowes to Torquay race.

Further successes were publicised. The Brussels Motor Show featured a Russian Moskvitch car fitted with the 4.99(V), a conversion by Scaldia Volga who planned to produce the cars in Belgium. An order worth £105,000 for P3.144(M) engines was announced for the Ceylon Fisheries Corporation, to power new boats in a project to modernise the industry on the island. The third announcement was perhaps the most prestigious: Perkins were awarded the Royal Warrant as 'Manufacturers of Diesel Engines to the Queen'. Monty Prichard affirmed that 'the Company is proud and greatly honoured' as he announced the award.

In March Prichard visited Vancouver, Canada, in his capacity of Vice President of the Society of Motor Manufacturers and Traders. At a press conference he talked about the importance of membership of the Common Market to British Industry. He highlighted the need for a quality drive to ensure better vehicles, better marketing and enhanced after-sales support if the future of the motor industry was to be assured. There had been changes to Perkins' management in Canada and the USA as Robert Cumming resigned to take a post with White Motor Company, leaving Harry J. Graham in charge of the Canadi-

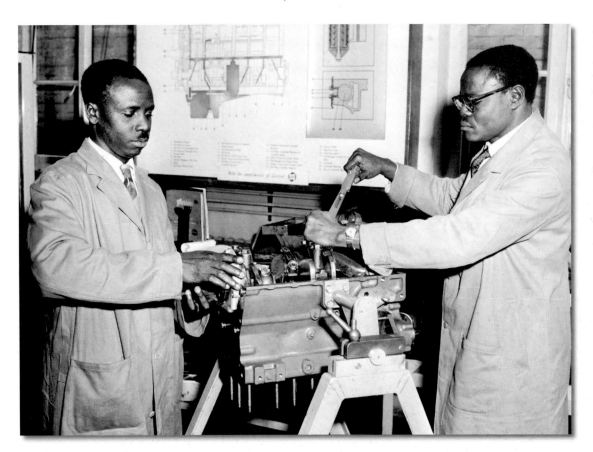

Many thousands of students from all over the world passed through the Service School at Peterscourt, learning all about the various products and how to look after them

an operation, and Bill Winemaster running Perkins Inc. in the USA. More news, of great concern to the British motor industry, came with announcement that the Chrysler Corporation were to take over the Rootes Group, a step which received the approval of the Government through Anthony Wedgwood Benn, the new Minister for Technology.

An article in April highlighted on the longevity of the early engines. Crane Engineering Co. Ltd at Kettering had an old 'Neals Rapid Crawler Crane' dating from 1936 in their yard. There were thoughts of scrapping the machine, powered by a Leopard engine. However, someone suggested trying to start it with battery power and fuel supplied the engine fired and ran! Some further refurbishment was carried out, with new piston rings, head gasket and reconditioned injectors at a total cost of £3.75 they had a functioning crane!

New headquarters for Perkins Germany were opened in May. The new premises at Kleinostheim gave more space to look after the West German market, worth £3.5 million in 1966. While the largest and most important German customer was still Claas, taking increasing numbers of engines for their combine harvesters, there were many smaller enterprises handling conversions, installation and servicing for a multitude of German customers.

There were several important national announcements during the spring: the publication of the Decimal Currency Bill was a move towards metrication. Other financial news concerned the gradual reduction of Bank Rate from 7% to 6.5% and then to 5.5% in May, as the Government took steps to relieve pressure on Sterling.

Perkins featured on BBC TV as the 'Value Analysis' team featured in a series on Engineering Design. They were identified as leading exponents of cost reduction techniques in a programme covering 'Design for Value'. An exhibition in May gave the team a chance to show all Perkins employees that they could be involved and contribute to the V.A. process. A further internal meeting in the same month dealt with 'Quality and Reliability' when Joe Hind, Richard Perkins and Bernard Dyer addressed 200 Manufacturing management personnel on this increasingly important topic. (Bernard Dyer was elected to the Board a few weeks later as Staff Director, Manufacturing.)

Sir Francis Chichester arrived back in Britain after his 28,500 mile solo voyage, having spent 119 days at sea: his faithful Gipsy Moth and its 4.107(M) had performed faultlessly.

Changes within Massey Ferguson

In June there was an expansion of Massey Ferguson following the reorganisation into product groups, splitting out the activities on non-agricultural machinery into a new entity, named Industrial and Construction Machinery (ICM) Division. At the same time the Engines business was identified as a separate Division, with Monty Prichard as Group Vice President. Taking worldwide responsibilities for their various geographic operations units, the new VPs reported into the corporate structure based in the Toronto Headquarters. Worldwide growth of the ICM business was forecast by MF, who committed $30 million to this aspect of their activities: the introduction of thirteen new products for the construction market was promised by the end of 1968. Previously the industrial equipment was based upon modified agricultural tractors, with suitable accessories and a yellow colour scheme. The new range would include crawler tractors, hydraulic excavators and four-wheel-drive shovel loaders. Most machines were to be powered by Perkins.

It was around this time that news of important developments for Peterborough started to feature prominently: it is worth a brief digression to consider the implications of the 'Greater Peterborough Master Plan'. In 1964 the Government had announced plans to divert future growth of the country away from the overcrowded South East, and Greater London in particular, to new towns or expansion of existing towns. In the East Midlands the decision was reached to concentrate development on three cities – Northampton, Milton Keynes and Peterborough. The creation of the Peterborough Development Corporation provided a focus for the efforts that would see the city increase greatly in population, infrastructure and, most importantly, industry and employment over the next thirty-five years. One small part of the 'Master Plan' was of course the redevelopment of the centre of Peterborough, necessitating the final closure of the Perkins Queen Street premises – as had been identified by the city fathers immediately after

A proud moment with the family captured outside Buckingham Palace after Monty Prichard received the CBE for services to exports

the war! It is interesting now, looking back at the detail of the Master Plan, that no company is named in the document although there were large enterprises employing significant numbers of workers. It is not clear how much discussion there was between the Development Corporation and Perkins; there surely was a great deal and interestingly the DC eventually took over the Peterscourt offices once they were vacated by Perkins – a convenient city-centre position.

Returning to the events of 1967, in July the Engineering Division started the transition to the new site at Eastfield, although in fact a number of the Research engineers and the associated test shop personnel remained at Queen Street for a considerable period into the early 1970s. In the same month there was a change on the Manufacturing side when Vivian Frayling, who had been the Group Personnel Director, was appointed Director and General Manager of UK Operations Manufacturing.

There was more international news as the new 4.154 engine was exhibited on the Perkins stand in Japan: the engine was developed by Toyo Kogyo in Hiroshima and was initially fully manufactured there. From Poland came the news that the 4.108 and 6.354 engines were to be offered in Warszawa cars, Nysa buses, Kuk vans and Star 25 trucks, while in Germany Monty Prichard attended a ceremony at Harsewinkel where the 100,000th engine was handed over to Dr August Claas of that combine harvester company.

Following the sales of engines early in the year to Ceylon, the Perkins Film Unit produced a new film, 'Food from the Sea'; a 17-minute feature on the fishing fleet which had grow into an important national industry over a 15-year period.

At Peterborough, Frank Perkins presented special awards to the long-serving members of the Company. There were now 186 employees with over 25 years of unbroken service: each received a gold watch, canteen of cutlery, silver cigarette box or a silver salver from the Company. There were posthumous awards to four members who had died in the preceding months.

Success in offshore racing again

The powerboat races were in the news in June and August, with awards to Perkins power in the 177-mile Wills International Race and in the annual Cowes to Torquay event. Among the major winners were Bob Bolton with Finandandy and Peter Twiss in Waterline Huntress who scooped the fuel economy prize. The T6.354 marine engines were confirmed as the diesel product to beat in offshore powerboating, especially when teamed with the Fairey fast cruisers.

There was good press for the V8.510 in September when a Dennis Maxim truck running at 30 tons GTW completed a 1,667-mile drive across Europe to Italy. The engine ran trouble-free and averaged 7.3mpg and about 18.6mph average speed including all stops. The run was carried out as an 'in-service' demonstration for a UK haulage company, and showed that the engine could hold its own with more powerful continental competitors, even at altitude and on the Italian autostrada. Favourable comments were also made on the efficient engine exhaust braking system, which helped spare the service brakes.

There was an announcement in October of collaboration between Perkins and the Berliet company in France. The venture was signed to develop a new series of engines between 8 and 20 litres, supplementing the existing ranges of both companies. Peter Bowyer, a long-serving member of the Engineering development group, was named as Project Engineer for the Perkins side. (Unfortunately the project never realised its potential and was eventually quietly dropped.)

A little piece of history was made when the first female engineering apprentice, Linda Renshaw, took her place alongside sixty boys in the Training School. Previously there had been many young women

trained on the commercial and secretarial side, but none on a technical apprenticeship.

Death of Frank Perkins

The month was also a time of great sadness with the death of Frank Perkins at home in Alwalton Hall on 15 October, at 78 years old. There were messages from all over the country and from all corners of the world. Over 1,000 attended a memorial service at Peterborough Cathedral on 21 October, after a private family funeral at Alwalton. Frank Perkins was a proud but modest man, whose legacy is clear. Yet there had been no national recognition during his lifetime, a fact that is difficult to comprehend today. It has been suggested that there had been a too-public attempt to gain a knighthood for him during the post-war period: whether this upset the 'establishment' is impossible to tell. The fact remains that a man who was a pioneer in his field, brought great success to company and country, and fostered a number of important ventures in the community, remains unsung to this day, apart from his name being applied to a Queensgate car park and part of the Peterborough ring road system. His modesty is reflected in the simple grave in Alwalton churchyard, the little village outside Peterborough which also happens to be the birthplace of another great but modest English engineer, Sir Henry Royce, whose ashes are interred within the church. Sir Henry received recognition during his lifetime and a name that lives on in the products that bear his name. At least there is one common factor.

In North America an innovative advertising campaign by Perkins Inc was praised by the US trucking industry: Perkins asked a very simple question of the country – 'imagine yourself in a world without trucks'. The writer recalls that at about the same time those same American advertising people coined a new word to describe the applications and sales personnel – 'dieselators'. It didn't catch on although the coined companion word to describe the conversion process – 'dieselisation' – had been used on and off by Perkins over a number of years.

There were further significant changes in the finances of the country during November, when the Pound Sterling was devalued from $2.80 to $2.40: this followed an increase in Bank Rate to 6% in October as the Government tried to control the money market.

At the end of the year, amongst the usual run of children's parties and other festivities recorded in the Echo, there was an announcement that Joe Hind had been elected to the Board, recognition maybe of the increasing importance being attached to better quality and increased reliability in the products. Certainly there were a number of initiatives underway to identify problems in the field, including the beginnings of an analytical approach to identify 'top ten' problems (on cost and frequency) against each engine type, with increased alignment of Engineering resources to timely resolution.

The production figures at the end of the year did not show the anticipated continued growth, as a total of 176,045 engines was a modest decrease on the previous year. Most types showed small reductions in sales as the industry went through a small slump.

1968

The major Perkins news in the early months of 1968 concerned the decision to purchase the Elwes Hall in Church Walk as the new home for the Sports Association, replacing the old Refectory at Peterscourt. There were some dramas over planning permission for the conversion, estimated to cost around £20,000 on top of the £26,000 purchase price. At the same time it was announced that the bowls club would be relocated to a new green at Eastfield, adjacent to the tennis courts, with the old site being sold for building. This was all part of a reassessment of the role of the Sports Association, subject of an analysis and report by the Tavistock Institute of Human Relations, commissioned by the Company.

In February it was announced that the fund established in tribute to the late Mrs Gwyneth Perkins would be renamed the Frank and Gwyneth Perkins Memorial Fund, its purpose being to support the nursing staff of the Peterborough Memorial Hospital.

In the same issue was news of additional car parking space being created at Eastfield to meet the needs of staff transferred from Queen Street and Peterscourt.

Strike action at Eastfield

In early March Perkins suffered from strike action when 57 workers on Track One walked out in protest over changes to methods being proposed by the Work Study Department. There had been ongoing discussions since December 1967 with the trades unions without result: the Company advised the Unions that proposed changes would go ahead from 4th, then 11th March. The effect would have been to move two workers to other areas. With the track paralysed a further 143 workers were laid off on 18th March, stopping production of three-cylinder engines. The impasse dragged on, and a press release on the 24th advised that the Amalgamated Engineering Federation (AEF) had stated that they did not have enough data to determine their attitude to the dispute. Whether this was the trigger for settlement is not clear, but on the 27th a return to work was agreed. Industrial relations at Perkins had been good, but this action was indicative of a changing mood and sense of confrontation throughout industry in the late 60s.

Monty Prichard paid a visit in the spring to Mexico, seeing the new Toluca plant of Motores Perkins SA as it prepared to manufacture 4.212 and 6.354 engines for Massey Ferguson and Chrysler. In April the Sports Association introduced new rules, part of which was an increase of subscriptions to the princely sum of 6 (old) pence per week. This announcement coincided with the granting of planning permission for the Elwes Hall conversion. The Company featured on TV again as an Anglia camera crew accompanied Brian Gomm, North-

ern European Sales Manager, on a tour of Scandinavia as part of a documentary on selling UK goods abroad.

In June there was a civic reception and lunch at Eastfield as the Mayor, Len Adams, formally opened the new road in front of the factory complex, naming it 'Frank Perkins Way'. In a speech of welcome, Monty Prichard spoke of Frank Perkins' vision: 'He looked out from that first workshop in Queen Street not through windows that framed the nearby street scene, but on to the whole world.'

The Apprentice School was featured as part of a BBC TV series Training in Skills. The programme highlighted the application of skills analysis and progressive training techniques as pioneered by the Company, working closely with the Engineering Industries Training Board for craft apprentices. There was other news of the apprentices as Linda Renshaw came top of her first year on the Loughborough sandwich course, and two apprentices built a pedal car to take part in a Baker Perkins challenge race at their Sports Day.

There were more awards for Perkins-powered boats in the St Helier 'Guards International' powerboat race, where Bob Bolton in Finandandy took awards for third overall, first all-British, production class and first fast cruiser. John Bowman of Jersey won the best all-rounder and fuel economy prize in his Fairey Huntsman cruiser.

The V8.510 scored more successes, powering the Mercury aircraft tug chosen to move Concorde around at the BAC plant: in the Chrysler UK Group announced their new Dodge 500 truck at 16 to 28 tons GCW with the V8: the 6.354 being specified in lighter versions. The V8.510 was already being specified by Ford (alongside the Cummins V8), Guy, Seddon, ERF and Dennis. Daimler became another new user, for their rear-engined Roadliner bus and coach chassis.

Some of these vehicles were present at the Sports and Family Day on 14 September, and at a Press Open Day on the 10th. Visitors had the opportunity to see the new extensions and offices at Eastfield, plus the new factory for the V8 at Fletton: this was dubbed the most modern diesel production facility in the world, capable of producing

A moment of tension at the 1966 Sports and Family Day on the Perkins sports field during the inter-departmental tug-of-war

The 4.154, launched in 1967, was the first product developed in conjunction with a partner, in this case Toyo Kogyo in Japan

30,000 engines a year. 15,000 people attended the Family Day, with the canteen staff serving 9,000 teas!

There were a number of staff changes during the year, with Geoffrey Smith moving to North America as President of the US and Canadian operations, to be succeeded in the UK by Joe Hind as Engineering Director. Bill Hayward also moved to the USA as their Engineering Director, succeeding Bob Schmidt. Wally Whitbourn was appointed Production Manager for Eastfield and Dennis Eassom for Fletton.

The Commercial Motor Show at Earls Court in October featured the V8.510 strongly, with engines in vehicles on eight manufacturers' displays: Richard Perkins was interviewed on the Daimler stand for the BBC TV Wheelbase programme. The Company advertised for more labour as demand for engines soared. The close of the year saw production reach 191,652 engines, with the 4.236 and 6.354 families featuring strongly and the V8 volume gathering pace, with 1,424 sales. There was a considerable increase in the sale of CKD kits to the licensee operations too, although the actual figures for 1968 were not recorded.

1969

Monty Prichard was elected to the main Massey Ferguson board in early 1969, an indication of the growing stature of the Group within the Corporation. There was another appointment too, as David Hodkin joined Perkins as Group Director, Product Reliability: his previous engineering experience included time with ERA, Rootes Group and Ford (where he had been involved in the launch of the Cortina car).

More strike action hits Eastfield production

The issue making the most impact in the first weeks of January was, unfortunately, not good news. There had been increasing unrest between management and the shop floor trades unions over a failure to settle the pay dispute affecting over 5,000 workers. Deadlock had been reached in November 1968 when the final Company offer of 6 pence per hour had not been accepted and negotiations had ceased. In January the shop stewards had decided to refer the issue to full-time officials, and a call for industrial action had apparently been made. At a time when further new jobs were in the offing and the order book was healthy this seemed to be an unhelpful move even if feelings were increasingly bitter.

Before this situation could move ahead, however, there was another upset. On 13 January one worker on the 4.99 crankshaft line objected to 'time-and-motion' analysis of his job. The man happened to be a shop steward, although this was claimed to have no bearing on the situation. He was suspended and when he left the factory forty of his colleagues also walked out. The strike quickly escalated so that by the afternoon of the 14th there were 200 men out. Worse was to follow: by lunchtime on Wednesday 15th there were 5,000 men on strike as talks between management and union representatives broke down. The local press of course picked up and carried various stories, giving the unmistakable impression that most workers did not want to be off work and that there was dissatisfaction with the level of communication from the unions. Confusion reigned regarding the status of the strike, with the works convenor claiming it to be official. It was even suggested that management had engineered the strike because they knew another strike at a supplier was going to cause a shutdown!

As further days passed there were more statements by trades union officials that appeared to increase the acrimony: the management were accused of 'provocative acts and intimidation' by threatening disciplinary action if time study was not enacted. On Saturday 18th a statement from the Company was published which refuted previous TU statements and tried to present a factual position, noting that there had been no declaration of an official strike. The statements in the press, the letters from workers and an amazing statement from the local AEF branch secretary claiming, of those opposed to the action, that '. . . their forebears had fought and died to create the basic freedoms of our present society in vain'.

In the next week, as a solution appeared no closer, it was noted that the strike was costing Perkins £250,000 every day, that 700 men were laid off at the MF Coventry plant and that a question had been tabled in the House of Commons. On the 22nd a mass meeting of AEF members heard the convenor tell them 'you are not mice, you are men at Perkins'. They decided to stay out. A week later there was considerable confusion over the real majority for continuing the dispute and eventually a return was negotiated. However, the writing was on the wall: from being a company with good labour relations, Perkins had become another casualty of the 'war' between management and unions, and relationships would not be the same for many years to come.

The Echo for February carried news of a new initiative destined to become a fixture in the Peterborough cultural calendar – the Perkins Industrial Concert. In association with the Eastern Authorities Orchestral Association and the Arts Council of Great Britain, Perkins was to sponsor the concert in the Cathedral, aiming to: 'present well-produced performances to the public at popular prices'. The announcement that the first performers would be Yehudi Menuhin and his Festival Orchestra was well received by the employees and a local population starved of events featuring such famous personalities.

Production Director Vivian Frayling presented the awards at the annual Apprentices' Dinner and spoke of the production target of 1,000 engines per day, or 230,000 engines per year from the Peterborough sites, plus CKD production of 400 kits per day. This was being accomplished with 6,000 workers in the manufacturing area alone. He also commented upon the conflicting requirements of high rates of production, tailored products for individual customers, standardisation, greater variety, shortened time cycles, tighter cost control and better quality. He repeated the belief that 'the apprentices of today are the backbone of the company of tomorrow': his audience included Barry Parsisson, a graduate apprentice who retired in 2004 as Marketing Director.

Spring carried news of pay agreements and awards. On the clerical side there was a 5% rise across the board, plus an extra 2.5% for female workers in a move towards equal pay. For the shop floor workers there was a settlement after months of negotiations on a two-year deal, following the acrimonious strike. The awards made were the highest in the Company's history, with sixpence an hour for the term agreement and a further fourpence for settlement of a national claim: the deal was recommended for acceptance by local and national trades union representatives. In return the Company was looking for freedom from disputes, greater flexibility for movement of personnel and further improvements in working practices. Other clauses covered the application of Work Study, standards and timing – and improved procedures for settling grievances!

Announcements of changes both at home and overseas also appeared. Ted Kent was moved from the Walton factory to take up a post as Manufacturing Advisor to Motor Iberica in Spain while Dennis Eassom was appointed Facilities Manager for the five Peterborough factories. Ken Fuller returned from the Wixom facility where he had been part of the team planning the new facility to be built at Farmington on the outskirts of Detroit – a move announced in March. More expansion was also announced for the Motores Perkins plant in Brazil. Another change took the Show Engines Department from Queen Street to Walton: this small team of veterans under Sid Doncaster had, to that date, made 725 engines over 30 years. Each engine was carefully sectioned, chrome-plated and finished to a very high standard, and all were capable of being driven electrically to show the working parts.

The Sales side was also busy, with a highly successful Stockholm Boat Show displaying engines in products from the UK, Denmark and Finland as well as Sweden.

The boats, including Swedish water taxis with the V8.510(M) and Broads cruisers fitted with the 4.108(M), were seen by Prince Bertil during a visit to the Show.

The Echo was determined to be part of the successes, proudly announcing that the monthly circulation had now passed ten thousand, with 10,372 copies being produced for employees home and abroad.

April brought the opening of the new Sports Association premises when the new Club, named 'The Frank Perkins Social Centre' in honour of the late founder, was opened. Richard Perkins pulled the first pints for guests including the Mayor in the £67,000 building, which could seat 300 in the main hall, or accommodate 250 for dances. With 7,000 employees enrolled as members of the Sports Association there was assured success for the new facility.

New models for the 6.354 family

Product news included the announcement of the 6.3542 vehicle engine. This was a heavy-duty version to meet the increasing demands of truck applications. At the same time a higher rated T6.354(M) was announced, with 175bhp at 2,400rpm this engine development was 'race-bred', benefiting greatly from the past years' successes in offshore powerboat racing and answering demands from customers for more power.

A number of Perkins employees past and present, including Laurie Hancock and Richard Perkins, attended the celebrations for the 50th Anniversary of Seddon Diesel Vehicles Limited in Manchester. The company took its first 12 prototype P6s from Perkins in 1937 – the start of a long relationship. Long-service was also in the news in Peterborough when the 'Quarter Century Club' announced a change of name to 'Perkins Long Service Club' with membership limited to 200, plus 50 'social' (retired) members.

Monty Prichard embarked on another overseas 'sales' tour in April when he visited North and South America. He was encouraged by the good reception for the products in Latin America especially, where he visited major customers in Argentina and Brazil: in the latter country Motores Perkins was already the largest diesel engine manufacturer.

A special Echo in late May showcased more news of expansion. In a two-year programme costing £20 million an additional five bays would be added to Factory 2, with a further three bays to be added to the storage building on the east side of the site. In the principal article, Monty Prichard confirmed that, even at 350,000 engines a year worldwide already, this expansion was essential to safeguard future needs. He intimated the possibility of product expansion up to 400bhp. In underlining the success already achieved, he reminded readers that in 1968 the total exports of the British shipbuilding industry were worth £61 million: in comparison Perkins alone exported almost £57 million! The major problem to be faced was that of spiralling costs, and to combat this it was essential to build engines more efficiently and maintain growth. Another challenge was the increased regulation on pollution, smoke and noise: forward design was focused on keeping ahead of the field in meeting the challenge.

An additional message from Richard Perkins commented on the forecast of total diesel engine market growth averaging 6.5% annually for the next ten years – taking the 1971 estimate of 2,294,000 engines to 3,845,000 in 1980. Perkins had to retain share and increase production to keep pace, bearing in mind the export level already at 85%. He stated that on average a new diesel engine left the Eastfield factory every minute of every 18-hour working day. The new engine marshalling, storage and despatch facility costing £1 million would increase capacity to 1,400 engines a day.

An announcement in June gave details of a new factory to be built in Turkey for Motori Motolari SA, with an area of 300,000 square feet and capacity of 50,000 engines a year. Intended to employ 1,500 Turkish nationals, the plant would start to produce 3-, 4- and 6-cylinder engines by the end of 1970 – becoming the largest diesel engine plant in Asia outside Japan and one of the largest in the world. Monty Prichard was quoted: 'This is another example of Perkins as part of the multinational MF organisation, being able to play a leading role in contributing to the welfare of developing countries.' The development added to the growing Turkish motor industry, now comprising 14 factories plus 4 tractor plants.

At home, Perkins won a British Safety Council award for the third successive year for a record 40% better than the national average: in 1968 the actual rate was 4.2 accidents per million hours worked, with over 13.7 million hours actually worked. This compared to the first records in 1951 when there were 13.1 accidents per million hours.

The first Industrial Concert on 12 June was a resounding success and a sell-out. It featured Bach's Concerto in D minor for violin, oboe and strings plus the Mozart Violin Concerto in G, K216, and a number of other minor works. It was announced during the concert that the following year would feature Sir John Barbirolli and the Hallé Orchestra.

Once again the summer featured powerboat racing strongly, with the Daily Telegraph 'Round Britain' race in July and the Daily Express 'Cowes to Torquay' race in August. In the former the competitors included six Perkins-powered craft: the most powerful was Polly Perkins, built by Chris Tremlett Ltd and driven by Ron Watts. This boat was powered by four T6.354s with a total of 700shp! Unfortunately the boat had to retire after running aground and suffering crew injuries. However, the other five craft finished and collected 8 awards between them: the thirteen days and 1,700 miles of racing saw the Perkins service crews working round the clock, transported between the stopping places by helicopter. The Express race featured 14 out of the 76 entrants with Perkins power. More awards were gained, including the fuel economy prize, won by Fairey Huntress driven by Charles Currey of Fairey and Richard Perkins.

On dry land there was the launch of the new 4.154(V) engine to power light vans. Rated at 62bhp at 3,000rpm this engine was com-

The Queen's Award for Industry being presented to Richard Perkins by Lord Hemingford in September 1970

pleted in Peterborough from an engine 'core' supplied by Toyo Kogyo. Diesel conversions in Holland also featured with local taxi drivers using Opel Rekord saloons with the 4.108(C) fitted by local agent Kemper en Van Twist of Dordrecht.

In October it was announced that by the end of the month – the end of the financial year – the target of 230,000 engines would be met, plus CKD shipments averaging 646 kits a day. Marine sales successes were also given prominence when distributors J.F. Duffield of Norwich ordered over £250,000 worth of HT6.354s for 37ft boats to be built at Norfolk boatyards. An Echo article commented that Perkins

marine engines were now in use on 67 countries, with diverse applications including the tenders for the Royal Yacht Britannia, fishing boats in Ceylon, racing craft and lifeboats.

The November Echo carried a story about employee Dick Bruce who was about to retire after many years driving Perkins-powered vehicles around the country; he estimated he had driven in excess of 1.5 million miles and in later years much of this had been around Peterborough as he drove the inter-works bus between Eastfield, Queen Street, Peterscourt, Walton and Fletton – clocking up 93 miles a day on the scheduled runs.

Vivian Frayling spoke to fifty professional trainees at a seminar in December on 'Peterborough Manufacturing Activities now and over the next three years'. He visualised engine production in Peterborough reaching 300,000 engines a year by 1972, plus much increased CKD activity. A further £18 million investment was scheduled, with major expansion of 4.236 and 6.354 production capacity, plus a further 220,000 square feet of manufacturing and stores space. Other speakers included Ken Fuller (Fletton plant), Bob Shipley (Production Control), Walter Whitbourn (Production Manager) and John Fish on quality standards. Joe Shakespeare also addressed the group on safety standards, noting that Eastfield had finished seventh out of the 26 plants in the worldwide Massey Ferguson Safety Performance League.

The statistics at the end of 1969 showed total production of 230,812 engines – a new record – with increased volume for every engine type except the P6, which was finally phased out after just over 30 years in production. The CKD volume was recorded as 103,106 kits as the licensee operations also moved ahead with production.

1970

The New Year began with concern over a national flu epidemic, believed to be responsible for 6,600 deaths. For Perkins there was the usual flurry of activity at the London Boat Show where 100 Perkins engines featured on nearly 50 stands, from the 4.108 through to the T6.354. Duffields of Norwich placed a further order worth £100,000 for T6.354s to power Norfolk-built Moonraker 36 cruisers selling for around £10,000 each. Film star Susannah York named a new 45ft catamaran powered by Perkins 'Sparkle of Stoke Mandeville', a specially converted craft able to accommodate wheelchair users. There was also news of an unusual Perkins application in a hovercraft, although not as motive power, when Vosper-Thorneycroft announced the VTI-001. This was a ferry between the mainland and the Isle of Wight: twin 4.107(I) engines powered G and M generators to provide the onboard power for the 76-ton, 96ft craft able to travel at 40 knots.

A significant agreement was signed when Yanmar Diesel Engine Company of Osaka and Perkins agreed to market the Peterborough product as Yanmar-Perkins in Japan for industrial purposes, and for full Perkins service worldwide in support of their export business. The agreement was hailed as an important support to the surge of diesel usage and export growth from Japan.

During February the results of the MF Safety Performance League placed the Perkins Brazilian plant second, with Walton fourth and Eastfield eighth, just ahead of Queen Street. A new local facility came into being with the opening of an overspill warehouse at Wisbech. This was staffed by a small team of Peterborough storemen and intended to ease the pressure on capacity at Eastfield. Another new facility in the news was the opening of a branch of Barclays Bank in the Eastfield offices: at the time this was publicised as the first bank branch to be opened in a factory, but this was soon contradicted by Perkins Brazil where a branch had opened facilities eighteen months earlier! The Peterborough bank initially opened three days each week, and helped 1,000 weekly-paid staff switch to the monthly payroll. A third new facility opened a few weeks later when a temporary office, known as the Elliott building, was erected in the North car park. This provided more office accommodation and housed, amongst others, the Echo staff.

In March a pay offer was made to hourly-paid workers of one shilling and sixpence an hour, on top of the sixpence an hour already awarded in February. With the addition of shift premiums this increased the average wage by £4 and 13 shillings a week (a 23% rise), plus overtime. This increase was supported by the trades unions but initially not accepted by the workforce.

The largest club in the Sports Association, the Ten Pin Bowling Club

made a bid for the world 12-hour marathon record in March, failing by only 933 pins with a total of 23,606. The event raised £440 for the Spastics Society and there was a suggestion to make it an annual event.

A new record was announced in May, however, when a Perkins-powered boat broke the world one-hour diesel speed record on Lake Iseo in Italy, driven by the Perkins Italy Marine Sales Manager, Livio Macchia. The boat averaged 76.589kph, beating the record previously set in 1966 by 4 knots. Using a single T6.354(M), the craft also set a new record for 24 nautical miles at 76.918kph. In the same month Perkins staff said farewell to the Peterscourt offices after 16 years, when the premises were vacated and handed over to the Peterborough Development Corporation.

Queen's Award for Industry

Perkins was named again in the listing of the Queen's Award to Industry, for the second time in four years: worldwide sales had reached £100 million in 1969, the tenth successive year of growth. Monty Prichard in a statement said: 'I am proud that my company has once again been singled out to receive the honour of the Queen's Award. My pride is heightened by the knowledge that the Perkins engine is also playing a part in the successful exports of many fine products in the automotive, agricultural, construction machinery and marine fields.' (The award was actually presented in September in a ceremony at Eastfield by the Lord Lieutenant of Huntingdonshire and Peterborough, Lord Hemingford.)

During May there were changes of General Managers around the European operations as Tom Leask, Brian Gomm, Joe Gormezano and Dolf Pittevils switched areas as part of a planned development of knowledge and expertise. At the Mechanical Handling Exhibition in London 27 exhibitors showed Perkins-powered machines on their stands, including a new range of forklift trucks from Clark Equipment. Growth of 15 to 20% per year was claimed for the mechanical handling industry overall.

An honour for Bill Baxter

The Queen's Birthday Honours List in June included the award of the MBE for Bill Baxter, then the Area Assembly Manager for Factory 1. Bill had joined the Company in 1939 as one of the 400 workers, rising through the ranks to his present position where he controlled 800 production operators. Commenting on the award, for Services to Exports, he said: 'I regard myself as fortunate and proud to hold this award on behalf of all the other chaps. It's really all team spirit and team effort that gets the job done, and I think the award has been given to "us" and not just me.'

During a royal visit to Peterborough the following month at the East of England Show, Prince Philip dropped in on the Perkins stand and met PAMELA – a creation of the apprentices – the acronym standing for 'Perkins Apprentices Mechanically Engineered Lactatory Animal'! The mechanical cow created considerable interest from other visitors to the show as well. There were other royal occasions during the summer, when Lord Snowdon paid a private visit to the Eastfield factory, and King Gustav of Sweden visited the stand during an exhibition in Jönköping.

An article in the August Echo by Joe Hind defended the reputation of the diesel with regard to emissions. He stated that the engine was not a health hazard, producing less pollution than the petrol engine, the only exception being soot in the exhaust. He noted that there was new North American legislation just being enacted, plus the new British Standard BS AU 141: 1967. Perkins products were compliant against both sets of requirements, although the UK regulation was not yet obligatory.

Later in the month there were comments from Bernard Garner, the General Planning and Procurement Manager. He covered in some detail the changing pattern of demand for diesel engines and the equipment they power, with especial emphasis on the impact on Perkins of everything affecting the customers. He noted the serious effects of the current recession in some overseas markets, especially the USA, and that cutbacks in America also impacted on developing countries and their demands. The implications of competitive pressures, strikes and other industrial problems were also explained, noting too that when production was already running close to capacity any losses from such actions were often non-recoverable. (It is worth remembering that there had been a dockworkers' strike in July, and that overall wages had risen by nearly 10% in the first seven months of the year.)

A world's first for Perkins

In September a new version of the 6.354 was announced. The T6.3543(V) was rated at 155bhp at 2,600rpm and was to be marketed for truck use up to 24 tonnes GVW. The engine was claimed to be the world's first turbocharged vehicle engine fitted with an air-to-air charge cooler as standard. Specifically designed for vehicle use in the 1970s, the engine gave a big advantage in power-to-weight ratio. There was enthusiastic response from the motoring press, who were impressed with the engine's flexibility and response during their test drives. Paul Brockington of the Commercial Motor magazine commented: [the charge-cooling] 'gives very real advantage in low thermal loading – why wasn't it done years ago?' The engine was displayed at the Earls Court Commercial Motor Show, fitted in the first production application, the Dennis DB24T truck. There was considerable Perkins presence again with exhibits on the Chrysler UK, Dennis, Ford, Seddon and Vauxhall stands, as well as the CAV and other component manufacturers' displays. Coincident with the exhibition, Marshalls of Cambridge undertook a 100-hour trial on a course between Cambridge, Bedford and Peterborough using a BMC Mastiff truck fitted with a V8.510 and run at 16 tons GVW carrying 10 tons of concrete: the vehicle ran 2,552 miles at an average 10.3mpg and with absolutely no problems.

The effects of the recession became clearer in late September when short-time working was introduced, affecting up to 3,000 employees who were put on to a four-day week. A number of factors were involved, among these being the economic climate, inflationary trends and reduced demand for agricultural products.

There was a wheat surplus and a poor maize crop in the USA, whilst at home spiralling costs and forecast changes in Government grants for farm improvements were making farmers hold off commitment to new equipment. There was a reported 15% reduction in tractor sales. Richard Perkins spoke of the threats of inflation and the need to reduce costs while ensuring exports were maximised.

During October there were announcements of several reorganisations. A new North European Operating Unit Engineering Department was created, with John Tucker as Chief Engineer and Roland Bertodo as Product Reliability Manager. Ian Mearns was appointed Technical General Manager for Argentina, and John Condie as Overseas Development Manager. Horst Braxmaier moved from Germany to Vehicle Sales Manager UK while Adrian Parsons joined the Company as Financial Analysis Manager for NEOU.

A later announcement gave details of major changes on the Group Engineering side: David Hodkin was made Assistant Director (Administration) while retaining his role as Director Group Product Reliability, Martin Vulliamy became Assistant Director, Special Duties and Dino Monachelli Assistant Director, Applications. New Project Groups were formed, with David Burnicle, Charles Harrison and Peter Bowyer managing the three groups of engines.

Another new product was announced with the release of the 6.3721 – an increased bore version of the 6.354 – rated at 121bhp at 2,500rpm and intended as a long-life engine for industrial application such as cranes, excavators and shovel loaders. In November the first phase of the new storage building to the east of the main factory was completed, giving 50,000 sq ft of space, with the remaining 32,000 sq ft on schedule for the end of the year.

First-ever call for redundancies

The December Echo carried an unprecedented headline: 'Company to cut costs: Redundancies'. The leading article gave details of the concerns. Costs of labour, materials and overheads were rising at an alarming rate, and the actions so far taken to reduce expenses had proved insufficient. Therefore activities were to be streamlined and a reduction in the number of people employed, both staff and indirect non-productive labour, was required. Approximately 360 people were to be made redundant.

Monty Prichard explained the problems of severe inflation of wages and prices, coupled with the increasing competition especially in the USA, Germany and Japan. The ability to operate on a basis of price stability was unlikely to be re-established in the near future so stringent measures regrettably had been forced upon the Company. Within Peterborough some staff would be selected in the Marketing, Manufacturing, Public Relations, Personnel, Planning and Procurement, and Finance areas. Around 200 staff would be made redundant; of these 140 posts had already been identified.

Volunteers would be sought, and close liaison with the trades unions was being maintained.

So close to Christmas the announcement was unexpected to most employees, and came as a severe blow after many years of increasing, safe, employment. The problem was national too: in the first six months of the Tory Government there had been more strikes and working days lost than in any year since the General Strike of 1926. Around 8.8 million man-days were lost, with engineering companies the worst hit. On 3 December the new Industrial Relations Bill was published, intended to provide powers to fine trades unions for ignoring new procedures for avoiding strike action.

In the same December Echo there was the first appearance of a name destined to become familiar: Victor Rice was appointed as the new Comptroller. He joined the Company from Chrysler UK after previously being with Ford Motor Company, and was to be responsible for pricing, profit planning, financial analysis, manufacturing costs and accounting.

The close of year figures showed a new production record in spite of the problems of the final months. 236,123 engines were produced with the V8 showing considerable growth to 10,270 units and all other products contributing. The 4.108 actually reached an all-time high at 29,355 engines. On top of this performance, the CKD despatches totalled 114,021, a healthy increase over the previous year.

The resignation of Gordon Dawson and the appointment of Geoffrey Smith brought about a substantial reorganisation of the Engineering Division structure, as well as a move to recruit more personnel to undertake the increasing workload. The opening of the new offices and workshops at Eastfield really triggered the expansion, since there had been no spare space in the old offices at Queen Street and Eastfield. The basic organisational change was to form Groups, each under a Project Manager, to handle each of the main engine families. Thus there were groups for the Large (V8), Medium (6.354 and 4.236) and Small (4.108 and 4.154) engine families. These contained design, mechanical and performance teams under Design and Development Supervisors, reporting to the Project Manager. The teams were located side-by-side in the new single-storey offices. Specialist functions were located nearby, covering such areas as basic research, the technical office, change control, parts listing, reprographics and finance.

Each team controlled its own work loading and priorities, bidding for test bed and other facilities against an overall divisional plan. Monthly meetings with the Director and senior managers monitored progress. The organisation was more complex and needed time to shake down, but provided stronger customer focus and resource allocation.

The new buildings were occupied gradually from late 1967 into 1968 with personnel being transferred in groups. Already there were insufficient test beds to accommodate the work in hand, so that some research and performance engineers remained with their workshop personnel running the test beds at Queen Street. This introduced a new problem for the management to handle, since they now had design and mechanical development personnel working side-by-side, but the teams responsible for fuel injection equipment and performance development still two miles away! Past experience with the separation of the design function from development had shown that even this small geographic separation hindered general efficiency – 'team spirit' was always better when all concerned had easy access to their colleagues. In spite of the operational challenges, however, there was sufficient work, with time constraints mainly driven by customer demands, to ensure that working relationships were quickly established. Newcomers were assimilated into the existing teams and brought with them fresh ideas, skills and experience that soon revitalised the whole Engineering Division.

Once the euphoria of being in a new purpose-built facility had died down, the staff began to realise that the new single-storey offices were not ideal. Not only was the building very long, the design also had inherent defects particularly as far as ventilation was concerned. The architects had planned originally for air conditioning, but this was cut as a cost saving. As a result, in winter the cold-fall of air passing over the glazed areas produced draughts and in summer the lack of airflow demanded windows being opened, with discomfort for those sitting at the sides. Over 36 years of occupation the problems of office ventilation were never fully resolved and caused endless complaints. There were also problems with noise levels in the long open-plan area, but these were gradually resolved by floor covering and screens.

Applications Engineers were also located in the new offices, with the Field Test workshop moved from its previous position at the rear of the factory to a new building across from the test cells and close to the offices. The only far-flung part of the workshops remaining was the Cold Chamber, which had been built at the rear of the old Field Test shop and was too complex and expensive to move.

Customer contact with the representatives of major customers such as Ford, British Leyland and Chrysler/Dodge became part of normal operations. This was a new experience for many of the teams, who had been accustomed to a 'buffer' (in the shape of Sales and Applications Engineering staff) between them and the demands of a vehicle manufacturer. New skills were developed to identify programme stages, dates and lead times. The introduction of 'critical paths', PERT charts and a new breed of 'timing engineers', budgets and priorities identified problems and alternatives more quickly. During the late 60s and early 70s it is true to say that Perkins Engineering developed skills and processes that were to stand them in good stead for the next thirty years.

Working with Massey Ferguson

The major customer, and the one with the most 'pull', was of course Massey Ferguson. Starting from quite small volume and variety in 1959, MF quickly realised the advantages of having their own engine supplier immediately to hand and able to respond to new projects quickly. The core tractor business was already supplemented by manufacture of combine harvesters in Canada and Scotland, with additional need for engines. With the global ambitions of MF it did not take long for a series of fresh tractor projects to develop. Their requirements became more complex as new factories were set up around the world, along with rapid growth of the plants in Coventry, Beauvais and Detroit. Tractor production was evolving in Italy with Landini too, plus the development of a new business in industrial tractor and construction machinery – initially for modified tractors but very soon developing into a range of wheeled loaders, excavators and tracked machines. All of these demanded engines – in most cases with a different build specification and very frequently with different rating and power curve shape, which stretched the abilities of the performance engineers and the fuel injection equipment suppliers.

MF started with the AD3.152 and AD4.203 in small tractors (MF 35, 135, 65 and 165) but expanded upwards in power to suit the rapidly expanding agricultural market which demanded bigger and more powerful machinery to improve efficiency and reduce manpower on the farm. The 4.236, as already mentioned in an earlier chapter, was specifically tailored to suit the MF preference for an engine to form an integral part of the tractor 'chassis'. As well as the incorporation of the balancer to smooth out the vibrations of a big four-cylinder engine, it was not long before MF looked for – and got – engine capacity variations to suit tractor size and specification. Thus a variant with short stroke but bigger bore – the A4.212 – and a bigger bore version – the A4.248 – were developed. The MF preference for this apparent complexity was simple: it stopped the tractor owner uprating a lower-rated engine to a higher power simply by adjusting the fuel level on the injection pump. In addition, limiting the engine power for a particular tractor specification meant that the tractor transmission etc. could be tailored to the power level and thus product cost could be controlled. The 4.212 showed a further advantage too, since its reduced secondary vibration levels allowed the Lanchester balancer to be removed, offering a cost saving for some tractors. The availability of a range of engine powers from the same basic frame added to the ability of MF to offer a huge range of tractor specifications simply by combining engines, transmissions, axles, wheels, cabs, etc. from their range of 'pre-engineered' and available components – almost a 'Meccano Set' concept applied to full-size machines. A range of tractors designated MF275, 285, etc. used the 4.236 family engines.

The turbocharged version of the engine came later (the AT4.236), as did a spark ignition version (AG4.236) to suit niche demands for the tractors in, for instance, the North American 'turf tractor' market and other sectors where farmers still preferred gasoline engines to

The expansion of Massey Ferguson into industrial and construction equipment started with tractor-digger-loader versions of the yellow industrial tractors. Here an early machine is seen clearing a site backing on to the Queen Street factory

diesels. This applied to the 3.152 and 4.203 engines too, where spark ignition versions were developed. These derivatives were used not only by MF, but also by the makers of forklift trucks and other industrial equipment where identically-sized engines running on gasoline or LPG (liquid petroleum gas) as an alternative to diesel were convenient for their own engineering efforts and to meet niche markets. (The fact that most fork trucks used the engine as a part of the vehicle counterweight was also advantageous to Perkins, since the converted engines were substantially heavier than the alternative spark-ignition units.) The Engineering Division developed a small group of engineers with spark-ignition expertise and drew on subcontractors such as ERA and Calor Gas to assist in the process of engine development and production.

Increasing power and ever-larger tractors, especially for the American market, did not stop at the 4.248. MF quickly identified a need for the 6.354 at 100bhp in the MF 1100 and then 135bhp for the T6.354 in the MF1135. The six-cylinder engine was also developed into new versions with changed swept volumes, and the resulting 6.306 and 6.372 came into use for tractor and combine applications.

Even more followed when the MF product research people saw the V8.510 and a potential for an even larger tractor. The visual impact of the engine – with the cylinder banks protruding either side of the tractor with chromium-plated covers and twin upswept exhausts – was seen as a marketing feature, with the 'hot-rod' image likely to help sales! Although never a huge seller, the resultant MF1150 tractor did achieve considerable success – perhaps proving that even in tractors there is no substitute for the 'almighty cubic inch' with a V8 configuration! David Burnicle, V8 Project Manager for a time, recalls another quirk during the tractor development: when the first installa-

tion was completed it was criticised because from the side you could see straight through the tractor between engine and sheet-metalwork. Rather than do some expensive retooling of the tractor cowling it was decided to add an 'anti-see-through' plate to fill the gap!

Many of these new projects were generated through the Special Projects Division of MF situated in Livonia, not far from the Detroit plant at Southfield: under the direction of Lee Elfes, who frequently struck fear into unsuspecting Perkins engineers with probing technical questioning. His influence did much for MF products, advancing their technology and applying leading-edge methodology, most notably in technical computing.

A list of engine parts lists for MF tractors in January 1967 shows the tractor range needing 87 different build lists to cover the French, UK, North American and Italian (Landini) requirements. The Italian builds included a range of crawler tractors. Added to this were 15 lists for the combine harvesters produced in Australia, France, Germany, the UK and North America.

The Industrial and Construction Machinery Division of MF (ICM) also became a customer for virtually every size of Perkins engine to suit a bewildering array of machines. From yellow-painted versions of the little MF135 the range grew to large crawler tractors and wheeled loaders fitted with the V8.510, as well as utilising larger engines from other manufacturers. The machines were made in new factories in Manchester Barton Dock Road, Detroit and Akron in the USA plus Aprilia and Ravenna in Italy. The Perkins applications engineers spent an increasing amount of time visiting these factories to develop the specifications and resolve teething problems. It was clear that MF were getting their money's worth out of the Perkins takeover as well as extending their product range into new fields: the MF globalisation strategy was aimed at tackling head-on the established competition such as Deere and Caterpillar, although there must always have been misgivings within the Corporation about the financing of such an ambitious programme.

The challenge of Ford Motor Company and the V8.510

The implications of working with large enterprises like Ford Motor Company soon hit the Project Teams. The writer was, from early 1968, the Development Supervisor for the V8 team. It often seemed that Ford was actually running our engine development programme in spite of their Engineering Director's assertion that 'We are buying a black box from you to do a job'. There were constant demands not only for information but also for specific tests to be carried out – often of an apparently outlandish and unrealistic nature. A number of these became enshrined within the Perkins testing programmes for the future, notably the 'hot scuff' and 'death rattle' tests which were intended to prove the engine's resistance to a high level of abuse, especially in its early life.

There were demands too for changes to design. One such case was the insistence of Ford that the engine they bought should have no means of identifying it as coming from Perkins. Perkins complied but somehow managed to retain a vee-belt carrying the Perkins logo – Ford promptly insisted that this be painted over in the despatch area! A further example occurred when the efficiency of the optional exhaust brakes provided on the V8 was called into question. The Ford engineers believed they were not good enough, because Perkins had included a small hole in each butterfly flap so that the back-pressure with the brake activated did not cause the engine's valves to 'float' excessively and cause mechanical failure. Ford were quite insistent, until one articulated vehicle running on their Borehamwood test track one greasy January day slowed using the exhaust brakes only, jack-knifed on the slippery surface and destroyed the truck cab. Fortunately the driver was unhurt – but no further demands for increased efficiency were heard!

With introduction programmes running with BMC for the V8 in the Mastiff truck (the 6.354 was fitted in the smaller Boxer truck), Dodge for the 500 Series truck and Daimler for their bus/coach chassis, there were constant problems and much juggling of priorities to meet customer needs. Silly things happened too, that helped to lighten the days – one such issue for BMC management came when Ford announced the Perkins V8 as their '511E' engine. There was an immediate outcry that Ford must be getting an improved version due to the higher numerical designation!

Much of the development programme for the V8 relied upon accelerated vehicle testing, partly by the Perkins fleet under normal road conditions with more specialised tests run on the controlled (and more private!) conditions of the Motor Industry Research Association (MIRA) test facility near Nuneaton. Here too there were Ford-requested tests: one of these required high-speed running and regular downchanges to simulate engine overspeeding when leaving motorways. The tests showed up some interesting non-engine shortcomings: tyre life proved a considerable embarrassment until Michelin 'X' tyres were tried which resolved the issue completely. Another component failure was the Turner gearbox, suffering a series of spectacular breakages before a solution was engineered.

Some unexpected problems had to be resolved during the tailoring of the engines to suit individual customer needs. The writer recalls an instance where a mysterious loss of power occurred on a specification for Daimler. This consistently produced about 10bhp lower than the other vehicle versions under test bed conditions, with specific fuel consumption figures suggesting a 'friction' loss somewhere. Consider-

ation of the build differences concluded that the sump configuration was to blame: this led to the oil system relief valve being identified as the culprit. The excess oil from the valve sprayed across the crankshaft assembly, increasing 'windage' losses tremendously: a trial with a shield over the valve to direct the oil flow down into the sump was tried and magically the full engine output returned!

An article in the Echo of May 1970 confirmed how intensively the Field Test fleet was used. One driver, Syd Billings, was featured and recounted how he regularly drove 70,000 miles a year around the country, with occasional fully-laden tests at 70mph on the MIRA track. The fleet ran around 500,000 miles a year with the drivers responsible for recording various test parameters and log book records as an integral part of the job.

It was not just the Perkins truck fleet that was used of course, since all the major truck manufacturers ran field evaluation fleets on road and test track. Also Ford had friendly commercial fleets that participated in trials, achieving high mileages under typical operating conditions in return for prompt resolution of failures and problems. One such fleet was that of Robsons of Carlisle, who ran a number of Ford D1000 articulated trucks fitted with the V8.510. It became routine to arrange the removal of an engine over a weekend at Peterborough, fitment of a loan unit for a couple of weeks while the test unit was tested, stripped, examined, rebuilt and refitted a fortnight later. Tremendously good relations were built up with the drivers and excellent results obtained. To obtain experience of all sorts of running conditions, other 'tame' operators included the Mars confectionery group, with a vehicle running local shuttles on a 24 hours a day basis, and an operator in Yorkshire with a 16-ton van-bodied vehicle transporting eggs from Yorkshire to London overnight. The mix of conditions predictably showed up a variety of defects, in a timescale that allowed much faster problem-solving to be applied.

Problem solving

As production and field experience increased with the V8, a number of design shortcomings were uncovered that needed correction. The most important in terms of incidents was the engine oil cooler, an item designed specifically for the engine. Early in quantity production there were problems of leakage from the sealing rings on the cooler body, resulting in an oil-in-water failure. The Product Reliability Group under David Hodkin took charge of this problem, as indeed they did with any serious field issue, tracking statistics and controlling actions. Numerous minor changes were made but a lasting cure came only when an alternative design was developed with Serck, a more experienced manufacturer of oil coolers, whose component eliminated field complaints virtually completely.

Problems with the fuel injection equipment needed a range of talents to produce a solution. The Simms Minimec in-line pump, was initially a major challenge to Perkins engineers, used to the rotary pumps from CAV. There was a steep learning curve on its foibles, especially the mechanical governor and the handling of the high-pressure fuel pipes feeding the injectors. The latter led to a little piece of Perkins folklore when a small number of engine failures due to burnt pistons was eventually attributed to incorrect fitment of the pipes. It was essential that the engine firing order was matched by that of the injection process: the pipes were designed to cross the top of the engine, taking the shortest distance to the injectors. It transpired that, in spite of the comprehensive instructions in the service manuals, a number of mechanics succeeded in refitting some pipes incorrectly, crossing them at the pump ends. Almost immediate failure occurred but the reason took some time to spot. The design team were charged with devising a means to prevent such wrong positioning and produced a small plate, fitted to the side of the pump, to guide the pipes. The device was officially called the 'Fuel Injection Pipe Guide Plate'

– something of a mouthful even if technically accurate. Within a few days one of the engineers was heard to remark that 'only a twit would get it wrong' – a detail redesign of the plate saw it formally renamed as the 'Anti-twit Plate' on all documentation!

Another concern, of lesser frequency but potentially very serious consequences, occurred with the lubricating oil pump when a number of engines suffered breakage of the drive gear shaft. With total loss of oil flow, engine bearing seizure followed very rapidly. A design review resulted in a change to the undercut and shoulder behind the gear to eliminate the stress-raiser which had instigated fatigue failure. (The writer recalls that one such failure occurred in an early production engine operating in an excavator in the USA. The machine was working in a very swampy area when the engine stopped. The only way to extricate the excavator was to change the engine in situ, literally by using another excavator as a crane to lift the failed engine out and then carry in its replacement.)

Yet another concern was oil consumption, which started at a reasonable level but showed an increasing trend as road mileages topped 100,000 miles. The cause, not unknown to Perkins when using standard aluminium pistons, was increasing top ring groove wear caused by the 'hammer' of the ring in the groove under inertia loads: the top ring groove temperature under high sustained speeds was relatively high, reducing the strength of the aluminium. The solution was also well known, but expensive: namely the introduction of an armoured groove – usually known as an 'Alfin' insert. The writer had had considerable experience of this solution on the early testing of the T6.354 but met a natural resistance to adding more product cost to the V8. Nevertheless some sample pistons were obtained and tested surreptitiously on endurance engines. When the time came to accept the inevitable, the V8 team were well prepared to provide supporting evidence for the change, which was introduced with excellent results and a much-improved engine life.

A problem which plagued the engine and irritated operators considerably was oil leakage from the cover plate in the centre of the vee, below the fuel pump. In order to provide clearance under the Simms in-line fuel pump this cover was formed of pressed steel and was curved, necessitating special seals at each end plus separate flat side joints. In service these were insufficiently robust to resist the considerable oil 'wash' caused by the windage within the engine, plus the vibration effects, so that a weep of oil from the area was common. With fuel oil leaks from the injection pump too, this meant that the centre of the engine was frequently damp causing smell, accumulation of dirt and a generally unsatisfactory condition. It was only when later versions of the engine were fitted with a flat aluminium cover plate that the leaks were stopped – Perkins engines at that time were not renowned as being leak-free and the V8 unfortunately did nothing to enhance that reputation!

6.354 Progress

The development programme on the 6.354 family continued actively through the 70s. Improvements were made which resulted in the 6.354.1 (later the '.' was deleted to designate the new marks as 6.3541, 6.3542, etc.). The major change for this first offshoot was to the cooling system, and soon the 6.3721 followed with the cylinder bore increased to 3.975 inches. A more radical version followed with the launch of the 6.3542 for vehicle use, with greater detail changes improving the engine reliability and life. Lessons learnt from the extensive endurance and field-testing of turbocharged engines resulted in the launch of the T6.3543 later. This featured a new cylinder block design, which deleted the tappet chamber covers and created an appearance similar to the 4.236, plus a new cylinder head with copper sleeves for the injectors to reduce their operating temperature.

The marine programme on the T6.354 was a major source of pub-

licity due to the considerable success of the engine in offshore powerboat racing. There was a spin-off from the racing as more was learnt about endurance life and potential power increase. From the initial 145bhp the engine went through various stages of up-rating, although not all the augmentations were to reach production. The introduction of the T6.3543 GT was a major step forward, meeting the challenge of Ford with their Sabre engine conversions for a time. Later, as the Sabre engines reached 370bhp – with twin turbochargers, twin charge-coolers and nitrous oxide injection – Perkins recognised they could not keep up. The affordability of the marine programme was being questioned anyway by then, and was ultimately scaled down as the economic environment became more difficult.

Invention of the V8.540

Further development of the V8.510 was part of the Engineering forward plan. A larger swept volume was possible since the design allowed for an increased stroke to be used, with a longer throw crankshaft, without changing the height of the cylinder block. A small increase in bore diameter meant that the engine capacity could be increased to 605 cubic inches and a rating of 215bhp obtained at a slightly lower speed of 2,600rpm. While this was being developed there were complaints from MF about the poor torque curve shape obtained from the V8.510 at the lower speeds preferred on agricultural machinery. The writer discussed the problem with Roger Young, then the performance team leader for the V8 team. It was considered that a hybrid, using the standard bore size but with the increased stroke of the V8.605, might prove effective. As a result a new set of pistons was obtained (this being the only new component needing to be sourced) and a trial engine built. Thus the V8.540 came into being and immediately gave the power and torque characteristics desired! Obviously there was more work needed to prove the engine's durability and acceptability, but eventually this product succeeded the V8.510 for vehicle use as well and proved to be a popular derivative. There is some dispute about the real story behind the invention of the V8.540. David Burnicle's version varies from the author's in that he was under fire at the time from MF's Lee Elfes for the poor power output of the V8.510 - requests from Perkins to reduce the considerable parasitic losses in the tractor fell on deaf ears. The argument ended with David investigating the feasibility of the hybrid engine: it successfully produced 10 extra bhp, more torque and also addressed the concern over smoke emissions as well as cutting two decibels from the noise level due to the reduced maximum engine speed.) Whichever version is believed, the V8.540 proved to be a successful development and was arguably the best of the family.

Development of the Specialist Group

As the 70s progressed the increased attention being paid to emissions – of smoke, toxic gases and noise – became a major part of the research efforts of the Company. The creation of a team of specialists, with recruitment of relevant expertise from universities and other companies, gave Perkins an edge in many disciplines. This, coupled with increasing use of new technologies and techniques, enabled fundamental investigations into hitherto unexplored directions with the results applied quickly to existing or future products. Traditionally, engine testing had been the primary means of establishing fitness for purpose in a new design. This was feasible because it was relatively cheap and quick to build and test a new engine. The drawback of the approach was that if a component failed on test, there was frequently some doubt about the mechanism of failure.

The early 70s saw the advent of more powerful computers, plus the introduction of methods such as finite element analysis into the industrial world. Under the strong leadership of Roland Bertodo, who had pioneered such processes while running the Research Centre at Ruston Hornsby in Lincoln, Perkins became one of the earliest adop-

This aerial view shows the Fletton factory in June 1967 as it was being equipped to become the home of the Perkins V8 engines

ters of these new predictive techniques. As well as using the methods for establishing stress levels in pistons, cylinder blocks and so on, they were applied to predicting noise levels emanating from different engine designs. Gradually the philosophy of engine design changed to become one where, if possible, the component would be 'tested' in computer analysis before it was made. The ability to redesign to resolve failures identified by the computer saved time and produced a more optimised part to be engine tested. Initially there were many setbacks in the adoption of this methodology but it did produce massive successes and has become the established norm for engine design within the Company – and indeed every branch of engineering – as computer power and sophistication have increased. It seems now, with the benefit of hindsight and some knowledge of other engine companies' progress in applying predictive techniques, that Perkins were well ahead of their competitors throughout the 1970s.

There were always new engine designs under consideration; many of these were designated with 'Q' codings, one of the most radical being the Q6 concept. 'Convention' for Perkins – and indeed most other engine designers at that time – meant that the timing gears and associated drives were taken from the front end of the engine. Research into the fundamentals of noise generation demonstrated that a major source was the timing train, due to the varying loading from the engine components such as fuel pump and camshaft and the resulting gear tooth movements. Design considerations suggested that moving the gears to the centre or even rear of the cylinder block would make a considerable difference to engine-generated (and therefore radiated) noise in a vehicle environment. Accordingly the basic design group under Bill Stewart produced two prototype designs with repositioned gears. Testing confirmed what theory had suggested, but this was insufficient to outweigh the inherent manufacturing and cost implications so that the engines never progressed beyond the 'interesting idea' prototype stage.

Combustion research

It was in the areas of combustion and injection systems that the most progress was made in the early to mid-70s. The use of direct injection technologies and the open bowl combustion chamber – usually of toroidal shape with or without a central 'pip'– had become common practice on the engine range. In order to maintain reasonable performance in terms of power and torque, without compromising specific fuel consumption or smoke levels, the use of quite advanced fuel pump timing (start of injection up to perhaps 28 degrees before top dead centre) became common, along with the use of a DPA fuel pump with advance box which gave even earlier start of injection at higher speeds. This direction of development tended to increase both engine noise and mechanical loadings: a change of approach was needed, essential when improvements of smoke and gaseous emissions were included in the equation. The Perkins research engineers tried many new combustion chamber designs on single-cylinder research engines, together with modifications to porting, valve timing, injector designs, etc. Ultimately a new chamber design, patented as the 'Squish Lip' on account of its re-entrant bowl cross-section which 'squished' the air over the bowl edge, became the leading contender and was chosen for the next generation of lower emission engines, starting with the 4.2032 and 3.1522.

There was little development work during the 70s on the largest four-cylinder engine, the 4.270D and its successors the 4.300 and then 4.318. This big-capacity rugged engine was used almost exclusively by MF in tractors, combine harvesters and later industrial machines: one concession to increasing sophistication had been the incorporation of a Lanchester balancer on the later derivatives, which improved vibration level considerably. Although ideal for agricultural use this size of engine did not fit in with the needs of most other customers; as a consequence volumes were small and there was little incentive for further development.

ICM Generation Two

In mid-1973 the author was asked to return early from Mexico, after a spell there as Chief Engineer in succession to Russell Bennett, to lead a small team working on a major project for the ICM Division of MF. The team was to be responsible for the engine selection, application design and installation in a series of new machines designated 'Generation Two' for the industrial and construction equipment offering. This was the first time a team had been formed within Perkins but reported directly to an MF manager, based in MF Detroit. The engine work involved liaison between plants in Detroit, Aprilia and Ravenna in Italy, Manchester and Coventry in England, as well as involvement with head office personnel in Toronto.

There was a clear intention to introduce new ideas in machine design, especially in terms of operator comfort: hence close attention was paid to noise reduction and the provision of air conditioning on even the smallest machines. The new range of machines covered tractor digger loaders, hydraulic excavators, wheeled and tracked loaders and crawler tractors: a major and very ambitious programme intended to be implemented over a four-year period.

There were some initial teething problems with relationships, since the work cut across the established, and assumed, responsibilities of the Applications Engineering area in Peterborough, but considerable progress had been made by mid 1974. The major part of the programme was then cut as MF purchased the established German company Hanomag, with several new machines ready for production. There had also been recognition by then at MF Board level that the cost of the programme was already running well ahead of budget, with excessive spend on travel between the sites by many personnel and indiscriminate use of contract labour in the Detroit area to meet the project time demands. The people seconded to the project returned to the fold having learnt considerably about multinational operations!

Comments have been made in an earlier chapter about the relationship with Toyo Kogyo in Japan with regard to the development of the 4.154 engine, its six-cylinder cousin the 6.247, and development of versions of the 4.236 and 6.354 as indirect-injection engines. After considerable discussions between the companies, agreement was reached in 1972 to produce the 4.224 and 6.335 engines, with production in Japan using some components sourced from Peterborough. Totals of 30,000 engines of each type were covered in the initial agreement, production starting in 1973. This project added to the overall development programme at Peterborough, although TK engineers were responsible for a great deal of the work on what was to be a Japan-only product.

Other developments under consideration included a three-cylinder version of the 4.236, known as the 3.177, which had been mooted as a successor to the 3.152 for Peterborough production. The project never reached fruition in England, although a version was later developed in Yugoslavia with the licensee IMR: the author has been unable to discover what production volumes were actually achieved.

There had been a further reorganisation of the Engineering structure in the early 1970s when Project Teams were disbanded to introduce Project Managers with small teams of Project Engineers directing each engine family but drawing upon a pool of expertise for design, mechanical and performance development, etc. The move created greater flexibility in the utilisation of manpower and test facilities, but removed some of the 'ownership' from the individuals. Perhaps there was some benefit in cost control: it also sharpened the attitudes of the Project Engineers in writing up their job requirements for the functional areas!

Chapter 15: Inflation, Redundancy, a Knighthood & a Strike (1971 - 1973)

1971: Facing the challenge of the time

A review in January by Vivian Frayling covered the past year and the prospects for the next twelve months. His balanced assessment of the immediate future listed the prime factors to return the Company to satisfactory profits – response to market change, reduced costs, improved productivity, better quality and on-time product delivery. For the past record year, where actual despatch of 236,000 engines had to be viewed against the forecast of 271,000, this was a challenge to every employee.

The blunt assessment by the Production Director identified the factors contributing to the shortfall, many due to outside influences. Supplier problems due to labour disputes, material price rises, wages rising by 50% over four years and fringe benefits by 100% in the same period all contributed, as did the cost of overheads in the Peterborough factories which had increased by 37% since 1968.

On the brighter side, no production in 1970 was lost to industrial action, despite having up to twelve suppliers on strike at one time. The production arrears of about 10,000 engines at the end of 1968 was due to a combination of labour disputes, high demand, insufficient labour and lack of supplier capacity. This had reduced to 9,000 at the end of 1969 and by the end of 1970 there was a 'nil arrears' position. However, factory productivity since 1966 had risen by only 12.5%, barely ahead of the national average of 3% per year.

Frayling identified actions to be taken through 1971 in pursuing a new target of a 5.5% productivity increase. Reduction of factory off-standards, better working practices and maintenance procedures, engine test time reduction and a better despatch process were all detailed, together with their target savings. Major new plant and machinery purchase – taking average investment per man from £2,500 to £3,000 – and another £2 million in expanded production facilities would help maintain the competitive edge. Raising engine prices was not an acceptable and easy solution.

There was some positive news from Italy where on 3rd January Renato Molinari had set a new diesel marine speed record on Lake Como, his speed of 68.204mph eclipsing the previous record set by Don Aronow of the USA. The boat was fitted with a special T6.3543 (M) GT: this new engine development was one of the announcements at the Earls Court Boat Show, where it attracted considerable interest. The other new product was the T4.108 (M), which offered increased power for the smaller craft with, of course, a better power to weight ratio. There were 78 Perkins engines on display around the show, which was the biggest to date.

Predictably, inflation was foremost in the minds of many people, among these being Richard Perkins when he spoke at the Peterborough Chamber of Commerce Dinner. He told the audience that it was not enough to tell industry: '. . . you must stem the tide of wage inflation. We must all decide now if we are to fight against, or submit to, the pressures of cost and inflation. If we cannot operate in a climate of stable prices we in industry will soon find that the cost of the products we sell to our customers will render us less and less competitive, until we price ourselves out of the market.' He went on to suggest that all businesses must seek to reduce costs, in retail as well as manufacture. His concerns over fringe benefits – pensions, insurance, medical and unemployment benefits – echoed the words of Vivian Frayling. He emphasised that employees and unions had to recognise that you never get something for nothing: wages could only increase if improved work efficiency justified the increase.

Clearly these words were intended to help establish the Company's position as wage negotiations on a new two-year deal for hourly-paid employees opened in February. The claims from the TUs for a 'substantial wage increase', plus changes in employment conditions to bring hourly-paid into line with staff, were tabled at the National Joint Council meeting for all MF and Perkins sites, with local negotiations to finalise details. Management stated that difficulties due to inflation and falling sales had already resulted in local redundancies (shop floor employment at Peterborough had dropped from 6,866 to 6,274 through 1970). The union side demanded increased investment and marketing action: in reply management detailed the huge investments of 1968/70, continuing into 1971.

Nationally, labour unrest was evident. On 23 January the first-ever postal strike began, with 230,000 workers involved, looking for a 19.5% wage rise. This stoppage lasted until 8 March and caused considerable disruption countrywide. On 1 March, and again on 18 March, there were token strikes involving about 1.5 million workers, protesting against the new Industrial Relations Bill.

In March an important ballot was held for staff employees on a proposed revision to the pensions scheme to introduce a 'final salary' basis for the pension. This followed from the publication of the new Superannuation and Pensions Bill published in December 1969, which proposed earnings-based pensions. While the pay negotiations with the hourly-paid unions continued, the staff TUs indicated that a claim would be submitted for all staff.

In March John Fish retired from the post of Quality Control Manager. In paying tribute for a job well done, Vivian Frayling recognised that the Quality function in Perkins owed a great deal to John Fish for his inspiration, professional competence and courage. John retired to his home county of Yorkshire and was succeeded by another Yorkshireman, Brian Grundy. (Sadly, John Fish died a year after his retirement, an inadequate time to enjoy his return to what he always called 'God's own country'.)

On the social side, the Sports Association Annual General Meeting was given news of planned ground improvements and a new bowls pavilion. Overall the Association was in good shape, with 25 active clubs including very successful football and tennis sections, and the finances were reported to be healthy too with most of the cost of the new social centre already paid off. The SA announced the first Perkins Ball for October, with the Syd Lawrence Orchestra booked as the main attraction.

Company restructuring

At the end of March, Monty Prichard announced major changes in the Company's management structure in moves aimed at meeting the tougher competition and the inflationary environment. This introduced three principal line functions plus central staff to supersede the 'Operating Units' concept. The main changes were:

Sales, under MIP as acting Director, would cover all areas except Brazil, with senior posts taken by Tom Leask, Philip Poniatowski, Harry Lymath, Vince Griffin and Ken Woollatt.

Supply, under Richard Perkins (also acting as Deputy MD), would cover plant operations, manufacturing planning, material control and also Brazil. The senior posts were held by Vivian Frayling, Bernard Dyer and Roland Jennings (General Manager, Brazil). Engineering under Joe Hind was essentially unchanged Central Services reported to MIP and included Victor Rice as Finance Director, Jim Winstanley as Product Planning and Market Development Director, David Hodkin on Product Reliability, M. Jackson as Management Services Director, Nick Cowan as Personnel Director and Peter Collins as Public Relations Director.

There were further labour concerns in April at Fletton where a reduction in demand for engines forced a four-day week for 320 men: negotiations with the unions sought to reduce the workforce there by 80 men in view of a reduced sales forecast. Later in the month the unions called for a ballot on the Company's offer of a new two-year agreement which would give them 4.35 to 5.62 pence per hour from October – this being chosen to minimise the effects in the current financial year. The TUs rejected the offer and referred it to the National Joint Council in London, where a further offer from the Company was tabled, proposing increases from 1 April and promising improvements in sick pay and holidays. This was ultimately accepted after a ballot.

National endorsement of Perkins' working practices came when the British Safety Council sent representatives to study the Safety and Total Loss Control System, pioneered at Eastfield by Loss Prevention Manager, Joe Shakespeare. The amalgamation of the security, fire and safety departments under one manager allowed a wider approach to be used in identifying all costs associated with incidents, including such hidden costs as business interruption, investigation and training of replacement staff.

The increasing use of Perkins engines in the vehicles used on airports around the world was highlighted in April. As well as V8s powering the tugs used to move Concorde and other aircraft, Perkins-powered baggage handling equipment, servicing vehicles and starting trolleys produced by specialist builders including Houchin, Mercury, Douglas and Dennis served BOAC, BEA, Aer Lingus, KLM, Alitalia, Sabena, Swissair and the RAF.

National unemployment figures published during April showed a figure of 814,819 out of work: the highest level recorded since May 1940.

First Redundancies

In early May ninety workers left Fletton under voluntary redundancy terms. The staff unions meanwhile were considering an offer of £2.00 a week across all areas, backdated to April. Later in the month the overall situation on redundancy was documented as the Company sought to clarify the position and squash rumours that were causing unrest. In the first two weeks of the month there had been 330 workers made redundant, 80% being volunteers. In addition 280 hourly-paid personnel had left the company of their own accord and were not being replaced. The article recorded that, while management were doing everything possible to safeguard jobs, times were hard, money was in short supply and profit margins were eroded, so buyers were not ordering vehicles and machines. Then Perkins' customers would cut their engine orders and inevitably the Company would be forced to take action to reduce over-manning.

In early June it was reported that the staff TUs had accepted the offer of £2.00 a week from April. The Company was not prepared to discuss the associated issue of equal pay for women, but indicated a willingness to open talks later in the year.

A lengthy Echo article chronicled the activities of the Peterscourt-based Product Education Department. At the time there were students from Liberia, Nigeria, Ghana, India, Belgium, Peru and the Sudan, as well as from the UK. There was praise for the instructors and for the quality of training that ensured good servicing practices were introduced and maintained worldwide.

Richard Perkins addressed the annual meeting of the British Internal Combustion Engine Manufacturers' Association (BICEMA) in London in July. His theme was that while all engine manufacturers were facing a crisis of cost, it was vital to remain competitive. He identified the difficulties faced by Perkins in particular since most markets were export rather than domestic: with UK inflation higher than overseas the prob-

The V8.510 engine, seen here in vehicle configuration, gained significant truck business during the late 1960s and early 70s

lems were magnified. With UK industrial growth lower than the rest of Europe, and price rises higher than most, there were further concerns and pressures. With regard to the Common Market, he identified the positive aspects of membership, especially easier access and market growth. (This followed the announcement on 24 June when Geoffrey Rippon stated that the way was now clear for Great Britain to join the EEC. This turnaround followed the death of Charles de Gaulle, who had previously vetoed UK membership. In Parliament 100 Labour MPs had supported the application for membership, in defiance of their Party's position.)

An announcement of interest to all long-serving employees appeared as the Company gave details of a new scheme to make awards to all 25-year employees, irrespective of their membership of the Long Service Club.

Further employment concerns

In a further message to all employees on 5 August, Monty Prichard reviewed the economic situation and short-term volume reduction due to further market deterioration. He expressed his great belief in the long-term future and a guaranteed volume upturn, but in the immediate future the priority was to reduce costs and safeguard jobs in the face of falling demand. In consultation with the TUs, it had been agreed to ask for additional volunteers to prune the workforce further. Although current forecasts showed 1971 production volume at the same level as 1968, the total employment was now about 500 more than the earlier year. In the same period wage costs had gone from £10 million to over £14 million. Although only one major customer had been lost in that period (Ford now making their own engine to replace the 4.108), volume recovery needed a market revival. Forecasts suggested a return to 1,000 engines per day might take until 1974 or 75.

A couple of weeks later the unions and the National Joint Council were given details of new redundancy requirements for hourly-paid workers totalling 205. There had already been 600 volunteers from which it was expected 100 would be accepted, after some 'matching' of people to jobs had been carried out. There would be further announcements of staff redundancies, with the message that it was jobs that were being considered, not personalities.

There was brighter news on the product front. A V8.510, fitted to a Seddon 16:4 truck belonging to Rother Transport of Rotherham, had completed 350,000 miles in about 4 years, was still going strong and spent less time in the garage than any of the other 40 vehicles the haulier operated. The vehicle ran at up to 28 tons GCW and had at one time been used 24 hours a day moving trailers on Immingham Docks.

The V8.510 featured in another success story, this time in Daimler Roadliner coaches operated by Black and White Coaches of Cheltenham. They had operated one of the first such vehicles, now with over 180,000 miles on the clock without major problems. The operator had purchased ten more similar vehicles in 1969 followed by a further ten scheduled for 1970 on the basis of the excellent reliability and performance experienced.

Four new Perkins-powered craft took part in the annual Daily Express Powerboat Race from Cowes to Torquay on 28 August, all fitted with new T6.3543 (M) GT engines. Peter Hicks had re-entered racing after five years with Eight Dials, while Jim Renouf with Firecracker, Miss Dunhill (sponsored by the cigarette company), and Miss Delson owned by Martin Harfield were the other new entrants. In a tough race, with high seas, gales and poor visibility, only ten of 41 starters finished. Miss Delson finished ninth and won the Grosvenor Trophy and the Marine Engine Manufacturers' Trophy as the lowest-powered finisher. None of the seven Perkins-powered entries suffered engine problems but they did suffer damage to craft or crew. A few weeks later Miss Dunhill finished fourth overall in the Torbay race, with Miss Delson sixth and other Perkins-powered craft seventh, eighth and tenth.

Mid-September brought a sudden increase in engine demand, mainly from overseas, and some areas worked overtime – including some where redundancies had occurred. Personnel Director Nick Cowan was at pains to explain in the Echo that, for such short-term fluctuations, engaging new labour was not the answer.

Another of the early employees retired as John Hammonds left the Engineering Division after 38 years' continuous service. Engineering announced the appointment of the first Technical Legislation Manager, David Bampton: the new position emphasised the growing importance of the 'legal' aspects of engineering for all products and applications.

In October, following a five to one vote against the Common Market by Labour at its Party Conference, opinion polls said that most Britons were also against membership. However, in Parliament on 28 October a vote registered 356 for joining and only 244 against. There were 69 Labour MPs rebelling against their party line, while 39 Conservatives voted against.

In November the new V8.605 vehicle engine was announced. Producing 205bhp at 2,600rpm, the engine was designed to power trucks at the legal maximum of 32 tons and the new legal requirement of 6bhp/ton. John Moon of the Commercial Motor was impressed by the new engine in a road test – its flexibility, low-speed pulling power and noise level all receiving praise for a unit of the same package size as its V8.510 predecessor. The Company advertised the engine as 'designed for Europe', to meet all noise and emission regulations and achieve at least 200,000 miles before overhaul. In December the engine had an enthusiastic reception when displayed for the first time at the Scottish Motor Exhibition in Glasgow.

Monty Prichard was the guest speaker at the annual dinner of the '200 Club' (for recipients of the maximum awards in the Suggestion Scheme). He talked of the past difficult 18 months and a difficult 1972 to come. 'Some people have been really worried whether Perkins has a future; let me assure you it has.' He noted that in difficult times people began to realise the advantages that the diesel engine could

bring, it had happened in Europe but not yet in the USA. 'I do not see the economy changing in 1972, but by 1973/4 Perkins will be climbing again. There are no problems we are not going to solve. We are doing a hell of a lot to keep in business. Get this message across when you are talking to your colleagues,' he insisted.

The Smithfield Show in London featured many Perkins engines, the Company noting that a total of 160 manufacturers worldwide were using the products. The radical new MF1200 tractor made its debut, and Claas announced that they had taken 130,000 engines over the past 20 years for their combines.

John Condie took his leave of the Company in mid-December, after 38 years' service.

At his retirement presentation, Monty Prichard said: 'We have a lot to thank him for. There isn't a Perkins engine being manufactured today with which John Condie hasn't been connected.'

In addressing the Plant Operations Management Group in December, Vivian Frayling outlined four priorities for the next year: to maintain productivity improvement, to hold and improve cost reduction, to improve quality and reliability and to deliver product on time. After the satisfactory 5% productivity increase in 1971 he set a target for the New Year of 6.5%, and gave an exhaustive analysis of all aspects of the production processes.

Although not as poor as had been expected, at only 197,485 engines the Peterborough production was over 16% down on 1970. Every engine type had suffered, with V8 production almost halved at only 5,389 units.

1972

January brought an early change in senior staff when Jim Winstanley resigned to join the board of the Associated Engineering Group: Victor Rice assumed the role of Director, Product Planning and Market Development.

Once again there was a big presence at the 1972 International Boat Show, fifty craft displaying 70 Perkins engines. Chay Blyth's British Steel, with a 4.107(M) as auxiliary engine, had recently returned from his successful 'wrong way' solo voyage around the world. The new product shown was the TV8.510 (M), rated at 225bhp and 2,600rpm for pleasure craft applications, while a unique application shown was the fitment of twin 6.354s in the new sail training ship Royalist. This 110-ton, 76-foot square-rigged ship was the largest built in 60 years, intended to teach seamanship to 1,000 boys each year. Moonraker Marine, the luxury cruiser builders from Brundall in Norfolk, were taken over by Colin Chapman of Lotus Cars – he announced his intention of expanding the business, continuing to use the T6.354 (M).

The January Echo included a special supplement on Brazilian subsidiary Motores Perkins SA. In the words of General Manager Roland Jennings: 'By Peterborough standards the Company is small but its growth pattern is following that of the parent company.' With 1970 production 15% better than 1969, and 1971 25% better than the previous year, their slogan for 1972 was 'Yesterday's records are tomorrow's routine!' The workforce had grown to 1,100 including 250 staff, with an average age of 36. The operation was a microcosm of Peterborough, with a flourishing social club, successful football team and a suggestion scheme. They were also the winners of the MF Safety Performance League again, with only 1.3 accidents per million hours worked.

The New Year began badly with the start of the coal miners' strike: the Government was soon advocating fuel rationing. However, negotiations over membership of the Common Market were completed on 18 January when it was announced that Great Britain, along with Norway, Ireland and Denmark, would become a member on 1 January 1973. At over £400 billion GDP, a population greater than that of the USA and 41% of world trade, the enlarged EEC should become a major force.

National industrial unrest

A Government announcement on 20 January showed unemployment at over one million workers. By 9 February the miners' dispute forced the Government to declare a state of emergency, with industry on a three-day week and householders asked to heat only one room to conserve fuel. The train drivers' union refused to move oil supplies past picket lines, exacerbating the situation. Meanwhile the Wilberforce enquiry recommended a £6 a week increase for the miners: on 25 February the miners voted to stop the strike and return to work. There had been serious disruption within Perkins, with workers leaving early on no-power days and no hot meals in the canteen. However, it was claimed that no customer had been let down although delivery delays did occur.

At Perkins, talks had started again in January regarding the 1972 pay and conditions for hourly-paid workers: the unions were claiming a 12.5% pay increase, an extra week's paid holiday and a 35-hour week without loss of earnings. Inevitably the Company's initial comment, ahead of the formal reply in February, was that times were tougher than ever in the engine business. Their offer, delivered a couple of weeks later, was for an 8% wage increase from 1 April in return for renewal of the existing one-year agreement. In noting that in two years wages had risen by 35% but productivity by only 6%, the Company said: 'The main platform of the claim related to the cost of living. It is a fact that increases in wage rates resulting from negotiations consistently move income ahead faster than the increase in the retail price index. It was stated in the claim that from April to December 1971 the cost of living rose by 9.5/10% and that this did not reflect all the increases to which your members were subjected.' The company did not agree the figures, stating that the RPI over those eight months rose by 3.87%, equivalent to 5.8% annually. The lengthy statement intimated that the claim was greedy, serving to increase the inflationary spiral; Government guidelines had to be respected if this effect was to be broken. At about the same time the staff unions also submitted claims, DATA for £8.50 a week and CAWU for £5 a week plus a move towards pay parity for women.

By the end of February the union negotiators recommended acceptance of the offer of £2.55 a week, commenting that 'security and continuity of employment are two essentials in determining the true value of any job. It is to everybody's advantage to slow down, and ultimately halt, the rate at which engine prices rise.'

The Perkins concert on 19 April featured Daniel Barenboim, the New Philharmonic Orchestra and Vladimir Ashkenazy with a programme including Beethoven's 1st Piano Concerto and Schumann's Symphony No.1 in B flat. There was a rush for tickets and the total sell-out quickly demonstrated that the event was both a fixture and a highlight of the year, other problems notwithstanding. The performance was acclaimed as the best yet.

Another stalwart retired in April when Bill Baxter, MBE, left after 33 years' service in Queen Street and Eastfield. Another 'landmark' of a different sort was lost at the same time when the two green huts, temporarily erected to the south of the main offices 18 years previously to accommodate a staff overspill, were finally dismantled and sold.

In May the whole Engineering Division mourned Bill Westwell, who died suddenly at the age of 51, after suffering a heart attack as he was leaving the offices. Joe Hind said of him that he was the kind of person who was virtually impossible to replace, and indeed his involvement with the design of the 6.354, 4.154 and V8.510, and later in liaison with Toyo Kogyo, made him a major contributor to the design team

efforts from the 50s until his death. A fund was started in his memory, to provide books for the Technical Library.

The International Mechanical Handling Exhibition at Earls Court featured many new machines fitted with Perkins engines. These customers included Eaton Yale, Clark Equipment, Priestman Brothers, Jones Cranes, Matbro and Lancer Boss. The Perkins products on display included gasoline versions of the 3.152, 4.203 and 4.236, plus all diesels up to the V8: a special feature was the 'SOS', or Standard Option Scheme, range of industrial units. This new method for ordering the products was ideal for manufacturers needing small quantities of engines. By selecting their content from a pre-engineered range of dress components the engine could be tailored to their needs without requiring time-consuming design and parts list action.

At the Annual Dinner of the Long Service Club, Manufacturing Director Vivian Frayling spoke on the need to develop good relations with the Trades Unions to promote mutual confidence and understanding – in the light of considerable industrial unrest around the country at the time his topic was not unexpected. After tracing the history of the Company, its successes and problems, he concluded: '... so it comes down to the people, and I believe we have the sort of people in Perkins who, when the chips are down, show moderation, wise judgement and a spirited professional pride in overcoming the vicissitudes which punctuate our working life'.

In May work started on the extension to Factory 2. This area would take extra machining lines to reduce dependence upon outside suppliers and reduce product cost. A special citation was awarded to the Company for the second year in succession by the Royal Society for the Prevention of Accidents: Perkins had finished second again in their statistics, this time behind Ford Motor Company.

Knighthood for Monty Prichard

The name of Montague Illtyd Prichard appeared in the June Queen's Birthday Honours when a knighthood was conferred 'For Services to Export'. Sir Monty, as he was to be known, said: 'Of course I am delighted for my family as much as for myself. But really, you know, this honour is quite obviously a tribute to the good work done over the years by the whole Perkins engines team at home and overseas – in our factories and offices, and in the field.'

Monty Prichard had already been named as one of the Top Ten Britons, and one of the five great export salesmen, in 1967 by Mr Anthony Wedgwood Benn, then Minister of Technology. His dedication to the Company and tireless pursuit of exports to world markets was at last recognised (and perhaps made up for the lack of a similar honour for the Founder!). There were many tributes from around the world, and of course from within the Company and locally from companies and individuals.

The Minister for Transport Industries, the Rt Hon. John Peyton, spent a day at Eastfield during July, and in a press conference at the end of the visit stated: 'No minister learns anything by sticking at his office desk, so I came here to see what this firm with its worldwide reputation is doing, and can do, to help combat the problems of noise, smoke and smell. If we can help to make the motor vehicle a more civilised affair, so much the better. And a firm like Perkins can make an enormous contribution of course.' During his visit he saw much of the engineering efforts as well as touring the factory and talking to workers.

Richard Perkins, speaking as Chairman at a conference of BICEMA, reminded British manufacturers that while the economy was growing at 2.5%, export markets were increasing at 10% per year. With British entry into Europe and the progressive removal of duties and restrictions, benefits would apply to all European industry. 'It will be to the disadvantage of firms whose fortunes are tied to the home market,' he said, adding: 'Entry opens the way for those companies who are prepared to put in a great deal of planning and work.' He covered the benefits of the EEC in the long term and the recent retrenchment in British Industry but would not say that a full recovery was already visible. 'Inflation', he claimed, 'is our greatest vulnerability at a time when manufacturers need to feel their way into the new situation of entry into Europe.'

During the summer Chancellor Anthony Barber announced the flotation of the Pound Sterling after the Government had spent £1,000 million in an effort to stop speculative selling. A dock strike from 28 July to 16 August was a further warning that labour relations remained strained.

In August the Company announced the appointment of a new Finance Director when Jim Felker arrived at Peterborough from the Massey Ferguson Corporate staff in Toronto, taking over the position vacated by Victor Rice.

Warnings on inflation again

In September, Sir Monty gave another message via the Echo about inflation in answer to a question about how Perkins was contributing to the efforts of large manufacturing companies prior to Common Market entry. He noted that over the past year Perkins had pegged price rises to 5% maximum, and was committed to extending this action for a further three months. This was in line with an initiative started in July 1971 by the Confederation of British Industry (CBI), of which Perkins was a member. This had been the CBI's own initiative to deal with the danger of inflation running away, and was triggered by getting the largest members to promise to keep price rises to a minimum. In doing this, it had been hoped that the Trades Unions would match the action by restraining large wage demands: indeed by the end of 1971 wage settlements had moderated, only to increase again after the miners' and railway workers' settlements. Sir Monty noted that: 'The CBI's policy helped to bring down the overall rate of inflation from 11% to 6%. We have agreed a further three months in the hope that CBI, Government and TUs can agree a voluntary means of restraint.' He warned that the higher standard of living everybody wanted could only be achieved by winning the fight against inflation – 'the vicious spiral can only be stopped by the enthusiastic cooperation of us all'.

On 28 September Prime Minister Edward Heath announced a radical proposal for voluntary price and incomes policy in talks with the TUC and CBI. It was proposed to limit pay rises to £2 per week and price rises to 5%. This was at a moment when the power workers were seeking £5.50 a week, the dustmen £4 a week and the miners – again – £4.50 to £7 a week. Confrontation and unrest remained very much on the agenda.

The Commercial Motor Show at Earls Court in September saw the vehicle version of the 6.3723 make its debut. The engine, rated at 121bhp and 2,800rpm, drew heavily upon the heavy-duty components developed for the T6.3543 and was aimed at providing life to first overhaul in excess of 150,000 miles for long-distance haulage operation. Once again, most major manufacturers were featuring the Perkins products, with Seddon Motors showing their new 13:4 truck with the 6.3723, a new midi-bus with the 4.236 and their new coach with the T6.

After the considerable coverage of offshore powerboat racing over the past years, the Echo told the story of the 'backroom boys' – the team of fitters who supported the racing season under Marine Service Manager Tom Dowey. Since the 'Round Britain Race' of 1969 the five-man crew had supported more than a dozen races in British waters during which the Perkins-powered boats had won over 50 trophies.

Perkins' record on safety found prominence in October when the BBC featured the company as a leader in safety and loss prevention in a series called Workers at Risk.

A safety exercise was included where employees became film stars for the day! The programme was acclaimed by viewers and by companies requesting copies for training purposes. In the annual MF safety league the Peterborough plants fared well, with Walton finishing fourth, Eastfield sixth and Fletton eighth in the worldwide competition.

The Australian operation at Dandenong featured in an October supplement in the Echo. In 1971 there had been over 12,000 engines imported directly or indirectly to Australia, supplying 47 different customers. These included local subsidiaries of multinationals such as Hyster, Clark Equipment, International Harvester and Lincoln Electric, plus local companies such as Chamberlain-John Deere, who used 6.306, 6.372 and 4.236 in their tractors.

Inflation featured in a message from Richard Perkins in October, as he cited differences between Britain and its nearest European competitors. He quoted France with productivity increasing by 30.9% over the period 1966 to 1970 and wages by 30.3%, Germany with figures of 51% and 51.9%, but Britain with 16.9% and 19.5%. As an example of what good government control could do, he quoted Brazil, where from 1961 to 1964 inflation ran in excess of 100% per annum: with close control of wages, prices and capital investment the 1971/2 figure became 18%. (Still of course high for Europe and applying to a developing nation!) Undoubtedly this message was aimed mainly at the Trades Unions, but was nevertheless a warning about the necessity of remaining competitive home and overseas – especially as Common Market entry drew near.

Further management changes were announced in October as Victor Rice moved over to Director of Sales and Marketing for the Group. Nick Cowan left Personnel to take a post with the Philips Electrical Group and was replaced as Director by W.P. (Bill) Mearns, transferred from MF Toronto. Bernard Lynn retired after 32 years, having served as Director of Planning and Procurement since 1962.

In November an exhibition entitled 'Better Roads Mean More Jobs' at Eastfield was co-sponsored by Perkins and the British Road Federation. It showed the detrimental effect that the poor road network had on exports, with the knock-on effect as new equipment was not ordered, product development lagged and jobs were not generated. The position of Felixstowe was cited, where lack of good connecting roads meant that the £12 million port investment could not be exploited since cargoes were not moved in acceptable timescales. A batch of engines leaving Peterborough at 4.30pm took four hours to reach Felixstowe, finally reaching Frankfurt 41.5 hours after leaving the factory. By contrast a load from Clermont-Ferrand in France would take only 30 hours for a similar distance of 540 miles. (One could comment that although the A14 and A1 trunk roads were eventually upgraded to serve Felixstowe better, they were soon inadequate and by 2004 the A14 had become a nightmare, with the journey not always possible in four hours!)

The exhibition also gave some statistics on Perkins exports at the time. The company made 40% of the UK multi-cylinder diesels of which 85%, worth £180 million, were exported. This meant that 60,000 tons of engines and parts were exported each year, and 40% of this total was shipped via the East Coast ports.

Italian record breaker

World records on the water again featured in December when Livio Macchia, the Perkins Italy Sales Manager, drove his boat Four Points to a new water speed record for diesels of 78.355mph, almost 10mph faster than the previous record. Four Points was built by Cantiere Navale Abbate in Italy and was powered by a single T6.3543 rated at

In December 1972 Italian Sales Manager Livio Macchia set a new diesel record with a T6.3543(M) in his boat Four Points, seen here at speed

292bhp at 2,600rpm. The engine installation was very simple to save weight, using a direct vee-drive without gearbox. There had been a minor confusion before the record was set, when the craft was started and promptly set off backwards – the wrong 'hand' propellor had been fitted! However, with this mistake corrected, Livio retook the record to add to the long-distance and one-hour records set previously using the T6.354 engine.

The Engineering Division proudly displayed their new noise cell in December. This anechoic chamber was fully instrumented and capable of housing a vehicle up to 25,000lbs in weight in addition to testing bare engines under load.

Production for 1972 showed an improvement at 234,544 engines: this was an 18.5% improvement on 1971 but still marginally below the 1970 record. Shipments of only 42,090 CKD kits were disappointing, well below the previous year.

1973

The Earls Court Boat Show in January attracted big crowds again, in spite of the economic problems. Perkins was well represented as always, with 43 craft fitted with a variety of engines, many being new 'Low Line' versions of the 4.236 and 6.354. The award for 'Boat of the Show' went to an American yacht, the Swan 44 from Sparkman and Stephen of New York, fitted with a 4.108 as auxiliary. There were so many exhibitors competing for space that some craft had to be based on the Thames at the Cadogan and Westminster piers.

Peter Bowyer, the marine applications expert, produced an article for the Echo explaining the reason for Perkins' success in the marine field. He cited the adaptability of the basic engines as a major ingredient, the easy fitment of special marine parts – such as heat exchangers and gearboxes – plus the availability of special sumps etc., making the engines attractive in price and ease of installation.

Perkins personnel in the headlines included Roland Bertodo, speaking on BBC Today about noise and the diesel engine, and Sir Monty, who appeared on a BBC TV programme *Made in Britain* talking about Peterborough as a European city, and Perkins' importance to its success.

An Echo article featured the 4.236 machining facility, which had just produced the 500,000th cylinder block and was now running at 113,000 blocks per year. On the factory safety side three workers had been saved recently from serious injury, thanks to being equipped with the right shoes, helmet and safety spectacles. Of interest to all employees was the news on the wages front that the Trades Unions had already entered claims for the hourly paid for a shorter working week and more holidays for all UK MF and Perkins plants, with wage increases to be negotiated on a plant-by-plant basis. The staff unions were also reported to be preparing claims.

In the USA Neville Hartwell, Manager of Ecological Engineering for Perkins Inc., was elected Chairman of the Engines Committee of the influential Society of Automotive Engineers, and became Chairman of the US Technical Advisory on the International Standards Organisation, as well as serving on various Engine Manufacturers Association committees: the importance of involvement in policy-making bodies in the USA had been recognised as increasing emphasis was placed on the diesel engine and pollution in its various forms.

In Peterborough a familiar face was lost with the early retirement of Chris Thompson after 32 years' service. Chris had worked in various engineering areas, especially associated with the field-testing of engines at home and abroad, and at his retirement was PA to Joe Hind, the Director of Engineering. Chris did not sever his ties to the Company completely, however, going on to research the early history and to produce a biography of Frank Perkins which was published in the Butterworth's Dictionary of Business Biography in 1985.

Engineering facilities expansion

In early February further expansion of the Engineering workshops was announced, to add 67,000 square feet to the facilities. Completion gave 106 test beds of various configurations and included unique instrumentation, special acoustic treatment and the ability to run vehicles on load up to the size of a combine harvester. At about the same time there was a proposal from a local historian that the old Queen Street works should become a local industrial monument, with its history going back to the Peterborough Iron Works in 1850: an appeal for details and information was made locally but the initiative eventually died.

The importance of Perkins in the marine world was reinforced when Gulfstar Inc. of St Petersburg, Florida, announced an order for £500,000 worth of engines at the 63rd annual National Boat Show in New York. The four-, six- and eight-cylinder engines were to power yachts, motor sailers and trawlers made by the company.

In mid-February details of the Company offer to the hourly-paid unions was announced. In addition to a 6.5% increase in basic pay from 1 April, they offered two more days' holiday in 1973 and a further two in 1974, plus an additional 3p per hour for female workers as a move towards equal pay. The details were accompanied by tables showing that Perkins were ahead of 22 other local industries in terms of hourly paid wages in all but one category. The offer did not meet the demand for parity with Coventry workers – the Company data reflected that this would mean a 45% pay increase for skilled and 50% for semi-skilled workers. An accompanying article in the Echo gave considerable detail on the effects of giving way on parity. It would have meant adding £5 million to costs and put price competitiveness in jeopardy. There had been 992 jobs created in the past 12 months, all local in spite of an unemployment level of only 2.2% in Peterborough. Perkins' labour turnover, for all reasons, had been only 4.8%. A further statistic confirmed the concern over the pay/price spiral – since 1969 hourly-paid wages had risen by about 50% while the RPI had risen only 22.76%. The figures since 1966 – wages up 65% and RPI 35% – were also given, just to rub the message in. Staff union claims were mentioned briefly, including a shorter working week, improved holiday entitlement and early retirement at 60.

In March the shop floor TUs rejected the Company offer, which was referred to the National Joint Council according to the agreed procedure. There was also a failure to agree on the staff claim, as the Company wished to tie the extra days to statutory holidays to make a more economic shutdown. Meanwhile there were problems with suppliers due to industrial action and the effect of a gas industry dispute, seriously affecting programme plans.

Purchase actions to source components from overseas suppliers were undertaken, successful in that layoffs were avoided. The forecast for the year suggested that 10% of the £50 million purchase cost would be spent overseas. Concern was expressed that shortages could cause more accidents as extra efforts had to be made moving material around.

The possible benefits of the Suggestion Scheme grew as the possible maximum award was increased again, this time to £1,000. The award was based, of course, on a percentage of the saving to the Company during the first year after adoption. During 1972 there had been

total awards of almost £10,000 and a total of 3,800 suggestions received: thus most suggestions had little monetary value but received a token 'encouragement' award. The 'biggies' were what the company wanted, and these received considerable publicity.

In Mexico during March there was a special launch organised by Chrysler-Automex at the Camino Real Hotel in Mexico City to introduce their revised Dodge truck with the new Perkins C6.3542 (V). This was developed for countries with a considerable part of their road system at altitude, the 'C' standing for 'compensated' to identify an engine specification adding a turbocharger to an upgraded naturally-aspirated engine. Since much of central Mexico was above 6,000 feet there were great advantages in having an engine that retained most of its power when operating in these conditions. Trucks so equipped outperformed the Cummins-powered DINA trucks of nominally greater horsepower, giving Dodge a useful edge over their rivals.

Chay Blyth was again in the news as his boat British Steel became the British Army entry in the Whitbread 'Round the World' race, refurbished but still using its original 4.107(M) engine for auxiliary power.

Perkins pay dispute drags on

In April the pay dispute was back in the news when, after dragging on for over three months, it was referred back from the NJC to local level. The demands remained for positive moves towards parity with Coventry, freedom to negotiate locally without Government constraints, rationalisation of the wage structure outside the current bargaining agreement and, in return for a renewal of the current Term Agreement, for the company to grant a 'special' increase outside the general agreement and pay code constraints! Unsurprisingly, the Company could not accept such a deal, offering only the holiday arrangements previously stated and a 6.9% wage increase (plus an extra 3p an hour for female employees) – this being the maximum allowed by the Pay Code with its '£1 + 4%' rule. The Company offered facilities for a secret ballot of members but this was rejected, the TU imposing an overtime ban and work to rule except for essential services. In their

JCB extended their use of the Perkins products with the launch of the revolutionary JCB 110 rear-engined tracked loader

turn the Company confirmed that the Guarantee of Employment was suspended for the duration of the dispute for all Peterborough plants, and that they had no obligation to backdate any settlement to 1 April. Meanwhile the ASTMS staff union accepted a £150 a year offer: other staff unions remained in negotiation.

On 26 April the Company had offered backdating to 1 April to the NJC and the TUs, provided that the offer was accepted before 30 April. The unions repeated their dissatisfaction and disappointment that the offer would not go outside Government guidelines.

During April the V8.540 vehicle engine was announced: rated at 180bhp at 2,600rpm, this was a 'stretched' version of the V8.510, the extra capacity being achieved by use of the crankshaft from the V8.605, giving an increased stroke. The engine also provided better torque characteristics, reduced noise level and improvements based on lessons learnt from service experience.

Sir Monty addressed the annual dinner of the Long Service Club at the beginning of May, covering many topics during his speech but stressing particularly the 'difference of opinion' between shop floor and management. He noted the importance of keeping up with increasing customer demands, indicating that more expansion was essential as the plants were now flat out. He reminded the audience that other manufacturers waiting in the wings would pick up on any failure of Perkins to meet their sales commitments.

A 31-year-old S6 (M) engine was reported still running in the Adriatic, propelling a workboat named Nyata. Built in Scotland in 1913, the boat was still going strong with the S6 clocking up 40,000 miles in the past two years, and over 6,000 hours of service for the engine since an overhaul in 1965. Another story of long life recorded the 10,000 hours achieved by a Landini tractor fitted with a 4.203 engine: since 1963 the engine had worked in the Tiber valley in Italy trouble-free with only routine maintenance.

The AUEW met with Perkins management on 4 June, the first meeting since 28 March. The Company offered overtime for essential services over the Bank Holiday weekend, allowing all to work on the Tuesday to qualify for Bank Holiday pay: this was rejected by the TU. The arguments dragged on into July; eventually agreement was reached with the Company agreeing a phased movement towards parity with Coventry. Some of the overall relief disappeared, however, when Bill Mearns, the Personnel and Industrial Relations Director, appeared live on TV and appeared to disagree that the concession had been granted! Eventually harmony – and sanity – was restored.

Amongst other stories recorded in June was the intention to restart the 'Miss Perkins Diesel' beauty competition, for which all female employees were eligible to enter. A series of photographic heats would be held, from which finalists would be selected by readers' votes.

The 1973 Perkins Concert was held in Peterborough Cathedral in July. This year it included Schubert's 'Unfinished Symphony' and Stravinsky's Firebird Suite, but the major work was a newly-composed Symphony by Krzysztof Penderecki, played by the London Symphony Orchestra and conducted by the composer. The work was broadcast live by BBC Radio 3 and received a mixed reception – enjoyed by the critics but much less so by the audience, whose applause was more polite than enthusiastic.

In mid-July Loss Prevention Manager Joe Shakespeare embarked on a 3,000-mile tour in South Africa, lecturing on Safety and Loss Control. This was seen as a further recognition both for the Perkins record on safety and Joe's growing reputation in the relatively new discipline of Loss Prevention. (Later in the year Perkins was awarded a golden sword by the British Safety Council, in recognition of an exemplary record in industrial safety, having been runners-up in 1971/2/3 in the George Earl Trophy competition.)

Another of the earliest employees died in August: Geoffrey Guest started in 1935 and in the early days had worked on conversion of the AEC diesel bus engine to the Aeroflow combustion system. He also sold the first industrial engine, to the Clipsham quarries in Stamford, and in later years was a familiar figure on the industrial sales team. He died at 64 years old, a few months short of his retirement.

An advance on the Quality side of the business was announced in late August when Brian Grundy gave details of the 'Quality Procedures Manual'. This laid down a series of quality objectives and standards for components and engines, including testing and inspections methods and procedures, for Peterborough plants and those of licensees and associates. The intention of improving and standardising processes went beyond the previous systems, bringing Perkins into line with the increasing and exacting demands of the customers – and the new standards being formulated by regulatory bodies.

In the autumn the overseas companies were much in the news. In September the Yugoslavian company Industrija Motora Rakovica (IMR) celebrated their 20th anniversary since signing as a licensee: during that time they had produced over 150,000 engines and were currently making 25,000 a year. Around 75% of all agricultural equipment produced in Yugoslavia at the time was Perkins-powered. A few weeks later MPSA Brazil announced the production of their 150,000th engine too, with over 70% of the tractor market, 35% of industrial equipment and more than 20% of diesel truck sales featuring Perkins engines. The September Echo featured a supplement on Japan, covering the meetings and joint programmes with Yanmar and Toyo Kogyo through which Perkins had achieved considerable success in the Japanese market after ten years of intensive effort.

The next month the Personnel Department advertised a £5 'bounty' to any employee who was successful in recommending a recruit in the Company's continuing search for production-skilled and semi-skilled workers. They were also looking for good accommodation for new workers being recruited from further afield as local 'digs' became more difficult to find. Later in the year the recruitment process was taken further with a 'Meet Perkins' day at the Key Theatre in Peterborough, designed to show the city people what the Company – and its 8,000 employees – was all about. This first commercial use of the Key by a City company was yet another innovation for Perkins!

Stories about product applications old and new were still appearing frequently. New Swedish tanker Thuntank I was a unique application using no less than five V8.510s: the engines provided power via individual hydraulic pumps into a common power circuit. the claimed advantages including the need to run only sufficient engines to satisfy immediate demand. Locating the small engines into available spaces was more efficient than finding room for one large engine.

The first big Suggestion Scheme award was made in October to Alf Horsfall: £790 for a proposal to do away with the cranking dog-nut on the crankshaft nose, and replace it with a standard hexagon nut. In the same month, nurse Sandra Bennett from the Peterborough Maternity Hospital was sponsored through the 'Gwynneth and Frank Perkins Memorial Fund' for six weeks' leave in Canada, studying their use of mechanical aids to treat babies with respiratory distress disorder – the Canadian methods being both different from and in advance of those common in the UK.

Ken Woollatt retired in November after 32 years' service. Since joining in 1941, he had filled important roles as Chief Accountant, Company Secretary and Finance Director before taking responsibility for Overseas Manufacturing Operations in 1959. He visited 32 countries for negotiations, travelling over 1.5 million miles. In comments to the Echo he said: 'One of the amazing things about the company's growth is that now it produces as many engines in a day as it used to in six months when I joined.'

Reactions to another oil crisis

October and November saw the beginning of yet another national crisis. The oil-producing nations voted to raise oil prices by 70%, in protest at American support of Israel in the Middle-East War with Egypt. The impact was worsened in the UK when the power workers and miners struck in mid-November, forcing the Government to declare a state of emergency. At the end of November Peter Walker, Secretary for Trade and Industry, announced that 16 million petrol ration coupons were being printed as the Middle East crisis deepened and a worldwide oil shortage resulted. Perkins announced an intention to reduce oil consumption by 20%, which meant a saving of 6 million gallons a year, shared between heating (54%), production testing (20%) and engineering testing (17%), with the remaining 9% being shared between external and internal transport. All suggestions for saving fuel were to be considered.

Sir Monty Prichard addressed the Motor Industries Research Association's annual lunch as their President in November. He told his audience that the current industrial unrest was affecting Britain's ability to keep up with the competition in the rest of the world. He referred to the considerable deterioration of labour relations in the past year and forecast that the current actions would worsen the fuel crisis, with a 'day of reckoning' bound to come. World energy resources were smaller than had been assumed, he said, and the ability of management to get to grips with the necessary technology and keep abreast of the rest of the world was being hamstrung by the union-led unrest. He was supported by Manufacturing Planning Director Bernard Dyer, who advocated the appointment of an 'ombudsman' to deal with the fuel crisis, identifying responsibilities and measures to conserve fuel and energy. Perkins issued a booklet nationally, entitled 'Better Maintenance for a Better Environment': a campaign aimed at reducing operating costs and improving engine efficiency and life. A further booklet was produced for all employees, called 'Beat the Fuel Shortage: Save Fuel'.

On 5 December the Government announced a 50mph compulsory speed limit as part of their emergency measures. The following day £2,000 million was wiped off share values as Arab funds were withdrawn and on 17 December a crisis budget cut £1,200 million from public spending. The power dispute was causing paralysis in industry with only five days of electrical power per fortnight. There was a further OPEC oil price increase just ahead of Christmas, while around the country the basic question being asked was – who rules the country, Government or Unions?

During December work started on the site for the new 'Factory 3' on 22 acres of land leased from the Development Corporation, close to the southern boundary of the existing Eastfield site. This plant would provide space for the final transfer of operations from Queen Street, and add capacity for production. The first phase of 63,711 square feet for rebuild operations was scheduled for completion in autumn 1974.

The year closed with the usual round of shows, the Smithfield heralding the launch of the agricultural version of the V8.540, and new products from Marshall Fowler and Muir Hill featuring Perkins power. The new Claas Dominator 80 combine harvester made its debut, along with the Massey Ferguson 760 combine and a new range of tractors – MF 1200, MF1080, MF188, MF168 and MF135. Of these the MF1200 was the most radical, using the 6.354 in a new 'chassis' configuration.

The International Boat Show presented the usual array of boats with Perkins power, and also the launch of the TV8.510 (M) rated at 235shp for pleasure craft use. One of the star boats was a Nicholson 42 with a 4.236(M) as auxiliary power, whilst the T6.354 was seen in nine cruisers, the 4.236 in ten others and thirteen craft were fitted with the 4.108.

Despite all the trauma and difficulties during the year the production statistics showed only a small drop from 1972, with 227,504 engines produced. For the first time the production of the 4.236 engine passed 70,000 engines in the year while CKD kits recovered too. However, this was not a true picture: the figures should have been much higher. It was estimated that as many as 40,000 engines had been lost through the industrial action. An additional major concern was that goodwill had been lost with customers, many of whom started to seek alternative suppliers. The overall cost of the worst industrial dispute in the history of Perkins was immense: everybody had lost and the effect on the trust between the workforce and management was tragic. Some years later, John Harper-Tee, a journalist who had been Industrial Editor of the Peterborough Evening Telegraph at the time, summed up the events of the long hot summer of 1973 as 'madness': not just the demands of the workers for parity but also the performance of the management. It was a sad period and coloured the relationships between the sides for a very long time.

Chapter 16: 'Let the Good Times Roll' (1974 - 1976)

The opening days of 1974 did not suggest that any improvement in Britain's overall situation was close. Along with the oil crisis and a temporary 50mph speed limit there was a major restriction on the availability of electricity for industry. The crisis deepened on 10 January when train-drivers' union ASLEF came out on strike, crippling the country.

Within Perkins, however, improvisation became the order of the day. In spite of having mains electrical power for only three days of the week, full production was somehow being maintained. Vivian Frayling identified three objectives – to maintain deliveries to the customers, to protect jobs and earnings and to obtain the best level of production. The Company found, and put to work, eight generating sets in critical areas of the plant. Some operations were moved to areas of better natural light whilst during non-power days the engine storage and despatch process was hand-managed, cutting out the Triax storage area. A sort of 'Dunkirk' spirit was generated and a will to overcome obstacles prevailed, turning emergency into opportunity. Others were impressed, with national and regional TV, radio and press making visits to see how Perkins was coping.

Life was not work and no play, however. Sports successes were in the news during January, with the Perkins Squash Club winning the Greater Peterborough League. Star players Bernard Miles and Ted Ellis also ran coaching sessions for promising young players. In local rugby Perkins were fielding three teams, with the First and Second XVs undefeated so far in the season. Success of a different kind came to a young maintenance worker, Bill Bailey, when he appeared with his mother on the BBC TV Generation Game, hosted by Bruce Forsyth, and won the major prize!

A very significant retirement was announced at the end of January when Richard Perkins decided to leave the Company after 34 years. He had held a number of posts during this time, culminating as Deputy Managing Director and Director of Supply. The announcement included the news that he was to be succeeded by 32-year-old Victor Rice as Deputy Managing Director and Director, Operations. Sir Monty Prichard paid tribute to Richard and his contribution to the Company over his lengthy career, wishing him a long and active retirement. He intended to devote more time to his other interests, notably farming. Richard had owned a farm at Stibbington, to the west of Peterborough, for many years. In July he announced he was emigrating to New Zealand – the place of his wife's birth – to start farming there.

Among the other stories in January was an article about a novel role for the V8.510 engine in California – frost protection. A company was set up by the Franzia brothers of Ripon to market an idea originated to protect their own 2,750 acres of grapevines. This was done by spraying the vines with water at a rate of 50 gallons per acre per minute during periods when frost was imminent, and used a total of 75 V8s! A number of orders from other growers had been received to exploit the idea commercially.

A special ceremony was held at Eastfield at the beginning of February when the Lord Lieutenant of the County, Lord Hemingford, attended the presentation of the Gold Sword of the British Safety Council to the Company for their outstanding record in Industrial Safety. In making the award their Managing Director, James Tee, said: 'Your company has led the way to changes in safety management, as distinct from injury prevention. What it has done in introducing Total Loss Control has been an example not just here in the UK but to other countries of

In a bid to attract recruits, Henry Cooper was invited to Eastfield. He is seen here demonstrating "Enry's 'ammer" to a group of youngsters. See p.129

As truck sizes and power requirements increased, the final development of the Perkins vee engine to the TV8.640 provided power up to 290bhp

the world.' Since the introduction of TLC the achievement of a level of five accidents per million hours worked was unsurpassed anywhere.

It was announced that Daniel Barenboim was to return to Peterborough for the sixth Annual Concert in May, this time with the English Chamber Orchestra to play the Bruchner Mass in E Minor: the concert would be recorded by EMI the next day in the Cathedral.

National news continued to be of great concern. On 4 February 81% of the miners voted to strike again over pay, while a week later petrol prices increased for the fourth time in a year, this time to 50p a gallon, following a further massive price rise on crude oil demanded by OPEC. The Government had had enough. Edward Heath decided to call a General Election on 28 February to determine whether it was to be Unions or Government in control. The result declared on 1 March gave the Labour Party 301 seats and the Conservatives 297 seats – no overall majority. Harold Wilson became Prime Minister again, and on 6 March the miners ended their strike, for a 35% wage increase! On 8 March the country returned to a normal five-day working week.

One million engines by 1980?

Victor Rice presented awards to 128 employees who had completed 25 years' service at the annual Long Service Dinner in February. His address covered many of the challenges facing both Company and country: 'While long term the outlook for Perkins is excellent, we must not lose sight of the serious situation that faces the company now. For reasons beyond our control we cannot make enough engines – and one thought I have is that amongst the audience, with over 2,500 years of experience, perhaps you have some views on how we can overcome the problem.' He went on to speak of the fuel crisis, the growing importance of the diesel engine with its greater economy, and the success of Perkins where 1974 production should approach 500,000 engines

per year worldwide – a phenomenal rate of growth which could be even greater in the next 25 years. 'A private dream that I have had . . . is that I can see a time in this organisation when we shall be hitting the one million engines a year mark. If that happens there are all sorts of possibilities that open to us. The key thing is to grasp our opportunities now if we are to be in position to take advantage in 2 to 3 years time from now of the dramatic growth which will take place in our industry.'

In support of his speech, the February Echo reprinted articles from the Peterborough Citizen and Advertiser covering their interviews with Victor Rice in which he expanded on the challenges and opportunities presented in spite of the currently difficult circumstances. He accepted that 1973 had been a bad year for the credibility of the Company but emphasised that there had only been two major industrial relations situations in 40 years: there were positive possibilities to build a better future. He also touched upon the possible extension of the diesel market to the passenger car, commenting that Perkins had tried but the engine was still too noisy and the economics at an average of 12,000 miles a year still unfavourable.

March brought news of the new crankshaft machining line going into the extension to Factory 2. This would handle the six-cylinder crank with capacity rising to 440 per day; the aim being not only to boost production but also to reduce reliance upon outside supply. Additionally the nitrided crankshafts for the turbocharger versions of the engine and the short-stroke version needed for the 6.335 engine would be produced. (There had always been a problem with the quality of the 6.354 crankshaft, where consistency of the fillet radii, close control of heat treatment and the positioning of the induction-hardened pattern on the bearing surfaces were quality concerns in ensuring this critical component reached the necessary performance level.)

The Canton venture

Later in the month there was an announcement of a new venture across the Atlantic where Perkins was to manage a plant in Canton, Ohio, to produce a new range of six- cylinder and vee-eight engines. These were of 429, 707 and 950 cubic inch displacement, the new range extending the Perkins offerings to over 400bhp.

Although not mentioned in the news item at the time, this plant was then owned by White Motor Company and the proposal was to have the six-cylinder in production by the end of 1975, followed by the V8s at a later date. It transpired that the whole announcement was premature: the new engines were never produced and the plant was instead put to a different use.

In the same issue of the Echo there was a first mention of 'Heritage' by a Perkins employee, as Bert Saville spoke of the proposal by a small number of employees to start a museum for old engines, documents and other artefacts tracing the early history of the Company. Some collecting had already started, with Bert pictured with T12, Wolf and Leopard engines stored at Walton. The proposal did not get very far at the time, but the incentive did ensure that some articles were saved over the next twenty years.

The Budget made news again in April; an Echo leading article explained the effects of the new proposals on the Company. Adverse impacts totalling over £4.5 million a year were forecast as a result of the rises in the costs of steel, coal, National Insurance, graduated pensions, rail fares, postal fees and telephone charges.

Further expansions

Factory 3 was reported to be on schedule, while in Brazil a factory extension of 45,000 sq ft was underway to take local production to 54,000 engines a year. This covered the introduction of the 4.236 and 6.354 families to Brazil, at up to 30,000 engines a year, with high local content in view of the stringent controls on importation. Another Latin-American item concerned the visit of Victor Morales, the new General Manager of Motores Perkins SA in Mexico. He made his first visit to Eastfield having moved from the Massey Ferguson office in Mexico City to take charge of the diesel plant; the proposal to double their production to 36,000 engines a year confirmed the growing demand for engines in the whole region. Morales also spoke of the importance of the compensated 6.3542 in Mexico where it was helping to reduce air pollution caused by diesel trucks and buses at altitude.

On the sporting front, there were a number of successes reported: one of the Perkins tenpin bowling teams reached the regional final of the 1974 European Corporate Championships, whilst Purchasing Officer Philip Romaine won the Peterborough 'Round the City' race. The Perkins football team retained the KVT 'European Cup' when they beat Kemper van Twist 3-1.

The operation of the Government's Price Commission came into the news at the end of April when they cut the Perkins submission for a product price increase from 14.3 to 13.9%: the difference was accounted for by some changes in the rules applied by the Commission. In an explanatory article the reasons for the rise were reviewed: supplier price rises accounted for the apparently large increase and this was put into perspective by some of the increases inflicted on Perkins. Examples quoted included a 41% rise on fuel injection pumps, 32.8% on fuels, 16% on pistons and steering pumps and no less than 46% on interest on borrowings.

Joe Hind addressed the Annual Dinner of the Long Service Club, held at the Technical College in May. He dwelt at some length on the efforts being made to produce cleaner and quieter engines, commenting that 'When you read rude remarks about manufacturers not doing things about pollution, remember that it is the customers who won't pay for cleaner and quieter products.'

In the same month the new Director of Operations, Victor Rice, announced some organisational changes. Vivian Frayling was appointed to the new position of Director of Logistics, covering purchase, production control, planning and procurement. Reporting to him as Purchasing Director was R.G. (Ronnie) Hadnam. Bernard Dyer continued as Director, Manufacturing Planning, plus acting as Director, Production Operations, while Roger Clarke was appointed Director, Sales and Market Development, taking over the responsibility from Rice.

Later in May the Engineering Division unveiled four new test beds, built at a cost of £40,000, to meet the new American Federal Authority requirements for emission testing. These cells were able to measure smoke and gaseous emissions to a new accuracy – the US regulations laid down a test cycle and demanded that total smoke, carbon monoxide, nitrogen oxides and hydrocarbon emissions were measured over the whole cycle. The test equipment included 'new generation' measuring devices and a dynamometer capable of driving the engine at low speeds for a part of the test procedure. Needless to say, the whole set-up had to be inspected and signed off by an American Federal authority representative.

Chay Blyth was successful in the Whitbread round-the-world sailing race: his 4.107 engine completed its second circumnavigation, and was reported to have operated faultlessly – 'without a sputter' – even starting immediately amongst the icebergs of the polar seas.

Four employees were the first to achieve 40 years' service for the Company. Those honoured were Guy Screeton, Frank Hart and Russell Broughton, all of whom had started as fitters with Frank Perkins at Queen Street in 1934, and Wally Clarke, who had started in a clerical function and went through several roles before becoming Shipping and Traffic Manager in 1959. Guy became an expert on fuel injection equipment and was currently Group Senior in FID at Eastfield. Frank worked in the vehicle conversion shop at Queen Street before moving on to the Service side, while Russell progressed from Foreman of Rebuild to General Foreman at Eastfield before becoming a manager in Quality Control.

The Industrial Concert on 3 May was hailed as another great success, with Mozart's 'Coronation' Piano Concerto a perfect foil to the Bruchner E Minor Mass, although there were some adverse comments about the acoustics of the cathedral which sometimes blurred the sound reaching the audience.

Squish Lip Combustion System

In early June Perkins released details of their new 'Squish Lip' combustion system, the result of a year's intensive research effort by a team consisting of Tony Downes, Fred Brear and Ian Middlemiss and led by System Engineering Manager Roland Bertodo. Perkins was the first company in the world to declare that they could meet the Californian Air Resources Board 1977 legislation requirements with a naturally aspirated direct-injection diesel. As well as achieving gaseous emissions below 5g/bhp/hr, the system produced a 3dB(A) noise reduction as the lower rates of pressure rise softened the characteristic diesel 'knock'. A further development programme costing £2 million was under way to evolve specifications for 1976 production start-up. It was claimed that the squish lip technology endowed the direct injection engine with some of the desirable characteristics of the indirect injected engine without losing the fuel economy advantage.

Efforts continued to reduce costs throughout the Perkins operations: a specific area being electrical power. It was found that even when the plant was not working there was still a demand for 850kWh of power! A drive was instituted to shut off all unnecessary lights and other electrical equipment.

A local application for the new V8.510(M) engine was in the news

Factory 3, the new home for engine rebuilding, soon after the move from Queen Street in April 1975

with the commissioning of fishery protection vessel Protector operating out of King's Lynn. The launch was fitted with twin V8s and was used to enforce fishing by-laws from the Humber to Great Yarmouth: with a 20-knot top speed and 500-mile range the vessel was well equipped to police local waters.

Modern equipment at Eastfield hit the headlines as ten numerically-controlled machines were installed in the new extension to Factory 2. These new-generation machine tools were intended to reduce set-up times and the need for jigs and fixtures, as well as being able to perform multiple operations on production components. A new electronics and instrument laboratory was set up near the machines to handle their special needs.

'Our 'Enry' visits Perkins

The drive to find more shop-floor labour continued. Henry Cooper – former Empire and European Heavyweight champion, and one-time contender for the World title when he fought Mohammed Ali – was invited to Eastfield to help encourage recruitment. He was the first leading sportsman to be asked to help an industrial concern in such a manner. The need to increase employee numbers, at about 120 a month, went hand-in-hand with the efforts to regain customer confidence and alleviate the crucial shortage of engines. Actions on expansion of production and location of new suppliers were also publicised.

Nobody in the country was astonished in late June when inflation for the past year was declared at 16%, a post-war record. The Labour Government finalised a 'social contract' with the TUC, aimed at restraining pay increases, and a few weeks later brought their 'Trade Unions and Industrial Relations Bill' into force, repealing the Tory 'Industrial Relations Act'. (The 'control' processes of the government

were to continue through the summer, with announcement of capital transfer and wealth taxes; small wonder that by mid-August the FT Share Index had dipped below 200 points for the first time in 16 years!)

The Sports Association announced the start of the 1974 competition to find 'Miss Perkins Diesel', while six teams from the Tenpin Bowling Club entered the annual twelve-hour marathon in aid of charity. (One team set a record of 24,929 pins, while over £1,000 was raised for charity – the real object of the attempt.) The Gwyneth and Frank Perkins Memorial Fund gave financial support to fourteen members of Peterborough District Hospital staff attending the World Conference on Intensive Care in London.

Big plans worldwide

Production was scheduled to rise by 20 percent by 1976 – Victor Rice was quoted again in stating that the Perkins current worldwide output of 400,000 engines was expected to rise to one million by 1980 to meet the expected demand. However, the first priority was to regain lost ground with customers now sourcing competitive engines. Chrysler were buying Mercedes-Benz products, British Leyland and Dennis were using Leyland engines, and even Claas was now using Mercedes after being exclusively Perkins. Other smaller customers were specifying Ford, Deutz and Fiat engines so that the competition ranged against Perkins was quite formidable.

More details of the expansion programme were published on 18 July. The transfer of the remaining work to the expanded Factory 3, plus the further expansion of the Engineering workshops and test facilities, would allow the final closure of the Queen Street factory. There was a further plan for more expansion, with a search for a new plant somewhere in continental Europe to increase production of the

4.236 and the 6.354, looking three years ahead.

There was news for Brazil too: a new plant to supplement the existing factory in São Bernardo was planned, to take production to 100,000 engines a year. In addition the Perkins Group had acquired their first foundry with the purchase of Progresso Metalfrit in São Paulo: this iron foundry was established in 1917 and had a capacity of 8,000 tons a year. The intention was to expand this to 24,000 tons with the possibility of supplying castings to other parts of the Perkins expanding empire. Victor Rice also intimated that the White Motor plant in Canton might also go beyond the production of the new six-cylinder and V8 engines; he had confidence in the future and had no intention of finding the Company short of capacity to meet whatever new demands customers might make.

At Eastfield there were more managerial changes. Keith Williams was appointed Manager, UK Production Operations, reporting to Bernard Dyer. In Engineering Division Roland Bertodo was appointed Director, Product Engineering, and David Burnicle became Director, Applications Engineering; both reporting to Joe Hind. The following month there was news of a reorganisation of the Personnel and Industrial Relations Division, with four new managers – Chris Plaster, Alan Don, Norman Perry and Gerry Yates – reporting to Director Bill Mearns.

In August the diesel industry received a boost as the Government's Rothschild 'think tank' on energy conservation concluded that the engine was 30% more economical than the petrol engine and that there was no better competitor around. However, there were adverse comments about the engine being more expensive, noisier, heavier and with poor vibration and smoke characteristics. Joe Hind commented in the Echo that the industry was working hard on these criticisms, and announced that Perkins were funding a research scholarship at a London university to investigate diesel odour (Colin Ingram, later to become Director of Engineering at Perkins, was sponsored to undertake this work). There was also action planned to quieten engines through cladding and shielding – one laminated material on trial used a sandwich of asbestos and lead sheets.

Perkins announced that the new V8.540 vehicle engine would be at the Earls Court Commercial Motor Show, suitable for trucks up to 24 tons at the new legal requirement of 7bhp/ton: the Company would be continuing its unbroken record of attendance at every show since 1935. There were news snippets about customer achievements: for instance the Geest food distribution fleet ran ten million miles a year, relying mainly on British Leyland Boxer and Mastiff trucks with the 6.354 and V8.510 engines. This £100 million enterprise delivered to shops across the UK six days a week throughout the year – this was of course before supermarkets had become commonplace with their 24/7 supply needs!

In early September Keith Williams announced a reorganisation of the Production Division, aimed at increasing emphasis on engine build and improved customer satisfaction. He appointed Eric Marriott, Cyril Clarke and Alan Barnes as Production Managers looking after Factory 1, Components and Factory 2 respectively, with Wally Whitborne running Fletton and Bill Hill in charge of the transition of Rebuild from Queen Street to Factory 3.

Reports from the Earls Court Commercial Motor Show highlighted the increased numbers of foreign trucks and engines on display. Roger Clarke, Director of Sales and Market Development, commented that for over a year Perkins had been unable to supply enough engines to meet all customer demands, and were still having to advise long-standing customers that even the reduced allocation promised could not be met. This shortfall was as much as 40% on some engine types, due in part to inadequacy of the Eastfield facilities but also because the suppliers of specialist parts, such as fuel injection equipment, pis-

tons and rings, cylinder liners and small iron castings, were unable to react fast enough to the increasing demand. There was also an inability to support the requirements of overseas plants for CKD kits and also the needs of the spares market. Although every British manufacturer had the same problem as the diesel market expanded following the oil crisis, it was clear that some competitors were reacting faster than Perkins.

At the Southampton Boat Show in September, Perkins exhibited the 4.154 (M) for the first time, rated up to 58bhp and 3000rpm for pleasure craft. The engine was advertised as a twin installation for cruisers up to 32 feet, as a single installation for craft to 26 feet, or as an auxiliary engine for yachts up to 40 feet. Alongside this new product there was the usual array of other marine engines up to the V8.510.

You can't build engines without the parts!

The October Echo gave considerable coverage to the efforts being made to find additional suppliers to help resolve the shortfall in component sourcing. During the year there had been approaches to over 400 companies on a worldwide front – 23 countries being visited as well as many UK companies. Negotiations were in hand with 70 of those contacted. The Logistics Division team of fifteen buyers, led by Vivian Frayling and Ronnie Hadnam, travelled thousands of miles to places including Australia, India, Japan, Mexico and Eastern Europe. While this search was proceeding, the Material Provisioning Department was chasing existing suppliers on a daily basis to support production engine completion. As the end of the financial year approached there was a concerted drive to complete many of the engines held on the floor for missing components – over 5,100 were freed off by a 'task force' action, although some of these were to be completed after they reached the customer. It was very clear that actions to balance inventory and avoid further such campaigns were a priority for the New Year. A picture of Victor Rice sitting on one incomplete engine in a sea of problem products did nothing to improve the Company's image!

Additional space in Peterborough was provided through the leasing of a warehouse previously used by Farrows Foods in Fletton, to be used for CKD storage and despatch. Action to take over a factory formerly used by Newall Engineering at Fletton followed, giving a further 95,000 sq ft to extend small parts machining. Victor Rice commented that Perkins were fortunate to find such premises, shortening the time needed to bring new capacity into use.

Further space was also needed – this time for the Perkins Social Club in Church Walk, to accommodate the increasing membership. Plans were announced to extend the bar and open a small restaurant, aimed at providing space for a further 350 people.

In November a flurry of statistics was published. The Suggestion Scheme had paid out £12,500 in the past year, including two maximum awards of £1,000 and a further 22 between £100 and £400. The Safety Office had sold 5,000 pairs of safety boots and shoes in twelve months – in all styles, colours and sizes. At prices ranging from £4 to £6 these were a bargain since no VAT was paid.

The 1974 Perkins Ball attracted a maximum capacity of 1,000 people: they danced to the music of Syd Lawrence and his Orchestra for the third time in four years. One of the attendees was 18-year-old Sandra Loan, the recently elected 'Miss Perkins Diesel'.

In November the first move from Queen Street to Factory 3 was advised: 150 workers were to move in mid-December, to be followed by personnel from Rebuild after Christmas. The new plant was said to be the most modern area possible, with fume extraction, more natural light, wider gangways and more space between machines. Quite a transition for the lucky workers, who went from the oldest to the newest premises!

Yet more statistics were quoted as Bernard Dyer addressed the annual dinner of the '200 Club'. He reviewed the problems and challenges of the 1974 fiscal year, noting that business had never been so difficult, with demand at a record high and ability to satisfy it frustrated on every hand. The first plan for the year had shown 372,000 engines; this was revised down to 308,000 – with many customers being told what had been allocated to them – but in the end only 230,000 engines were produced, no better than 1973. The 1975 forecast was for 399,000 including CKD kits: this was recognised as a challenge which could be met 'if we all pull together'.

A striking success was achieved, however, by sixteen members of the Purchase Department, just in time for Christmas, when they won £505,324 on the Football Pools, for a 25p stake! England's football manager, Don Revie, presented the cheque at the Grosvenor House Hotel in London.

December also saw a record attendance of 94,000 at a very successful Public Works Exhibition at Olympia, the last to be held there. Perkins products appeared in 49 machines on 32 stands: these included two new JCB crawlers, a Ruston Bucyrus backhoe and a Hitachi excavator. Later the same month the Smithfield Show featured Perkins strongly once more: in ten years it was claimed that 2.25 million Perkins engines had gone into service worldwide, with every third diesel tractor sold, and two thirds of all combine harvesters, being fitted with Peterborough-designed engines.

An opportunity missed!

Although the difficult year closed on a good note, it should have been so much better. The sustained high level of activity failed to have the expected effects, for all manner of reasons. The full statistics for 1974 show 232,128 engines produced, only 4,500 more than the previous, fraught, year. The 4.236 family pushed ahead with over 73,500 produced, most other products remaining fairly static. Production of CKD kits, at 91,633, was nearly 80% up on the previous year, but well short of the levels achieved in the early years of the decade.

All in all, 1974 represented an opportunity missed. To put it in perspective nationally, it is worth quoting some data on the inflationary pressures: the 'Cost of Living Index' in 1974 increased 20%, wages rose 26% (September to September 20%) with some sectors higher (e.g. schoolteachers 32%). Steel prices rose 45% through the year, while the removal of price controls in Denis Healey's November Budget had seen petrol prices spiral from 42p a gallon in January to 72p in December, including a high VAT increase on fuels.

1975

The first news story in January 1975 concerned the move to metrication. David Hodkin, the Director of Product Planning and Reliability and Chairman of the Metrication Steering Committee, announced that gradual introduction had started, with completion targeted for the end of the year, after two years of planning. All new products would be to metric dimensions using the International Standards Organisation (ISO) standards. With over 100 countries already using metric, and a further 35 committed, including the USA, it was imperative that Perkins fell into line as more and more customers expected the change. Training was already underway in conjunction with the Peterborough Technical College; 50 engineering personnel had already passed through the courses, with a further 1,000 to follow.

The Polish Project

One of the first projects to benefit, and indeed increase the complexity of the in-house metrication process, was announced quietly at about the same time. Discussions had begun in 1972 with the Polish Government over a plan to modernise that country's tractor and diesel engine industry. The process was long drawn out: within Perkins and

Massey Ferguson some senior staff who felt it unlikely that the contract would be awarded to the Group. However, the decision came finally in September 1974 and an agreement was signed between MFP Limited and the Polish foreign trade enterprise Agromet Motoimport, representing the Polish Ursus Group of Companies. Worth a total of £150 million, the agreement also involved GKN, CAV and other leading British companies and aimed at production of 75,000 tractors and 90,000 engines by 1980. The agreement was very detailed and meant that a team had to be established from scratch and start the documentation very quickly indeed. The author was one of the first members of the management team: one of his first tasks was to action a 'soft-metrication' process for every drawing needed for D3.152 and 4.236 engines production.

A major change to the treatment of clerical employees was announced in January when a Job Evaluation Scheme was agreed for APEX Union members between Company, National Staff Council and the Union. Individual job summaries and questionnaires were completed as a first stage in producing a full evaluation of job content and value. An improved pension plan for hourly-paid personnel was announced: meetings were held to explain the details, including the computerisation of all records.

Also during January, Victor Rice conducted a series of informal discussions involving shop stewards, supervisors and managers to consider both the problems and the opportunities for growth in the current economic climate. He commented: 'It's a pity we did not start this kind of dialogue a long time ago but at least we have made a start now.' The difficulties of keeping a 13,000 workforce fully informed, 8,500 of them in Peterborough, was not lost on the management team.

Retirement of Sir Monty

Sir Monty Prichard announced his decision to retire from his post as Executive Vice President, Engines and Managing Director of Perkins at the end of January. He agreed to continue as Chairman until the end of the year, however. His successor was to be Peter Wright, a long-serving MF man currently Executive Vice President for Europe. At the same time it was announced that Victor Rice would be moving to the post of Comptroller of the MF Organisation in Toronto. MF President Albert Thornbrough paid tribute: 'Sir Monty has provided the central thrust of the major expansion of Perkins since its association with MF began in 1959. His contributions have been immense and all of us will miss his always strong participation in Company affairs.' Within Perkins there were many tributes to the man who had been the strongest possible salesman for the Company's products and who had steered the enterprise through some difficult years.

February brought further news of the drive to recruit more component suppliers. Forty-eight new British companies were involved and a total of one hundred across the world, with further talks ongoing. All manner of parts were involved, and many suppliers would be making major investment in plant and staff to support Perkins' needs. The additional evaluation and validation of these suppliers put a further burden on Engineering, Quality Control and the Logistics Division as the number of parts involved increased dramatically.

Sir Monty undertook one of his last duties when he presented the 25-year awards at the annual Long Service Dinner. There were 137 awards, including four ladies, bringing the total 'quarter-centurions' to 557 – or over 20% of the 2,600 employed by the company in 1949.

The Echo of 13 February contained a special supplement in which Jim Felker gave a guide to the 'language of finance', explaining that 'Finance is Everyone's Business'. Some significant facts were presented, not least the need to generate 5% profit consistently in order to pay for replacement, modernisation and expansion – an occasional 'flash in the pan' being insufficient. He noted that with Accounting handling over £120 million a year, a close watch had to be kept on every facet of the business, with computer control becoming a necessity. On current figures of every pound handled, 55p was spent on materials, 22p on wages, 4p on depreciation, 15p on overheads, leaving only 4p as profit.

A second Echo in the same month carried a leading article on the Engineering Division and its work on fundamental diesel engine performance. Roland Bertodo detailed the major points to be tackled to meet noise and emissions legislative requirements worldwide up to 1980, together with expected fuel consumption improvement and better understanding of factors such as exhaust odour. He noted that: 'It is expected that the completion of this engineering programme will allow all currently known, proposed or expected legislation to be met on time and in an orderly fashion.'

While this programme was starting, changes in Logistics Division aimed at improving the programming function, allowing a balance to be achieved for engines and components. Better forecasting for customers was also essential: by making each family of engines the responsibility of an Engine Control Manager the right control of priorities could be set with the Sales and Marketing Development Department. Richard Robson was placed in overall command of the new area, with Ken Groves, Terry Sismore, Peter Latter and Peter Morgan controlling the four engine groups. An 'Engine Output Monitor' showed 5,889 engines already in arrears for the first three months of the financial year, so improvement was needed.

Further statistics were given for 1974, showing that £124,000 had been saved in energy costs – an overall 18.2% saving – through economies on fuel and electricity. A part of this was down to a 5 degrees Fahrenheit reduction in office and factory temperatures. A Government advertisement in the National press under the 'Save It' project highlighted the Perkins efforts. (During February the miners accepted a pay rise of up to 35%, with coal prices set to rise 30% in March: this was followed by a record rise in electricity prices of 35%, so the savings efforts were soon justified!)

In March the first reconditioned engine came off the new assembly line in Factory 3: the final sections from Queen Street were scheduled to move in April. Even more statistics recorded the rebuild throughput of Queen Street to be 182,203 engines from 1948 to 1975.

The Echo duly recorded that production arrears in February alone were almost 5,000 engines as the plan for 1,245 engines per day achieved only 1,001. Bernard Dyer commented that it was a great pity that stoppages caused such a loss. Additional focus on losses looked at others costs, where 1975 scrap was forecast to cost £500,000: the Suggestion Scheme looked for ideas for savings, while publicising the payment of a £1,000 jackpot for a proposal on the machining of 6.354 cylinder blocks to avoid scrap due to misplaced holes.

Another of the original employees retired at the end of March as Frank Hart left after 41 years' service. Memories of the early days were stirred as he recounted the struggles to assemble five engines a week with twelve employees, and later days testing the first P6 engine in Wales and demonstrating it around the country.

During April 'Project 1202' started, a £7 million programme to move machining lines to the new Fletton Components factory, modernise the Walton plant and make changes at Eastfield including the provision of a new area for engine buffering prior to despatch.

The Queen's Award for Industry again

In early May there was cause for celebration again as Perkins received the Queen's Award to Industry for Export Achievements for the third time in nine years, following a year when 86% of production was exported directly or indirectly. In the five years since the last award exports had risen from £32.765 million to £63.192 million. The cita-

tion also spoke of the 'notable achievement' of Perkins' involvement with Massey Ferguson in the Polish contract as a further success for British Industry.

There was yet more new business as Perkins announced a deal with Volkswagen in Germany to produce the new 4.165 engine to provide the diesel power for the first VW range of light trucks. The engines were to be built at a new plant in Hanover, but with some components supplied from Peterborough. This was the culmination of long discussions with this major customer, and the engine would also be supplied to other customers.

A small item of 'heritage' interest in the 1 May Echo recorded the permanent display of the record-breaking boat Four Points in the Museo Nazionale della Science e della Technica Leonardo da Vinci in Milan.

Later in May Peter Wright addressed the Long Service Club annual dinner. His theme, inevitably, was the position of the Company and its unwanted reputation in the market as a poor supplier. Speaking to an audience of committed employees, his emphasis was perhaps unnecessary as he spoke of the effects of inflation, industrial relations and the need to get it right. In reply, new Club President Joe Shakespeare spoke of the LSC as the most important organisation at Perkins since it was based on trust and loyalty, the most important company asset. His views were echoed by the Mayor, Councillor Bill Passmore, who spoke of the inspiration he felt in such a gathering.

During June the first moves into the Fletton Components Factory began. All Eastfield connecting rod machining was relocating, together with 4.270/4.300 block machining. Careful consultation with shop floor operatives and TUs allowed workstation layouts to be optimised. In the same spirit of consultation there were employee places on the Local Advisory Committee for the works pensions scheme too.

Later in the same month Brazil was in the news as Peter Wright presented his Challenge Cup to MPSA after they rose to his challenge to produce 230 engines a day for a full month! General Manager Jorge Silveira accepted the cup on behalf of the company, recognising that a future challenge elsewhere in the Group could take it away!

By July the new packing plant at Fletton was in full operation handling the CKD kits and manufacturing parts needed for the many overseas plants. Parts were being handled for Bulgaria, Yugoslavia, Greece, France, Spain, Mexico, Brazil, Argentina, Japan and the USA. During 1975 new plants in Korea and Peru would be added, with V8s as CKD in 1976 for Spain. The operation also supplied parts for the Central Parts operation at Urmston, Manchester.

The V8.510 gained unexpected success in an unusual race. A trawler, Anne Marie, originally owned by Bob Bolton, a past competitor in the Offshore Powerboat race, had been fitted with a V8.510(M) and collected three trophies in the annual Port of Brixham trawler race in late June.

After all the news of plant changes and expansions it was the turn of office staff in July. Due to lack of space and a pressing need to refurbish and modernise the old North office block for more suitable computer accommodation, there was a proposal to reoccupy the Peterscourt offices with the cooperation of the Peterborough Development Corporation. Up to 400 staff would be relocated while new offices were built at Eastfield to provide 50,000 sq ft of modern accommodation. A 10,000 sq ft temporary office would be sited along the front of the Engineering offices as the old North Offices were modernised.

During June a serious labour dispute at the MF Banner Lane plant, including a worker 'sit-in' occupation of the main offices, had disrupted production. By the end of June a total of 23,853 engines had been lost versus plan – a cumulative result of local disputes, absenteeism and material shortages. The dispute also disrupted the efforts of the Polish project when the MF strikers also shut down the service school and offices at Stoneleigh, where the joint MF/Perkins team had been located.

On the sporting front, Peterborough hosted football teams and supporters from the Yugoslavian licensee, IMR. Although the two Perkins teams lost their matches, as they had in Yugoslavia earlier in the year, a good time was had by all as the IMR group were hosted around Peterborough – including a Civic Reception at the Town Hall.

There was even more than usual interest in safety and health issues as the Company prepared for the enforcing of the 1974 Health and Safety Act. With increased responsibility on all employees for personal safety in addition to the established procedures, a joint management and Trades Unions working party set new guidelines and a training programme. Aspects covered included health, safety and fire prevention measures.

Announcement of a Peruvian Licensee

Another licensee operation was made public as a proposed joint venture in Peru reached agreement. The plant was to be operated by Perkins in conjunction with the Peruvian Government and Volvo, with the new factory to be built in Trujillo in the north of the country. As well as 4.236 and 6.354 engines, the plant would assemble larger Volvo six-cylinder engines for use in locally produced trucks and other machines. Advertisements appeared in the August Echo, seeking volunteers for key staff posts on expatriate assignment as the plant was brought into operation.

The Echo also contained an early warning of the intended 1976 'Sports and Family Day', the first to be held for nine years. Volunteers were sought to help with the organisation for the event expected to include an 'It's a Knockout' competition, barbecue and evening dance, with the famous Ray McVay Orchestra, as well as the usual factory tours.

In September there was news of a new extension to the Fletton V8 plant, adding an extra 14,000 square feet to accommodate the new V8.640 engine, while at Eastfield a new fire station was being completed, to give the volunteer firemen a proper home to replace the 'temporary' green hut at the north end of the site – occupied since 1955! Another new building nearing completion at Eastfield was the 178,000 sq ft factory extension for extra machining, assembly and storage. An important 'opening' was that of the extended bar at the Sports and Social Club on Church Walk.

A group of 'marathon walkers' raised over £1,000 for charity (LEGS – Let Everyone Give Something) when 100 people set out to walk 51 miles from the factory to Hunstanton. Not all managed the full distance but six brave men did, taking up to 14 hours to complete the walk.

The shortfall on engine production continued into August, with the deficit for the year declared as 36,295 engines versus plan. By now there was an apparent slowdown in demand in some markets, especially trucks and light tractors, while material problems, holiday and absenteeism continued to have an adverse effect.

The efforts of Perkins Engineering to address possible alternative energy solutions continued when Research Engineering Manager Bill Tipler addressed an SAE conference in Milwaukee. In recommending that 'energy sources should be used to do the jobs they do best', he proposed the use of spark-assisted diesel engines to make the best use of lower grade fuels, including coal-based fuel.

Some product news also appeared: the National Coal Board praised the performance of the 4.108 engines used in 50 Bedford CF twelve-seat personnel carriers used to move miners around in the Scottish pit area. Running up to 80,000 miles a year in dirty operating conditions, the engines were rated highly reliable with little down time over their average three-year life. Elsewhere there was another British record for Perkins as Nat Barkwill in Sandy Bay Girl set a new speed record for cabin class cruisers at 60.455mph, using twin T6.3543s rated at 250bhp each.

A special edition of the Echo in November celebrated its 21st birthday with a review of the past years plus a miniature facsimile of the first edition. The same issue carried news of a reorganisation in Peterborough as Joe Hind was made MD of Perkins Engines Limited and head of the UK Area Operations Unit. Roger Clarke was appointed head of Eastern Hemisphere Operations, Jim Felker of Latin American Operations and Ken Glass of North American operations; all reporting to Peter Wright as Chairman and MD of Perkins Group Limited.

A few days later there were further changes within the Manufacturing Division as Keith Williams created new key positions in support management to cover inspection, material control, product change and similar functions, all aimed at improving product throughput. It was announced that the 4.236 block machining line had produced over 100,000 components in the past twelve months: Director, Manufacturing and Component Supply Planning, Jeff Herbert paid tribute to all involved in the achievement, noting that a £200,000 refurbishment, planned in January and carried out during the July shutdown, had paid great dividends.

Total production at the end of October, the close of the financial year, missed the planned volume by 48,440 engines, although it was 13% higher than the previous year. October production was 1,342 engines per day, against the original intention of 1,504. During the annual dinner of the Suggestion Scheme '200 Club', Joe Hind noted that the world production of diesel engines (excluding passenger cars) in 1950 was 2.5 million, but the forecast for 2000 was 20 million! He said that with oil prices escalating and the differential between petrol and diesel increasing – in Argentina it was ten times more expensive – the switch to diesel was not surprising. Perkins had an essential task, and opportunity, in supporting all markets.

There were more comments from Hind in December as he reviewed the past year and congratulated all employees on their efforts. During the past eighteen months there had been concerted recruitment efforts as the UK workforce increased by 1,000 to 9,500. Following this there would be a period of consolidation, with no replacement of retirees and leavers except in critical areas; he emphasised the commitment to continuity of employment and therefore realistic manning levels. The high investment levels of 1975 would continue so that by the end of 1976 expenditure would approach £15 million. Although much of this was on factory and office space, he noted that in 1975 around £6 million was accounted for on just 80 items of machinery and equipment.

The end of year figures reached 262,572 engines, with the 4.236 family totalling 77,461 and the 6.354 at 47,969 – all new record figures although well short of plans and expectations. The CKD kit volume increased to 101,635 as several of the licensees increased their own production levels.

The overall achievements of Perkins were considerable in view of the unresolved national issues, where unemployment had risen to around 1.25 million in August – the highest level since March 1940. Other economic factors were unpalatable, with annual inflation at 21% in May and the pound sinking on foreign exchange to a value of 74.8% of its 1971 value. Chancellor Denis Healey gave an ultimatum to employers and unions alike in July that pay rises should be restricted to 10% – later amended to £6 per week. Nothing was given to those earning £8,500 a year and above as Wilson and Healey took emergency action 'to stop the merry-go-round of inflation'.

There was other, brighter, news during the year too. In a referendum on EEC membership the country voted 67.2% for and 32.8% against (in comparison to the Labour Party's 2:1 majority to leave!). Oil had begun to flow from the North Sea wells during the year, and the Suez Canal reopened after eight years in what Nasser called a 'gesture of peace'!

1976

The year did not start with optimism. National business statistics showed a record number of bankruptcies for 1975, the total of 1,875 being 110% up compared to 1973. All the evidence suggested that the corner had not really been turned as yet, with a general lack of confidence in the immediate future.

On 19 January a ceremonial closing of the gates at Queen Street heralded the end of an era as Perkins finally vacated the premises after nearly 44 years. The area was gradually cleared to make way for the Queensgate Shopping Centre, to become the centrepiece of the revitalised City centre and, for a time, a model for other similar developments.

Energy savings were still very much in the news as every business sought to reduce costs. Perkins' efforts over the previous two years had saved £374,000 on heating fuel and electricity: savings in 1973/4 and 1974/5 respectively were twice the 10% sought by Minister of Energy Eric Varley. A Department of Energy film was partially shot in the Eastfield plant. Advice sessions were run for Perkins people and friends to suggest ways that everyone could save energy and money. They covered home insulation, energy efficiency and even how to increase the economy of private cars. In February a new computer system was installed to control factory heating and ventilation to within one degree of the desired temperature. Perkins was the first UK company to install the new American-designed system, which was expected to save another £90,000 a year.

In spite of the troubled economy the International Boat Show in London attracted over 600 boats and 400 exhibitors occupied over 11 acres. Fourteen leading builders featured Perkins products, including the Moody 52 motor sailer with the 6.354(M) and the Moonraker F series cruiser with twin T6.354 (M)s.

There were other successes in sales too. The new Muir Hill A5000 loading shovel was selected by the British Army: the unit was claimed to have an improved work rate, be fast enough on the road to be used on convoys and be capable of withstanding parachute drops. On the River Thames the London Fire Brigade put the 13.7-metre Fire Swift into service. Powered by twin T6.354(M)s, this rapid-response craft with its 17-knot top speed could get fire-fighters to many of the 600 fires reported on the river each year faster than previous boats: she was joined by sister craft Fire Hawk later in the year.

Office space expansion

In late January office staff began to move into the Peterscourt offices, and the temporary 'Mercian' building on the Eastfield front lawns provided accommodation for Shipping and Traffic, General Purchase, Service and Site Services while the north offices were stripped and refurbished. A start was made at about the same time on the 91,300 sq ft Factory 3 extension. In Church Walk the Mayor opened the new extension to the Social Club: it could accommodate 700 people and had taken just 36 weeks to complete.

Expansion of the Engineering facilities included a large anechoic noise cell, able to accommodate large machines and run them under full load

In early March further pressure on the economy resulted in the pound falling to 1.982 dollars, a new record low. On 16 March Harold Wilson resigned as Prime Minister, triggering a struggle between James Callaghan and Michael Foot for the premiership, eventually resolved in Callaghan's favour.

In the meantime, the March Echo reported on Perkins' successes in Indonesia where the 6.354 had cornered much of the market for conversion of the urban bus fleets around the capital, Jakarta. As a result, half of the five million population of this crowded city used the buses daily on 106 different routes. In spite of the country's self-sufficiency in oil the improvements in reliability, maintenance and economy had proved profitable. A further article noted the importance of the 6.354 and V8.510 engines in UK fire engines, reporting that 80% of new diesel appliances were now Perkins-powered. Another important customer was the Post Office – a new order for 750 Commer PB vans fitted with 4.108 engines doubled their Perkins-powered fleet. Each vehicle ran an average of 12,000 miles during each year of a seven-year life. With the diesel vans recording 29mpg for rural use and 27mpg in the city, against the 21 and 17mpg of their petrol equivalents, the vehicles provided substantial cost savings, especially when maintenance and reliability were added into the equation.

In late March another long-serving employee announced his retirement. Martin Vulliamy had served in various Engineering posts during his 39 years with Perkins, in the last nine years as Assistant Director, Special Duties. In this position he had represented the Company on many committees, a role he would continue on a part-time basis for a period. Martin had seen the development of many products, and also many young engineers, during his career and had been a major influence in the growing technical expertise and success of the Company.

Another person in the news was Yvonne Mahaffey, the current Miss Perkins Diesel, who was selected to help promote the new 'Health and Safety at Work Act', and appeared on a poster used nationwide.

Perkins people were also contributing charitably in many ways. The Tenpin Bowling Club raised over £1,300 in their annual twelve-hour marathon session, and set a new record of 24,972 pins in the process. The Perkins and Employees Community Fund – with 6,000 members paying a small weekly subscription – made small donations to many local charities throughout the year, assisting many worthy causes.

Further expansion of the Engineering facilities

The Echo in early April detailed the unveiling of the new extensions to the Engineering test facilities with a special supplement. With an additional 75 test beds complete with remote control consoles, the area included special cells able to test for engine emissions to the new legislative conditions and three environmental cells able to test large complete machines under controlled conditions of temperature and humidity. Two anechoic noise cells enabled investigation of engine and component noise characteristics. The facility represented a further investment in modern equipment to ensure Perkins' products were developed cost-effectively under world standard conditions. Recognition of Perkins' expertise was clear when the team responsible for the 'Squish Lip' combustion system won the Gresham Cooke Prize for their paper 'A Method of D.I. Diesel Emission Control'.

More product recognition was forthcoming the same month when Geest Food Group, based in Spalding, increased their transport fleet of 71 Leyland 'Mastiff' trucks, V8.510-powered, by more vehicles fitted with the V8.540. Their Chief Engineer, Jim Esherwood, claimed excellent experience over the past three and a half years and approaching 200,000 miles per vehicle. On food distribution services the highest level of reliability and on-time arrival was essential, and he claimed that the Perkins engines, backed by good maintenance and vehicle inspection practices, literally delivered the goods. A further accolade came from the boat hire operators on the Norfolk Broads, where around 1,000 boats were fitted with Perkins engines and would carry 250,000 holidaymakers during the summer period, reliably and economically.

Joe Hind addressed the Long Service Club annual dinner in May and once again seemed to be preaching to the converted as he spoke about the need to restore customer confidence and fast: 'To achieve this means maximum effort by everyone, acceptance of a more flexible attitude to changing circumstances in work content or allocation, including who does what and where. In other words we must adapt to social change.' He noted that from 1967 to 1971 Perkins commanded up to 65% of their range of the diesel engine market, excluding Massey Ferguson business, but by 1975 that share had fallen to 46%, with Deutz as the fastest-growing competitor. In extolling the continuing good work to maintain product competitiveness and the investment in production expansion, he balanced this against the loss of credibility stemming from the labour, supply and oil crisis effects. The poor production record in 1973/4 was a major concern to all.

The continuing water shortages resulting from the prolonged drought were also a major concern, with a continuing drive to cut wastage. Perkins used 110 million gallons each year, and a campaign to 'beat the waterhog' brought emphasis on recycling, switching off, stopping leaks, etc. By August Perkins had achieved a saving of between 5 and 10%, and earned praise from Anglian Water, but needed

to go further. Every avenue for saving within the plants was being explored. On the home front, the Company distributed plastic bags to the workforce to fill and place in their house toilet cisterns, thus saving with every flush!

Late June brought the long-awaited Sports and Family Day, with a crowd of 20,000 forecast. However, that day the heavens opened and continuous rain meant that only 12,000 hardy souls braved the elements. The Engineering Division 'Red Dragons' won the 'It's a Knockout' competition and those who attended enjoyed a series of attractions.

Nationally there was still concern over the economy. Although inflation reduced to only 18.9% in May the pound sterling still lost value against world currencies, falling to 1.71 dollars in early June. The Labour Government negotiated loans of £3,000 million in the same month, managing to retain some semblance of control in spite of growing disenchantment as the electorate turned more to the Conservative opposition in local elections.

Within Europe the oil crisis was making more countries turn to diesel engines for their passenger cars, led by Citroën, Peugeot, Mercedes-Benz and Opel. In Italy, Alfa Romeo had been using the 4.108 in their F12 and A12 series vans for some time and in July launched the Guilia car with the same engine. The installation was praised by David Burnicle as one of the best Perkins had seen, and was expected to give 30% better fuel economy than the petrol version. Italian fuel prices put diesel at a big advantage too, at 168 lire (11p) a litre versus 400 lire for petrol.

Arrival of Michael Hoffman

A long-expected announcement was made by Joe Hind in mid-July as he named his successor as Executive Director for United Kingdom Area Operations and Managing Director of Perkins Engines Limited. Michael R. Hoffman was a mechanical engineering graduate from Bristol University, currently working in an executive capacity at Associated Engineering Limited. At only 37 years old he represented the new generation of management and would assume his new role on 1 November, while Joe Hind would revert to his position as Assistant to Peter Wright after his period as 'caretaker'.

During August the extension to Factory 3 was completed: a further 100 workers would be accommodated in the £1.3 million plant, to machine bearing caps and the cylinder heads for the 6.354 family, including the new .4 version which was to switch to machined inlet ports like the 4.236.

It was not only in Europe that the fuel crisis was bringing benefits to Perkins. In Brazil, where natural resources had not been developed to anything like self-sufficiency, the Government was promoting increased usage of alcohol as a fuel. Standard cars in some areas were already running on fuel with an alcohol content of up to 5%, and the commitment was to have passenger vehicles running by 1980 on 100% alcohol fuel. The alcohol was produced from distillation of the juices from sugar cane and as such was a renewable resource needing only extra cultivation and construction of the supporting infrastructure. The local car manufacturers, including Ford, Fiat, Chrysler, Volkswagen and General Motors, were all developing engines to run on the new fuel. In the meantime diesel engines were to be used only in trucks and buses, with no vehicle under one tonne payload being allowed to use such engines. However, Perkins already had one official local user in the shape of the São Paulo State Highway Police. One of their Chevrolet station wagons had been converted to a 4.203(V) in the MPSA workshops and over 20,000 miles had achieved a 50% saving versus the equivalent petrol-engine vehicles – demonstrating what could be done! In the face of the ban on small engines for cars, however, Perkins were active, along with the rest of the Brazilian diesel industry, in exploring other fuel alternatives, including the possibility of an alcohol-derived substitute or oils from natural renewable sources (see Chapter 19 for more information).

Peterborough employees were still active in supporting local charities. An idea had been put forward to fund a specially adapted bus to help transport local disabled people. A number of events had been held to raise £10,000 towards the cost of purchase and conversion. In September fifty walkers took part in a sponsored 40-mile walk: although only 11 managed the complete distance a total of £1,500 was raised, taking the total raised to beyond the halfway mark.

Later in the same month Perkins announced the latest versions of the Fletton-built vee engines, the V8.640 and TV8.640. These were to be displayed for the first time at the Earls Court Commercial Motor Show and would take Perkins into a new truck size range. The engine output of up to 250bhp meant that vehicles up to 32 tons GVW could be powered, keeping pace with industry demands. A Scania 110 tractor unit with a TV8.640 and trailer rated at 32 tons were prepared as a demonstration unit for the show.

Another announcement at the same time told of the acquisition by Perkins of Groupe d'Industries de Seine et Oise (GISO), based at Genainville in the Paris area of France. The plant would be operated by Perkins Industries SA and with a capacity up to 20,000 engines a year would support the local French markets as a further extension of the Perkins local manufacturing policy.

The new Perkins Film Unit production 'Man the Inventor' was premiered in October. The forty-minute colour film traced the history of the heat engine from Hero's aeolipyle of 2,000 years ago to the development of the modern diesel. It included unique and previously unpublished material and paid tribute to the pioneers Rudolf Diesel, Herbert Ackroyd Stuart and others. The Apprentice School produced a working replica of Hero's device for the film.

Mike Hoffman gave an interview to the Echo just after he started as Executive Director at the beginning of November. He said that he had been studying the Company's activities in detail and was very impressed with its achievements in spite of the many difficulties faced. He was looking forward to an exciting future as the Company continued its tradition of success. One of his first public appearances was at the annual dinner of the Suggestion Scheme '200 Club' later in the month, when he presented a review of the past year in Company and national terms. He commented upon the serious problems facing the nation: high unemployment, which had reached 1.5 million in August, the pound at its lowest-ever level of 1.64 dollars, and the crisis in the British motor industry as it faced ever-increasing foreign competition.

He did not dismiss the effects of competition on Perkins either, but treated this as an incentive for further investments and renewed efforts to improve manufacturing skills and efficiency, to say nothing of improving quality standards. Since Perkins was not dependent upon the UK market – with over 90% of products exported directly or indirectly – and had considerable overseas manufacturing capability, he was optimistic for the future. Diesel engines were increasingly needed as the effects of the oil crisis were understood, and he expected a busy year ahead with more investment to be made.

During the year the Suggestion Scheme had been busier than ever, paying out a record £20,000 in the year with 616 of the 3,800 suggestions being rewarded: a tribute to the continuing imagination and interest of the workforce.

The annual Smithfield Show supported Hoffman's comments about opportunity and incentive. Agricultural exports were up 25% on the previous year, and at home farmers were looking for more power in both tractors and combines. The new V8.640 was publicised as an ideal engine for larger combines, forage harvesters and combines, whilst the new versions of the 6.3544 and T6.3544 offered more power from the same package size. Perkins featured strongly on the stands of MF, Muir Hill, Leyland Tractor, International Harvester, Dronningborg and Claas.

The end of 1976 showed a new record for production in Peterborough, with a total of 269,437 engines produced. Production of the 4.236 family reached 95,880 and the 6.354 was also at a record 50,612. Even 3.152 production increased to 72,073 engines, although this remained a long way below the figures of the early 1960s. The volume of CKD kits reached 123,009 as increased demand extended across the world.

Although it was certainly not expected at the time, the overall production figure was to remain the all-time record for Eastfield right through to the end of the century.

January 1977 opened with a review by Mike Hoffman of the performance of the past year and the prospects for the new. His message was characteristically forthright: although a dramatic increase had not been expected, there had been a distinct upturn in production and a healthy increase in CKD demand during November. Peterborough was still contributing around three-quarters of the worldwide production of Perkins engines, including parts and CKD, but with world production growing at 8–10% per year it was impossible to meet the demand purely from the UK plants. However, actions in hand would see a further £15 million spend on plant, equipment and offices in the UK, taking expenditure to £35 million in three years. Much greater efforts were in hand to improve quality control and methods, to meet increasingly exacting customer expectations and legislative demands. Customers did not want to know about Perkins problems pre-delivery, or after delivery – they wanted on-time and trouble-free products.

The 'oil crisis' still received frequent attention and concern. With oil representing 45% of primary energy consumption government actions worldwide were focused on increasing efficiency in both industrial and home energy consumption. In Spain households were being limited to 80% of their 1973 consumption, while in the UK pricing and taxation were forecast to be the means of controlling oil usage.

Peter Baker addressed representatives of distributors from twelve European countries at a three-day conference covering every aspect of distributor activity. In enumerating the major companies now specifying Perkins engines, including new customers Volkswagen and Alfa Romeo, he reminded the audience of the growth of diesel power in response to world energy problems – and that Perkins was holding its position by reputation.

During February an assessment team from the Ministry of Defence Quality Assurance Department visited Eastfield to review Perkins' systems and procedures against their Quality Standard DEF 05/21: a yardstick used by many overseas companies for purchase of products. After the week-long inspection process MoD approval was won. There was further action on quality issues with the announcement of QUAC77 – a quality action campaign aimed at increasing awareness and actions to reduce defects and errors.

The industrial unrest continued, with Prime Minister Callaghan telling British Leyland to stop the strikes or no more Government support would be forthcoming: meanwhile the BL chiefs were threatening plant closures. In early March 3,000 strikers were causing 40,000 layoffs, and were served with notice of impending termination. Government statistics released in March showed that prices had risen by 69.5% since 1974: a Bill was introduced into Parliament giving the Price Commission powers to freeze prices. At about the same time the miners were demanding an end to the 'Social Contract' as unrest grew in many employment sectors.

The Echo for March contained news of a major change in Mexico, with the opening of a new 187,650 sq ft plant on a 42-acre site at Toluca. The factory replaced the original plant adjacent to the Chrysler-Automex car plant near Toluca and would be capable of producing 36,000 engines a year. All major parts except crankshafts would be machined and the plant included test beds, engineering facilities and a spare parts warehouse. Their major customers included Chrysler, DINA, Massey Ferguson de Mexico, Poclain Mexicana and Atlas Copco. Ownership of Motores Perkins SA was 24% Perkins, 7% Chrysler do Mexico, 60% Mexican Government and 9% private investors – a major change from the original operation where Chrysler held a much greater interest.

In the UK, Chrysler announced orders for 4.108-powered 'Spacevans' for the Post Office, and Dennis sold 40 'R' series fire engines to the Merseyside Fire Brigade (with V8.640 engines) and 10 F131 engines to the Greater London Fire Brigade with V8.540s. The V8.510 figured in a 'good news' story when a seven-year-old Leyland Mastiff 1600 attained 540,000 miles hauling aggregate in the Lancashire area, with routine maintenance apart from one new set of injectors and pistons, rings and bearings at 310,000 miles. Owner Vic Stone claimed average fuel consumption of 11.5mpg while cruising at 50/55mph on the motorway.

In April a new-look Echo was introduced, with an editorial by Kim Hart identifying the Company's intention to use the publication, to provide open and honest communications: in the troubled 70s this was intended to address a frequent criticism of industry in general. The new format of eight pages also reverted to a 1950s idea of providing a 'pin-up' on page 3! A new series of articles was introduced, each featuring a section or department of the Company, its personnel and work: the first covered the Gear Section at Walton where the volume of 6,000 gears each day encompassed over seventy different part numbers.

The Long Service Club publicised a change to their membership policy: instead of limiting this to 225 employees the new criterion would be continuous service of 30 years, with club membership open to everyone reaching this milestone. However, the Company recognition and award would remain at 25 years, but with a new award for 40 years' service – already 19 employees had qualified.

The potential for diesel engine sales worldwide was confirmed by an industry forecast of 1.1 million engines each year for the USA alone by 1981 (the 1976 figure was 632,000), and by an announcement by Cummins of expansion at their Shotts factory costing £30 million over five years and providing 1,200 new jobs, producing 250–450bhp engines for Europe.

Mike Hoffman talked more about the intentions of the QUAC77 Campaign, with the introduction of a 'quality gate' for CKD kit and part exports, and a drive for a major improvement on despatched engines to reduce complaints of poor paintwork, leaks and damage. In addition special action on the 6.354 and V8 engines would address their production problems.

Further sales successes were publicised during May: the despatch of the 150,000th engine to Claas in Germany, a £1 million order from National Carriers for Dodge Commando trucks with T6.354s, and an order for 10 new Hestair Dennis fire engines for the West Midlands Fire Brigade - fitted with the V8.640 and Allison MT640 transmission and claimed to be some of the most modern appliances available.

Later in the month, Mike Hoffman addressed a meeting in the Social Centre, sharing data on the year to date. His overall view was that things 'are getting better, but there is lots still to do' – while UK sales and CKD volumes were improved the overall build volume was below plan. He highlighted the urgent actions of Quality and was supported by other directors, including Keith Williams who emphasised the need for a more flexible response to customers, whose changing demands were exacerbated by the complex product mix.

Work had started on the new building in Vicarage Farm Road, where a 60,000 sq ft office block, restaurant facility and car park was being erected on a site leased from the Peterborough Development Corporation. When completed, it would house all the personnel transferred to Peterscourt, plus those currently working in the 'Mercian' temporary offices in front of the Engineering building.

Peter Wright spoke at the annual Long Service Dinner at the Regional

College: his review of the past two years traced the change from acute under-capacity, engine shortage and reorganisation, to the present where, with extra facilities on stream, the order book had fallen and maintenance of full employment was difficult. He called upon all 'to maintain team spirit while awaiting the upturn in the market and the re-establishment of credibility with customers'. He was supported as guest speaker by Roland Jennings, MD of UK Operations for Massey Ferguson Manufacturing, who recalled his own days in Eastfield and later with Perkins in Brazil. He remembered especially the help readily given at that time and thanked everyone for that help. He singled out the Product Training Department for their efforts in providing education worldwide 'wherever the engines are used'.

In July the Echo article on a particular department focused on the Eastfield restaurant and, not unexpectedly, included some startling statistics – £54,000-worth of chips each year, 50 gallons of gravy, 20 gallons of custard and 600 fried eggs every day! Manager Arthur Petty spoke of the challenge of providing 24-hour service across the Eastfield, Fletton, Walton, Factory 3 and the new Components factories. He identified inflation as his major headache, with investment in a new 4,000 cu ft freezer to help stabilise costs. The new VFR facility would include a 'cook-freeze' process for meals to assist forward planning of menus. With a total catering staff of 137 employees the Department was capable of serving 600 people in 10 minutes at the midday break!

Amongst the smaller stories at this time was the announcement of the award to Russell Broughton – the longest serving employee – of the Queen's Silver Jubilee Medal: he was one of 30,000 people nationwide to receive this after personal nomination by the Company.

The Engineering Division started working with the Atomic Energy Authority at Harwell, in conjunction with British Leyland, Rolls-Royce and CAV, on the practical application of lasers. The development of 'Laser Doppler Anemometry' was to prove a tremendous aid in measuring gas and fluid movement, furthering the understanding of the combustion process.

Nationally, July brought a demand from the miners for a wage of £135 for a four-day week, in spite of a call for restraint from old union boss Joe Gormley. The Trades Union Congress refused to set a ceiling for pay claims in response to a call from Callaghan for common sense to keep awards as close to 10% as possible. Although Chancellor Healey was preparing a 'mini-budget' offering incentives to the unions to moderate claims the left-wing members were unmoved, with the railway workers demanding 63%, and similar levels expected from other sectors. In September the UK inflation level was given as 11%.

There were a number of interesting comments in the technical press: the Government-sponsored Automotive Energy Working Group dismissed the likely penetration of diesel engines in the UK car market, arguing that the higher initial cost would make the fuel cost saving unattractive to users doing less than 30,000 miles per year. A maximum penetration of 10% was forecast! The Financial Times meanwhile reported that the Japanese diesel industry was able to support 99% of domestic engine needs, the remaining 1% being supplied by Perkins!

Closer to home, a hardy group of Perkins employees raised over £1,500 for the Perkins 'Bus Fund', an effort launched to raise £6,000 to convert a bus for use by local disabled people: they walked from Perkins to Hunstanton, the fastest man achieving 9 hours for the 50-mile distance. A much more 'off-beat' record attempt in Abersoch, North Wales, by a Manchester disco owner, Bill Kerfoot, set a world record over the August Bank Holiday weekend by towing 32 water skiers behind his 53-foot shark boat, powered of course by twin 6.354(M)s!

New business during September included American Motors Corporation announcing the introduction of the 4.154 as an option on the Jeep CJ-5, CJ-6 and CJ-7 models for 1978: their personnel attended training courses at Perkins ready for the launch. More good news came from Bulgaria, where Balkancar Impex placed orders worth £2.6 million for 3- and 4-cylinder engines to be assembled at Varna, for installation in forklift trucks, tractors and Moskvitch cars. After four years of supply this was the biggest order yet received, with expansion of the plant to 30,000 engines a year expected for the early 1980s.

The demand for more office space led to the construction of the Vicarage Farm Road offices on land leased from the Peterborough Development Corporation in the mid-1970s

Coincident with this story, the Echo described the activities of the Shipping and Distribution Department whose work covered the exportation of engines and CKD kits worldwide. The demands of the business included safe and prompt despatch, correct packing handling, documentation and clearances for the products, needing meticulous attention to every detail.

Later in September Mike Hoffman addressed some 200 UK Operations personnel at an information meeting at the Social Centre. His theme was the effort needed to get the factory back up to full capacity to make up the accrued losses, prior to the close of the company financial year at the end of October. He acknowledged the considerable component supply problem arising from supplier strikes, but believed the target being set for built engines and CKD kits was achievable, looking to go out at the end of the year with the factory working flat out. The Quality Action Campaign was also discussed, with overall support and good ideas helping the in-house committees to move towards the right quality standards. David Allen, the Market Supply Director was another speaker, identifying Peterborough as the 'mother' to operations around the world: the 1977 forecast of 232,000 engines and 157,000 kits represented a good recovery, with the 1978 forecast looking similar but with higher kit volume. He emphasised that Peterborough needed to see itself as a provider of engine sets, not just an engine plant.

New Licence Agreement with Iran

An important development in the Licensee side of the business was announced in September when a new deal in Iran was made public. Agreement with the Iranian Government provided the Iran Tractor Manufacturing Company (ITMCO) with a licence for 30,000 engines a year, to start manufacture in 1978 at a new factory in Tabriz. The 3.152 and 4.236 engines would be used in MF tractors made under licence, while ITMCO would also provide sales and service support for Perkins in Iran for other engine types and customers. Support from Perkins personnel was an essential ingredient in helping Iran modernise its agricultural and industrial base quickly and efficiently, with staff training given priority: later in the year the Echo included advertisements for personnel wishing to take expatriate assignments in support of this project.

A Government 'Save It' campaign had been given support and publicity by Perkins: in September 42 employees received a total of £4,022 for awards in the Suggestion Scheme, most of these being for energy-saving ideas. Another Government-sponsored 'Engine Sector Working Party', set up by the National Economic Development Organisation, received support from Perkins shop floor and directorate. The first report of the Working Party identified potential constraints for the diesel industry including foundry capacity, crankshaft machining and 'bought out finished' items such as fuel injection equipment and pistons. They went on to consider ways and means to safeguard the medium- and long-term future of the UK industry in the light of worldwide market trends, including Government policy, manpower and financial needs. Although at the time the diesel industry was one of the more successful sectors, it recognised that government attitudes to fuel supply and consumption were important in the light of growing competitive pressures from overseas.

Among various industrial comments in the press at the time, an article in The Times noted that while the 1976 balance of payments benefited by £1,545 million from 'invisible exports' from financial expertise, this was £50 million less than the export earnings of the British motor industry – much of this coming from the commercial vehicle, tractor and component sectors.

An Echo article reported on further sales success in Mexico, where bus company Servicio y Transportes SA had converted 1,000 vehicles to the C6.3542 engine from the gasoline engines introduced after the

Mexican Government had banned the liquid propane gas engines previously used on the buses. The diesel conversions were estimated to save over £162,000 a month in operating costs.

In November there were three new appointments to the UK management team, John Devaney being promoted to Director, Quality Control (the first such director) and Ivan Porter to Comptroller, while Richard Robson became Director, Management Systems. Another appointment mentioned was the promotion of Victor Rice to Corporate Vice-President in MF Limited, Toronto – to prove of considerable significance within a few years.

Mike Hoffman spoke at the annual 200 Club Dinner (the Suggestions Scheme elite group). One of his main points concerned the cancellation of the Q11 project, this being the small engine intended to replace the 4.108. The reasoning given was the change in the marketplace which, following the oil crisis, no longer appeared to require a small diesel to permit more economic vehicle operation, especially in the passenger car and light truck sectors. Since the Q11 was conceived as a vehicle engine it was decided not to spend the capital. to support the new project into production but to instead continue with the 4.108 for a few more years, possibly with some enhancements. (Looked at from the perspective of 2006, it may be that this was an opportunity lost, since in the 1980s and 90s the explosion of diesel-engined passenger cars started: Perkins could have been an early player in this revolution, although the major car manufacturers would have produced their own units eventually.)

Hoffman emphasised the need for substantial product quality improvements, better engine finish and appearance to meet the Japanese and American competition – and to match the product durability and reliability standards already achieved. He mentioned also the past year where a lengthy MF industrial dispute, coupled with problems at suppliers, had adversely affected Perkins' performance. He praised the efforts behind the good recovery the Company had made, and the recruitment efforts had taken total headcount to a new record. A solid start was needed for 1978, although no great expansion was forecast. Supply problems should be at least offset to a degree by better sourcing policies. The new Vicarage Farm road offices were reported to be on target for January 1979 occupation.

The new factory in Peru opened, a joint venture by Perkins and Volvo with the Peruvian Government. MODASA (Motores Diesel Andinos SA) was formed to produce 4.236, 4.248 and 6.354 engines, together with larger Volvo engines, to power new trucks, buses and tractors as well as providing repower opportunities for older petrol-engined equipment.

Local news included a report on the successful annual Perkins Ball, where 800 people danced the night away to the New Million Aires Orchestra, and the presentation of an £8,500 coach to Cambridgeshire County Council by the Perkins Bus Fund – the specially equipped vehicle to be used for transporting handicapped and disabled to and from the day centres: the fund was a voluntary effort by many workers and a variety of money-raising activities.

The year-end figures showed that built engine production fell to 228,027 units, although CKD despatch rose by 32,000 to 155,815 kits. Manufacturing Director Keith Williams commended the efforts of production staff, especially the drive to complete and despatch a backlog of around 6,000 engines held by parts shortages.

1978

January 1978 brought a change of leadership for Perkins: Peter Wright had retired at the end of December and was succeeded as Chairman of Perkins Group by Mike Hoffman, although he continued his responsibilities as Managing Director of UK Area Operations. In thanking Peter Wright for his successful reorganisation of the company to face the challenges of the changing world and the increasing competition, Hoffman injected a note of caution concerning the softening of world agricultural markets and anticipated a difficult period to come.

January brought a number of successes, with eleven boat builders showing Peterborough engines at the London Boat Show, while a team from MF were visiting Pakistan to complete the details of a joint venture to build up to 10,000 tractors per year, with the engines also locally made. Within the Peterborough plant a pioneering survey was under way covering all aspects of environmental impact: the appointment of Geoff Osborn to conduct this survey and recommend changes to meet latest national and international standards and practices represented another industrial 'first' for the Company.

Perkins figured in another record when an MF1155, with V8.540 engine, set a time of 13 minutes and 34 seconds to plough one acre – breaking the previous record by almost two minutes. Other V8s appeared successfully in powering Mercury RM350 aircraft tugs to handle the Boeing 747, while reliability records showed Leyland Mastiffs achieving up to 300,000 miles without major engine overhaul. Many operators were purchasing vehicles with the V8.540 to replace original V8.510-powered trucks.

The Vicarage Farm Road offices were 'topped-out' in early February, with Mike Hoffman officiating. At another communications meeting with UKAO staff he called for greater sales action and improved inventory control to help offset the volume loss from poor agricultural sector sales. He was perhaps guilty of stating the obvious when he identified the high cost of airfreight in place of the usual sea shipment as an adverse impact of the activity levels needed to clear the arrears at the end of 1977!

In March a reorganisation was announced, aimed at addressing the slackening demand by providing speedy response, cost effectiveness and efficient use of human resources. Hoffman expressed confidence in the ability to turn around the current 'backs to the wall' situation. The changes included:

Adrian Parsons as Group Director, Staff Operations (covering finance, administration and strategic planning).

David Freemantle as Group Director, Personnel.

Roland Bertodo as Group Director, Product Staff, including Product Planning.

Roger Clarke, Sales and Marketing.

Dietrick L. 'Pete' Peterson as Executive Director North America (NAO).

Jim Felker as Executive Director Latin America and Caribbean Operations (LACAO).

Keith Williams as Executive Director UKAO.

The presentation of awards for 25 years' service was of especial interest, with 182 men and three ladies being honoured: they started in 1952 when the workforce was about 4,000 people. This brought the total of long service awards to 1,283 – again out of that 4,000 total – quite an achievement for the company over its 45-year lifespan and indicative of the level of loyalty felt by the employees.

Among other stories of the time was an adventure experienced by Ron Whitaker, a Peterborough applications engineer working in Peru, whose Hillman Hunter car with a 4.108 engine was caught in a landslide 16,000 feet up in the Andes and swept to within feet of a 150ft drop. Miraculously men and car survived and the latter proved still driveable after being rescued by a passing truck!

Massey Ferguson announced their biggest tractor to date, the MF2805, fitted with the TV8.640 engine rated at 190bhp and intended for the US market. Over the previous ten years Perkins had supplied over 1 million engines for agricultural use, powering 40% of all combines and 27% of tractors worldwide.

In early March a German TV crew and British press representatives were at Eastfield, 'shadowing' Margaret Thatcher, the new leader of the Conservative Party in opposition, as she made a one-hour visit to Perkins to see the factory and meet the people. In the same week the new Mayor of Peterborough, Councillor Mrs Jean Barker, visited Fletton, Walton and Factory 3, meeting the men and women working in the plants.

The Sports Association opened two new squash courts at Eastfield, claimed to be the best in Peterborough and reflecting the growing national interest in the sport. One well-known Perkins squash addict, Ted Ellis, was noted to be developing a programme of exercise for the over-30s 'to fight the flab and combat middle-age spread'!

During April Mike Hoffman reviewed progress in the first months of the year, confirming that the expected sales improvements had not occurred in the agricultural markets due to poor weather and bad harvests. A drop in CKD kit demand for Turkey and Argentina added to the bad news and meant a reduction in the sales forecast. As a result Hoffman introduced a cost-cutting exercise to manage the cost base, and further reorganisation to pursue new markets. (Meanwhile, struggling British Leyland received Government backing for a £1.3 billion investment programme including £850 million of state funds over the next four years: new chairman Michael Edwardes was given almost everything he asked for!)

At the end of April Joe Hind retired after twelve years with Perkins and some thirty-eight years in the engineering industry. He had been especially influential in developing the Engineering Division into a formidable presence and latterly had acted as MD of Perkins Engines Limited up to the recruitment of Mike Hoffman.

Release of the 6.3544 engine

There was an important product upgrade in May with the release of the 6.3544 premium engine for vehicle use. This revision offered improved durability, increased efficiency and reduced noise, and featured considerable changes, including a new cylinder block design, stronger piston assembly, revised water system and steel timing gears. The engine was offered in naturally aspirated form (at 124bhp and 2,800rpm), turbocharged and charge-cooled up to 155bhp plus an altitude-compensated version for use in mountainous areas such as Mexico and South America. This release was well timed, since the UK commercial vehicle market grew 10% in the first quarter but with imported trucks taking 26.5% against 16.9% of the previous year. This penetration was strongest in the over-28-ton category: the writing was on the wall for the British truck industry although they didn't know it yet.

The British Government decided to actively discourage the growth of diesel engines in passenger cars by adding an extra 5p per gallon tax on the fuel. This may have provided some relief to Perkins after the cancellation of the Q11 project but elsewhere in Europe competitors were working hard on developing small diesels, including Fiat in Italy.

The Sports and Family day in June was attended by 22,000 people and was blessed with good weather so that all enjoyed a day of entertainment including an 'It's a Knockout' competition and displays of many sorts including sheepdog handling, aerobatics and trapeze artists. Joe Hind made a special visit to the Peterborough Museum in company with Charles Chapman, the first Chief Engineer, to see a display covering the history of Perkins.

Another special visit during the month, organised by the British Trade Council, was that of a Chinese Agricultural Mechanisation Study Mission. They saw the Eastfield and Fletton plants and were introduced to 'squish lip' technology in the Research and Product De-

Alternative fuels interest in Brazil led the Research Department to use the Apprentice School to develop a project using World War II technology to evaluate the potential of 'producer gas' on a diesel engine. The project team is seen here with the installed unit on an MF tractor in November 1979

velopment Department, before going on to visit Massey Ferguson at Coventry.

An important development in the social thinking of the Company was announced during July when the Perkins Retired Employees Club (PREC) was formed to cater for all employees upon retirement, with a variety of activities envisaged including outings, suitable sporting opportunities such as bowls, as well as monthly socials and dances, and even a choir. It took a little time to get the new club on a firm footing but it quickly became an important addition to the calendar, alongside the Long Service Club.

There were a number of 'product' news stories in July, the strangest being that of a doomed but industrious 4.108 engine fitted to a Hydrovane compressor set: the machine was welded to the upturned hull of oil tanker Eleniv after an incident in the English Channel. The compressor was pumping air to keep the vessel afloat until Royal Navy engineers were able to blow up the wreck, which vapourised the remaining oil and sank the remains of the ship plus, of course, the valiant engine too. Another item concerned an export order for 140 Ford trucks fitted with V8.540 engines, shipped to Turkey to modernise the garbage disposal system in Istanbul. Yet further success for the V8 came from the Army when 146 generator sets were ordered from Lucas Aerospace.

Closer to home the Executive Director UKAO, Keith Williams, left the company to become MD of Brush Electrical Machines in Loughborough. Meanwhile the one- millionth cylinder block was machined in Factory 2 after 14 years of operation, and the new offices and restaurant at Vicarage Farm Road neared completion, with the personnel

from several divisions being readied to move in.

August brought some disquieting news on industrial performance. Although the Motor Industry recorded increases in production of both passenger cars and commercial vehicles in June, actual export output fell 10% in the first six months versus the same period of 1977. On the other hand imports of cars and commercial vehicles rose by 38% over that period. Throughout Europe the penetration of diesel engines for commercial vehicles continued to rise as users began to recognise the importance of better fuel economy as well as the impending tighter legislation.

The launch of the 'Range 4' marine engines at the Southampton Boat Show on 23 September attracted considerable attention from marine journalists from around Europe. These 6.3544 and T6.3544 products featured considerable updating and were rated up to 138kW (185bhp) at 2,400rpm for pleasure craft applications. David Allen, the Marketing Director for Perkins Engines Group, noted a 50% increase in marine engine demand in the past two years; Perkins aimed to deliver the new range faster through rationalisation of the products and reduction of options, while still giving the customer the right engine.

Changes at Massey Ferguson

The problems besetting Massey Ferguson over the previous months resulted in the appointment of Victor Rice as President in September, replacing Albert Thornborough who continued as Chief Executive Officer and Chairman of the Board. Ambitious plans for worldwide expansion of both agricultural equipment and industrial machines, covering licensee operations as well as their own plants, ran into trouble as recession hit. Victor Rice had given the Board warnings about cash flow problems during July. Everything started to go wrong and the change putting Rice in charge proved almost too late. It is not the author's intention to cover the unfolding position in detail: this may be studied in Peter Cook's 1981 book Massey at the Brink, but a short review of the situation is essential.

Signs of weakening world markets in 1977 had followed the boom period of the mid-70s. By mid-1978 there were clear indications of major sales slumps in Brazil and Argentina, while the poor 1977 harvests in Europe, North America and Canada had left farmers unable to invest in new machinery. Rising interest rates also increased the cost of servicing the debt repayments, exacerbated by the cost of large inventories of finished goods. To be hit by so much bad news at the same time was perhaps hard luck, but it was abundantly clear that urgent action was needed. There had been a considerable power struggle within the Board of MF in the preceding months, which had culminated in the appointment of Conrad Black (a young entrepreneur whose ascent to control of the Argus Corporation, a major stock-holder in MF, is a story in itself). Black took over as Chairman of MF and convinced the Board that fast action was needed and Rice was the right man for the job of President. There followed a number of senior management changes as Rice determined which of the existing executives could, and would, work with him.

There were some unpalatable truths to be faced, with the third quarter loss of $90 million being the worst performance in MF's history. The implications for Perkins were not immediately apparent although the overall cost-cutting, including reduction of workforce, inventories and manufacturing costs, were bound to have an eventual impact. The writer saw this all from within Brazil, where early recognition of the need to reduce Perkins' exposure to the agricultural sector, with its reliance on unreliable Government funding, was followed by aggressive expansion into the vehicle and industrial sectors. An instance of local actions put in place immediately while the overall corporate salvation strategy was still being formulated!

While these eventually earth-shattering events were unfolding, normal life continued in Peterborough. The traditional Perkins 'hobbies and gardening' show took place in September, while a campaign started to raise £1,000 to buy a guide dog for the blind – so well supported that the money was raised in only twelve weeks instead of the expected year! Along with pure donations all manner of sponsorship ideas were tried, including a seven-hour 'keep quiet day' in the typing pool. The success encouraged the campaign to continue to fund further dogs.

The Company attracted a number of awards in the later part of the year, including the Gold Diploma of the Russian Chamber of Commerce for the 6.3544 engine, presented to Peter Baker at a Moscow trade exhibition, and the Bland Payne Safety Award for the Eastern Region in recognition of both the Company's excellent record over the years and the cooperation between management and trades unions in helping to cut industrial accident risks. Another 'first' for Perkins was announced in November when the MCC Cricket Team was recruited to help promote Perkins products during their tour of Australia under captain Mike Brearley – the first time such an industrial promotion had been proposed.

In November a sign of the new MF regime's intention appeared as the Echo announced 'CUT OUR SPENDING' above a Mike Hoffman invitation to all employees to become Perkins Super Savers in a bid to reduce operating costs. His comments identified the serious problems facing the Group in the depressed agricultural market and the need to economise. The Christmas edition of the paper carried a message from the Industrial Chaplains – 'A Christmas Recipe for the Future'. In quoting an old African Proverb, 'No condition is permanent', Mostyn Davies and Bob Dew reckoned this as an apt axiom for

Perkins in facing the challenges of 1979. In reminding the readers that 'God helps those who help themselves', the article recognised the heavy burden upon all employees through a period of transition, with conflicts of interest likely but not necessarily destructive. 'If one thing is going to ensure the survival of Perkins Engines it will be its ability to change and its faith in change and its determination to change.' It was a novel angle on the overall situation!

The traditional end-of-the-year celebrations included the Christmas parties, attended by 1,500 children and featuring Father Christmas, entertainers and lots of food and drink. Another cause for celebration was the performance of the Perkins Football Club's first team: 48 games undefeated including promotion to the first division at the end of the last season. So far they had scored 50 goals with only 9 in reply, were top of the division and hoping to run a second season without a defeat. (The run lasted well into the New Year, achieving 18 months and 66 games!)

The statistics at the end of 1978 were depressing, engine production at only 201,033 units represented a reduction of nearly 12% on the previous year. With lower CKD kit despatches, it had been a poor year and reflected the prevailing market conditions. These facts, however, contrast with the overall views expressed in the Encyclopaedia Britannica Year Book, which identifies 1978 as a 'boom year' for the UK – the best since 1973 – with output up 5–6% in twelve months giving a total increase of 13% since the trough of 1975. Exports were up 5% against 1977, with loss of spending power reversed and earnings rising twice as fast as prices. The reasons were identified as the increase in North Sea oil income, the strength of Sterling on the world market, and the Government's decision to increase consumer purchasing power (in hindsight a recipe for disaster?)

There were also less attractive statistics, however. Labour relations continued to be poor, especially in the motor industry (British Leyland and Chrysler UK) and the newspapers. For the first time the sales of imported cars accounted for more than 50% of the market. If ever there should have been a wake-up call to the trades unions now was the time, along with a sharp reminder to industry about quality and design. Unemployment ran at about 1.4 million through the year, with credit and wage restraints proving ineffectual as unions ignored them. Government spending and imports were rising again at the end of the year.

1979

During January 1979 Victor Rice paid his first visit to Perkins as MF President, expressing his satisfaction with the levels of cleanliness and

Brazilian company Explo developed their own gasogene-powered MF 275 tractor, seen here in November 1979. (Photograph by the author)

good housekeeping as well as meeting the executive team and shop floor workers. Nationally there was major unrest as a strike of truck drivers threatened a shortage of essential commodities such as heating oil and food, exacerbated by a series of one-day rail and public service strikes, hitting schools and hospitals. By the end of January a period of unrest, later to become known as the 'winter of discontent', was in full swing. Wage settlements exceeded the voluntary 5% limit, but still the Cabinet refused to declare a state of emergency. Rubbish piled up in the streets, schools closed due to lack of heating oil and gloom settled over the country.

The January Echo carried a 'heritage' article looking back to 1953 when a number of ex-RAF launches were sold to the Thames River Police for patrol duties. They had served as seaplane tenders and had already given stalwart service: in the article ex-coxswain Jack Chadwick recalled how they had used one boat to tow a Sunderland flying boat from Loch Ryan, Stranraer to Belfast, taking fourteen hours and needing all the power of the triple S6(M) engines. The boats were also used for air-sea rescue and were responsible for saving over 8,000 lives around the world. The P6 and S6 engines had a reputation for reliability, starting first time whatever the conditions, even if left for some time without attention. A few months later more data on the RAF launches was provided by John Goodman, a district service engineer. He recalled that many boat crews were trained at RAF Corsewell, which also provided service support for the flying boats at Wig Bay, where over 70 craft were stationed on various duties. Some of the Perkins-powered boats were able to reach 28 knots, useful especially for air-sea rescue.

In February a novel machine named the 'Trantor' was put into production by WHS Engineering Developments Ltd. This device was powered by a 4.236 engine and was developed to meet a perceived niche market for farm transporters. It was reckoned that many tractors were used 75% of the time for transport, rather than for the traditional land cultivation purposes. Thus the Trantor had a wide wheelbase and low centre of gravity, and its cabbed construction allowed the transportation of up to seven people or a half-ton payload. Able to tow a trailer, of course, the vehicle had a road speed of 60mph and could still undertake off-road tasks around the farm. (Sadly the concept never caught on in the 70s, but the development of the JCB high-speed road tractors of the 90s might perhaps owe something to the original Trantor inspiration?)

The Suggestion Scheme, whose work had been little publicised in recent years, was noted to have paid out over £180,000 since 1964 for over 10,000 good ideas. With up to £1,500 available for suggestions, tax-free, there were many inputs and with an average of 60 ideas per week the small team was fully occupied in assessing and placing the proposals before the monthly committee for processing. Often the proposers would be called upon to expand on their ideas, and in any case everyone would be advised of the outcome, with full explanation and reasons for rejection, etc. Some of the ideas from the 'War on Waste' were featured on a Roundabout Anglia radio programme, when presenter Pat Beasley interviewed Mike Hoffman. The background of the project was explained with the sort of ideas coming forward providing potential savings for anyone to exploit. In the first two months alone over £14,000 had been saved on electricity and even heating oil had been saved in spite of the wintry weather.

Indeed the winter of 1978/9 proved to be one of the most severe for thirty years, with workers marooned at Eastfield when Peterborough was cut off from the rest of the country by snow. Works transport trucks were also stranded around the country and the switchboard was jammed by incoming calls. In spite of everything the company kept going with a greatly depleted workforce, and a 'Dunkirk spirit' to help those stranded or in difficulties. Letters of appreciation from those victims, and from Production Director John Devaney saluting the team spirit, appeared in the Echo.

The Government changes – Margaret Thatcher takes charge

The Labour Government and the Trades Unions finally reached an uneasy truce, at last recognising the severe damage done to reputations and public confidence: the polls indicated a Conservative lead of 20%and Prime Minister Jim Callaghan moved to repair the damage. This proved too late, however, with a vote of 'no confidence' in the Labour Government won by the opposition on 29 March. Callaghan was forced to call a General Election for 3 May amidst a wave of public feeling that a change was long overdue.

Perkins publicity continued to extol success in the field. The achievements of V8.540 engines were recorded by UK Vehicle Sales Manager Gordon Mitchell – many truck engines were achieving 200,000 miles before overhaul and had given excellent service over the previous five years. South Yorkshire had been using Ford 1617 trucks for gritting and snow-ploughing duties, running 24 hours a day in the recent bad weather and showing excellent operating and repair costs against smaller vehicles.

Victor Rice paid another visit to Eastfield in April to talk about the new MF Corporate programme entitled 'We Can Do It'. This was aimed at demonstrating a more aggressive and competitive stance in the marketplace, to assist worldwide marketing in an effort to meet or exceed sales plans for the current year. His tour continued to other Massey Ferguson plants worldwide. (This was part of a 'hands-on' approach by Rice following the reorganisation of November 1978; this had resulted in a total of 21 executives reporting directly to him, allowing much greater insight into the operations and the results of the changes introduced.)

Mike Hoffman hosted a reception for the victorious MCC cricket team on their return from Australia, presenting skipper Mike Brearley with a double-headed penny and a do-it-yourself 'ashes kit'. Brearley, in thanking Perkins for their support said: 'We have enjoyed working with the Perkins people . . . We hope that you scored as many victories off the field as we achieved on it.' Although the sponsorship was believed to have been mutually beneficial, the initiative was never repeated.

The General Election brought the expected change as the Conservative Party swept to power with an overall majority of 43 under leader Margaret Thatcher, the first woman Prime Minister of the United Kingdom. In May the Government Price Commission, set up under the 'Price Commission Act' of 1977 and intended to retain tight control over price rises in order to combat the inflationary spiral, reported on their findings following a Massey Ferguson-Perkins Ltd notification in December 1978. The request had been for a price increase of 10.63%, weighted average, for all Perkins products including engines, reconditioned and short engines and optional extras. The preparation of the case, with its attendant detail documentation, had been a time-consuming process, involving the burning of much midnight oil as every item was carefully considered. The report of the price commission, printed on 4 April 1979, fully justified the efforts made, resulting in a recommendation that there should be no restriction in implementing in full the requested price increases. Indeed there was a further recommendation that future additional increases should not be restricted. The body of the report indicated, however, three causes for concern regarding the efficiency of the Company's operations:

Firstly, the number of engine variants produced seemed larger than might be desirable, suggesting that a variety reduction programme be pursued with vigour.

Secondly, there was concern that some elements of the plant were old and needed replacement.

The third issue was that of labour efficiency, especially in the area of labour utilisation, where a move to explore alternatives was seen as desirable.

Perkins' reaction to these concerns appeared quite low-key. Adrian Parsons, UK Operations Executive Director, noted that 'Perkins business was founded on variety, we need to keep this under control and the report recognised the actions on-going.' Clearly there was overall relief at being able to restore a better level of profitability after a lengthy period struggling with the effects of inflation.

The report had also dwelt on other aspects of the future development of Perkins. In particular the potential for development into the passenger car market, and thus progressing in the automotive sector, was a recommended route. In addition the possibility of obtaining Government funding and financial assistance to aid both profitability and capital investment was stressed, especially since diesel engines had been identified as a priority sector in the Government's Industrial Strategy. How this recommendation influenced Perkins' strategy will unfold in later chapters.

There were other more public causes for celebration in various areas of the Company. Mike Hoffman presented awards to 150 employees who had completed 25 years' continuous service in Peterborough, and in Brazil MPSA celebrated the 20th anniversary of their formation. Over that period 431,000 engines had been built, with a series of expansions as the business grew. One Brazilian-built 6.357 engine, developed from the ill-fated R6, achieved 1.8 million kilometres between 1969 and 1979 in a Chevrolet truck transporting fuel for Petrobras: owner driver Fausto Volante was presented with a new engine in recognition of this achievement.

In Peterborough one team from within the flourishing tenpin bowling club – the '007s' – won their way through to the European Championships in Vienna by finishing second out of 480 teams entered, in spite of the disruption caused by the closure of the only bowling centre in Peterborough. The Sports Association was in the news later in May when announcing the intention to build a new pavilion on the sports ground. Costing around £150,000 to build, the pavilion would improve the facilities for members of the now profitable Association. The Football section saw good results from the season: the first team won the Peterborough League Division 1 title at their first attempt, scoring 106 goals to 32 against in winning 23 and losing only 4 of their 34 matches. The second and third teams also performed well in their divisions.

During June the Engineering Division announced the commissioning of their new 60ft motor cruiser Perkoil IV. This was the latest in a series of craft used to test marine engines under realistic conditions from a base at Sutton Bridge near King's Lynn. Powered by twin TV8.540Ms the new boat was capable of 18 knots and joined Perkoil II and Perkoil III in the field test fleet.

June also heralded the first budget for new Chancellor of the Exchequer, Geoffrey Howe, who introduced substantial changes to income tax, with the basic rate cut by three pence (to 30p in the pound) and the top rate slashed from 83 to 60%. Further important economic factors followed, with OPEC announcing a 15% rise in the price for crude oil in late June – effectively a 13p rise on the cost of a gallon of petrol in the UK. In late July the Government announced cuts in public spending amounting to £4,000 million.

Closure of the Canton Plant

In July Perkins announced that the American engine plant at Canton, Ohio, would close at the end of October 1979 as part of the consolidation of operations. The new machining lines would be transferred to Peterborough and engines for the US market would all be supplied from England. Meanwhile the 'We Can Do It' campaign was finding acceptance worldwide, with badges, stickers and slogans acting as a battle cry, and improvements in company performance visible.

During August some changes to senior management were announced with Jim Felker returning from Miami to a role as Executive Director, Sales and Marketing – replacing Roger Clarke who moved to MF Headquarters in Toronto – while Adrian Parsons was appointed Managing Director, Perkins Engines Limited, with responsibility for Group Finance, Personnel and Industrial Relations Division as well.

Mike Hoffman announced a Perkins initiative on 'Future Fuels Policy' at a press conference in London in September, developed as a basis for discussion with the Government. He urged all governments to learn a lesson from the fuel crisis and the clear need for worldwide conservation of fossil fuels. His proposals for a national energy policy on fuel conservation included the suggestion that fossil fuels be conserved for the most suitable applications – mobile machinery – with stationary plant powered by more traditional forms of energy such as electricity, gas, coal, wind or solar power. Considerable work by Perkins and other producers of internal combustion engines suggested that development and utilisation of alcohol blends, wide-cut petroleum products and vegetable oils represented viable routes. Any impact of this initiative appears unfortunately to have been lost completely, perhaps discounted in the euphoria over North Sea Oil, so that the potential for development of new resources, and perhaps financing of the industry to encourage new engine and fuel technologies, was not pursued. With the benefit of hindsight this was another opportunity lost.

There was better news from Massey Ferguson in September when the Board authorised the issue of up to $500 million of new shares. The results from the three months' sales up to the end of July 1979 showed a substantial increase over the similar period of 1978, with the sales for the first three quarters of the financial year at $2,133m against the $2,022m of the previous year. The losses in the period were only $9.5m compared with $54.6m, with Victor Rice confident that the last quarter would show a break-even for the year before taking into account exchange effects or exceptional items. The Financial Times UK exporters list showed MF/Perkins in eleventh position with $387 million sales in 1978.

A solution for an unusual customer requirement featured in October when Alan Spellman of Field Test demonstrated a unique rig capable of running a T6.3544 Range Four marine engine upside down. This was in answer to a requirement for escape capsules fitted on oil platforms, where capsizing was possible and the engine needed to keep running for 10 seconds before the capsule self-righted. Some engine modifications and the special test bed confirmed that Perkins could meet the challenge. Sales of up to 100 units were forecast.

In November the Company announced the first-ever Voluntary Redundancy Scheme for staff employees as management came to terms with the need to reduce headcount, specifically targeting longer-serving personnel who were close to retirement age and had built up acceptable pension levels.

December brought news of the death of another of the Company's pioneers, Charles Chapman, who died at his Winchelsea home at the age of 82. His role in the early success of Perkins cannot be overestimated: his designs of the Wolf, then the P-Series engines, the wartime S6 and T12 products had been followed by consultancy work on the V8 engines. He also helped other diesel engine developments at Ford and became an expert on torsional problems and the design of flexible couplings. He was the author of books and articles on diesel engine design and development, as well as 'The Director's Dinner' – a novel based upon his time at Perkins.

Another unusual piece of engine development featured in December in an article covering the construction of an MF tractor with its

A4.236 engine modified to run on producer gas. This technology had been used during WW2 and surfaced again in Brazil in the late 1970s when a local explosives company exhibited such a device as a possible solution to the Brazilian fossil fuel shortage. In Peterborough young research engineer Ian Moncrieff delved into the wartime archives of Automotive Engineer before leading a small team of engineers and apprentices in adapting a Field Test tractor. The machine ran successfully on gas produced from a charcoal generator, with diesel injection used solely as the ignition source. Although the design had an element of Heath Robinson in its appearance, the practicality of the approach was proven, with an estimate of eight hours' running on one fill of charcoal! Sadly the project went no further, although the Brazilian 'Explo' tractor did run demonstrations in São Paulo state for farmers and government officials.

A more commercial success was publicised for the 4.236 in powering the new MF60 tractor-digger-loader. In an independent test the new machine with new variable displacement hydraulic system beat Ford, Case, JCB and John Deere competitors, achieving productivity levels 24 to 49% greater and using half as much fuel per cubic yard of soil moved.

The year-end numbers did not reflect any massive change in production volume. The total of 200,755 engines was a drop of 27,000 units on the previous year, while the CKD total of 118,171 kits fell some 10,000 short of the 1978 total. The loss of business was across almost every engine type, with only the 4.108 showing a modest increase. There were only guarded words of encouragement as the Company faced a new decade, with sales difficult on home and export fronts coupled to the realisation that the parent, Massey Ferguson, had major issues to resolve.

Nationally too a number of economic factors were preparing the stage for further confrontation. Additional Government cuts in public spending, this time of £3,500 million, as well as an increase in prescription charges, fuelled general concern. The building societies had set the mortgage rate at a record 15%, while the mineworkers' union had rejected a 20% wage increase, indicating that their claim for a 65% increase was imminent. Margaret Thatcher demanded a rebate from the EEC of £1,000 million and fears of runaway inflation were further fuelled as oil prices had more than doubled (from $12US to $26US a barrel) over the year and were set to go higher. The welcome to the 80s was muted.

Chapter 18: Engineering stretches its Horizons (1975 to 1980)

Mention has already been made of the 'Polish Project', signed between Massey Ferguson/Perkins, the Polish Government and their tractor manufacturer, Ursus, in late 1974. This covered the modernisation of the plant at Ursus, just outside Warsaw, to produce MF tractors under licence along with Perkins D3.152 and 4.236 engines to power them. This was a huge contract with a total value to the MF Group of £9 million plus various buyback and barter agreements to ease the Polish repayment of hard currency. The production facilities to be built were to produce up to 75,000 tractors per year and up to 90,000 engines – the additional engines being destined for other applications built in Poland.

The agreements were complex and detailed. Once signed, the contract timing was such that the MFP teams, formed very rapidly in Coventry and Peterborough, had to start delivering information exactly to the agreement programme in early 1975. Inevitably there were major priority tasks within the Product Engineering part of the agreement, with the need to produce 'soft-metricated' drawings of every component of each engine type, in a new format allowing the Polish team to add their language translation on a border around the drawing. Thus every relevant note on the drawings had to be numbered so that the cross-reference could be made clear on the translation! A special task force of design staff was formed under Ralph Reaves, with constant support from the Drawing Office Services, to produce master drawings for modification. In addition all the 'standards' documents which were cross-referenced on the drawings had to be in a suitable format for translation. The author had been appointed Technical Manager for the Perkins Engineering side of the Polish Project, working with other managers covering the other areas – an arrangement duplicated for MF. Eventually the project group was brought together at the Stoneleigh Product School site owned by MF, outside Coventry.

The director for the Perkins team was Dennis Eassom, a manager with wide experience on the production and overseas licensee sides of the business. He, along with his MF equivalent and specialist personnel, reported to Project Director Ralph Ramsey, whose experience within MF had covered several countries and responsibilities. Along with the technical data for the products, the teams also planned factory layouts, identified suppliers, negotiated specific additional licences and a myriad of other details. A liaison team was also based at Ursus to work closely with the Polish personnel: this team was led by Tom Leask who had managed sales functions in Germany and the UK, and Ted Kent, who in spite of his English name was Polish-born and gave the group the big advantage of having a fluent Polish-speaker on site. Key personnel were transferred from within MF and Perkins, while others were recruited from the motor industry around Coventry. Monthly joint meetings kept close control of progress and quickly identified any slippages, whilst strong support from the directors of MF and Perkins ensured that all other parts of the two companies gave priority attention to the project when requested . . .

Another overseas project of considerable importance started at about the same time under the code name 'Rheingold'. This originated to develop a plant on the MF-owned Hanomag site in Germany to produce the new 4.165 engine. This engine was a Peterborough redesign and upgrading of the 4.154 engine developed in conjunction with Toyo Kogyo and was for the new Volkswagen LT light truck: hence the convenience of putting the plant in Germany. A number of key personnel were seconded from Peterborough, among these being Ron MacIntosh, who was appointed project manager. The production facility included the installation of a novel assembly track, which became known as the 'J-hook' line: instead of the usual floor-mounted

The Q11 engine was based upon the 4.108 engine but updated to include latest technology. This example is in vehicle configuration with rear well sump and dates from April 1977

assembly pedestals in a conveyor, the new system used an overhead conveyor with engine assembly fixtures hanging downwards. This gave clear floor space and access all round the engine during assembly for the line operatives: the assembly fixtures also rotated on a horizontal axis so that the engine could be turned into different planes.

The reference to 'soft metrication' in the second paragraph of this chapter regarding the work with Poland deserves an explanation and expansion. In the early 70s the British Government stipulated that the UK would become a metric country. Perkins made a decision in 1972 that all future products would be fully metric, but for existing products no metric alternative would be considered. When the project for Poland came along the new licensee insisted that all dimensions should be to the European ISO standards. Thus all dimensions on the engine drawings had to be converted to metric units by adding a direct ('soft') metric dimension alongside each imperial dimension, rather than the full metrication where dimensions would be only in millimetre (etc.) sizes. The resulting conversion process, although time-consuming and apparently a duplication of effort, provided Perkins with a well-developed set of standards and ensured that the draughting routines used by the company were equal to the best in industry. When coupled to the already high standard of reprographics, microfilming and change control, the drawings produced were models of clarity and legibility.

The Engineering Division was already converting, using ISO standards for many operating parameters such as engine power (kW instead of bhp), torques, etc. The Standards Group within the Engineering Division also developed tabulations of preferred hardware in metric units, using both metric fine and coarse threads as appropriate. Perkins engineers also sat on a number of British Standard committees and were accustomed to the BS/ISO preferences and able to influence decisions where needed. The only complaint during those years was that the whole process took too long – both in Perkins and British Industry in general. (Even in the 21st century there are still pockets of inconsistency, not least where 'miles, gallons and pints' are concerned: the very British resistance to change has delayed, or even prevented, sensible and timely standardisation!)

The impact of computers

There were other organisational changes within the Engineering Division, not least the impact of job cost control and computerisation. The Division had moved a long way from the somewhat casual approach to controlling project costs in the 50s and 60s, to a point where all personnel below supervisory level tracked their productive output on an hourly basis, booking work to a series of cost codes closely tied to the active projects, with other codes for 'non-productive' jobs such as training, visits, sickness, etc., timecards being inputted to a computer system each week. As a result the real costs for major engine projects – and also the cost of the short-term 'panic jobs' so beloved of any engineering operation – were recorded and tracked against planned costs and durations. The use of advanced planning tools, such as the 'PERT' critical path planning chart and similar computer-based systems, spawned a number of planning engineers selected from within the ranks of the design and development staff. Their task of advising management on the progress of every job at regular monthly project meetings enabled professional guidance to be exercised while delays or problems were spotted and addressed.

The use of computers within the Engineering Division had started in the 1960s when performance and design engineers had first exploited the power of computers to drive calculations and predictive engineering. Through the succession of expensive (and soon obsolete) mainframe computers housed at Eastfield, this technical expertise developed to produce suites of programs able to assist and speed many complex calculations to a conclusion. As a result, the 'Research Specialist' side of the Division was able to give support to the project teams – although they usually complained that everything took too long, expecting unrealistic 'instant' solutions! The whole process of programming and feeding data into the mainframe computer took much longer than 21st-century systems of course. Further extension of this 'computerisation' resulted in in-house development of computer control of test beds, automatic data logging and automation of some of the more mundane aspects of engine testing.

This turbocharged version of the Q14 engine from September 1981 shows clear lineage from the 6.354 family. Here a vehicle version is equipped with a twin-cylinder air compressor

Another unexciting but essential part of the engineering process helped by computers was that of parts listing. The generation of the 'bill of materials' for every engine specification produced by the Company was the responsibility of a small army of specialist writers. Although not highly qualified technically these men (most of whom were recruited from the shop floor or from the Services) used their knowledge of engine build principles and an acquired knowledge of existing specifications, available options and newly released parts, to produce a list of parts to suit the needs of a particular customer. From the earliest days the huge proliferation of engine specifications, tailor-made to the needs of the many customers large and small, had been daunting and difficult to limit and control.

Various attempts had been made to provide standard specifications, or base builds, which could be varied in detail more quickly to suit individual machine requirements. One such attempt, entitled 'Standard Option Scheme', or SOS, has already been mentioned. However carefully this was done, and even with an over-checking process in place, errors occurred, and with parts-listers working as individuals, full standardisation was never achieved. (In addition continual changes to correct or modify lists kept a further group of 'list-change' personnel fully employed!)

The wider use of powerful computers was an opportunity to address the specific problems of parts listing. The first attempt, developing 'Sectionalised Parts Lists', with groups of parts brought together in packs, then in turn linked into full build lists, was partially successful. Greater efforts were needed and eventually a more complex approach was agreed, with a senior manager, Ken Walker, put in charge of making the whole thing happen. The computer experts in the IT department created a suite of programs unique to Perkins requirements which took the control of engine component specification, buying and using to a new level of sophistication. A huge tabulation known as the 'Item Master' was created, listing every part number that was in use, together with its sourcing details, material, etc. A number of other programs linked to this and some of these were used to provide more advanced computerised parts listing.

Every part which could be used in the build of an engine – from the cylinder block down to the most insignificant washer – was identified and specified by function in a mammoth tabulation, which was designated the BBSDM (Building Block Standard Data Mask). More software then allowed these parts to be grouped together, still by function only, into packs that could then be built into a complete engine specification. This entailed using a 'Line Reference' (a unique approach) for each function, while packs were described as Core, Base Option or Dress Options to define their use within the engine build. Having put this structure into place, an engine could be specified by defining against each of the line references a specific part number for the engine type, etc. It sounds complex, and indeed it was, taking many months of work by experienced personnel. Once agreed and made 'live', the new 'Core and Option' approach quickly gained momentum and acceptance, speeding the creation process and improving the understanding of parts lists for all involved. The creation of initial lists, and later updating, was carried out through computer input documents rather than direct entry – a necessary although time-consuming safeguard.

Designation of pack numbers and a new sequence of build list numbers completed the transformation to this revolutionary process in the late 1970s. The needs of production processes, which saw the engine build in a somewhat different way, was catered for by a conversion process –again carried out by computer – which 'translated' the Engineering build list into an equivalent Production 'bill of materials'.

Product Upgrading

While changes were being made to the fundamental processes within

The Q16 engine represented a major change in Perkins design thinking for a small vehicle diesel, with overhead camshaft and cogged belt drive. Dressed as a passenger car specification, this 1981 version shows the separate drive for the exhauster as well as the 'sandwich' crankcase construction

the division, creativity had not ceased. For the established products, especially the 6.354 and 4.236 engines forming the greater part of the production volume, there were continual modifications and upgrades as problem areas were addressed and of course cost reductions were sought and introduced. The 4.236 engine range was upgraded to produce a turbocharged version, initially for agricultural and industrial purposes but later developed for vehicle applications.

Another major change for the 4.236 family was the redesign of the secondary balancer. This came in the late 70s when Massey Ferguson claimed that the existing forward-mounted balancer assembly in the latest tractor types produced an unacceptable vibration characteristic: they asked for a revision of the design to locate the balance elements more centrally in the fore-and-aft plane of the engine. Design studies threw up several alternatives, the most acceptable (purely in engineering terms!) being a radical change to incorporate a drive gear on one of the crankshaft webs, driving a smaller balance unit hung centrally from the main bearing caps. Unfortunately this brought with it a considerable extra capital cost for the crankshaft line, declared unaffordable by the directorate. Engineering were forced to fall back on the alternative, which was a heavier cast frame locating the balance weights further back but still driven through a drop gear from the crankshaft nose. The resulting design was cumbersome compared to the forward-mounted design, but tests showed improved tractor vibration characteristics and therefore this arrangement went ahead into production. A new, very expensive, transfer line was commissioned in the Eastfield factory to build the new balancer. (Did this actually prove cheaper in capital terms than the crankshaft change already vetoed? One does wonder!). Once production started it was found that some tractors suffered a different noise problem – a resonance over a small speed range, unfortunately often coinciding with tractor operation at about maximum torque speed. Considerable time and money was spent in later years attempting to eliminate this fault but without total success.

The 6.354 meanwhile had already progressed from the original

design through a series of mark changes – designated 6.3541, 6.3542 and T6.3543 – plus additional derivatives such as the 6.306 and 6.372 to meet 'niche' needs for MF and a few other customers. A further upgrade was proposed and resulted in the 6.3544 and its turbocharged and altitude-compensated versions. The new engines drew heavily upon experience gained in the field, with cylinder block design based upon the T6.3543, a machined inlet port cylinder head similar to the 4.236 design and a number of detail changes to correct known shortcomings in the field.

Among these the introduction of four-bolt clamping arrangements for the lubricating oil filter head and the fuel lift pump were notable, as was an increase in the number of the cylinder head-to-block clamping bolts – all these gave better sealing to address customer irritants and reduce warranty costs. This new product introduction coincided with rationalisation of the product offering and the new 'core and option' process mentioned earlier. Other cost reductions and detail improvements had been made over the years as new materials and techniques became available, all rigorously tested before being introduced.

Most engine families also needed development of new ratings and power curve shapes to suit specific customer needs, while much energy was expended on noise and emissions as new legislation was enacted from various parts of the world. The American 'Federal Register' became a major driver as far as smoke and emission regulation was concerned, while in the UK the smoke levels demanded by British Standard AU 141:1967 had forced technical changes too. Major research efforts explored the fundamentals affecting smoke and gaseous emissions, resulting in new ground being broken. Fuel injection equipment capability was extended in joint programmes with CAV, Bosch and new supplier Sigma from France. The research teams also explored new directions for combustion systems, which resulted in new piston bowl shapes and new ideas for port shapes, spray patterns and other detail parameters. Some of these proved patentable and appeared in new engine developments, as will be detailed later.

Evaluation of noise reduction measures, by engine structural changes and the addition of sound-deadening treatment for sumps, timing cases and rocker covers, extended to the treatment of vehicles and machines. Perkins engineers became an acknowledged source of expertise on noise problems, providing help to many OEM customers and also on occasion to others seeking ways to solve problems, such as reducing noise levels in factories and machinery.

The V8 engines meanwhile had extended beyond the V8.540 and V8.605 to the maximum practical 'stretch' possible within the block dimensions (and of the existing machining line in the Fletton factory). The engine was given an increased bore of 4.63 inches and an increase in stroke to 4.75 inches, for a total capacity of 639.8 cubic inches (10.5 litres), designated in round figures as the V8.640. This meant marginal increases in the cylinder block height and of the overall width of the engine, a limiting factor for many vehicle installations. The V8.605 had found few customers but the V8.640 promised more, especially when the turbocharged and charge-cooled versions (TV8.640CC) were made available. The vehicle rating of 290bhp at 2,600rpm became highly competitive as truck manufacturers sought more power to handle heavier vehicles at motorway speeds. Considerable development work was needed to produce the necessary reliability and performance: by this time the expenditure on the V-engines had been considerable. With the 'fashion' for vehicle applications moving to larger capacity inline six-cylinders, as vehicle regulations changed and higher gross tonnages were promised for the UK in line with Europe, the days of the vee-eights were sadly numbered and the V8.640 was on the scene too late. A number of smaller specialist manufacturers, such as ERF and Dennis (for fire appliances) and Haulamatic (for large dumper trucks) persevered with the V8, while MF and Claas took small numbers too for large tractors and combine harvesters. The possibility of marine versions was also explored, especially in the American market, where potential users such as Sea Ray were courted and installations carried out. A financial analysis of the engine cost and selling price eventually demonstrated that the product was uneconomic to produce and eventually the brave venture was phased out.

New Product Activities

An ill-fated attempt at a joint venture in the USA in 1977 was a proposal to produce a diesel version of an American V8 petrol engine. This became coded Q12, and arose from a discussion with Chrysler Corporation by Ken Glass, at that time the General Manager of the North American Operations Unit. A quite detailed feasibility study was undertaken in Peterborough under the Chief Designer Bill Stewart and Senior Development Engineer Alan Rogers. The proposal was to use either the 360 cubic inch 'A' series engine or the 440 cubic inch 'RB' series V8, the latter being of rather heavier construction and used in trucks as well as passenger cars.

The Perkins study showed that a diesel derivative of the 440, slightly modified to a swept volume of 396 cubic inches, could produce 160bhp at 3,600rpm, using a new indirect injection cylinder head but with no other major machining changes. The use of a Ricardo combustion chamber and a fuel injection pump from either Stanadyne or Bosch was proposed, together with CAV compact injectors. With the need for special attention to emissions already recognised there were proposals for the use of exhaust gas recirculation and possibly a catalyst, as well as optimisation of the combustion and fuel injection systems. It is interesting to note that the first programme estimated around four years to meet 1982 model year introduction complete with all Federal certification, at a cost of between £650,000 and £1,116,000. After this initial study the project proceeded no further, but no doubt the experience provided an interesting dummy run for the projects to follow in the 80s.

There had been a number of studies for a larger Peterborough-designed 'Big Six' in the 'Q' range of projects; the latest during the mid-70s became the Q14. This followed conventional 'Perkins' design concepts and initially took the swept volume to 423 cubic inches (6.94 litres); in parallel a four-cylinder was also designed to complete a bigger and more powerful family of products. The effort was serious, with a large project team of designers and engineers assigned, using the results of the considerable work on combustion and gas flow research. The Product Planning Department strategy was to support this engine for all applications, although it was the vehicle business that was seen as the most attractive sector. Development ran into the early 80s, by which time the six-cylinder engine had grown to become 440 cubic inches (7.20 litres) with ratings up to 228bhp (170 kW) at 2,600rpm for the charge-cooled turbocharged version. The design went through considerable performance and durability development plus vehicle field-testing, the accumulated tests exceeding 152,000 hours with the test fleet of up to ten trucks achieving good performances in the field. There were later moves to increase the swept volume of the engine yet further to 470 cubic inches as the demand for increased power in the truck market overtook the Perkins offering. Sufficient confidence had been generated to allow the completion of initial sales brochures, although whether there would have been enough business with the few remaining independent vehicle manufacturers to satisfy even minimum volume for efficient production is open to question, especially in the light of the economic situation. As will be seen in a later chapter, this project came to an abrupt end.

There were also new engine designs under active consideration at the lower end of the power range. During 1975 a feasibility study into increasing power on the 4.108 engine considered a series of possible approaches up to an engine capacity of 125 cubic inches, as well as using a Weslake-designed cylinder head. In March 1976 this study concluded that a 4.121 engine, with overhead camshaft, linerless cylinder block and chain timing drive could meet the requirement of 54bhp at 4,000rpm. It was proposed to retain the 'Howard' combustion chamber with improved cooling to obviate the known problem of 'fishtail cracking' in the combustion throat, and a switch to the Bosch EP/VA rotary pump was proposed. Considerable work was done on prototype engines, designated as the Q11 project, on the test bed and in light vehicles. A spark-ignition version of the 4.121 got as far as being the subject of an advance publicity flyer but in fact never progressed beyond the prototype stage. One problem is said to have been that the resulting engine was much more bulky than the 4.108, especially in height. This severely limited the vehicles into which the engine could be fitted, even for prototype purposes where the Field Test engineers and fitters were past masters at re-working 'impossible' engine compartments to achieve a viable installation.

Alternative Fuels Research

During the 1970s there was much interest in alternative fuels as a series of crises developed with the supply of fossil fuels from the Middle East. Perkins, along with other engine producers, recognised the need to investigate all possible alternatives. There had previously been moves toward the use of 'wide cut' fossil-based fuels for military purposes and the ability of the conventional Perkins engines to run on gasoline mixtures had been evaluated. The problems associated with rotary fuel injection pump designs had proved to be a limiting factor, since reasonable fuel lubricity was essential to avoid pump seizure. (In comparison with the older design of 'in-line' fuel pumps where a separate lubrication system could be used, the DPA pump with its close tolerances within the rotating distributor body needed the fuel to double as lubricant, this being possible with 'oily' diesel but not with gasoline unless a supplementary lubricant was added.)

The fuel shortages of the 70s and a need to find indigenous fuel sources had convinced several countries, notably Brazil, to explore other directions. The Brazilian Government instigated the 'National Alcohol Programme', seeking to extend the use of ethanol fuels for road transport purposes beyond the established practice of adding up to 15% of ethanol to normal gasoline fuel. Experience showed that this level of addition caused little or no problem for the average motorist, beyond some gum formation in carburettors. Running engines on a fully anhydrous ethanol fuel, however, did show that certain changes were needed, notably alternatives for the 'terne' plating of fuel tank interiors and the changing of some other fuel system materials. The Brazilian idea was to move more and more towards the use of alcohol for passenger cars, reserving the imported crude oil for applications such as truck, bus and rail where diesel engines were of most benefit. Farmers received incentives to produce more sugar cane, with new distilleries constructed to produce ethyl alcohol as a main output instead of an ancillary to sugar production. Huge areas of farming land of São Paulo State were turned over to cane production, taking advantage of the financial incentives. While this helped the average motorist, the benefits to the diesel industry were marginal; the major manufacturers – Perkins, Mercedes-Benz, Scania, MWM and Volkswagen – banded together to ensure their interests were not ignored. (See Chapter 19 for more details of the Brazilian experience.)

One of the more bizarre developments was the 're-invention' of the gazogene unit by a Brazilian company named Explo. The old wartime expedient of using producer gas from a coke-burning furnace saw a new twist when Explo engineers fitted an MF tractor with a charcoal burner mounted in front of the tractor radiator, providing gas to the engine with diesel fuel used purely as an ignition source. Perkins engineers in Peterborough hurriedly designed and built a similar device and proved it could actually produce useful work – but the whole idea quickly died, in spite of the Explo tractor being paraded in front of Brazilian Government officials! The research engineers in Peterborough also evaluated the potential of alcohol and vegetable oils, although the work received little Government support or interest in the UK, where the North Sea Oil bonanza was beginning and non-fossil fuels were seen to be of no immediate benefit. (A good example of politicians driving short-term expediency and inhibiting the growth of engineering knowledge, perhaps!)

Within Peterborough considerable interest was being generated in the potential for high-speed direct injection engines. A small team started work on a derivative of the 4.236 engine, going for a hybrid with the bore of the 4.248 and the short stroke of the 4.212 to keep piston speeds down – thus creating a 224 cubic inch engine capacity. Since this size had already been used in the 4.224 engine developed for Toyo Kogyo in Japan, the Peterborough team dubbed their version the 4.22X and this nomenclature stuck. The engine was designed around a re-entrant bowl shape, somewhat reminiscent of the 'Squish Lip' chamber used on the 4.2032 and 3.1522 low-emission engines, plus the use of the Bosch EP/VE rotary fuel pump design which had been found promising for engines rated to above 3,000rpm. The work on this derivative coincided with another Brazilian project to provide the local market with a higher-speed diesel for use on light trucks in competition with the very successful MWM 229.4 product. Several prototype engines were built in Brazil, using the Bosch EP/VE rotary fuel pump in place of the CAV DPA pump, and a few were installed in vehicles to gain experience under road conditions. Development work continued in Peterborough.

A Novel Light Diesel Concept

At about the same time Peterborough designed the Q16, a fresh look at the small engine market and intended to take up where the Q11 had left off. This was to a large degree the brainchild of Roland Bertodo and was a serious attempt to design an engine with low capital cost and higher power-to-weight ratio. The engine had bore of 92mm and stroke of 85mm, giving 2.26-litre capacity for the four-cylinder unit with ratings of 53kW at 4,500rpm naturally aspirated and 63kW for the turbocharged version. The target weight of 105kg for the bare engine and installed weight of 137kg were very competitive for the time.

The engine was designed in 'layers', with an overhead camshaft located in a light alloy cylinder head, attached to a cast iron cylinder block with open top deck, which in turn fitted to an alloy crankcase. The assembly was held together with through-bolts and also featured an SG iron crankshaft and connecting rods made by powder-forging. The whole idea was novel, with a number of features that were well outside Perkins' usual conservative engineering approach and experience. Adding to the interest was the decision to go for the 'high-speed direct injection' system already mentioned above for the 4.22X, plus the use of a toothed belt drive in place of timing chain or gear drive.

Prototypes were built and run successfully, including some field-testing in cars, but the financial constraints of the late 70s, plus some lack of confidence in the engine's mechanical durability, saw this project dropped too. However, important lessons were learnt about high-speed DI combustion and about the fuel injection equipment needed, as use was made of the engine as a development tool into the early 80s. The engine was also a brave design attempt, in many ways a 'clean sheet of paper' exercise. (Some similar features appeared later in the Rover Group 'K' series petrol engine, which appeared some years after Roland Bertodo's departure from Perkins – first to Dexion, but later to the Austin Rover Engineering Department. This engine proved successful in production for a number of models including the Metro and MGF.)

Towards the 1980s the Engineering Division became involved in a number of new technologies, including the advent of computer-aided design (CAD). A small team started investigating its potential – in a company wedded to the drawing board, with a vast array of hard copy drawings and the means to handle them, the initial views were not encouraging. A number of managers saw the computerisation of drawings merely as a speedy way to produce 'general assembly' drawings, a process which took a long time using traditional methods. However, as the technology developed and extra facilities and computing power became available, it was clear that CAD would be the future and the division made plans for change and implementation. As will be seen in Chapter 24, this was not to be easy.

wo of the most important and influential overseas operations for Perkins were those in Brazil and North America; they were very different and are of historical interest – hence the inclusion a specific chapter. The writer is fortunate to have had considerable help from past employees of these two areas and thus had access to data from the earliest days. The help of Jorge Silveira and Ary Favero of Motores Perkins SA, and Rudy Jansa and Bill Winemaster of Perkins Inc., has been essential in piecing together the story.

Brazil

Mention has already been made in earlier chapters of the setting-up of Motores Perkins in São Bernardo do Campo, and the transfer of the R6 production equipment in 1959/60. To understand the significance of the venture some of the background to the automotive industry in Brazil needs explanation.

Up to the end of the Second World War there was limited local automotive production in Brazil – the economy was slow to develop and of course the population was also growing on a basis of mainly agricultural production. After the First World War some local production was led by Ford and General Motors, but general political unrest had inhibited growth. During World War II prosperity due to exports of agricultural produce meant that Brazil, along with neighbour Argentina, was able to import new vehicles from the USA and Europe – fast depletion of dollar reserves soon forced the government to introduce quotas and restrictions.

It was soon clear that the time was right to introduce local production. Under the enlightened administrations of Getulio Vargas and Juscelino Kubitschek in the 1950s, Brazil started development and, with the National Automotive Plan, created incentives for foreign companies to invest in the creation of vehicle and component manufacture on a large scale, with phased moves towards higher national content. By 1957 a number of plans had been approved, covering Volkswagen, Mercedes-Benz, Ford, General Motors, International Harvester, Willy-Overland, Simca, Toyota, Vemag (DKW), Land Rover, Borgward and NSU. Some of these were to prove non-starters ultimately. In addition there were plans approved for a number of component manufacturers, including Krupp, Sifco, Eaton, Mahle, Cofap, Metal Leve and Brasinca – all aimed at nationalisation of essential parts. Most of the new plants were sited in the 'ABC' region of São Paulo, which comprised Santo Andre, São Bernardo and São Caetano – destined to become a major influence in the rapidly developing Brazilian industrial economy.

Production of diesel engines was a natural progression. The only local manufacture had been that of FNM in Rio; this was followed by projects with Mercedes-Benz, whose original proposal to make cars had been switched quickly to trucks and buses, with the supporting diesel engines (initially OM 312, 314 and 321), MWM Farymann (initially a small horizontal unit), Deutz (three- and four-cylinder units), Cummins and Scania.

The proposal to add Perkins to the list came about in late 1958, almost by accident. Two families of English origin, the Murrays and the Simonsens, created an informal group during the 1930s, partly through marriage and the similarity of their main enterprises. Many

The original building of the Brazilian Perkins plant at Avenida Wallace Simonsen as it was in April 1961

The new plant built to produce the 4.236 and 6.2544 engines in Brazil is seen (centre) in this aerial view. Located a few kilometres from the original factory, the spacious site is seen here in the late 1970s

of these were associated with the motor industry, including the importation and servicing of various brands, while the Simonsens controlled the São Paulo-based Banco Noreste and also owned land in São Bernardo do Campo. During the 1958 motor industry process mentioned above, Charles Edward Murray and his group tendered for the NSU venture, originally for small motorcycles but switched to the NSU Prinz minicar when one young engineer, Jorge Silveira, recently appointed Technical Coordinator for the project, visited Germany and became aware of the imminent launch of the vehicle. The small team was working hard towards implementation when the NSU chairman made a surprise visit to tell them that NSU was being sold to Auto Union and the project was dead! This left them with no product, but the situation was quickly resolved when Murray spoke with the President of Willys-Overland do Brasil (WOB), whose proposal had dropped the Rénault Dauphine and Gordini cars due to time pressures; plans were switched to the new cars, and Government approval obtained.

WOB also offered a Murray a 'crazy' project to manufacture Perkins diesel engines, something that had been under discussion with Ken Woollatt of Perkins but not viewed favourably by the WOB Board. A small task force, including Jorge Silveira, compiled and submitted a plan to manufacture the R6 engine, the approval being received in early 1959. The original plan covered only the R6, for use in vehicle, agricultural, industrial and marine applications.

The finalized Heads of Agreement with Perkins Engines Ltd included the supply of the entire machinery and full technical support from England, while Murray-Simonsen provided the site in São Bernardo do Campo and working capital, as a 50/50 participation. As soon as approval was indicated, the new company rushed to offer the R6 as an alternative diesel engine for the GM C60 and Ford F600 trucks

(then being produced as petrol-engined vehicles only), recognizing that both companies had sufficient foundry capacity and expertise to produce blocks, heads and other smaller castings.

The interest at GM was somewhat lukewarm but eventually they agreed to trial a D60 prototype truck with the redesignated 6.340 engine. The reception at Ford do Brasil was even more reluctant – at that time Ford was openly critical of the 'slow, heavy, smoky, smelly power units' being used by their Mercedes competitors. However, their position changed somewhat when it was agreed to produce the F4.203 engine in Brazil to power their 8BR agricultural tractor. Ford then proposed a formal supply contract to control supply of castings from their Osasco foundry, although the legal hassling over the terms overran the eventual delivery of parts!

Meanwhile Massey Ferguson do Brasil had entered plans to build tractors in a rented plant at Jaguaré, a suburb of São Paulo, specifying A3.152 and A4.203 engines. Initial tractors were built from CKD kits. This additional engine business needed a further project and the sourcing of additional machine tools, which were obtained through a local joint venture with US Equipment, specialists in second-hand machinery. The supplementary plan was submitted on Wednesday 11 May and approved two months later. Motores Perkins SA was created in São Bernardo do Campo, its 'social contract' being signed and registered on 29 June 1959. Meanwhile Silveira had been signed as employee number one on 2 May as Purchasing Manager and flew out to England a few days later to learn all about the product, systems and processes over a two-month period.

The new company was installed in an empty multi-purpose building owned by the Simonsen's Companhia Comercial Brasileira (CCB) at No. 13, Avenida Wallace Simonsen, close to the centre of São Bernardo. Across the road from the factory premises there was additional Simonsen land which would allow later expansion. Several expatriates were also brought in from Peterborough to help install the machinery. Bob King, Jack Miles, Fred Cleaver, Derek Ballard, Jimmy Prince and Max Grist were among these specialists and were instrumental in getting the factory up and running. Of this initial group Max Grist was tragically killed in a freak bus accident on his way to Rio de Janeiro, while Jimmy Prince elected to stay on after his initial contract expired. The others returned to Peterborough.

Another tragic accident occurred on 23 September 1959, when Charles Murray was killed in a plane explosion. He had been late leaving São Paulo on the 'air bridge' flight to Rio but somehow the name of Jorge Silveira got entered on the passenger list during the check-in process. The Scania aircraft blew up in mid-air, killing all 28 passengers and crew, in an accident that was never satisfactorily explained. Jorge Silveira was alerted about ten o'clock that night by a friend who called him at his house to say that his name was on the list of dead. Considerable distress was caused to members of both families before the error was sorted out.

In early October the staff moved into temporary offices in the S B do C factory and commenced work to identify component procurement with potential suppliers. In November the first machinery was transported from the port of Santos, causing considerable disruption to the traffic on the Via Anchieta. On 25 November Monty Prichard made his first visit to the new company, including a cocktail party to meet prospective customers and suppliers.

Over the next few weeks the small number of employees was busy with the many details necessary to start local procurement. In the days before computers this was a considerable clerical effort since each basic engine parts list had to be broken down to individual parts so that the Company Programme could be created. Gradually more personnel were recruited and departments organised. The first purchase order was issued on 4 January 1960, to Sifco for 6.340 crankshaft forgings, soon followed by the second, to Robert Bosch for fuel injection pumps and injectors.

Throughout May and June, meetings covered more details, including costs and sales pricing for the F4.203 for Ford. The rest of 1960 soon passed as the company and its structure took shape and the factory machinery was put into place. It must be remembered that, unlike other licensee operations, MPSA could not rely upon supply of machined parts from Peterborough for the 6.340, since all of the major machinery was already in Brazil. Consequently the only parts supplied from Peterborough comprised any remaining surplus stock of major parts and, of course, support on bought-out-finished components.

A possible customer that came to nothing was International Harvester (IH), whose approved project ran late as far as the nationalisation plan was concerned. A change from petrol-powered trucks to buses included the intent to switch to diesel using the 6.340; however, their poor installation work was rejected by MPSA on the grounds of unacceptable service and maintenance access. Eventually the IH plant was sold to Simca and then to Chrysler.

Meanwhile the programme for 3.152 and 4.203 engines for MF do Brasil began and the first three F6.340 prototypes were delivered to Ford. When production began there were problems with the timing chain drive on the six-cylinder, as there had been in Peterborough of course, while the early three- and four-cylinder engines showed some oil consumption problems with the Cromard cylinder liners, eventually resolved by a change to thin cast iron liners and a new piston ring pack. Deliveries of F6.340s to Ford began in May 1961, following the satisfactory start of F4.203 production for the tractor.

Through 1961 and 1962 considerable expatriate assistance was received from Peterborough, plus regular visits from Ken Woollatt. There were several foreign senior management changes of short duration, including a period when Jim Winstanley moved from Peterborough to take control. Another important event was the visit of senior CAV personnel, which resulted in the creation of CAV do Brasil. The early relationships with this local supplier proved troublesome as far as their deliveries, prices and spares were concerned, needing Peterborough to intercede through the CAV headquarters at Acton.

The premises of MPSA were soon extended by the construction of a new factory on the other side of the road. As well as accommodating several departments this became the temporary home for some transmission component machining for Massey Ferguson as the local company was under pressure to increase the pace of their 'nationalisation' programme before their new Sorocaba factory was ready.

There were continuous changes of personnel in MPSA at this time, with key posts changing hands frequently, especially in the Purchasing area. The company was growing fast – maybe too fast – with no rigidity of reporting structure, not helped by several changes of General Manager. In addition to this the country was suffering high inflation and there was a lag in correcting salaries, which caused dissatisfaction. In October 1962 the powerful Metalworkers Union, which covered the automotive industry in the ABC area, started a general strike in support of wage demands. This closed many plants with pickets in place, but the MPSA workers decided not to take part; the plant had to cease production, however, due to shortage of parts as the supply chain was affected. The workers also ensured that a team was always present to prevent vandalism by strikers.

Through the remainder of the 1960s MPSA continued to make significant progress. The products were enhanced considerably when the 6.340 was upgraded to become the 6.357 in 1968. This was a bigger-bore version of the engine, still with indirect injection using the Perkins 'Aeroflow' combustion system, but featuring a locally-designed timing gear arrangement instead of the troublesome chain drive. The engine also used a new CAV DPA mechanically-governed fuel pump with a number of other design changes that improved performance and allowed the engine to be rated at 3,000rpm. The engine was sold to Ford, General Motors and Chrysler trucks and was developed for other small industrial, agricultural and marine uses.

By this time Ary Favero, one of the first MPSA employees, was established as Chief Applications Engineer and successfully oversaw the majority of engine adaptations into machines. One of his achievements was to limit variety in a way never possible in Peterborough – alternative manifolds, for instance, were unheard of!

The recruitment of a local Chief Engineer, Alfredo Domschke, during the late 60s brought a new challenge as an attempt was made to convert the 6.357 to direct injection, with assistance from Peterborough especially on combustion technology. The redesign was sweeping, with many new major components, although there were constraints to use the same machining line as the 6.357. The resulting engine was designated 6.358 but never proved successful, although the efforts of the succeeding Engineering Directors in the shape of John Lawrence and the author managed its launch into limited production in 1976.

An upgrade of the 6.357 was introduced as the 6.3572 – this had a revised combustion chamber and exhaust manifold to provide increased power (to 122bhp at 3,000rpm) and better fuel consumption. (This change was really forced by the strict Government price control regimes which prohibited price increases unless there were benefits to the consumer – the resultant price distortions due to 'historic pricing' during the period of high and sustained inflation in the 60s and 70s caused major erosion of company profitability. The power increase was a sufficient bargaining point to allow a modest price increase!)

In the early 1970s Brazilian production was making slow forward progress, increasing from 11,970 engines in 1968 to 19,424 in 1971. The products were old in design and did not compare with modern offerings from Mercedes-Benz and particularly the new MWM D226 fitted to the Ford F4000 light trucks and MF80X tractors, although the 6.3572 had gained quite a reputation as rugged and easy to fix. By then the General Manager was Roland Jennings, another expatriate who was well versed in Peterborough politics and processes. Massey Ferguson was ambitious to expand on a worldwide front: the MF plants in Sorocaba, São Paulo (tractors) and Canoas, Porto Alegre (combine harvesters), along with the MPSA engine factory, were seen as key resources for expansion in Latin America.

A plan was formulated to expand the Perkins product line to include the 4.236 and 6.354 families. This was submitted to the usual rigorous Government processes and finally approved. First priority was to be given to the smaller engine since this would power the popular mid-sized range of tractors that were the cornerstone of MF expansion.

A team of experts was relocated in Brazil on expatriate assignments to develop both the plant and processes to introduce the 4.236 family during 1975. A new plant was planned on land that was purchased in the small township of Alvarenga, located just outside São Bernado do Campo, to accommodate the assembly and test facility, while the South Factory at S B do C would take the new machining lines for cylinder block and cylinder head.

The key personnel transferred from Peterborough included Ken Fuller, whose experience covered a wide range of successful tasks including the construction of the new Perkins Inc. plant at Farmington, Michigan, managing the V8.510 plant at Fletton and completing the new Engineering workshops at Eastfield. With him went Alan Bailey, John Lawrence, Lynn Jones, Fred Pell and Lewis Hall, to provide expertise on the factory planning, engineering, quality and foundry/ purchase aspects of the new products respectively. Other postings included Aaron Jones, who moved from MF Corporate finance staff, and Mike Robinson from the administrative staff at Peterborough. This nucleus was supported by recruitment of additional local staff with the right experience, plus many regular visits by specialist Peterborough staff to keep an eye on progress and help solve problems.

In spite of the difficulties associated with the continuing rampant local inflation (mini devaluations of the Brazilian Cruzeiro against the US Dollar were taking place on a weekly basis!) and the need to develop local suppliers, the expansion project went ahead against a tight schedule. Major new pattern equipment was procured to cater for both the tractor and vehicle block versions of the 4.236 engine, and major casting supplier Tupy was selected, working from a large modern foundry at Joinville. Other major suppliers were selected, an important point made being that all parts were to be totally interchangeable with the equivalent Peterborough parts – this to include ensuring that design levels were maintained in line so that Brazilian parts could be used in the UK and vice versa. Engineering tests were carried out in Brazil and Peterborough to validate the local parts, working to procedures established by the Engineering Division and the Associate and Licensee Operations Department. Earthmoving and construction work at the new Alvarenga factory site proceeded to plan, opportunity being taken to provide a football field for the workers and, later, a sports hall for basketball and other indoor sports, as another incentive to the workforce.

Meanwhile sales efforts were ensuring that there would be customers lined up for the 4.236 and 4.248 engines, the first of these being of course Massey Ferguson who were keen to have the new 200 series tractors standardised between Brazil and the rest of the world. The first 4.248s were produced in 1975, so that by the time the author arrived in Brazil to succeed John Lawrence in December that year, the factory had been formally opened on 9 October and produced 5,358 engines in its first year. 1975 was a boom year with total production

reaching 53,864 engines, with 4.203 and 6.357 totals at 19,718 and 20,416 respectively. Both vehicle and agricultural engine demand was high, helped by Government incentives as the National Alcohol Programme took off and additional sugar cane cultivation was started, aimed at reducing Brazil's reliance upon imported oil by substituting ethyl alcohol for petrol in greater proportion than hitherto.

Along with the existing big customers – Ford, General Motors, Chrysler and MF – other well-known names came along, including Case, whose exports to the Middle East of the 580H backhoe helped to bolster the engine production considerably. One other major name whose potential business did not follow through was Komatsu, who took a prototype 6.3572 but then asked for the manifolds to be switched to the other side of the engine to suit their excavator bodywork: on enquiring how big the business might be, MPSA were told 'maybe 20 machines per year!'. Komatsu were politely advised that the enquiry was not viable.

There were also a number of small manufacturers that were hungry for engines, and through the distribution network there was a ready market too for conversion engines for older trucks. Occasionally other odd applications surfaced too, often down to the ingenuity of individuals. One such example was the farmer who purchased an MF tractor version of the 4.248, complete with balancer unit that limited the engine to 2,000rpm maximum speed. This did not deter the farmer from fitting the engine into a pick-up truck: by making his own 'overdrive' gearbox he finished up with a highly illegal vehicle capable of cruising well above the legal limit of 80kph and providing a fuel consumption better than half that of the petrol engine!

The banning of diesels in small pick-ups and vans was a deliberate policy: Brazilian Government encouragement for diesel engine usage in trucks did not extend below one tonne payload. This did allow MPSA to offer the 4.236(V) for small trucks in competition with the established MWM D226-4, which powered the Ford F4000 truck. Chrysler already produced a small truck, and when VW bought out the Chrysler plant they in turn decided to offer the 4.236 and 6.3544, as options to the MWM diesels, in their own new small forward-control truck. (A 'Letter of Intent' was obtained but deliveries never materialised.) A local entrepreneur named Gurgel, already producing small cars fitted with VW petrol engines, decided to produce trucks too. Prototypes were built using the 4.236 in another 'cab over engine' configuration using a glass-fibre cabin.

All of this business was very small and fragmented compared to the tractor market of course, but the MPSA Directors were keen to reduce the heavy reliance on the agricultural sector, since they had already seen (as had MF!) a serious impact on their production caused by a sudden Government decision, driven by inflationary pressures, to reduce the level of subsidy given to farmers to increase mechanization. In 1977/8 this caused MPSA production to drop severely from 63,836 (76) to 51,330 (77) and then 44,112 (78) – at a time when the new engine types should have been pushing production towards 75,000. Agricultural use accounted for over 50% of MPSA production; a concerted effort was needed to diversify into other sectors.

As a result, the decision of General Motors to produce a larger version of their D10 pick-up truck, with payload marginally above one tonne, was welcomed by Perkins. Along with specific tailoring of the engine front end to suit the vehicle, MPSA would fit the new Bosch EP/VE fuel injection pump, which had been tried in Peterborough and found to offer good governing characteristics for vehicle use.

There was another reason for going down this route, of course: Perkins had come to rely too much upon CAV production, as a result product costs had been adversely affected and this, coupled to expensive service failure returns, made Bosch politically attractive. Bosch do Brasil was also keen on the idea for two different reasons: their

The move to Detroit resulted eventually in the construction of a new headquarters at Farmington, seen here in the early 1970s

new Managing Director, Jack van Kampen, had already been given the task by Stuttgart to get some new Perkins business, and since they would need the EP/VE pump to support production of a small diesel engine due to be launched by Fiat do Brasil for worldwide use in the early 80s, the MPSA requirement would allow Bosch to nationalise and debug the pump production ahead of this much higher volume demand.

Prototypes of the new truck were soon on the road with the 4.236 fitted and proved to be quite successful, even though the engine was really too large and heavy for the size of vehicle. Good fuel economy was coupled to an over-the-road performance allowing the truck to go almost everywhere in top gear! The launch was quite low-key, but the demand in the market was such that over 14,000 trucks were sold in its first year (1979), making it at that time the highest vehicle engine sales volume to one application in a year for any Perkins plant!

The MPSA production in 1979 was over 57,000 engines; aided by the GM business the vehicle diesel share was 30% while industrial business grew 15%. Perkins' share of the total Brazilian market was 30%, while MF retained 35% of the agricultural tractor business and saw production recover by 6% compared to 1978.

Reference has already been made to the programme of work associated with alternative fuels and ethyl alcohol in particular. The small engineering department in Brazil under the author during the later 1970s explored a number of possible alternatives, working with the other Brazilian diesel manufacturers, university and government bodies, and even local inventors, while keeping the Peterborough Engineering Division closely informed. Ethanol as a fuel for spark ignition engines was viable due to its inherent high-octane level but was not a suitable diesel fuel due to its poor cetane value. The use of an unmodified ethanol fuel was found feasible by carburetting it into the engine, then using a low volume of injected diesel fuel as the ignition source. Another route explored was the use of 'additivated alcohol', where a chemical ignition improver to the alcohol changed its cetane index. (Since this additive in undiluted form was an explosive akin to nitroglycerine, and highly volatile, there was concern over the potential for disaster!)

Other possible alternatives included the use of vegetable oils, produced from crops such as soya beans, but which needed treatment in order to protect the engine fuel system and combustion chambers from being gummed up by unburnt deposits. Although the processes were viable this direction never found much support, although Volkswagen did build diesel engines from CKD kits and run them in Passat cars – the fuel derived from vegetable oils had a distinctive exhaust odour reminiscent of a fish and chip shop!

It is interesting to note that many of the ideas for use of 'biomass' based fuels fell on deaf ears in the UK, but in continental Europe some progress was made through the 80s and 90s. During the early 2000s there has been increased interest as fossil fuel availability and price have become a problem. What progress could have been made if the Brazilian experience on both ethanol and vegetable oils had been appreciated and actions put in hand? In the writer's view this has proved another lost opportunity – only in 2006 were the UK Government and other entities beginning to take these renewable energy sources seriously, almost thirty years too late!

During the 1970s there had been several changes of management, of course. An American, David Bigelow, was recruited as General Manager and finally left in 1975 to take over at Poclain in France, and later on at the parent Tenneco Board. Jorge Silveira became his replacement and oversaw the growing enterprise up until the end of 1980.

Following the example of Mercedes (who from their inauguration had acquired the Sofunge iron foundry, from the Simonsen family, to provide all their iron castings including blocks and heads), in the later 1960s MPSA purchased the Progresso-Metalfrit iron foundry at Lapa. This was capable of producing flywheels and large housings for MPSA, as well as the five major castings for MF tractors.

During this period the 'corporate' responsibility for Brazil and the other Latin American companies fell to the Latin America and Caribbean Operations Area, based in Coral Gables, Miami and headed by Jim Felker who had previously been based at Peterborough. In the late 70s Aaron Jones, MPSA Finance Director, returned to England to take a post with MF and was replaced by Oliver Chapple. Oliver was an ex-graduate trainee with considerable experience in Perkins operations in the UK and South Africa, and had spent some time in Brazil previously. He took over the Finance Director role at a time when the MF troubles, as well as the difficult sales conditions in Brazil, were just beginning to show and financial constraints were necessary. As production fell through 1977 and 1978 there was a need to shed labour, especially the hourly-paid production workers, although it was necessary to maintain momentum on the plans to introduce the 4.236 and 6.3544 engines fully.

The benefit of worldwide standardization for the new products soon showed when Peterborough agreed to accept Brazilian-machined cylinder blocks for use in Eastfield production. The first batch was duly shipped by container, preserved to the conditions specified by Peterborough: on arrival in Eastfield it was found that the factory washing facility could not remove the preservative! Consternation followed and a specialist facility was found to clean the blocks while MPSA were advised of the problem. A Peterborough delegation duly arrived in Brazil to 'sort out the natives', only to find that local action was already in place, thanks to contacts with Mercedes who had recommended a more up-to-date preservative, which was not only more effective but could be removed by cold-washing!

After further batches of blocks had been shipped with totally satisfactory results, a more ambitious exportation of complete engines to MF Detroit was arranged, with some additional stipulations about packing in containers. Exhaustive overchecks on the engine specifications and service interchangeability were needed but again the export was completely satisfactory, generating good reactions all round – not least from Brazilian Government departments who were pleased to see the balance of payments receive some positive input.

In the wake of this activity discussions were started on an even more ambitious proposal to ship engines as CKD kits to the Modasa plant in Peru; these engines were to be mated to tractor CKD kits shipped from the MF plant in Argentina. This necessitated considerable liaison between the three countries before the first shipment was made. After some initial minor problems were uncovered in the first shipment,

extra safeguards were built into the Brazilian packing processes and faultless despatches were achieved, something that even the highly experienced Eastfield CKD operation did not always manage!

In 1980, with the financial problems of Massey Ferguson looming over the Brazilian operation, the production output was a record at over 68,000 engines – even with almost a month lost through industrial action – as the move away from high reliance on the agricultural market bore fruit. While MPSA was in good shape financially, MFB was not, with big loans outstanding and idle capacity in the Sorocaba and Canoas plants. During the year various management changes were made. There had already been a restructuring of the MFB and MPSA companies into a new company known as Massey Ferguson Perkins SA, initially with the MFB boss J.A. ('Ule') Engelbrecht as its President. This enabled the good financial position of the engine side to offset the poor position of the MF operation. Serious misunderstandings between Engelbrecht and Silveira resulted in the latter's resignation in August with three months' notice. Silveira was immediately hired as President of Eutectic and Castolin, while Engelbrecht was sacked before the end of August, to be replaced by Oliver Chapple. At about the same time the writer was offered a position back in Peterborough, departing at the end of December.

As part of the overall policy dictated by Victor Rice as he strove to bring MF back from their over-extended and over-ambitious plans to a profit-making position once more, Chapple was instructed to find a buyer for the whole Brazilian operation. This he eventually did, selling to a Brazilian financial group named Iochpe in 1982: the new enterprise was renamed Maxion SA. The deal included a certain amount of 'guaranteed' buy-back for the MF and Perkins products; this never tran-

The early operation in North America was based around the Toronto office, seen here in 1953 with some of the first staff

spired due to the depressed world markets and industry over-capacity. The relationship between original and new owners became somewhat acrimonious, a situation that remained right through the 80s and 90s. Maxion continued as a licensee, going on to develop their own derivatives of the Perkins products. The old products, 6.3572 and 6.358, were phased out in favour of the 6.3544, and an agreement with Rover to make the two-litre Land Rover diesel augmented their production and extended it into new markets.

Eventually Maxion was purchased by the American giant, Navistar International; by this time the whole manufacturing side had been relocated to Puerto Alegre, using the Canoas site formally occupied by the MF combine plant. At first the plant was renamed Maxion International Motores SA, but after total purchase of the Iochpe shares this was changed to International Engines South America Limitada.

Thus the manufacturing presence of Perkins in Brazil finished for a time until circumstances decreed, in the 2000s, that the Caterpillar-owned Company would once again set up in Brazil, this time in the growing industrial area of Curitiba.

North America

It will have been apparent to the reader that Frank Perkins considered North America to represent a potential market for Perkins products right from the early days; it is probable that without the impact of the Second World War there would have been an effort to export across the Atlantic much earlier than was eventually the case. In spite of the successes of companies like Cummins and Caterpillar with big and relatively slow-revving engines in the 30s – mainly for agricultural and industrial machinery – diesel engines were not widely used. With cheap fuel and cheap large displacement petrol engines available it is not surprising that users saw little virtue in paying more for the possible additional durability and cheaper running costs of the alternative engine. On this premise, the attraction of the American and Canadian markets to Perkins is a little difficult to understand – except that as a potential market it was huge!

By the early 50s the biggest US supplier of smaller diesels was Detroit Diesel with the 53 Series two-stroke, while Cummins had the lion's share of truck business in the Class 8 long-haul truck sector with engines in the 200bhp sector. The potential of the smaller vehicle sectors Classes 5, 6 and 7, which covered the myriad of lower tonnage trucks and vans used for intra-city pick-up and delivery services, was virtually untapped as a diesel market.

The creation of F. Perkins (Canada) Limited in Toronto took place in 1952 with Geoffrey Guest as the General Manager. His stay appears to have been brief, since by October 1953, when Aubrey Southgate went out to Canada on a twelve-month secondment from the Eastfield drawing office, Dennis Milnes was in charge, with assistance on the sales side from Peter Alliston from the Peterborough office. There were further changes of leadership in quick succession.

As Perkins settled into the Canadian scene they quickly found that, although some small-scale local business could be gained in the industrial sector, many of the 'local' customers were subsidiaries of US companies. As such their powers of independent decision on purchase were limited, being driven from their head offices. Since many of the Canadian products found their way onto the US market anyway, a move to a base in the USA was seen as essential, preferably close to where the main action was, namely Detroit. The Massey Ferguson takeover in 1959 gave additional impetus to the move.

By 1961 the main North American office had relocated to an old Massey Ferguson gear plant in Kercheval Avenue in Detroit, although a small sales office was left in Toronto to service local customers. Peter Allen was the General Manager and a sales agreement with the Marine and Industrial Division of Chrysler Corporation gave Perkins access to

sales outlets throughout America. (Chrysler at that time was a supplier of high-horsepower gasoline engines to smaller original equipment manufacturers (OEMs) and had a good sales and service network.) There were, however, some exclusions from this agreement, including the marketing of the Perkins outboard motors, plus a number of OEMs such as Hobart, Oliver, International Harvester and White Motor, who were already Perkins customers. (The truck market in general was excluded since Chrysler's competitors would naturally be reluctant to buy engines from a competitor!) The working relationship with Chrysler was already established in Europe, where conversions of their cars for taxi use was popular in a number of big cities in Belgium and Holland, mainly using the P4 engine. This business had moved Perkins to look at taxi conversions in the US too, and several Detroit taxi companies were converted to diesel with encouraging results.

At this time, Rudy Jansa came onto the scene when he answered an advertisement for a marine sales manager to join 'the American subsidiary of a foreign engine manufacturer' to market a range of outboard motors. He met with Peter Allen in early 1962, and although unimpressed with the plans to sell outboards at premium prices into an already established market, he was sufficiently impressed by Peter Allen to become interested – but the job offer did not materialise and eventually Maurice Downham was appointed. However, Allen told Rudy of his own imminent return to England, which would leave the General Manager's post vacant. Rudy waited some weeks before he was offered the position in March 1962. His view of the Company position at that stage is interesting: although decisions had been reached to continue with the exploitation of the outboard motor market and the attempt to convert taxi operation to diesel power, the termination of the Chrysler agreement was seen as inevitable with staff planning accordingly. The reasoning behind the termination was perhaps obvious: Chrysler distributors were keen to offer a range of diesel engines for industrial and marine conversions, but this conflicted with the corporate strategy to maintain sales of their gasoline products into the same market! With advertising slanted to their own products, and Perkins products 'offered' only if customers insisted on diesel, it was clear meaningful growth would be slow.

Jansa spent a month in England getting to know the product, people and politics while Peter Allen remained on for a spell before a phased handover to his replacement. The facility at Kercheval Avenue was old and run-down but adequate for a time for the small office staff. Close by, a small prototype installation shop had been established to handle the initial conversion work on OEM products ahead of demonstrations of performance and commercial viability.

This shop also took on the taxi conversion work on new vehicles for Dodge; to avoid production line disruption no US car manufacturer would even consider the fitment of a small volume of 'special' engines in their high-volume flow process. Therefore the vehicles were channelled to the Perkins shop, where the gasoline engine would be removed and returned for credit, the diesel conversion completed and the vehicles shipped. Unfortunately both driver and customer acceptance of the diesel taxis turned out to be poor: the P4 was considered too noisy, lacked performance and in cold weather the cabs were uncomfortably cold (due to the engine producing less heat than the petrol engine!) – improved fuel economy failed to attract and only around 50 conversions were undertaken before the business was terminated.

It is clear that these early days in North America were far from easy. The company was running at a loss since business was slow to develop, with the running costs and salaries for the small staff of about twenty people supported from Peterborough. By the late summer of 1962 the Chrysler agreement was being terminated, with the intent of setting up a new independent dealer and service network. Some of the Chrysler Marine and Industrial engine dealers expressed a desire to continue as Perkins outlets, but developing the basic sales, marketing, advertising, etc., as well as the dealer support was quite a process.

The staff at that time included Pat Percy, looking after Service, Neville Hartwell on Applications Engineering, Bob Cartwright on Sales and Ron Hickman as Financial Manager and Accountant. Later in the year Bill Winemaster returned to Perkins as General Sales Manager with Cartwright reporting to him. Efforts to establish a network for outboard motor sales were sabotaged by reports of early engine failures due to design shortcomings, as well as an investigation by the US Customs Department into pricing anomalies following a complaint. With the considerable expenses associated with resolution of the problems and this potential 'legal' situation, Peterborough made the decision to withdraw from the outboard market in the US; stocks were sold off cheaply or returned to England. It was an unsatisfactory end to a venture that was possibly always unlikely to succeed; the lack of support from MF for the venture was no doubt another factor.

In 1962 MF declared that they needed the space at Kerchaval Avenue for their own expansion, requesting Perkins Inc. to find an alternative facility. Eventually a suitable plant was found at Wixom, about forty miles from the centre of Detroit. The facility had been built as a truck terminal and had good space for workshop and test facilities, although insufficient offices for the eventual planned staffing level. Although there were some difficulties – due to the distance from Detroit for some personnel – a good price was offered as the owners were anxious for an occupier, so a five-year lease was signed and plans made for additional office space.

Although there were relatively few direct engine sales being made from Wixom at this time, there were 'liaison fees' due from Peterborough for support to existing American customers who were directly supplied and invoiced from Peterborough. This may have assisted the UK personnel, but in practice it meant that it was difficult to judge profitability within the American operation.

Mention has already been made of the abortive attempt to obtain a niche market through the Dodge taxi business. There was a second attempt in the early 60s through Studebaker which proved a non-starter too, although serious consideration was given before Studebaker Corporation filed for bankruptcy, killing the project and the last attempt of Perkins to get into the taxi market in the USA. (Some years later, in 1967, there were serious discussions with the Checker Cab Company, and conversion of some long-wheelbase taxis to take the 4.236(V) engine for export to Israel, but this too proved unsuccessful.)

Through the early 1960s the dealer organisation continued to grow in support of the gradually improving truck engine sales to OEMs such as White Motor and International Harvester (IHC), where fleet sales for intra-city delivery business such as brewery fleets and United Parcel Service were encouraging; Perkins gained about 12% of the diesel truck market at one point. Industrial and marine sales were also increasing, with new regional sales managers recruited to assist Bill Winemaster and Bob Cartwright. Among these were Bill Vollendorf and Carl Pearson, who stayed on, providing stalwart support, until their retirement.

The truck market at this time was an interesting and perhaps dangerous place to be for a foreign manufacturer. Rudy Jansa recalled the experiences of Daimler-Benz AG in the 1950s when they negotiated an agreement to sell Mercedes-Benz diesel engines in Canada and the USA through Curtiss-Wright. A first agreement with DC Freight Lines to repower one long-haul truck from Cummins to the M-B OM 326 engine resulted in very early failure – eventually blamed on a failure to understand the market and especially the fact that in American conditions the engine was expected to run effectively at full rating for perhaps 20 hours at a stretch – much longer than any European operation at the time. The experience resulted in Daimler-Benz retiring from the scene expensively, and not returning for some years. There were also problems for Rolls-Royce Diesels in Canada, where cold-climate running caused the British manufacturer considerable problems.

Although the Perkins products, and especially the 6.354, were perhaps better prepared and in any case not used for arduous inter-city service, experience soon showed that there were also fundamental differences in operating under American 'pick up and delivery' conditions. The average American driver was used to the higher-revving petrol engines in city driving conditions, and especially the ability to down-change on freeway exits to assist the vehicle brakes. The 6.354 had not been developed for high instantaneous engine over-run under such conditions. Breakage of valve gear components resulted, and crankshaft bearing failures also occurred. Urgent development work was instigated in Peterborough to resolve the shortcomings. The basic lesson learnt, very rapidly, was the need to understand the market and how the product would be used. A short while later similar issues arose on the 4.99/4.107 engines applied to Transicold power packs for refrigeration units on railway wagons: servicing periods were long and engines had to function under automatic control for many hours. Eventually an engine specification was developed which eliminated most of the concerns, but it was a long, expensive, process which lost some reputation and trust.

Perkins also suffered in the truck market from the demands of the OEMs to run their own parts business for the engines, to handle their own warranty business and also be responsible for the application adaptation of engine to vehicle. Due to this, not only did the Company not have close contact with the end-users and lose some profitability on spare parts, but they did not pick up on field problems as early as possible. Since engines sold to IHC were not branded Perkins, there was ignorance in the eyes of some operators regarding whose responsibility such problems were – and in some instances too the vehicle manufacturer would happily blame Perkins for failures of application parts they had fitted! A further adverse factor was the growth of the truck leasing business – as a result of the tax benefits possible by leasing instead of buying, and amortising, trucks as capital expenditure. The resultant loss of control over maintenance and driver standards may have saved money for operating companies, but the impact on the vehicle and engine manufacturers was significant.

As the usage of Perkins 6.354s in the US truck market grew through 1965, so did the problems. There was a level of naivety within Perkins too – the belief that the American trucking operators would adhere to servicing requirements, including the need to retighten the cylinder head gasket fixings in early life. This did not happen in most instances, since the operators believed that an engine should go into service and not need such early attention and of course loss of earnings for the day. The abuse of the engines during braking has been referred to before – bent or broken valves, rocker levers and piston damage added to warranty bills. There was some fault too in the quality of some engines, for instance with incorrectly lubricated water pump bearings, which resulted in a spate of early life failures. Campaign actions were necessary to avoid cancellation of future orders. Perkins went through the same steep learning curve which had afflicted Mercedes earlier. A proper analysis of the American market, and perhaps a field 'seeding' programme, would probably have ensured most of the faults had been identified and eliminated before major volumes of product had been sold. The result unfortunately was that Perkins could not strengthen the toehold they had gained in the truck market and never again made a successful foray into the on-highway business in the USA, even when the V8.510 came to market in the late 60s.

It is interesting to note that just before Rudy Jansa left Perkins and joined Caterpillar in Peoria (where he stayed until retirement) he had visited Caterpillar with Monty Prichard for some talks concerning a

The purchase of the White Motor Corporation factory in Canton, Ohio, provided a short-lived base for production of the 4.236 and 6.3544 engines in the USA in the late 1970s

possible business relationship. Various ideas were discussed but no firm agreement resulted. At that time Caterpillar was developing its own mid-range diesel family, which eventually competed with the Perkins V8. Nothing came of these discussions. Caterpillar later became a major US customer for small engines to fit in forklift trucks and then tractor digger loaders, right up to the late 90s when the buy-out took place.

The departure of Jansa took place at a time when there were a number of changes of management in Wixom: by 1967 Bill Winemaster had been appointed General Manager. The writer spent a few months in Wixom in 1967/8, working mainly at the satellite Engineering Department about six miles down the road at New Hudson. During that time as an 'engineering advisor', he saw various ongoing issues with the major vehicle OEMs, including visits to brewery fleets in New York and to the IHC Service operation in Chicago. There were other major programmes with Massey Ferguson of course, plus the Oliver tractor plant in the wilds of Charles City, Iowa, as well as smaller customers mainly locally in the Detroit area. Gradually Perkins Inc. acquired a considerable number of OEM accounts across the agricultural and industrial sectors, including Cockshutt, White Farm, Allis Chalmers, New Holland, Hesston, Agco, Case, Lincoln Electric, Miller, Hobart, Melroe Bobcat, Gehl and of course Clark and Hyster, to become a major engine supplier to industrial and agricultural sectors. There was also an increasing sales volume in the US marine market, especially in the sailboat and small cruiser sectors, growing to over 4,200 engines in 1981. Eventually total sales reached 45,000 engines a year by 1982, representing a market share of around 27%.

By the early 1970s the Perkins operation moved from Wixom to a new plant at Farmington, closer to Detroit, where more space allowed more customising to suit local OEMs, along with increased inventory and sufficient space for sales and service support.

In 1975, as mentioned in an earlier chapter, Perkins bought the Canton, Ohio engine plant from White Motor Corporation. The plant had been built with local investment to bring industry into the area but never reached production; understandably the City was anxious for the plant to continue working. Perkins Inc. relocated their headquarters to Canton and started manufacture of engines for the American market. The intention was for Canton to become the principal supply source for 4.236 and 6.3544 products for North America, with planned capacity of 100,000 engines by the 1980s, and employment of over 1,200 personnel. The plant was already equipped with an excellent 'J-hook' assembly track and automated test beds, while the machining lines were capable of conversion to suit the Perkins engines.

A number of key personnel were seconded from Peterborough to help establish the operation, including John Devaney, while Ken Glass was the President of the re-named Perkins Diesel Corporation and Bill Winemaster the Sales Director. However, the plant proved to be a loss-maker from the first day and was sold as the recession in the agricultural market affected MF and Perkins. The Perkins North American operations returned to Wayne, Michigan in 1979. The machining lines were shipped to Peterborough and installed in the new Factory 3, while the Canton plant eventually housed the spare parts operation for Detroit Diesel Corporation.

Bill Winemaster took early retirement in 1986, becoming the distributor for the Midwest of the USA. The marketing agreement with Detroit Diesel was signed in 1988 but this collaboration was not as successful as had been hoped for. As a result, in 1996 Perkins once again took over responsibility for their own sales and service network, covering all of North America from a base in Novi, Michigan, up to the point where Caterpillar became the owners.

Chapter 20: Associate & Licensee Operations

Although this book set out to recount the history of the Peterborough operations of Perkins Engines, the growing international nature of the business and its various overseas offshoots has already formed a part of the story. Chapter 19 covered in more detail the stories of two enterprises, and this chapter will cover the other operations and the part they have played in the development of Perkins, and their importance to the development of industry in their own countries. It is not overstating the case to suggest that Frank Perkins and his successors did much to further the acceptance of the diesel engine in many parts of the world, and in doing so helped to create and support industries of major importance in the development of several nations. There was a small team of personnel, reporting to the late Ken Woollatt (and later Frank Wilkinson), who roamed the world talking to new prospects, developing the licensees and guiding their efforts. The late Ken Richmond and Ian Mearns were major contributors to the work, especially on quality and engineering aspects, while in later years Ken Wright was a major presence in the setting up of production equipment. Of the personnel involved in negotiations, I am grateful to Brian Cocks for some of his recollections of the 1960s and 70s, as well as latter personnel, including Paul Rogerson and David Smith, for filling in some of the gaps. Unfortunately many stories may never be told since documentation is sparse!

For Perkins the heyday of licensing as a means of business expansion came in the 1960s and 70s. Many developing countries were looking for industrial expansion and modernisation, while at the same time putting up tariff barriers against the importation of certain goods. This complicated considerably the process for export of 'completely knocked down' (CKD) kits for engines, needing the development of a department specifically tailored to handle the complex bureaucracy. During the 80s, and especially after the break-up of the Soviet bloc, most countries reduced their protective import duties. The point was reached where some licensees were looking for significantly improved technology if they were to extend existing licences, along with access to international markets.

With the spread of free trade, often referred to as 'globalisation', licensing virtually disappeared in the early 2000s. In order to continue in the new situation, Perkins needed to change strategy, looking for Joint Ventures and manufacturing opportunities to provide global sourcing from plants placed in key growth economies.

India

As explained in Chapter 2, the first exportation of Perkins engines to India took place in about 1934. Burgeoning interest in the country was frustrated during the period of World War II but recovered soon afterwards and resulted in the creation of the first licensee operation in 1953.

Simpson and Company Limited, those original licensees, had their origins in a business formed by A.M. Simpson and a Mr Hide in 1840 in Madras. The company soon passed into full ownership by Simpson, with interests in various activities. In 1876 the Company was recognised by 'Special Appointment' as coach-builders, first to the Prince of Wales and then to His Majesty King Edward VII upon his coronation. In the early 1900s Simpsons began the import of motor cars to India, and by 1907 local build of vehicles had started. By the 1930s the whole enterprise had become complex; included in many other endeavours was the import of those first Perkins engines into India. Acceptance of diesel engines was slow, and the war years brought a stop to all such activity.

In 1949 an agreement was reached with Perkins for import and

servicing of diesel engines for southern India: a first batch of 243 P6 engines was imported for the conversion of existing petrol-engined vehicles. Initial sales were very slow and at the same time Perkins was negotiating with companies in other areas of India for the supply of engines. In 1951 an extension of the import and service agreement was signed with Simpsons covering all of India, together with a declaration of intent for a progressive move toward local manufacture. The first CKD kits of parts were imported in 1952, with the completion of the first locally built P6 in July of that year. A number of key Peterborough personnel were seconded to India for a period to assist Simpsons in their venture. A further agreement with Perkins was submitted to the Indian Government for approval with an initial target of 3,000 engines a year by December 1956: approval in June 1955 was followed by intensive activity, which ensured the programme reached its target. It seems clear that there was some friction and lack of understanding between Simpsons and Perkins in those early years, and that governmental support was sometimes lacking; however, the parties persevered. Visits by Frank Perkins and Monty Prichard, who was born in India, helped to foster a greater understanding between the two companies – all English visitors were always given an enthusiastic welcome. A close relationship developed between FAP and Mr Anantharakrishnan, the head of the Group which owned Simpsons: both men anticipated a great future for the diesel engine in India.

The initial licence for P6s was soon extended to other engine types, including the unique development of the P2 engine: Simpsons also took over Massey Ferguson India in 1960. Greater ambitions for industrialisation brought collaborative agreements with other British companies, covering components such as pistons, bearings and crankshafts. Through the 1960s, 70s and 80s the powerful Simpsons Group flourished, renaming itself 'Amalgamation Limited', and developing its own engines from the old licensed products to suit local market needs. They also purchased some of the assembly equipment displaced by the closure of the Canton plant in the early 1980s.

In 1995 Simpsons signed a new licence agreement with Perkins to produce the 1004.4 engines. This ended in 2005 with the engine being further developed to meet Indian emission standards and being renamed as the Simpsons S440. All licences lapsed, so the Perkins name and trademark can no longer be used on local products: however, the company remains the Perkins distributor for the whole of India. The considerable and complex history of Simpsons is told in Getting India on the Move, written by S. Muthiah and published in 1990 to coincide with the 150th anniversary of their founding.

Yugoslavia

An agreement was signed in 1954 with Industrija Motora Rakovica (IMR) situated in the Rakovica suburb of Belgrade to produce the P Series engines. IMR had been founded in 1927 by a group of Serbian and French investors to produce aero engines, soon diversified to include trucks and tractors. Over the years this agreement extended to cover the indirect and direct-injection versions of the 3.152 and 4.203, the 4.236 and its derivatives as well as the 6.354 range of engines. The licensee imported complete kits initially but developed and incorporated locally-produced components until a nationalisation level of around 95% was achieved. IMR supplied engines to a range of local machinery including forklift trucks.

Their biggest customer was IMT, a state-owned tractor company, which started out with a co-operation agreement with MF but soon turned into one of their most significant competitors in central European and African markets. In the 1960s IMR started their own export programme, including tractors to Egypt, where exceptionally they

The first Perkins licensee was Simpson and Company on Madrea, India. This picture shows a group of workers in the factory in the early 1950s

were allowed to sub-license the local assembly of the 4.203 engine.

During the 1970s, when engine demand was at its height and exceeded the supply capability of the Peterborough plant, 4.248 engines were shipped directly from IMR to MF Beauvais and to Volvo in Sweden for their tractor applications. Stuart Wolf was seconded from Peterborough to support this effort, living in Belgrade for a period to support the quality programmes and monitor supply. Relations improved during the 1980s, with production volumes reaching 50,000 engines a year. Further agreements were reached to upgrade the IMR engines to the latest standards; unfortunately the financial restrictions of the Balkans conflict stopped implementation.

As with many companies in the old Soviet bloc, IMR was a state-owned operation, with only 11.8% of shareholder capital. This state ownership brought other complexities to the relationship due to regular changes of management: the key Perkins contact in IMR was Mijat Milkovic whose roles included interpreter, Commercial Manager and Secretary of the Works Council – no doubt this also added confusion to the scene!

During the Balkans war of the early 90s, the licence agreement was suspended in line with the United Nations edict and production in IMR declined dramatically to only 5–10% of its previous levels. Mr Milkovic looked for better prospects and joined Simpsons in India.

Many of the heart-rending pictures of refugees escaping the conflict included red MF tractors powered by IMT 3.152 engines.

By 2005, IMR production was gradually increasing, the diesel engines based upon the Perkins products being known as M3, DM3 and S families. These had specifications founded upon the P-series Indirect injection, P-series direct injection and 4.236/6.354 families respectively, and include a two-cylinder version of the P series, the D2.101, which adds some challenge to the application engineer to resolve the resultant vibration characteristics!

The Serbian Government was reportedly looking to sell the Company into private hands but without success so far. It was recognised that the company needed to develop more modern engines with reduced emissions levels, but lack of capital precluded this activity and, without an external strategic partner or many of their former Yugoslavian customers, the long-term prospects look poor.

Turkey

The original licence agreement was signed with Uzel Makina Sanayii A.S. in 1961, together with an agreement with Massey Ferguson to produce tractors. The agreement allowed the production of AD3.152, A4.236 and A4.248 engines at up to 20,000 units per year and local content of about 30%.

A multi-application licence was signed in 1994 to cover engines for generator sets, marine and industrial sales potential, but never took effect. When Perkins declined to licence emission-compliant engines in 2000 – as the Turkish Government moved towards imposing emission regulations – Uzel signed an agreement with German manufacturer Deutz for local engine production. The economic crisis in 2001 caused this venture to stall and the Perkins 1103 product was selected to fill their needs for Stage 1 emissions requirement in the 53 to 75bhp class.

Throughout the late 1990s and early 2000s, Uzel built up a position as suppliers of utility tractors to MF (later AGCO) with the result that by 2006 around 25% of their production was being exported through these channels. The D3.152 engine continued to be built at around 6,000 units per year, with 40% of the engine content supplied via Peterborough CKD. Estimates suggest that over 400,000 Uzel/MF tractors are used in Turkey with locally-built Perkins engines.

Alongside the links with Agco, Uzel have embarked on other ventures, and can be expected to play a larger role in European and world markets. Plans are also being made to move the main factory from Rami, now an inner suburb of Istanbul, to a more cost-effective location in central Anatolia.

Another agreement was signed in 1982 with Chrysler Kamyon Imalatcilari A.S. to produce vehicle engines at up to 8,000 units per year. This company had started out as a Chrysler subsidiary but during the late 70s was purchased by the three Turkish distributors when Chrysler Corporation divested itself of many overseas subsidiaries. Handling discussions with three local entrepreneurs, often with differing views, brought some interest to the negotiations: the General Manager Erdem Bektas fortunately acted as arbiter and ensured that ways were found through this period and others where economics and foreign exchange difficulties proved challenging. During the 80s the relatively high profit margins possible on the CKD kits made the business with Kamyon important to the overall sales plan.

The products licensed started with 4.236 and 6.3544/T6.3544 but were extended to include the Phaser range of 4- and 6-cylinder products, including a charge-cooled turbocharged 4.40. Local content was considered to be 25% for this project. The trucks produced, as Dodge D250 and D600 series, had scarcely changed externally in over 30 years. With over 170,000 produced, often in tipper configuration, they are a common sight on the roads, often grossly overloaded: a tribute to the durability of both truck and engine.

Emissions regulations in Turkey eventually drove Chrysler Kamyon to seek alternative engines as Perkins could no longer justify the expense of meeting Euro-2 and -3 levels for on-highway products. In 2004 the Company changed its name to ASKAM and sold out the trade marks to Daimler-Chrysler who wished to sell cars under the Dodge name in Turkey.

Japan

Mention has already been made in earlier chapters of the development of business with Toyo Kogyo. This was an association of considerable mutual benefit, with Perkins providing indirect injection versions of the 4.236 and 6.354 (they became the 4.224 and 6.335 respectively, with shortened stroke to allow operation to over 3,000rpm), while TK developed the 4.154 and 6.247 engines - badged and sold as Perkins products for small trucks and industrial uses, through the South African and American companies as well as Peterborough. The 4.154 was eventually further developed to provide smaller (4.135) and larger (4.182) derivatives which sold in small numbers. In the early 1970s some 4.154 engines were assembled in Peterborough using CKD kits from TK and finished with UK-sourced parts. Later in the 70s the 4.165 engine was developed from the original 4.154 but never reached large-

scale production, although a plant in Hanover, Germany, produced the engine for Volkswagen briefly.

Brian Cocks recalls the pragmatic approach to problem solving adopted by TK in the early days: when faced with a porosity problem on the casting of the 4.224 cylinder block the Japanese engineers quickly switched to a shell-moulding process, at a time when European foundries used such technology for much smaller parts. The author recalls comments too from designers Bill Westwell and Bill Stewart when they were visiting TK in the early days of the venture: they would attend a meeting and be faced with a throng of Japanese engineers all listening and scribbling in their notebooks throughout the discussions – in such ways did they learn quickly from their partners!

Argentina

The local licensee Perkins Argentina S.A.I.C. was founded in 1961, using an existing factory in the city of Cordoba, about 400 miles north-west of Buenos Aires. Additional land was acquired to extend the factory area at the same time, and in 1963 further investment in machinery allowed local manufacture and machining of parts including cylinder blocks, heads and sumps. By 1967 the plant occupied 19,000 square metres and produced 3.152, 4.203, 6PF305 and 6.354 engines. Further expansions and extended license agreements introduced 6.3544 and V8.510 engines between 1976 and 1978, with the factory covering 35,000 sq m and able to produce in excess of 55,000 engines per year with local content up to 80%.

The moving force behind the Argentinian operation was Don Jaime Amat, director of the family textile firm, Amat SA. In the early days he was supported by a number of expatriates, including the late Ian Mearns, whose tales of his time there as Chief Engineer included the need to barricade the windows with mattresses during some of the wilder periods when bullets were flying. The early death of Don Jaime in May 1973, coupled with Argentinian economic difficulties in the 70s and 80s, when inflation became extreme, put the future of the enterprise at risk.

There was an intention in the late 90s to introduce the Prima and 500 Series engines but in October 1992 PASAIC declared bankruptcy under 'Chapter 11' and was taken over by the creditor banks. Local investors eventually purchased Perkins Argentina from the banks, believing that assets were a better investment than cash. The renamed company, Pertrak, has since developed engines for local applications and has become a component supplier to Perkins for their plants in England and Brazil.

Bulgaria

An agreement was signed in 1967 with Balkancarimpex, a manufacturer of forklift trucks, for the production under licence of 3- and 4-cylinder engines. This business was transferred to a subsidiary, VAMO JSC. A new factory was constructed capable of producing up to 30,000 engines a year, and this was modernised and extended in 1982 to produce 42,000 engines annually to meet increasing demand. They introduced a unique product in the shape of the 3.177 engine, a 3-cylinder version of the 4.236, with cooperation from Peterborough, but the engine is no longer made and the casting and machining equipment has been scrapped. The licence termination dates from 26 April 1989.

However, an experiment started in 1989 when Perkins Technology established a joint venture with VAMO to put in place a new consultancy, which was named Intertech, in Varna, Bulgaria's second city. The thinking behind this move was based very much on commercial considerations: PTech had found considerable difficulty working with companies within the Comecon area due to the problems of obtaining payment in convertible currency. By establishing a consultancy organisation inside an Eastern European country this issue would be at least eased. However, just as Intertech was about to start operations, the Berlin wall fell and 'glasnost' became a meaningful word in Western countries. There was considerable debate as to the future of the embryo entity: it was decided to continue with a reduced level of investment, staff and facilities.

Ken Galloway had been appointed from Peterborough as the expatriate director, with the rest of the staff selected from within Bulgaria. When operations started in 1990 it was against a background of considerable difficulty across the entire ex-Comecon group of countries: the grim battle for survival when most economies had effectively collapsed did not augur well for the successful development of the business. Sales visits were made to the majority of near neighbours, including companies in Turkey, Hungary, Czechoslovakia, Poland and Yugoslavia. Eventually a reasonable flow of work was achieved, mainly in the fields of noise and vibration but with some engine test work and technical support, but not to a level justifying increased investment. Ken Galloway remained for three years before returning to Peterborough but left behind an organisation which has continued in business but no longer with Perkins support.

VAMO still produces engines based upon the D3.152, 4.236, T4.236 and G3.152, with the majority of parts manufactured in the factory. The engines have been modified considerably to keep up with legislation and meet later levels of smoke and gaseous emissions, and the plant has obtained ISO 9002 certification for its quality systems. The engines are used not just on forklift trucks but also in many other applications including tractors, trucks, generator sets and water pumps, as well as marine uses.

At the time of writing, VAMO appear to have ambitions to extend their operations to include engine supply to Russia, the Czech Republic and Poland – in the latter case looking to assume the role of the Ursus operation which closed in 2005. They have modern machine tools and good engineering systems including CAD/CAM. The joint development with Perkins Technology of the Varna Technical Centre has enabled them to compete with Perkins for business.

Mexico

A joint venture between a group of Mexican investors, Fabricas Automex SA (Chrysler de Mexico) and Perkins Engines led to the formation of Motores Perkins SA in 1966. A factory was built on Automex land adjacent to the car and engine plant in Toluca, a city in Mexico State about 65km from Mexico City and at an altitude of about 8,700 feet above sea level – not an ideal place to build and test any engine! The original capacity was for 18,000 engines per year, initially the 4.212, 4.236 and 6.3542 models. A small number of expatriates assisted in the start-up of the factory, which produced its first engine in 1967. The first customers were Automex for trucks and Massey Ferguson de Mexico for agricultural tractors. Other industrial customers followed, including Clark Equipment, Ingersoll Rand and Poclain.

To combat the considerable effect of altitude on engine performance the altitude-compensated version of the 6.3542, identified as C6.3542, was introduced into production in 1973 and showed immediate advantages over other naturally-aspirated engines in the plateau areas of central Mexico.

Due to Government pressure on Chrysler de Mexico the ownership of MPSA changed, with Diesel National (a Government-controlled company which produced other diesel engines, including Cummins under licence) taking a controlling share. The company was moved to an independent factory in 1976, in another area of Toluca, with an initial capacity of 36,000 engines: by 1980 the actual production reached 34,000. The capacity was increased to 54,000 a year in 1983

by upgrading of the assembly and machining lines: the engine types produced were all variants of 4.236 and 6.354, including compensated and turbocharged derivatives.

Pakistan

The original agreement was signed in 1973 with Millat Tractors Limited, to produce tractor versions of the AD3.152 and A4.236 to fit in the Massey Ferguson tractors being made under licence. The project included the transfer of the block machining lines from Hanomag to Millat after refurbishment, and allowed steady production levels of around 10,000 engines a year (a production capacity of 15,000 engines per year with up to 30% local content was the original intent).

In the 2000s volumes reached over 25,000 a year as the local demand increased; Millat purchased the decommissioned 3.152 block and head lines from Peterborough to augment their production facility.

South Korea

There were some confidential discussions in September 1962 with the Chosun Machine Works Limited, the proposal being to build up to 3,000 6.354 engines a year. However, it is not clear what the driver was for that initial approach, and clearly it led nowhere. CMW later changed names and eventually became Daewoo Heavy Industries Ltd.

The first licensee was Hyundai International, an agreement being signed in July 1973 for vehicle engines, specifically the 4.108, 4.236 and T6.3543. Engines were built from CKD through to the late 1970s: as a result of local politics Hyundai lost the rights to the vehicle sector and the licence lapsed.

The second agreement was with Halla Engineering and Heavy Industries Limited, signed in February 1995. This company has connections with Hyundai International since I.Y. Chung was chairman of both companies and was the brother of S.E. Chung, the better-known chairman and owner of the Hyundai chaebol (conglomerate) which included the Hyundai Motor Company. The licence covered Eagle and Phaser engines destined for truck applications, which were themselves licensed from Iveco.

Halla also had other plans for expansion, including the construction of a new forklift truck factory at Merthyr Tydfil in Wales, for which considerable support was obtained from the Department of Trade and Industry. Unfortunately the Asian economic crisis of 1997 revealed that Halla, along with many other major Korean companies, was not as strong financially as had been believed. As a result the company folded and the licence lapsed. The Welsh factory was eventually taken over by Linde for their UK FLT operations.

Peru

An initial agreement signed on 14 September 1973 created Motores Diesel Andinos SA in conjunction with the Peruvian Government and Volvo Truck from Sweden. This company was set up to manufacture diesel engines in the 30 to 300bhp range as Peru's contribution to the Latin American Free Trade Area (LAFTA). The intention was that the new factory, to be built in Trujillo (500 km north of Lima) in 1975, would serve all countries in LAFTA, with engines at the lower end of the range to be built to the Perkins licence and those at the upper end to the Volvo licence.

Key staff members were contracted from both Peterborough and Sweden to assist start-up and train personnel. The local General Manager was Jorge Grieve, an ex-Government Minister and leading industrialist: his determination and persistence were a major factor in ensuring the project proceeded. Initial local content was very restricted due to the low industrialisation of Peru, and support was sought from

The original premises of the Mexican company were moved from a position adjacent to the Chrysler plant to an independent site in the mid-1970s, seen here in an aerial view

Brazil as local truck and tractor production started. The factory produced the 4.236 and 6.354 families at low volume.

The initial 10-year agreement was supplemented in 1992 with 'automatic' renewal on a 12-month basis. Eventually the plant in Trujillo was closed, with assembly and test operations transferred to a smaller factory in Lima.

Poland

The agreement signed by Perkins and Massey Ferguson in 1974 has been the subject of comments already in this book. This agreement with the Polish Government, promoted and supported by the British Government, was to completely modernise the Polish tractor industry under the Ursus Tractor ZPC marque, an established operation just outside Warsaw. This was the most ambitious of all the agreements, being worth US$9 million directly, plus considerable associated buy-back advantages. A large team was formed by Perkins and MF, co-located in premises at Stoneleigh near Coventry, and key personnel seconded to work in Poland. As well as providing the technical support for the products, the team arranged the civil engineering and machine tool purchase, etc., and training of personnel.

The engines were the AD3.152 and 4.236 families to suit the tractor models: a further proposed agreement with the Andoria engine plant in the south of Poland involving the 6.354 family was dropped in favour of the Leyland 6-98 series. The development of the Ursus factory was very slow, a newspaper report from early 1979 noting that there would be a year's delay in bringing the plant on stream – claiming it had reached the halfway point after five years! (However, some assembly from CKD kits, with some local content, did take place in 1978 as part of a training programme.)

Ursus production volumes reached 35,000 per year during the late 80s, but following the political and economic upheaval in 1990

the volume decreased to 2,000 a year until 2005, when production ceased. The town of Ursus had been built around the factory site and was visible from the railway line. John Harvey-Jones, the British industrialist and TV 'guru' mentioned the plant in one programme when he commented on the huge volume of tractors awaiting despatch and the inefficiency that it represented!

During 2002/3, the ownership of Ursus changed to a PLC: new owner Bumar, which has a significant State shareholding and interests in construction machinery and heavy engineering, has a strategy for the revival of the tractor brand. Meanwhile, Ursus has become a customer for Peterborough-built engines and remains an occasional supplier for 3.152 engine components.

Iran

The original agreement signed on 1 April 1975 with Iran Tractor and Manufacturing Company (ITMCo) covered D3.152, 4.236, A4.248 and 6.3544. The plant capacity was set at 30,000 engines a year with 40% local content envisaged.

The plant was located in a new industrial zone in the north-west city of Tabriz, with many of the management appointed specifically to develop the engine manufacturing facility. The cooperation agreement included the relocation of seven expatriates, led by L.G.T. (Leslie) Roberts who had considerable experience in overseas operations. Machine tools for the cylinder block and cylinder head machining lines were purchased from Cross Machine Tool Company, all being proved in England before shipment.

The production Job One was scheduled for mid-1979, which turned out to be six months after the departure of the Shah. With the revolution clearly underway, the Perkins expatriate team were withdrawn although their personal effects were held by customs for some six months at the Iran/Turkey border. The machine tools meanwhile were stored in their packing cases for about four years, in the open and being subjected to the considerable temperature variations in Northern Iran.

Under the new post-revolutionary Iranian government, existing agreements were reviewed and other tractor and engine manufacturers given the opportunity to replace MF and Perkins. In view of the dedicated nature of the equipment already on site this proved impractical: the project restarted but with none of the original Perkins engineers involved at the demand of the new ITMCo management. The negotiations, led by Peter Baker and David Smith for Perkins, were arduous and ultimately set the pattern for renegotiations with other companies, including Massey Ferguson for the tractor plant.

Under Ken Wright as the new Project Manager, the project restarted: in spite of the considerable complexity of the task – unfinished factory, stored machinery to be prepared and personnel trained, to say nothing of the difficulties of travel to a country still at war – production start-up was achieved using CKD supply. Material had to be shipped by road from Turkey, causing added problems and delays. After the successful start on the 4.248 engine, new agreements were put in place in 1984, 1993 and 1998 which extended both timescale and the products covered, including Phaser and 1000 Series engines. By 2005 yearly production reached 19,000 engines, mostly for MF tractor applications, with plans to achieve the originally specified 30,000.

South Africa

An agreement signed in 1979 with the government-owned Industrial Development Corporation in South Africa created Atlantis Diesel Engines Pty Limited (ADE) as a licensee, in conjunction with Daimler-Benz. The facilities built were possibly the best of the many licensees developed, the strong financial backing allowing high quality plants and associated foundry. The intention was to produce tractor and industrial engines from the Perkins range and vehicle engines on the Mercedes side. However, some conversion work ensured that 4.236 engines were also fitted to small trucks and other vehicles. Several Perkins expatriates were contracted to assist Atlantis on the manufacturing and product engineering, some returning after their contracts and others opting to stay on. Many had enviable lifestyles as a result, but those who stayed too long found that the devaluation of the Rand following the end of apartheid made a return to the UK financially difficult.

Such was the political drive for self-sufficiency that engines from other suppliers were banned from importation: as a result Perkins engines were fitted to products such as Case, Deere, Deutz and Same tractors. These adaptation kits proved beneficial some years later when Case's Doncaster works suffered a strike at their engine plant in Germany. Faced with a need for alternative engine supply in a hurry, the availability of the proven Atlantis 4.248 installation gave the company a unique advantage.

The original licence covered 4.236 and 6.354 families, and the overall development of ADE resulted in the export of major components back to Peterborough, especially crankshafts and cylinder blocks. Extensions of the agreement were agreed beyond the original 15 years until an effective termination date of 1 November 1998 was reached. The need for self-sufficiency in the changing conditions as other nations accepted the new South African position meant that free market conditions could now apply.

Indonesia

A licence agreement was signed in 1986 with PT Pandu Dayatama Patria (PDP) for five years, covering 3.152, 4.236 and 6.354 products for industrial and agricultural uses. Two of the customers were Japanese OEMs, Sakai for road rollers and Komatsu for forklift trucks. The

relationship with Sakai resulted in supply to their Japan-based operation, a rare occurrence. With few local manufacturers or international subsidiaries, however, viable volumes were not attainable and the project ceased.

Iraq

An agreement was signed on 13 May 1989 covering an initial ten years with State Enterprise for Mechanical Industries (SEMI). This was an attractive opportunity to supply engines for the Zetor 70bhp tractor and Brazilian MF combines being assembled locally.

On the same site at Iskandaria were an artillery shell facility and another which was described as producing baby milk, the whole area being protected by anti-aircraft guns: proof of their success was shown by the remains of an Iranian aircraft in the grounds.

As part of the proof that Perkins was an appropriate partner, the negotiating team was asked to show how the engine could be fitted into the Zetor tractor. There was a secret ingredient here, in that Hunters, the long-established Belgian distributor, had developed a conversion kit for the 4.236. Arrangements were made for a tractor to be sourced in Belgium and an engine installed. Once proved off, the engine and kit accompanied by an engineer from Hunters were flown to Baghdad. Since SEMI was a state enterprise the consignment was cleared quickly through customs: within three hours of the engine and kit arriving on site the installation was complete and the negotiating teams invited to witness the start-up! A few silent prayers later, a successful demonstration was followed by continuation of the talks.

The site chosen for the factory was on land where salts were clearly leaching to the surface. The Iraqi management would not accept that this meant that subsidence was likely due to the high water table, with consequent risk of the installed machine tools being affected. However, it was found on a subsequent visit that the 20,000 square metre site was being raised with thousands of tonnes of gravel, because 'the ground was too low' to provide an adequate foundation!

Construction of the new factory was underway when Iraq invaded Kuwait. The contract was suspended in August 1990, in line with British Government and UN edicts. Subsequently the area was closely targeted and the site damaged during the air campaign of the 1991 Gulf War.

People's Republic of China (PRC)

With the opening of the country to foreign participation in the late 80s/early 90s, there was a Corporate desire to establish a relationship in order to enhance business opportunities in Asia, especially the vehicle business, and also to take advantage of alternative engine and component sourcing. The state-owned engine and machine companies in the PRC were fragmented and frequently huge, often operating at a high level of integration, but looking for technology, partners and finance. The challenge was to find an effective partner to introduce Perkins to the 'customs and practices' of the Chinese industrial world, as well as providing a lead into volume business, preferably in the vehicle sector.

After some years of searching throughout China and discussions with several potential partners, a first licence was signed with Tianjin Engine Works (TEW) on 17 March 1994, and approved by the Chinese Government on 14 April 1994 for a ten-year period. This covered technical know-how for transfer of diesel engine technology and trade mark, including upgrades of the products as new emissions legislation took effect.

TEW first introduced themselves to Perkins during an SMMT Trade Mission to China in mid-1988 when they literally knocked unannounced on the Perkins representative's hotel room door, requesting a meeting and expressing a wish for a joint venture. TEW were a relatively small state-owned enterprise seeking to establish a new engine plant with a foreign partner and World Bank loan funding.

The agreement for the JV was finalised and signed in 1997, with Perkins taking 60% and TEW 40% of a new company, Perkins Engines Tianjin Limited (PETL). The relationship did not develop successfully, however, and in 2002 Perkins reduced its shareholding in PETL to only 10%, with the remaining shares being sold to the Tianjin State Government. Subsequent to this and following a number of irregularities in share dealings, Perkins served notice of termination of both the licence and trademark agreements on 11 August 2003. At the time of writing (2006) there were still ongoing disputes and legal actions by Perkins in China since products were still being built, marketed and exported, carrying the Perkins trademark without authorisation. Production volumes of around 15,000 engines a year were involved, mostly being fitted into trucks although the engines did not meet all the then current legislation requirements. Perkins continues to seek a means to re-enter the Chinese market.

Uruguay

In the 1970s there was a short-lived agreement to assemble 4.108 engines from CKD kits, with minimal local content for car and light van applications. Perkins Rio de la Plata was formed. No details are available of the actual production achieved.

Greece

Petropoulos, a long-established Perkins distributor, assembled small volumes of D3.152 engines for their own tractor production, using kits imported from IMT in Yugoslavia. This was done to comply with 'domestic content' regulations long before the EU opened markets.

Spain

Agreements were signed in 1966 which established Motor Iberica SA (MISA) to supply engines for their own MF and Ebro tractor and vehicle applications. Engines were also supplied to other OEMs in Spain who had set up manufacturing to access the protected national market. Production included V8.540, 4.108 and 4.165 engines, with some limited buy-back of components by Peterborough.

The partnership was successful only while the customs tariff and local content regulations were in place. When Spain joined the EU in 1983 the transition arrangements were short, and it quickly became apparent that assembly of engines and tractors was no longer viable. The plants in Barcelona and Madrid were sold to Nissan as a part of their European vehicle manufacturing operations. MISA also set up a tractor assembly plant in Aleppo, Syria, which is still in operation and takes engines from the ITMCo plant in Iran.

Morocco

Discussions had been held intermittently with SIMEF, a Lister/Petter licensee based at Fez over some years. The justification for local manufacture was based solely upon the punitive levels of duty levied on engine imports, with any local manufacturer receiving preference from the Central Bank and other Government departments for duty and foreign exchange allocation. The primary market was for MF tractor assembly, as a substitute for engines shipped from Banner Lane, plus some incremental volume from local Berliet truck and bus assembly plants.

An agreement was finally signed in 1990, but in the following year the Moroccan Government relaxed customs duties as part of an 'open market' philosophy. The tractor and truck assembly plants closed and the engine project was dropped.

The start of the new decade for Perkins, as with many other British enterprises, was not greeted with optimism. In a series of front page columns for the January 1980 Echo the directors reviewed the problems facing them in their various responsibilities. A quotation from MF President Victor Rice prefaced their comments: 'We are facing challenges which are demanding the utmost effort from all our people.'

Chairman Mike Hoffman elaborated on the position: 'At the start of the New Year it is customary to make resolutions . . . to take stock of where we have been and to chart a course for the future. The 1970s were difficult for MF and Perkins, culminating in disastrous losses in 1978. During 1979 many actions were taken for survival – unprofitable operations were sold off, organisation and assets slimmed down to reduce cash outflow. 1980 is being entered with a smaller more efficient organisation.'

Adrian Parsons, Peterborough Managing Director, went further along the same lines: 'During the 1960s and 70s the world was a fairly predictable place, we could plan the route ahead based on previous experience. . . . In the late 70s we saw the start of a period of change – "the age of discontinuity". The reasons for this are known to us all. . . . The challenge to Perkins is to be faster on our feet to take advantage of events, if we do not someone else will. To react quickly all must pull together, as we did during the 1979 industrial dispute.'

The other directors elaborated on the theme, giving more details of the problems and challenges. Today we can recognise the concerns as symptomatic of the concerns common to all industry in the 'Thatcher Era'. From being number one in diesel supply for years, Perkins faced intense competition at a time when record inflation was rendering any UK exports increasingly uncompetitive. The pressure to reduce costs and produce more from the same or less resources was obvious; an example quoted by Jim Felker was of the Austrian distributor who had seen Peterborough ex-works prices increase by 16%, although he could only increase his selling price by 4%. Added to that was an adverse effect of 3% on exchange rate, so that his costs went up by 19% for a price increase of only 4%, totally destroying his profitability.

Nationally 1980 had begun badly, with the first countrywide steel strike since 1926. British Steel announced that 11,287 jobs were to go in Wales by the end of March with the closure of the Port Talbot and Llanwern plants. Government statistics showed that half the married women in the UK went out to work, the highest in the EEC.

Not all of the January news was 'gloom and doom', however. An article was reprinted from Truck magazine covering the early years of Perkins, with its successes and failures, while news from Argentina covered the first production of V8.540s outside Peterborough as PASA delivered locally-built engines to Clark Equipment for their Michigan 75S wheeled shovel loaders.

Later in January Mike Hoffman visited the Perkins plant in Mexico and at a function there he called again for governments around the world to learn a lesson from the current fuel crisis and put together a unified policy with regard to fuel usage for the future. He restated his point of view made public in the previous September, suggesting the development of alternative fuel sources for stationary applications, with petroleum-derived fuels reserved for mobile applications. He also urged the encouragement of non-fossil fuel developments for road transport and of course the increased use of the more efficient diesel engine wherever possible. (It is sobering to record that no interest was taken in this by government; indeed it took until 2006 for any real stirring of 'official 'interest in alternative – biomass – fuels: an opportunity missed and over 25 years of wasted time. Of course we had North Sea oil . . .)

In Peterborough Adrian Parsons said farewell to over one hundred employees who had decided to take advantage of the redundancy terms offered for early retirement. Some of those leaving had over 40 years' service and over seventy had over 30 years with the Company. He thanked them all for their loyalty and dedication, working through good times and bad, and wished them well in their retirement. In a special article, the Echo looked at the career of the oldest employee, Russell Broughton, who had completed 46 years, starting as an engine fitter at the age of nineteen. The next issue of the paper looked at another employee, this time Madeleine Green who completed 39 years, finishing in the Standards Room where her responsibility was for the maintenance of the standard gauges and slip gauges used to keep production machinery and components within tolerance.

An unusual Perkins application was pictured in February, this time an amphibious vehicle used for harvesting mussels on the Brittany coast. Designed and built in St Malo, the craft bore a passing resemblance to the WW2 DUKW and enabled work to continue whatever the state of the tides, running at 6 knots in the water and 15kph on land or mud.

The five millionth engine produced at Peterborough was a 6.3544(V) built for International Harvester Australia. IHC Marketing Director George Aravosis is pictured between Perkins Quality Director John Lawrence (left) and MD John Devaney

Seven weeks into the steel strike a poll of 11,500 middle managers in the industry produced a vote of 'no confidence' in the top management, branding them incompetent as the losses were said to be £2 million a day. Prime Minister Thatcher announced that state benefits to strikers would be halved, increasing the pressure to settle. During March the 'get tough' policies of the Tory government hardened, with Margaret Thatcher stating her intention to withhold VAT payments to the EEC if their budget controls were not eased. The UK Budget on 26 March revised income tax allowances while increasing duty on petrol, drink and tobacco. Some relief came at last when the steel strike was called off on 1 April. Towards the end of the month the unemployment figures were announced, topping 1.5 million. At the end of the month the EEC was in disarray, with a failure to resolve the issue of British contributions to the European Budget.

The Suggestion Scheme featured strongly in May, when an article in the Daily Mail covered the link between Perkins and The Industrial Society, the body largely responsible for the original initiative, which sparked interest in Peterborough. The Echo meanwhile carried news of the first £2,000 payout by the Scheme, to foreman Mick Beavis for an idea for reconditioning machine tool coolant pumps instead of scrapping them.

The Transport Engineer magazine for road transport engineers produced an article by Editor John Dickson-Simpson praising the V8.540. He noted that the views of the industry changed sharply with the introduction of the bigger engine, which was proving to have twice the durability of its predecessor. Although Perkins claimed up to 280,000 miles before major overhaul, experience in the field showed up to 430,000 miles achieved before major failure. He confidently predicted that the new V8.640 would be even better, and argued that Perkins were in the 'premium engine' sector now, as well as helping to keep the smaller vehicle manufacturers competitive with the major producers.

Local news centred on the new canteen facility at the Vicarage Farm Road offices. The new kitchen was equipped to use a revolutionary 'cook-freeze' process, where batched meals went straight from the cooker into a high-speed freezer at -20°C. When needed the food could be reconstituted and served in one hour, as edible and succulent as the day it was cooked. With over 2,500 meals served each day, the ability to plan and cook ahead added flexibility to the planning of meals, assisting especially the nightshift catering. The restaurant manager commented that 'being able to read people's minds, especially when the weather changed suddenly, was always problematical'. The new facility would help this, and also enable preparation of food in season to provide better value for money.

Industrial unrest continued in the UK, with a TUC 'day of action' called for 14 May, a few days after an unfair dismissal claim by shop steward Derek 'Red Robbo' Robinson against British Leyland was rejected by an Industrial Tribunal. Figures for UK inflation showed a new figure of 21.8%, and at the end of May the EEC agreed a reduction in the British contribution from £1,100 million to £250 million by 1981.

June brought the commissioning of a new telephone system throughout Perkins, installed by Plessey, which allowed internal and external calls to be handled through one instrument. Its introduction coincided with the inauguration of a private network linking all Massey Ferguson plants, enabling fast communication between the units as well as 'speed dialling' to many suppliers and customers.

There were a number of stories about Perkins products and their successes. One unusual application was the use of the 6.354 in the

The T6.3544 found a market in the Defence industry close to the end of its production life. The Alvis Scorpion light tank provided a fast, light and easily-transported armoured vehicle with diesel power increasing its range and reliability

'Water Witch', a small versatile dredger for use in harbours and docks. Each unit could clear up to eighty tonnes of rubbish each day through dredging, as well as underwater bulldozing, ice-breaking and survey work. Manufacturers Liverpool Waterwitch Marine and Engineering of Ormskirk, Lancashire had over thirty units working throughout the world – one in New York had worked for eight years and twelve hours a day without problem. Perkins' service support worldwide was noted as an important consideration, although in fact few engine problems had been experienced.

The Material Handling Exhibition at the National Exhibition Centre was the venue for the launch of the 3.1522 'clean' engine. This featured 'squish lip' combustion technology, with reduced emissions and a smoke level 50% lower than its predecessor, while preserving excellent fuel economy. The engine was aimed specifically at forklift trucks and similar applications. In the huge Bauma exhibition held in Munich, 27 manufacturers showed a total of 43 machines powered by Perkins; the users included JCB, Blaw Knox, Broyt, Coles Crane, Hyster, Caterpillar and MF.

The annual Perkins Sports and Family Day in June was enjoyed by around 20,000 people. In spite of torrential rain in the morning, the weather improved in the afternoon, although low clouds prevented a parachute drop by the 'Red Devils' display team. There were displays by the Lancaster and Spitfire of the Battle of Britain Flight, while a Harrier jump jet gave an exciting display. On the ground teams from several departments took part in an 'It's a Knockout' competition, while the local fire brigades competed in a 'Jetball' competition using hoses to shoot a ball into goal – everyone got wet! The crowd also enjoyed a baby show, sheepdog trial and marching bands.

In the factory new production test cells were opened at a cost of £2 million, handling the small engines on pre-rigged trolleys to increase throughput. Another milestone was reached in Brazil where their 500,000th engine was commemorated with special stationery and billboard displays around São Paulo.

Any hopes that the overall national economy was improving were dashed as British Steel set the closure of the Consett plant for the end of September, with the loss of a further 3,700 jobs. Unemployment rose to 1.6 million in June. By mid-July this figure had worsened to 1,896,634 – the highest since 1936 – with forecast levels of 40,000 redundancies a month in a depression reckoned as the worst since the war.

In the July Echo the headline 'The Company Must Survive' introduced a sobering statement from Mike Hoffman to the Trades Unions. He warned of the need to change methods of working or face extinction in the diesel engine markets as a world recession started to affect British industry. Trading conditions were especially severe in North America and already Perkins was facing three- and four-day working weeks in some production areas. Many companies with a record of success in the export markets were now facing increasing problems triggered by a unique combination of high inflation, a strong pound and high interest rates. The fundamental inefficiency of many British working practices had helped to slash profitability, without which future investment would prove impossible. Hoffman noted that the situation was clear: 'Since 1978 a British exporter in the US market would need to increase prices by almost 50 per cent in order to maintain margins, far in excess of other competitors.' He concluded that Perkins needed to reduce costs and change working methods: this would mean redundancies. Without the co-operation of all the unions even more job losses would follow.

Not all the news was downbeat of course. The military supplier Alvis was welcomed as a new customer, fitting the T6.3544 in their Scorpion light tank. Claimed as the smallest and fastest in the world, Alvis expected that changing the existing petrol engine for the diesel

would extend the tank's range, increase its reliability and cut costs. Meanwhile the Walton component factory took delivery of a new multi-spindle lathe from Alfred Herbert of Coventry and a new gear hobber. These would replace five old machines, save nearly £50,000 a year and improve gear quality.

An article on the Italian subsidiary Motori Perkins told how the operation opened in 1961 and by 1980 had seventy employees under General Manager Roberto de Liso. Their sales had increased to over 9,000 engines each year, with a turnover in excess of £13 million. As well as sales to MF and Landini, the Perkins customers included Alfa Romeo, Benati, Laverda, Hydromac and Lugli. A few weeks later a further article considered the German company, Perkins Motoren. 'The market is difficult and fastidious,' claimed General Manager Juergen ten Houvel, 'but over 27 years we have proved able to stand up to strong competition like Deutz and Daimler-Benz.' The 45-man operation achieved £14 million sales in 1979 and had a 14% share of the non-captive diesel market. He noted, however, that with UK inflation running at 15% compared to 6% in Germany, and an unfavourable exchange rate, it was more difficult to compete. Their major customers included Claas, Clark, Eaton, Steinbock, Orenstein and Koppel, Lindner, Hanomag and Reformwerke.

A 'recycling' story was provided by Research and Product Development as they found a solution to the calibration of new flow meters fitted to the test cells used for exhaust gas emission tests. The American Federal Authorities suggested the use of a 'bell prover' – a device used in the past for the accurate measurement of flows by the gas industry. One of the few surviving devices made by Parkinson and W.B. Cowan was located and purchased for £250! With careful in-house restoration the antique was found to be ideal for the task.

In August UK unemployment topped 2 million with an expectation of further increases to 2.5 million. Margaret Thatcher blamed it on wage inflation – 'we have paid ourselves 22% more for making 4% less', she said, going on to claim that the monetarist policy was 'exactly right', and that the Government would not be panicked into emergency measures.

Mike Hoffman discussed the troubles afflicting Massey Ferguson in late October. The article was headlined 'The Fight We Have on Our Hands' and explained the situation over the past two years and the reality behind some of the 'scare' headlines. The severe pressure on MF started in 1978 when the year-end figures showed the Corporation in the red to the tune of $268 million – the biggest single loss in Canadian history. Looking at the current position, the actual debt of the Corporation stood at £1,700 million – this summation including all outstanding loans from banks and other financial institutions. On top of this was the cost of servicing the loans, at a time of high interest rates. New MF President Victor Rice had obtained commitment for some of the investment and was looking to the Canadian Government for the rest of the £215 million estimated to be needed to offset the debt burden. The complexity of the situation was made worse by the pattern of shareholding in the Corporation, where many small shareholders held most of the shares. The biggest single shareholder, Argus Corporation, had decided to give its 16.4% shareholding to the MF Canadian pension fund as well as withdrawing their representation on the MF Board. This withdrawal actually helped get the necessary Government backing as there had been differences of opinion between Argus and the other financial parties involved!

The Echo interviewer led Mike Hoffman into a discussion about the possible sell-off of Perkins to assist the MF recovery. Such a move was denied as 'never having been discussed'; Hoffman was at some pains to point out that the problems were mutual, with Perkins dependent upon MF for around half of all engine sales currently. Other points made concerned the unexpected adverse factors, especially the impacts of oil prices, high interest rates and the poor exchange rate performance of sterling. The purchase of both Hanomag and Canton, intended to increase engine production, had not proved to be safe investments especially when financed by borrowed money – a strategy that at another time might not have been disastrous. Hoffman stressed the need to act like a team – going out to sell products, cut costs and compete with the Germans and Japanese to turn around the business and ensure survival.

Elsewhere in the October Echo the sales efforts in the European region were highlighted, as was the Motor Show at Birmingham where V8.540, V8.640 and TV8.640 were strongly featured, along with the T6.3544 and 6.3544 and the new 'Power Exchange' engine scheme, which extended and modernised the original 'Perpetuity' process.

A number of political issues made October significant. At the Tory Party Conference Margaret Thatcher stated that she was 'not for turning' on her economic policies, and a few days later Jim Callaghan resigned as Labour Party leader at 68, tired and wounded by the disputes within Labour and the trades unions over the past years. A few weeks later Michael Foot was elected party leader, with Denis Healey as his deputy.

In early November the Group saw more changes at the top. Victor Rice appointed Mike Hoffman to the post of Technical Vice President for the worldwide MF operations, with Jim Felker taking over as Managing Director of Perkins Engines Group Limited. Jim Felker had been with MF since 1967 and had occupied positions in Canada and Mexico before joining Perkins as Finance Director in 1972.

Mike Hoffman in a farewell interview spoke of the actions already undertaken to save money, instancing the sale of Canton and Hanomag as well as the slimming down of Perkins' management structure. He noted also the successes over the past year in improving deliveries, improving quality and communications. It was noticeable that there was no comment on redundancies, although in fact the process had continued with more of the older employees being offered, and taking, early retirement. There was, however, mention of the effects of inflation on pensions, with extra payments from the Pension Fund to help cushion the impact.

The year-end figures showed an increase of production to a total of 213,874 engines, up by 6.5% over the previous year with the 4.236 and 6.354 families responsible for the modest increase. The volume of CKD kits also rose by 5.9% to 125,146 to achieve a reasonable result in a difficult year.

1981

The new year opened with the declaration of a new slogan – 'Right First Time'. In introducing this Jim Felker and John Devaney, the Director of Manufacturing, stressed the continuation of the past drive to improve delivery, reduce costs and ensure continued quality improvements. They expected a difficult year and needed every employee to strive to improve every aspect; in ensuring that each month every customer should receive everything ordered, Felker noted that 'none of us would be happy if we did not receive all our pay!' Devaney reminded everyone of the need for the clean build of every engine, commenting that engines stood down as incomplete were always more susceptible to error and could get despatched with problems. The Suggestion Scheme provided some backing with a new campaign offering special incentives on quality issues, homing in on ideas to reduce damage in engine handling, transportation and despatch. Cost savings were also in the news with the telephone system reckoned to have saved £350,000 in the year, with more to come for calls to the rest of the MFP network.

The annual London Boat Show was a busy time for Perkins, with the new TV8.540M as the largest marine engine offered and a revised T6.3544 featuring squish lip piston technology. With 27 engines fea-

tured in 24 boats, it was the venerable 4.108M fitted to narrowboat Godiva that attracted the attention of comedians Morecambe and Wise when they visited.

Nationally there was some better news as inflation dropped to 'only' 15.1%! This was overshadowed, however, by the announcement of plans to close 50 coal mines, with the loss of 30,000 jobs; the Welsh miners immediately started an unofficial strike. While Industry Secretary Keith Joseph announced plans for a further £990 million in aid for British Leyland, the Government confirmed their intent to privatise nationalised industries, starting with the sale of half of British Aerospace, and with further plans for the gas, electricity and telephone industries, plus the Trustee Savings Bank. The intention to expose other state-owned organisations to more competition was also made clear. In an unexpected U-turn, the government promised more money for the coal industry in an effort to avert a damaging national strike.

In Peterborough construction of the Queensgate Centre, on the site of the original Perkins factory, was well under way. Amey Roadstone Corporation was one of the major contractors, using Ford trucks powered by V8.540s for much of the concrete mixing and transportation. New TV8.640s were delivered to vehicle customers such as ERF for proving trials ahead of full production launch. Although many new truck models now featured big six-cylinder Cummins and Rolls-Royce engines, Perkins anticipated a gap in the market for a powerful and more compact V8 to handle vehicles up to 32 tonnes gross weight. With a purchase price saving of 15 to 20%, as well as a significant weight saving, it was hoped that the new engine would sell well.

On Wednesday 4 February at 11.30am, Perkins produced their five millionth engine. This was a T6.3544 vehicle engine destined for International Harvester Australia, and was the subject of a celebration as well as a special silver paint job.

Another 6.354, this time older and second-hand, featured in a news item about the Ravenglass and Eskdale narrow gauge railway in Cumbria: the engine was fitted to their locomotive Lady Wakefield to become the third Perkins-powered unit. Although for the tourist trade steam engines were naturally predominant, the line always used diesel power for the first and last trains of the day, transporting people to work and children to school. The trains could handle up to 200 passengers on the gradients up to 1 in 35 at average speeds of around 15mph.

In March an article in the Motor Transport newspaper praised Perkins' performance for recording a 23% improvement in reliability in the previous two years. Perkins had concentrated on early life warranty experience, using a count of 'repairs per 100 engines' within warranty. Not only had 1978 been 5% better than 1977, and 1979 23% better, but the cost of repairs had also dropped: 'Translated into actual engines it meant that an operator buying an engine in April 1980 had a 99.3% chance of needing no repair within warranty – quite an achievement by any measure.' The article noted that typically some competitive engines required between 3 and 16% repairs, and praised Perkins for its openness in disclosing data, hoping that it might encourage others to do the same. Quality Director John Lawrence was pleased with an independent source confirming the achievements: 'It also underlines how importantly the outside world regards quality.'

Jim Felker presented 25-year service awards to 245 people at the March Long Service Dinner. He noted that 'in the 50 years that the Company is about to complete it has never had a major compulsory redundancy. When redundancies have unfortunately been needed, these have been on a voluntary basis with payments to volunteers exceeding legal requirements and calculated to provide volunteers with a maximum opportunity for new employment or enjoy a reasonable retirement. It is the Company intention to continue this policy.' Perkins in 1955 may have been viewed as a paternalistic employer, but times change and policies become more formal and may appear more remote. 'The key question to ask is, has Perkins been a responsible employer throughout the past 25 years? If "yes", then it is up to all of us to keep it that way. If "no", let me know about it, to get it right first time!' he ended.

Queen's Award to Industry Again

In May Perkins won the Queen's Award for Export Achievement, the fourth time in fifteen years. Judged on performance over three years, from 1978 to 1980, the citation recorded that the value of exports rose from £155,864,000 to £196,811,000 during the period. The £40 million was a 26% increase, with exports representing over 80% of production annually. Perkins claimed 20% of the world tractor engine market, 30% of combines, 40% of forklift trucks, 14% of pleasure boats, 10% of trucks, 11% of compressors and 7% of generator and welding sets. Jim Felker stated that 'We are proud and delighted to have won this award, particularly at a time when market conditions are highly competitive, with quality and reliability of products becoming an important selling factor. Trading conditions for British companies have been difficult due to high inflation, interest and exchange rates . . . it is a fitting recognition of an excellent team effort across the whole company.'

As a part of the overall savings programme a new 'Modicon' control system was installed at Eastfield to monitor and control heating and ventilation across factory and offices, eliminating the human element. The scheme was expected to save almost 10% of the annual £3.6 million energy cost, adding to the other savings made by switching to coal in place of oil for boiler fuel.

Perkins apprentices were in the news for designing and building a special wheelchair to assist Peter Chilcott, who had been paralysed from the neck down after a car accident. The chair enabled him to be lifted into a standing position, an important consideration in his overall care, and something previously only possible during visits to the physiotherapy unit. The project had been initiated by the local 'REMAP' panel and later received recognition from an American specialist manufacturer.

During the annual Long Service Club Dinner, Jim Felker revealed that Perkins' trading position had been turned around to show a small operating profit. 'It is razor thin, but that's a big improvement on the major losses being made last year. We are doing better, but it's still not brilliant,' he stated. After the dinner he presented tokens to six members who had reached forty years with the Company.

There were some notable successes to record during the early summer too. An Acmat truck, made in France and powered by a 6.3544 engine, won the truck section of the Paris–Dakar Rally, finishing nearly seventeen hours ahead of the second-placed Ford truck. Acmat specialised in producing trucks for rough desert conditions and used only Perkins engines. Most of the other competitors – using Ford, MAN, DAF, Renault, Mercedes and Leyland trucks – failed to finish the course! Another success in a rather different competition went to the Perkins Squash Club whose team of three men and a girl won the finals in the European Federation of Company Sports Games, dropping only one game throughout the two-day competition in Hamburg. There was less success, however, for the Perkins tenpin bowling team 'No Hopes' who after winning the British Championship on handicap could not repeat their success in the European final, finishing at the bottom of 120 teams; but rivals '007s' came 41st, best of the other British teams competing.

Another sporting venture appeared in July with an Echo feature on tractor-pulling and the use of a much-modified TV8.540 in John Walker's Turbosonic Mark II. Looking more like a dragster than a tractor, this fearsome machine was equipped with four turbochargers, two in series on each cylinder bank, together with special low-compression pistons, hardened crankshaft and a huge fuel injection pump to cope with the claimed output of over 1,000bhp! With water injection to cool the induction air and running at about 110 lbs/sq inch boost, the 'tractor' was expected to be very successful.

Compared to this V8 modification the second 'special' application of a 3.1522 was much more prosaic, but no less intriguing. The engine was fitted to a British Oceanic submersible designed for operation in the North Sea. The novelty was the operation of the engine on a closed loop induction system, with oxygen injection and exhaust scrubbing so that the diesel could power the submarine while submerged. The project had been proved experimentally and was hoped to be in production in three years.

The annual works shutdown at the end of July heralded the final closure of Track 3 after nearly thirty years in operation. The track had been a trail-blazing system at the time, a powered conveyor rather than the 'towed trolley' tracks previously used. The cost of £7,372 for the installation in 1952 had been a bargain: it had handled the L4, 4.270D, 4.300 and 4.318 engines over the years. A few weeks later the Company announced a £10 million investment in a new cylinder block machining line, handling 6.354 and 4.236 families, by utilising the core machine tools and equipment removed from the Canton plant in 1979. The line was intended to add 80,000 extra components to the yearly output from Peterborough.

Later in September the employees were delighted to learn that the MFP Pension Scheme had come out top in a survey of works and staff pension schemes conducted by leading independent actuaries Geoffrey Morley and Partners. Steady improvement in the fund performance since 1971 was noted, with investment in promising UK and overseas companies providing increasing benefits for the MFP pensioners, irrespective of the Group's performance. (It was perhaps ironic that 23 September then saw the second-biggest ever fall in London Stock Market values!)

A snippet of industry news in the same month recorded renewed interest by both Ford Europe and British Leyland in the use of diesel engines in passenger cars. Their changing stance was reported to be in response to a growing world demand for more economical motoring, even though the tax situation in the UK had inhibited this development. Rather surprisingly there was no link to the fresh interest in the same applications within Perkins, where the cancellation of the Q16 project may have been the last independent attempt, but not the final curtain!

Two 'heritage' stories appeared in November. The first covered the existence of an old Barford and Perkins motor roller, still in use at the Napier cricket ground in New Zealand. This was built in the 1920s and was still going strong, being used for tending the pitch for regular matches, including those against touring sides. (In 2005 we learnt that the roller had been retired and passed into the hands of a local museum where enthusiasts were going to refurbish it!) The second story concerned the continued use of old drawings: Brian Henson of the Inspection Department had noted that the drawing for a rocker spring, part number 0780005, had originally been part number 102781, used on the 'Vixen' engine and dated July 1932!

Also in November the invention of a new 'language' by Perkins was publicised. In order to provide clearer instructions in the many service documents and to facilitate translation into additional languages for worldwide use, a special vocabulary of only 1,500 words had been developed for PACE (Perkins Approved Clear English). The words had been carefully chosen to ensure every instruction was both clear and unambiguous, and when taken in conjunction with quality illustrations would help all users, including of course associated OEM customers who produced their own instruction manuals, to be 'right first time'. An expansion of the 'fleet monitoring' scheme by the Quality Analysis Department was announced, aimed at collecting detailed information about engine performance, reliability and durability. By targeting fleets operating more than twenty Perkins engines in their equipment, not just in trucks but also forklift trucks etc., Perkins hoped to improve the breed through timely feedback on problems and shortcomings. The scheme was also expected to improve relationships and increase trust for all concerned.

There was also news of a change in the organisation of the Engineering Division, for the first time since 1975. With increasing emphasis on new products, it was decided to appoint two new Chief Engineers, one to look after the Q14 large engine family, while the other oversaw the development of small engines for passenger car and light van applications through joint ventures. A third Chief Engineer would look after the 'Current Products' and maintain close liaison with production areas.

In spite of the enthusiasm and belief that the revised and revived company would see good results in 1981, the statistics at the close of the year were disappointing. The total production was only 173, 063 engines, a reduction of 19% on the previous year. Every engine family, except the 4.236, showed reduced volume while CKD kit despatches also dropped by 17.5%.

If it had been a disappointing year for Perkins in almost every sense, nationally there was also little to celebrate. British Leyland had announced the closure of three plants, with 2,850 redundancies, while the London Docks were scheduled for closure and redevelopment. Apparently unable to see the writing on the wall, 58,000 BL workers struck over pay at the beginning of November, shortly before an announcement by their management of a joint venture with Honda to develop a new executive car – Project XX. In the first month of 1982 unemployment reached 3 million – an increase of 130,000 over the December level, another unwanted record as this represented the highest monthly rise since records began in 1948.

1982

For Perkins employees 1982 opened with a reminder that this was the year in which the Company would celebrate its fiftieth anniversary. This Golden Jubilee was coming during the worst economic period since Perkins' foundation. Jim Felker noted that there would be no time for a lavish celebration, although the contribution made by Perkins in leading a revolution in diesel power could not be overlooked. There would be a special Jubilee Dance in the summer, and a commemorative plaque would be placed in the new Queensgate Shopping Centre. Special headings were to be used on the Company's stationery and a special programme was planned for the annual Perkins Industrial Concert.

In his speech to the Suggestion Scheme '200 Club' annual dinner, Felker noted that Perkins was in the top ten of British industry for quality performance: 'Our reputation for improved quality is already winning approval from customers,' he noted. He reflected that the 'Right First Time' campaign was producing good results and giving employees greater pride in their workmanship: during 1981 the Scheme had paid out £125,328 for the total of over 2,000 ideas submitted.

Tony Downes, the Director of Engineering, talked in the Echo about the debut of the new Q14 engine at the forthcoming Amsterdam Motor Show and at the annual SAE Exposition in Detroit in February. 'This is the cleanest, quietest and most economical engine ever produced,' he claimed. 'With squish lip technology and benefiting from other lessons learnt, plus computer-aided design and other new techniques, this shows what can be achieved when a highly experienced design team sets out to produce a next generation engine.' The first prototype had been run in 1979, with the first road running in early 1981:

he forecast that the engine would play a major part in the world of agriculture and industry as well as road transport.

In early February there were more changes at the top. John Devaney moved from Manufacturing Director to become Director, Sales and Business Development, while John Towers took over the Manufacturing role. Both men were regarded as 'home-grown' as both had started as trainees – Devaney as a graduate in 1968 and Towers as a student apprentice in 1966. Towers had moved through a number of posts in the Engineering and Quality areas, being heavily involved in the 1981 'Right First Time' campaign.

The February Echo announced that well-known bandleader Syd Lawrence and his Orchestra had been booked to play for the Jubilee Ball on 14 August – something to look forward to as the country shivered in temperatures down to -20ºC, with snow and spectacular hoar frosts during the coldest winter for some years.

In March some changes in manufacturing were detailed: a major reshuffle in the north-west corner of the original factory provided space for the new 4.236 balancer machining area. This £6 million investment in automatic machining and assembly equipment was scheduled to produce the first unit in November 1982. A further change came with the installation of the 'J-hook' assembly line for 4.108 production. This line had originally been installed in Hanover for the short-lived 4.165 venture, and had been mothballed before transfer to Eastfield. The flexibility of the innovative overhead system meant that other small engines could be handled with minimal additional expenditure.

In an article entitled 'Planning A Future', coverage was given to the Company's yearly planning cycle used to set business policy, reassess long term planning and update, as well as set, the objectives for the year ahead. Although fundamentally aimed at maintaining the position of industry leader in technical innovation and worldwide supply within the power range – especially that of the 4.236 and 6.3544 – it was acknowledged that the UK cost base meant that the products might not be the cheapest. Therefore reliable quality and delivery became essentials to ensure customers received value for money. Improved two-way communication with employees and customers formed an important factor too, while the roles of Massey Ferguson as major customer as well as owner and partner were vital in maintaining volume. In the changing industrial world there was speculation on the possibility of joint ventures and new licensees, these being seen as important – provided they matched overall policy and were financially viable and indeed self-financing. Measurement of managers' performances against their annual plan commitments was a part of the shared responsibility for future growth and reward.

Massey Ferguson announced the introduction of a new tractor-digger-loader in March. The MF 50D replaced the highly successful and best-selling MF 50B, offering more power, greater stability and a higher capacity loading bucket, with options including torque converter or manual transmission and four-wheel drive. The 4.236 remained as the standard power unit, with 69bhp at 2,000rpm giving road speeds of up to 20mph.

In April Jim Felker, Dick Yates and track operative Dougie Emmerson joined with 200 other personnel from British Industry invited to Buckingham Palace for a special reception at which the recipients of the Queen's Award for Export Achievement were honoured. All met and shook hands with the Queen, Duke of Edinburgh and Prince Charles plus members of the Government before enjoying a reception and buffet. Dougie remarked to the Echo that it had been a long but most enjoyable special 'day out'!

Discovery of the oldest 'Wolf'

The search for the oldest surviving engine came to a climax with a special event at Eastfield when Harry Beeton, one of the original employ-

The diesel version of the ubiquitous Rover V8 engine failed to reach production in the early 1980s, after considerable effort and expenditure

ees now aged 92, was reunited with Wolf engine serial number 3084 which he had built and which left the Queen Street factory on 2 May 1934. It was found in Southampton during the search which drew entries from Africa, Australia and the Americas. The engine had originally been fitted to a Carrimore truck owned by Lawes Chemicals Company (of which Frank Perkins was a director). In 1939 the engine was fitted to an Albion truck owned by the Nobel Explosives Company but then disappeared from view until 1954 when it was purchased (fitted in a Daimler saloon) by Ken Cleverley of a local Southampton taxi company, who was expecting to remove and export the engine – until he realised how old it was! The car and engine went to a local scrap dealer, Frank Harris, who ran it for a year then sold it to local engineer Ralph Clegg. He fitted the engine to an ex-Army Humber staff car, where it was found to be 'underpowered but reliable'. The engine next went to Ian Musson, who intended to fit it to another ex-Army Humber Field Command Car – it took until 1959 to start the installation, for which he called upon Perkins for help! He used it for personal transport and to win a rally – 'it would only do 50mph but kept on going where others failed'. Then it was removed in the 1960s, eventually being overhauled in 1973 and fitted to an emergency generator set owned by F Musson and Son of Cannon Street, Southampton. What a chequered career for any engine – and this one was swapped for a new unit and then became a prized exhibit at Peterborough!

The special Anniversary edition of the Echo for early June contained a variety of articles recalling the early days of the Company, its trials and tribulations. A number of the reminiscences of early members of the staff were included, some of these being included in earlier chapters of this book as 'Personal Glimpses'. There were more recent stories of course, and the inclusion of a 'Customers' Charter' – developed by Perkins and based on 50 years' experience and service. A final quotation from the founder summed up his views: 'The principal requirement of a business is a satisfied customer but first the product has to be good.'

At the Long Service Club's annual dinner, Jim Felker likened the current position of the Company to that experienced by Frank Perkins fifty years before – started with good ideas, lots of hard work

and a large bank loan! Although the similarity held good in some respects, the industrial world was very different and the competition much stronger. The need to be better, rather than cheaper, was again a key part of his theme, as was the importance of the contributions made by the long-serving employees present at the event. He welcomed the Club's initiative in inaugurating a new award, the 'Golden Jubilee Award', which would be presented annually to the division, department or group of people perceived to have made the greatest contribution to the Company's prosperity each year. There were presentations to six members who had reached forty years' service, including the first award to a lady – Joyce Bell – who recalled that when she started, aged fourteen, in the Print Room at Queen Street there were 114 employees on the payroll. The Quarter Centurion Award for the year went to Bill Walton who completed the London Marathon at his first attempt, aged 63!

The Perkins Industrial Concert in the Cathedral was a big success, with a capacity audience of 1,400 enjoying the performance by Yehudi Menuhin and the Royal Philharmonic Orchestra: the programme included Schubert's 5th Symphony and the perennial favourite, Edward Elgar's Enigma Variations. There was less happy news from the Social Club, however, with a report of diminishing attendances for their regular Saturday dances and cabaret nights; the club believed that the recession was forcing employees to watch their spending more closely, and hoped that members would provide more feedback on what they wanted.

New Joint Ventures announced

The June news on the product front was more positive, with an agreement signed with Balkancar Impex of Bulgaria to develop designs for three- and four-cylinder engines based upon the 4.236 family, to include the new 'squish lip' combustion technology. The Research and Product Development Division announced that Perkins would become the first engine manufacturer to buy laser doppler anemometry equipment. Developed in conjunction with the Harwell Laboratory this new technology would allow the measurement of gas flows in a running engine, using a quartz window in the cylinder head, and assist in the development of advanced combustion systems.

Another important announcement concerned a joint venture (JV) agreement with Land Rover Limited, to produce the first British 'high performance' diesel under the project code 'Iceberg'. Perkins Research and Product Development were working on the conversion of the highly successful Rover 3.5-litre V8 to diesel, with dramatic improvement of fuel consumption and a rating of 125bhp at 4000rpm. The all-aluminium construction engine would feature an indirect injection combustion system, with initial production targeted for 1983 introduction.

Although not publicised at the time, this was not the only JV with the old British Leyland companies. Through David Hodkin and the Perkins Product Planning Department, negotiations with Austin Rover Group on a small car engine had been in progress for some time under the code name 'Ferret'. This was based on the conversion of an existing 2-litre four-cylinder engine to become a high-speed direct-injection diesel. There were other novelties for Perkins in this ground-breaking venture since the engine would be overhead camshaft with a cog-belt drive for the fuel pump and timing gears. Both these projects came under the control of Mike Hawkins, the new Chief Engineer, Small Engines.

The introduction of company-wide video presentations, aimed at keeping everybody informed about the Company's position, problems and progress, produced a number of questions at individual section briefings. As a result, the most important questions were answered by the relevant directors and managers through a series of monthly articles in the Echo, thus ensuring that all employees received the same feedback.

In July an article entitled 'Triumph of Teamwork' told the story of the first batch of T6.3544(V) engines to meet the new US Federal Emissions Certification standard being shipped to Central Freight Lines in the USA. This customer had been impressed by a prototype unit and required a further batch of thirty engines, but against a tight deadline otherwise they would switch their purchase to Japan. Faced with such a challenge the Production, Quality and Shipping Departments pulled out all the stops to meet the date – by hours!

Another initiative announced by Perkins in August was the launch of a new optional two-year warranty scheme, an improvement over the one-year scheme run for many years. The new option, taken out on the purchase of the engine, was simple and superior to any warranty offered by competitors at the time. The scheme reflected confidence in the product and was expected to improve customer relations and operator confidence too.

The culmination of the 50th Anniversary celebrations was the Jubilee Ball on 14 August, when 800 people danced the night away to the music of the Syd Lawrence Orchestra and the Bryan Dee Sound. Another event attracting sponsorship was a five-mile road race held at the East of England Showground in conjunction with the Nene Valley Harriers.

In the same month yet another joint venture was made public: this time an agreement with Chrysler Corporation to design diesel conversions for the car engines made at their Windsor plant in Ontario, Canada. The work would enable versions of the 'Slant 6' and two four-cylinder engines to be produced on the same equipment as the gasoline originals and provide diesel options for the North American car market. Perkins adopted the code name 'Squirrel' for this project, which also came under the responsibility of Mike Hawkins. It was noted at the time that Chrysler chose Perkins as a partner due to its strength in diesel technology, proven past ability on engine conversions and its ability to sell to the loose engine market. This hardly did justice to the strenuous efforts of the Product Planning Department to find potential new markets for the Company!

In September the head and block machining lines transferred from the Canton plant were being proven in Factory 3, with cylinder block production scheduled for November and cylinder heads in early 1983. The new £2 million balancer machining line in Factory 1 was also nearing completion with commencement of production scheduled for November, with potential levels up to 100,000 units a year. John Towers commented that this reinforced Perkins' commitment to the 1980s and would significantly improve the manufacturing base as well as quality. During the same month the new T4.236 and TV8.540 engines were announced, the former filling a gap in the product range and allowing customers to match engines more closely to their power requirements and use a smaller package size. The TV8.540 meanwhile provided compact power for trucks up to 34 tonnes gross vehicle weight with a compact engine envelope.

Amongst other new equipment installed in the factory the new multi-nut runner for the 6.3544 assembly track was most significant: this tightened all 32 fixings for cylinder head to block simultaneously in just seven seconds, providing improved clamping uniformity and eliminating the need to re-torque the fixings during test. Any error during the process was automatically shown on a printout, allowing immediate rectification using a back-up single spindle station.

Long-distance sailing records were once more in the news with the exploits of David Scott Cowper in his yacht Ocean Bound. David was already an amateur sailor of some repute, having taken part in trans-atlantic races during holidays while pursuing his profession as a chartered surveyor. He made a decision to attempt more arduous voyages, however, and purchased Ocean Bound with the express intention of making a single-handed circumnavigation of the world. Needless to say, the yacht was fitted with a Perkins 4.108(M) as auxiliary power plant – with good reliability an essential ingredient for powering lights and radio equipment as well as allowing safe entry and exit from harbours.

The first voyage took David round the world following Sir Francis Chichester's route in the most-favoured west-to-east direction. He completed the trip in 224 days on 23rd April 1980, beating Chichester's 1967 record by two days and setting a new fastest average speed of 131 miles per day for the 29,420 miles. This was the 67th single-handed circumnavigation and the seventeenth by a Briton. However, this was not the end of his adventures. After a thorough preparation he then set sail from Plymouth on 22nd September 1981 bound for Port Stanley in the Falkland Islands, then headed westwards to complete a record single-handed round the world voyage in the more difficult direction – against the trade winds. This journey took a total of 237 days, of which only 16 were spent in ports between legs for rest and essential maintenance. This time the distance sailed was 31,350 miles at an average of 141.85 miles a day – another record, eclipsing this time Chay Blyth's original 1970 record of 292 days. David relied on 'old-fashioned' navigation skills and sun shots rather than masses of electronics. During the two voyages the engine ran a total of over 800 hours and proved totally reliable, ending the marathon in virtually showroom condition.

Closer to home, the efforts of Dereck Lambe, a retired Perkins Field Test engineer, to save various engines and vehicles for his own museum were recorded. An ex-army Humber staff car occupied pride of place: this had been used during the Second World War by BBC war correspondents. He bought the car in 1950, fitted it with a P6 engine then ran it for over 300,000 miles as his main means of transportation. Along with a few other vehicles Dereck had collected many old Perkins engines, including prototypes that never saw production. 'This collection will be available to Perkins as and when they establish a museum,' said Derek.

In amongst the 'question and answer' sequence to which John Towers provided the responses was 'Why didn't we spend money on assembly equipment when Perkins was doing well?' In his reply, Towers noted that in those days the over-riding priority was the ability to produce enough engines, so that capital spend went on plants in Canton and elsewhere rather than detailed local improvements. (He could have said 'quantity rather than quality'!) With the change in the environment now, and industry over-capacity, the emphasis had switched to making better engines more efficiently and at a competitive price. Combined with the new equipment had been the proof that Perkins was not a 'strike-ridden' plant, which encouraged customers and allowed increased investment to improve assembly practices.

News of the increased sales efforts to attack world markets with the new engines came in October. At the Paris Motor Show, the 'Iceberg', T4.236 and TV8.540 were exhibited and attracted considerable attention. The rest of the autumn and winter shows, comprising the UK Motor Show in Birmingham, Hamburg and Genoa Boat Shows, Royal Smithfield and then the Earls Court Boat Show, would all receive high levels of attention from Perkins too.

The October issue of the Echo contained a rare mention of the Perkins computer facilities, giving details and pictures of the Computer Room and its links to the more than 400 terminals spread around offices and factories. The increased usage for every aspect of the business was emphasised, with 16 operators working in shifts around the clock to service 60,000 terminal transactions each day. Two CPUs provided back-up for breakdowns, with total data storage over eight times greater than 1976, with over 18,000 million characters on disc at any one time.

In November Jim Felker was interviewed by TV's John Kiddy for the latest company video presentation for all employees. Felker made it clear that Perkins would not meet the profit target set for the year, and that there was no sign of the total market improving for the next year. 'We have to face these realities and plan for them,' he stressed. 'That's the only way to stay in business.' He noted that Perkins was in very good shape with its customers, even though the industry worldwide was at the bottom of a severe recession. 'Compared with the situation in 1980/1, Perkins is now in a much more competitive position with engine prices now matching competition in France and Germany, and we may also have a price advantage over leading American competitors.' Asked if Perkins would still be around for a 100th Anniversary celebration, Jim Felker was emphatic: 'Most certainly yes. I may not be around but with continued hard work and a few successes I am sure the Company will make it!'

Later in the month, Queen Beatrix of the Netherlands helped to celebrate Perkins' 50th Anniversary when she unveiled a plaque in Queensgate on the site of the original Queen Street works. She also saw exhibits about the links between Peterborough and the Netherlands. Kemper en van Twist Diesel, based in Dordrecht, was appointed the first Perkins distributor in 1935 and many Dutch equipment manufacturers fitted Perkins engines.

With Christmas approaching there was more gloom nationally as the pound slumped to a new low of only 1.581 US dollars, with the Government stating that they would not intervene to support the currency. In addition there was yet another threat by the mineworkers' union in calling for a national strike. (The only bright piece of news was the fall in price of silicon chips, so that computers and calculators would become cheaper, with increased interest and sales pushes by Sinclair, Amstrad etc.)

Victor Rice visited Peterborough and presented the 1982 'Chairman's Award for Excellence' to the UK Sales team for their achievements. The team of Brian Gomm, Eric Ridgewell and Eric Plant had increased their market share and won new accounts, exceeding forecast sales of new and rebuilt engines and parts.

In spite of this the overall achievements for the year were depress-

ing, with total engine sales down to 140,696 – a drop of 18.7% from the previous year and the lowest volume since 1960. Virtually every product showed a sales decrease, the only exception being the venerable 4.318 engine! The most alarming decrease came in the 4.236 family, where sales were down over 26%, and the 4.108 with a volume drop of almost 40%. The CKD kit sales at only 62,753 were also almost 40% down, rounding off a year where any successes had been hard-won. The actual headcount of employees had also dropped very considerably over the year, although company records unfortunately do not provide the actual numbers.

1983

Perkins had some positive news at the beginning of January 1983 when Jim Felker met with Harold Musgrove, the MD of Austin Rover Group, to sign the Joint Venture contract for the two-litre diesel engine, known within Perkins as 'Ferret'. There was Department of Industry backing for this enterprise, with a contribution to the development costs under new legislation aimed at boosting innovative engineering in Great Britain. Starting with the ARG 'O' series petrol engine as the basis, the project covered both naturally-aspirated and turbocharged versions for cars and commercial vehicles. The major component machining was to be carried out at the ARG Longbridge plant, with assembly, test and finish done at Peterborough. Perkins would have the rights to sell engines to third parties, with royalties being paid to ARG.

There was more success at the Paris Boat Show, where 43 boats were on display fitted with Perkins engines. Most successful was the 4.108(M), reckoned to have 86% of its market, especially as the auxiliary power unit for many yachts. The upbeat performance continued at the Earls Court Boat Show, where the new 'lightweight' version of the 6.3544(M) took pride of place and considerable interest was reported in all products.

The structure of communication put in place by Perkins to keep all employees in the picture was rated as one of the best in British industry. Along with the daily press cuttings, weekly notice board 'Newsline', regular Echo issues and the display of press cuttings in the Technical Library, the company also produced a quarterly magazine called Power News for customers and a six-monthly video magazine seen by all employees.

National news continued to headline difficulties with both the economy and employment. On 25th January the pound sank to a new low of 1.517 US dollars and in early February UK unemployment reached a new record of 3,224,715. The first-ever national strike of water authority employees ended on 22nd February, followed immediately by a strike of miners in Yorkshire and South Wales in protest at pit closures. The NUM called for a national ballot on 3 March to assess support.

In the February Echo the work of the Production Engineering Department was highlighted. The new 'Sursulf' crankshaft-hardening plant was instanced as an example of cooperation between production, engineering, supplier and machine-tool manufacturers in assessing the potential of a new process, followed by development and proving of the equipment for production introduction.

Once again the Company presented long-service awards to the employees reaching 25 years at a special dinner dance in mid-March. This year awarded the starters from 1957, the year of the Suez crisis. There were only 33 awards, the smallest total for some years. Jim Felker referred to the recipients as 'The Class of 57' because 19 of the 33, including the author, had started as apprentices in that year.

Another Echo article gave details of the work of the sales personnel covering far-flung areas. Perkins Engines Pacific covered a huge area including Japan, Indonesia and New Zealand, where diverse applications took in everything from irrigation pumps to on-board generator sets, all manner of boats and industrial machinery. General Manager Mike Bruce (another ex-apprentice!) was confident that Perkins would continue to be a force to be reckoned with in an increasingly competitive market, noting that Perkins' engine adaptability and versatility were much appreciated, along with price, delivery and parts back-up.

A novel application of the 4.236 was exhibited at the French SIMA agricultural show in April, when a 'Total Energy' package was shown for the first time. Using a G4.236 as a basis, a generator set was shown running on the gases produced from burning wood. The combination could operate on natural gas, biomass, ethanol, etc., trying to make use of all the otherwise wasted heat through the incorporation of heat exchangers on the exhaust manifold and other components. Another new engine was also announced, the 3.1524 being intended for light industrial equipment such as forklift trucks, compressors and generator sets. With both naturally aspirated and turbocharged versions, the engine offered improved smoke and noise characteristics, along with greater reliability and durability.

Venture with Austin Rover closer to production

In May Jim Felker met again with Harold Musgrove of Austin Rover to sign the supply contract for production of the two-litre diesel, scheduled to start in 1985. 'One of the most significant recent developments in the field of joint co-operation within British Industry' was Felker's summing up. In the same month Margaret Thatcher called for an election on 9th June: this resulted in a landslide victory for the Conservative Party, with the majority of 144 seats the largest since the Labour victory in 1945. As a result of this defeat, Michael Foot and Roy Jenkins resigned as the leaders of the Labour Party and SDP-Liberal Alliance respectively.

A prestigious international award was made to Perkins by the Institut International de Promotion et de Prestige at a ceremony hosted by Peterborough MP Dr Brian Mawhinney, the presentation being made by Leon Brittan, Chief Secretary to the Treasury. The Trophée International d'Industrie' was awarded for international achievement and reputation in their field and in Perkins' case 'is proof that stability and tradition are compatible with modernity and competitiveness,' said Brittan. Perkins was acknowledged as one of the country's most successful exporters, with over 85% of production going overseas. In reply, Jim Felker thanked the Institute for the honour, but sounded a note of caution with regard to protectionism: 'Perkins is concerned that international competition is becoming more difficult as attitudes throughout the world are leading to increased levels of protection,' he stated. 'Taxes, customs, duties and levies, quotas, rules and regulations are hampering the free flow of international trade.'

Another achievement, of lesser international prestige perhaps, was the success of the Perkins football team, who won the final of the European Federation of Company Sports games with a 2–1 win over Francophone of Belgium at Ladbrokes' Holiday Camp at Caister in Norfolk. The Perkins Bowls and Rifle Clubs also took part but with less success.

The Long Service Club held their annual dinner in May, at which the new Golden Jubilee Award went to the Production Control Department for their work in supporting prompt delivery of engines and CKD kits over the past year. Jim Felker reviewed the Company's achievements and prospects for the next year, noting that although the home market looked a little brighter, the US market was still in a poor state. Guest speaker Mike Hoffman, now President of MF's Farm and Industrial Machinery Division, paid tribute to the Perkins products. 'The strength of the engines business was a major feature in MF's sales recovery. The engine is one of the strongest parts of our product. Keep giving us the same quality and we'll keep selling as hard as we can!'

The Perkins Industrial Concert held in June was a great success, featuring an all-Beethoven programme. The Hallé Orchestra was supported by a full chorus of 140 singers, necessitating the erection of temporary buildings in the Cathedral grounds to handle the resulting logistics.

The July Echo 'Question and Answer' section featured the Joint Ventures strongly. In answer to a query on the US Chrysler 'Squirrel' venture which had been cancelled almost before it started, the reply gave the facts about diesel car penetration in the USA, where only 4% of sales were achieved against the expected 25%, mainly due to the poor performance of the Chevrolet V8 diesel launched by General Motors. Another question concerned the length of time needed to develop the ARG engine; in reply, Engineering Director Tony Downes identified the need for an engine totally acceptable in all respects: the challenge of direct injection for a passenger car lay in achieving good noise, driveability and emission characteristics. Yet another question concerned the thinking behind going for JVs when the Company was unprofitable. Finance Director Paul Jobson noted that any project took time to deliver; although the JVs were not yet contributing there were excellent prospects for a good return when they reached production.

There was a change of Managing Director in August as John Devaney replaced Jim Felker. He left Perkins to join Massey Ferguson, replacing Mike Hoffman. (Hoffman left to take up a fresh challenge as MD of Airships Limited, based near Bedford.) Jim Felker had worked for eleven years with Perkins in various senior posts while John Devaney started in 1968 as a graduate trainee, moving through various jobs in Manufacturing, Quality and Sales, including a spell in Canton.

A major article in the Echo in August looked at 'International Competitiveness' with specific emphasis on product quality. Director John Lawrence covered considerable ground in describing the importance of a quality product to the customer, not only in terms of durability and reliability but also in the perceived quality as delivered. He noted that the 'Right First Time' campaign had produced good results; however, the level of 80% was still short of the desired target of 90 to 95%. The need to rectify faults after engines had been delivered to the customer was both expensive and damaging to reputation. Problems with unexpected stoppages and machinery breakdowns could also prove expensive to the customer. Lawrence also emphasised the improvement in warranty claims, now significantly better than five years ago. The current level of 6% for engine 'failure' in service was well short of the target of 3%, although the actual warranty costs of 1% of sales revenue was low for the industry. However, the new target was 0.5% or better, with a need to tackle the aggravating small failures now that most major failures had been eliminated. 'Our engines don't fail, our engines don't collapse on the end user. The problems we have are those irritating small things . . . the trouble is that the more we do the harder it is to get further improvements. But we can't afford to let up – our competitors won't,' he emphasised.

Another promotion followed the retirement of Brian Gomm, who left after nearly 30 years of service in the Sales area, finishing as Director, UK Sales. He was replaced by Eric Ridgewell, who moved from UK Agricultural and Industrial Sales, after joining Perkins in 1971 as a Product Cost analyst. He was soon in print, commenting on new business with ERF in September with the launch of their new M16 truck with the T6.3544(V) as standard fitment. Anticipating initial sales of up to 400 units a year, Ridgewell noted that lighter engine and truck weight allowed greater payload for a vehicle expected to provide good service for both motorway long haul and high street deliveries. 'Encouraging first business, the decision to make Perkins the sole option underlines their confidence in our product.'

The new challenge for Purchase

In the same month Ron Hadnam, Director of Purchase and Supply,

The purchase of the diesel business from Rolls-Royce brought the Shrewsbury factory into the Perkins Group. The original offices are seen here in 1984 along with an aerial view showing the old and new factory buildings in their urban setting

featured in the series on International Competitiveness, covering the challenges facing his side of the operation. He noted that in the fiercely competitive diesel engine field it was necessary to enlist the total co-operation of the suppliers in helping to achieve and maintain competitive pricing in world markets. 'With efficiency and productivity the keys, we tell our suppliers they must keep us informed of all potential ways of absorbing and offsetting costs. The search for suppliers goes all over the world with 13 percent of purchase coming from countries like Brazil, Japan, the USA, Sweden and Germany. We give British Industry a fair chance to quote for Perkins business but we are an international company and must buy from the most competitive suppliers who can give the best quality, the best delivery and the best price.' He emphasised the importance of supplier assessment, stock control and inventory reduction as the company moved towards a 'just in time' philosophy for supply to the production lines.

This Purchasing statement only tells a part of the story of course. One of the effects of the 'Thatcher years' was the erosion of the manufacturing base in the UK: the effects of inflation and high interest rates on old industries was eventually devastating, although the process was gradual and insidious. Many traditional suppliers to Perkins found times getting harder, to the point where eventually they were taken over by more forward-looking competitors, often from overseas, or they went out of business completely. Nowhere was this more visible than in the Black Country around Wolverhampton where production of the many essential hardware items – literally the nuts, washers and bolts needed by all manufacturers – took place. As cheaper foreign competition became available, and proved to be at least equal in quality and delivery, the old suppliers went out of business and a wasteland of old and derelict factories grew up in an area that had been the cradle of the Industrial Revolution. A similar fact overtook much of the foundry industry in the UK: as tougher legislation on pollution, noise and factory conditions was enacted, many of the older foundries became uneconomic and were forced to either modernise or go out of business. The Perkins supplier base was severely hit by this turn of events and as a result Ron Hadnam's Purchasing department had to search further and further afield to develop new suppliers. Throughout the 80s new suppliers came on stream, many in developing industrial na-

tions such as India, South Africa and Brazil, while others were found in Japan and the USA. A new breed of purchase agent was established, relying more on air transport to visit suppliers; the development of new means of communication assisted the practice of 'globalisation'.

'The Old Timer that Nearly Went to War' was the headline in October over the story of a 44-year-old boat in the Falklands. The ex-Thames police launch based in Port Stanley was nearly requisitioned by the invading Argentinians to assist their forces in the harbour, but skipper Jack Sollis convinced them that the boat was not seaworthy and could not be launched. The launch had been built in Littlehampton in 1939 and fitted with P6 engines, doing an enormous amount of work in the Thames before being shipped to the Falklands in the 1960s to a food processing plant.

The November Echo started a new series of articles covering the major customers. Starting with the largest of course, Bernard Garner spoke of the tremendous importance of Massey Ferguson since 1959 and the range of engines now used in their products worldwide. In 1982 the Banner Lane plant in Coventry had made half of the tractors produced in the UK, all of course Perkins-powered – and had manufactured over 2.75 million tractors in total. Close cooperation between many departments in MF and Perkins ensured that any problems were quickly resolved. The December article covered Dodge, the largest truck manufacturer using Perkins. Even in the currently depressed truck market there had been 4,500 Dodge trucks produced, ranging from the 50 Series using the 4.236 to the 26-tonners fitted with the V8.540. At the Scottish Motor Show the new Dodge Commando G24 was announced, fitted with the V8.540, and a revised 50 Series took an uprated 4.236 giving 79.2bhp. The Dodge and Karrier brands were used in a multitude of applications ranging from buses, tippers, dustcarts and vans to trucks.

The close of 1983 did show a slight improvement in production over the previous year, with total engine volume at 153,333 just 9% up. Most of the difference was due to a recovery in 4.236 volume to 75,711 units, while most of the other types were static or, in the case of the three-cylinder, dropping by over 4,000 engines. The CKD volume dropped again to only 54,147 kits, the lowest since 1973.

The Purchase of Rolls-Royce Diesels

The start of 1984 brought renewed optimism for Perkins with news of an expansion. After months of rumours, the buyout from Vickers of the Rolls-Royce Diesel International plant at Shrewsbury was finally confirmed, details appearing in the national media as well as featuring in the first internal 'news' video of 1984, along with a report on Perkins' progress and prospects. The purchase of the Shrewsbury factory – known as the Sentinel plant in view of its original ownership – was viewed as a very significant move, opening up exciting new sales prospects for the R-R products by using the Perkins worldwide sales and service network while extending the Perkins product offering to higher horsepower, in line with the long-term strategic plan. (It is interesting to remember that Mike Hoffman in the late 70s had talked of creating a 'British Diesel Engine Corporation' – it came to nothing at the time due to the more pressing economic realities).

A centre-page article in the Echo gave details of the R-R engines, extending up to the 1,200bhp CV12 used for military fighting vehicle applications, as well as showing the layout of the Shrewsbury factories, where the original Sentinel steam wagon works had been augmented by a new plant built on the other side of the main railway line to Crewe, the two plants linked by a bridge for a site totalling 50 acres. The new subsidiary would became 'Perkins Engines Shrewsbury Limited', with an agreement to continue to use the Rolls-Royce name for a limited period only. UK manufacturers took 80% of engine production from Shrewsbury at that time, for heavy trucks and industrial uses along with the specialist military applications; exported engines going predominantly to the Middle East and Africa.

Indications of other imminent new business came from the East-field production area, where the first 'production prototype' two-litre engines for Austin Rover were being built in a special area. Undertaking build from scratch allowed the small team to develop the assembly and build sequence, deciding upon tooling and test requirements. Since ARG needed a significant number of engines for their vehicle prototype programme, the early use of production facilities also assisted the Perkins Engineering Division to meet delivery dates.

A fascinating story of the German wartime occupation of Guernsey appeared in the January Echo. An Albion bus powered by a P6 had been hidden from the invaders, disguised as a haystack, for the duration of the occupation! After the war the bus was put into service, running over 400,000 miles before being purchased by a group of enthusiasts in Coventry for £700. After restoration the bus, with registration DFP 496, appeared for rallies as one of only ten pre-war Albion vehicles in existence. Another long-serving engine featured in a further story, this time from Zimbabwe, where the National Zimbabwe Railway used 4.107 engines in refrigerated wagons, with around 140 in use. One such engine, serial number 7051959, had run a total of 33,541 hours – often completing up to 10 days' continuous running. The NZR staff said the engines had proved to be outstandingly reliable under the exacting conditions.

Perkins commenced an all-out attack on inventory levels in February. A special team was put together, tasked to reduce overall inventory by around £2.5 million in the next year. Real savings were estimated at £250,000 for every million of stock reduction, from reduced interest, handling, storage and preservation costs. The computerised purchasing system was being refined towards a 'just in time' approach, ensuring material arrived in the factory when needed and not a month ahead. Active involvement of all employees was sought as the team searched for savings on tools and other consumables.

After the extension of the engine range upwards in horsepower with the Rolls-Royce engines, a further announcement took the product offering lower, with the addition of two new small engines of 3.5 and 5bhp respectively. These single-cylinder diesels were made in China by Perry and were launched at the Electrex Exhibition in Birmingham's NEC. Perkins expected that the engines would have up to five times the life of equivalent petrol engines and could be used in a variety of small industrial applications, such as generators and welding sets. (This new initiative proved to be a fiasco, sales failed to materialise and the venture was quietly dropped.)

An Echo series of articles on key customers continued with an analysis of JCB, a long-time customer for the 6.354 engines, taking up to 450 units a year for excavators and wheeled loaders. The opportunity to supply the 4.236 family, referred to previously, resulted in the sale of over 7,000 engines in 1983, making JCB into the largest industrial machinery customer. The engines were used in the Model 3C tractor-digger-loader as well as in a tele-handler. A small Perkins team, consisting of salesman Eric Plant, application engineer Chris Woolhouse and service engineer Cyril Field, ensured that JCB needs were met – especially their reputation for quality and reliability – and ensuring that delivery on time was maintained. It is worth recalling that the initial supply of four-cylinder engines had been very much a gamble on

The Prima engine was the world's first high-speed direct injection engine suitable for family cars. The turbocharged version pictured here shows clearly the complex fuel injection pump and the cogged belt drive to the overhead camshaft

Perkins' behalf since engines were added to the programme without a firm order.

A new naval application combined the products of Shrewsbury and Peterborough when HMS Gleaner was commissioned. Built by the Emsworth Shipbuilding Group near Portsmouth and only 15 metres long, this craft became the smallest vessel in the Royal Navy. Although fitted with twin R-R CGM-310 diesels as main engines, the craft used a single 4.236(M) when carrying out its main role of updating Admiralty charts, running at 3 to 7 knots while mapping the seabed electronically.

During March the Perkins flag was raised symbolically at Shrewsbury, signifying the change of ownership. The final purchase price of £17.4 million was about £2.5 million lower than expected, due to reduced inventory levels in the plant. John Devaney was appointed Managing Director, with Peter Jackson as his deputy, in addition to their current roles in Peterborough.

The Echo carried the story of another long-serving P6 engine, installed in the sub-basement of the Harrods store in London in 1940 for the fire-fighting system.

Thankfully the engine had never been used in anger but was run routinely and reliably for ten minutes every week, drawing water from the building's own borehole. There was another 'pumping' story, this time in more active service. Following the eruption of Mount St Helens in Oregon on 18 May 1981 the natural outlet from Spirit Lake, about a mile from the volcano, was blocked, causing the waters to rise dangerously. A raft floating on the lake and carrying twenty T6.3544 marine engines driving pumps had replaced the first emergency pumps. The system was commissioned by Perkins' US-based application engineer Jack Shirlin, who commented upon the scenes of utter devastation still visible, and the continued fear of a further

eruption that had recently caused a further shutdown and evacuation of all personnel from the area.

Nationally there were a number of significant events during March including a warning regarding the 'greenhouse effect' of rising carbon dioxide levels from studies by the University of East Anglia and others: of course it was to take many years for this warning to be treated at all seriously! A national coalminers' strike began on 12 March, the start of industrial action that caused irreparable damage to the coal industry, as confrontations, violence, arrests and fines occurred throughout the year. The miners returned to work in November, having gained no advantage in their fight with the Thatcher administration. On 13 March the Chancellor of the Exchequer raised taxation thresholds, and on 20 April the Brussels EEC summit collapsed over a disagreement on the UK's budget payments to the Community.

In May Peterborough City Council gave final details of the agreed route for the Eastern Parkway past the Eastfield factory: although the new feeder roads sliced about 85,500 square feet of land from the western edge of the Perkins site, the improvement in access to Perkins was seen as a major advantage.

The process of slimming down the operations in Peterborough continued in July as Perkins started to move out of the premises in Fletton previously used by Newall Engineering, preparatory to the sale of the site. It took seventeen weeks to relocate the connecting rod machining line back into Eastfield, to an area previously occupied by 6.354 cylinder block machining, which was moved to Factory 3. Other facilities moved included the Show Engines Department, resited to Walton, while the literature store was moved into Factory 3. The machining lines for 4.318 cylinder blocks and connecting rods were removed and mothballed after an 'all time requirement' stock had been produced ahead of phase-out.

The CV12 engine was the most powerful unit made at Shrewsbury, producing up to 1,500bhp for military applications including the Chieftain and Challenger main battle tanks

The Eagle engine produced at Shrewsbury was applied very successfully to heavy goods vehicles produced by many UK truck manufacturers in the 1980s

Considerable interest was shown in the Perkins products on show at the British Army Equipment Exhibition at Aldershot in June, where 80% of the vehicles on show were Perkins-powered. The T6.3544 was launched in the Alvis Ferret 80, and there was an order for 60 new Challenger main battle tanks for the British Army in Germany, fitted with the TV12 from Shrewsbury. Other customers exhibiting included JCB, Hyster and GKN, the latter featuring both the TV8.540 in an armoured personnel carrier and the 4.236 in their rough terrain forklift truck.

Unusually, the Echo featured the products of a competitor after a small team from Perkins visited the Cummins 'Consolidated Diesel Corporation' plant at Rocky Mount in North Carolina, USA. Although the visit was arranged to see engine-testing systems, the team took the opportunity to see the rest of the £250 million plant designed to produce up to 150,000 a year of the new 'B' series engines. The link to J.I. Case gave a guaranteed volume of 75,000 engines a year, the remainder being sold competitively against the 4.236 and 6.3544 and their successors. Although the Perkins team were impressed with what they saw, the overall reaction could be summed up by John Towers' words – 'We hope to make them rue the day they ever thought they could take on Perkins Engines and Perkins people.'

Victor Rice announced in August that Massey Ferguson had returned to profit in the first quarter of 1984, earning $2.4 million on sales of US$365 million, compared to a loss of $17.9 million on sales of $403 million in the corresponding period of 1983. 'Our first objective has been achieved, to survive and get back on our feet,' he noted,

adding: 'In phase two our objectives will address a strategy for prosperity across the longer term.' He spelt out the elements of that phase as consistent profitability, venturesome management, building the spirit of MF, teamwork satisfying customers, market leadership and productivity of all the company assets. In noting the continued weakness of some market sectors and uncertainties on economic outlook, he stated: 'There is unfinished work to do . . . I believe that the people of MF are more than equal to it. Together we shall finish the job.'

Within Perkins there were signs of growing confidence. For the first time in three years a dozen apprentices were recruited. A major refurbishment of the main Eastfield restaurant was accompanied by the termination of the cook/freeze operation at the VFR kitchen after a five-year period. Meanwhile on the main factory site a new automated system, known as SPAR, was announced for the eastern stores. Using wire-guided robotic vehicles, this new facility would improve handling, reduce inventory and improve delivery to customers. The automatic guided vehicles were given names from the signs of the Zodiac after a competition.

In September a new advertising campaign was unveiled for the expanded product line. Under the tagline 'Now we are one, we have the power to move the world', the campaign was designed to reach and influence top people in key potential customers. Alongside this confident move, however, came the announcement that Perkins and Austin Rover had decided not to proceed with the 'Iceberg' project to produce a diesel version of the Rover V8. The decision was reached due to problems with the cylinder block and fuel injector (see Chapter

The ten millionth Perkins engine produced – on a worldwide count – photographed outside the Eastfield restaurant with a group including Michael Bird (left), John Devaney and local MP Dr Brian Mawhinney (third from right)

24) although at the time a change of market conditions was blamed, with the anticipated demand for the product not materialising and an adequate return on investment unlikely.

Through the rest of the year the better news from Massey Ferguson was consolidated. The second quarter results showed the half-year profits as $10 million on $772 million sales, and by December this had improved to $14.2 million on sales of $1,131 million for the first nine months of the financial year: hardly a record-breaking level of profit, but significantly better than the previous year's loss of $41.1 million on $1,173 million. It was notable that, while farm machinery sales were down by 7.6% for the period, sales of engines increased to $72 million dollars – a 23% increase on the previous year.

Managing Director John Devaney, speaking in his position as Chairman of the Engines Committee of the SMMT, suggested that it was time for the British Motor Industry to blow its own trumpet – its overall reputation was lacklustre but its contribution to UK prosperity was great. The industry was Britain's largest source of manufacturing employment, taking into account the component and retail trade the employment was over one million! The SMMT was starting a campaign with other organisations to set the record straight; it was vital for the industry to have the support it needed to maintain its vital role in the prosperity of the country.

There was another development at Eastfield at the end of the year when a new automatic assembly facility for cylinder heads was an-

nounced. Featuring eight robot arms, the line was capable of handling over thirty different sub-assemblies to suit different configurations for 3-, 4- and 6-cylinder engines. Designed and built by Fairey Automation of Swindon, this £1 million investment was part of the total £3.5 million spent during the year in the factory.

'The best safety record ever' headlined the achievement of 1.25 million hours worked since the last accident at Eastfield. This rate was around twice as good as the average of the motor industry and one of the best in British plants as a whole, representing a considerable success for the continual campaign to promote safety at work.

The customary review of production achievements at the end of the year confirmed the depressed state of worldwide trade. The total engine production at Eastfield was only 126,418 engines, a massive 14.2% reduction on the 1983 figure, although CKD shipments at 89,269 kits were almost 65% up on the previous year's total. Production of every engine type was affected by the decline, with the 4.236 family worst affected with a drop of 20% to only 60,641 engines for the year. In the first year of Perkins ownership, the production at Shrewsbury was 2,697 engines, down by only 18 engines from the previous year.

The stringent measures put in place, with more redundancies and contractions alongside the tight control on spending and inventory, had helped the survival and indeed Group profitability at a time of inflation and high interest rates. There were some grounds for op-

timism, but continued survival had to come first. The pound had dropped to US$1.206 in October, on a slide destined to reach a low of $1.0765 in February 1985, representing 27% devaluation for the year. Even with the Bank base interest rate set at 14% the slide was not abated so the overall economic picture at the start of the year was anything but promising.

1985

The year began with a number of management changes as David Ford moved from Management Services Director to take over as Director, Shrewsbury Operations, his position at Peterborough being assumed by Roger Burrows. In a move to increase the importance of plant cleanliness and tidiness the Perkins Good Housekeeping Awards were made more competitive, with leagues being formed in the factories with quarterly monetary rewards, plus local Area Manager and Director's awards. Another move to integrate the Peterborough and Shrewsbury plants merged the Echo and Sentinel newspapers in order to present common news features.

The Government's Transport Secretary opened the Frank Perkins Parkway in 'Diesel City', being transported in a 1954 Guy Vixen bus with P6 power. This last link in the ring road included another bridge over the River Nene, and the new road bridge over Fengate incorporated a bas-relief mural inspired by the cross-section of the P3 engine.

The joint venture with Austin Rover was confirmed to be on schedule for launch in late 1985, with good results being obtained on prototype testing. The new engine was formally named 'Prima', selected from over 200 names put forward in an internal competition.

Considerable discussions over the need to improve the appearance of the products shipped from Peterborough resulted in the announcement of 'Engineered Engine Finish' (EEF). Reacting to customer complaints about poor paint finish and traces of rust appearing quickly on new engines, a decision was reached to change all external hardware to nickel-plated finish, with a more durable black primer paint applied to cast iron and steel parts (with aluminium left unpainted)

– the completed engines then being finish-sprayed with a hard and durable transparent lacquer. A new embossed 'Perkins' nameplate was specified and the whole engine image dramatically improved, giving an appearance similar to the best of the competition. Careful choice of materials ensured that customers still preferring a painted finish could have it – either delivered or applied themselves. As a means to reduce variety and provide a quality appearance the whole process was successful, and in the months that followed there were good reactions from customers and end-users. Within the plant, operatives soon recognised the increased need for care in handling components, avoiding unnecessary marking and ensuring that traces of liquid and fluid leaks were fixed. Although the detail work was considerable, the result in 'perceived quality' terms was well worth the efforts.

Further new products appeared from Shrewsbury in February, the DV8 560G and 600G Electropak versions of the DV8 engine, specifically for power generation, taking outputs to 750kVA through the use of twin turbochargers. There was more news of military applications, with the Condor V12 engine rated at 1,200bhp for the new Challenger main battle tank: the engine was packaged with the transmission and cooling system at Shrewsbury, producing a 'power module' weighing five tonnes which could be changed in the tank in under one hour! Along with versions of the CV8 and Eagle engines, the military applications accounted for only 10% of production but 30% of the revenue. A further military development was a CV8 power pack, intended to 'retrofit' into existing vehicles and being tried by the US military in their M41 tank. Peterborough employees were reminded of the difference in scale of the Shrewsbury products by a note that the DV8 Electropak engine weighed 1,300 kilograms against the mere 662 kilos of the V8.540!

Back in Peterborough the annual dinner of the Suggestion Scheme '200 Club' celebrated the Scheme's 21st anniversary, a period which had seen over 66,000 ideas put forward and £405,000 paid in tax-free awards, saving the Company over £1.3 million. In his speech John Devaney complimented those present and noted that in the previous twelve months there had been 1,750 suggestions and awards of over £40,000 so far. At another annual event, this time the dinner to honour long-serving employees, John Devaney presented awards to almost 200 people – it was reckoned that almost 20% of the workforce had served at least 25 years with the company! Among other changes on the site, the new visitors' centre in the main factory was opened and rated as 'elegant and comfortable' – while ground was broken adjacent to the Sports Association pavilion as work commenced on the new sports hall.

The London Fire Brigade augmented their good experience with Perkins V8 engines on shore with the launch of their new 'London Phoenix' fireboat. This 46-tonne catamaran used twin TV8.540(M) engines as main propulsion with two T6.3544(M)s powering the 3,600 gallon/minute pumps. The craft could also use its water-jet monitors alone to drive it through the water at up to 6 knots as well as providing extra manoeuvrability. The Brigade already had Fireswift and Firesure fitted with twin T6.354s, so that Perkins was well represented on the Thames.

Not to be outdone by Eastfield products, Shrewsbury won an order from the Royal Naval Reserve in April for engines to power fourteen coastal training vessels. This contract was for 34 CV12 engines plus spares, and followed the successful completion of Ministry of Defence type tests, including a 400-hour endurance run and tropical conditions simulation. It was expected that the engines would extend serv-

The Perkins-sponsored economy runs at the Austin Rover track test days were popular, although not in the way depicted in this cartoon produced by Perkins' artist John Lathey at the time

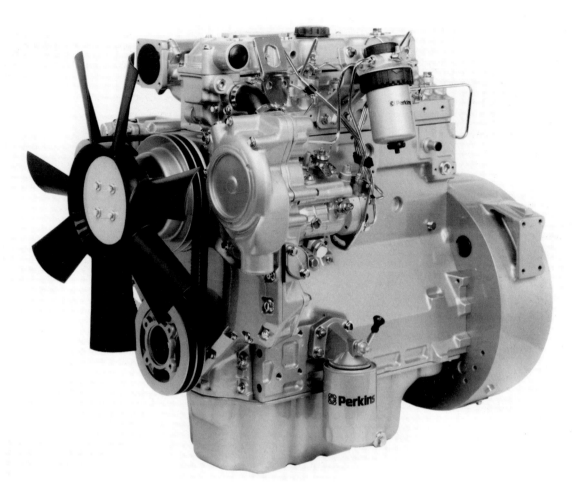

The 1000 Series and Phaser engines was a major product introduction. Typical of the engines is this four-cylinder vehicle version

ice intervals and lower operating costs.

The Massey Ferguson financial results for the year ended 31 January 1985 showed a profit of $7.2 million on a turnover of $1,490 million, the first profit for five years – albeit a modest one. Commenting on the results, Victor Rice noted that they were achieved in spite of persisting weakness in the demand for farm machinery, including a further drop in North American combines. 'Initiatives in reducing costs, reorganising operations and restructuring debt over the past five years have allowed a profit on a sales volume declined by more that 50 percent since 1980,' he stated. Third-party sales of $314 million for engines included $51 million extra from PESL and reflected some upturn in the industrial market. The global agricultural market was still burdened by overcapacity but MF was exploring joint ventures and other possible arrangements within the industry.

A landmark on the Peterborough site finally went after 30 years when the 'temporary' green hut at the north end of the main factory was demolished to make way for a new internal roadway as part of the rearrangements associated with the new Parkway. The hut had housed the company's fire station and later became the literature store.

A visit by David Foster, Manager of International Development, and two other Perkins engineers to China highlighted the differences in approach to the diesel and agricultural machinery industry. The party attended seminars and visited factories, the largest making around 20,000 tractors a year. They noted that there were many small factories and that most made the majority of their own parts – a major difference compared to the European industry.

In late June John Devaney announced a series of major management changes, representing a fundamental shift in style as three new General Managers were created, each having responsibility for the strategic direction and profitability of their areas. David Ford was confirmed in charge of Shrewsbury, John Towers took command in Peterborough with Peter Jackson running Aftermarket and Associated

Products. Other changes appointed David Bonner to Director, Marketing Operations, Richard Allen to Director, Finance (from MF France) and Paul Jobson as Director, Business and Product Planning. There were numerous other changes and realignments of personnel and reporting relationships in Peterborough and Shrewsbury.

Massey Ferguson reported a small profit for the first quarter of the year – only $400,000 on a turnover of $306 million – in spite of a further decrease in demand for farm machinery and a loss of $29 million due to exchange fluctuations. Victor Rice declared that of the four operating divisions only Combine Harvesters were now in a loss-making position.

Long-serving employee Bernard Garner retired from Perkins after over 47 years. He received a special tribute in the form of a Chairman's Award from Victor Rice, 'In recognition of almost half a century of meritorious service and exceptional contributions to the Company.' From a lowly start as office dogsbody and tea-boy, Bernard rose through the ranks as the company grew, with periods in sales and then planning and procurement where he became well known to customers, perhaps even infamous in the periods when demand exceeded supply!

A story of past glories concerned surviving veteran Motor Torpedo Boat No.102. This craft had been one of the last to leave Dunkirk in 1940 and after her war service had been fitted with twin P6s for civilian use. Following acquisition by the Norwich Sea Scouts she was fitted with twin TV8.540s and proved able to cruise at 12 knots when joining in the 45th Dunkirk reunion. Since externally the boat was largely in wartime trim, she had also been used in two films: The Eagle Has Landed and Soldier of Orange during the 1970s.

The presence of Perkins power on various railways highlighted the need for fuel savings even in the 'tourist trade'. Along with the P3-powered shunter on the Nene Valley Railway (named Frank!) there was a new locomotive on the Romney, Hythe and Dymchurch Railway named John Southland while the Ravenglass and Eskdale line now had Lady Wakefield alongside Perkins, providing reliable and economical service.

After other recent military orders, Shrewsbury publicised their biggest-ever order, this time for £70 million to power combat vehicles and battle tanks. One thousand Condor V8.550s for the GKN Sankey MCV-80 and an unspecified number of CV-12-1200 power packs for the Challenger tank and armoured recovery vehicles ensured full employment for the PESL plant for some months. A few weeks later there was news of a sales joint venture with Hawker Siddeley Marine to boost sales of Perkins workboat engines: HSM would market engines under their name to developing world territories in Africa, Asia, South America and the Pacific – the full range from D3.152 to CV-12 products.

Within the factories 'Improvement Teams' were being introduced widely. Pilot schemes had been started in late 1984 using an outside consultant, John Cox from Trent Polytechnic, to encourage employee involvement in changes. The success of the trials and the enthusiastic support of many workers encouraged an expansion of the initiative more widely to improve working conditions and practices for mutual benefit.

In October a special celebration was held to record the build of the Ten Millionth engine at Peterborough. Amongst the invited guests was Peter Walker, Energy Secretary, who praised Perkins as 'one of the country's leading engineering companies, continuing to pioneer in a field of industrial endeavour which has struggled for survival in Britain'. Press, TV and Radio were also on hand to record the event, together with local Conservative MP, Dr Brian Mawhinney. The opportunity was taken to show the new 'Prima' assembly facility, with the 'J-hook' line building 300 pre-production engines.

Caterpillar featured strongly in the November Echo with their new backhoe loader plant at Desford taking more 4.236 engines. The launch of the new 416 machine was expected to add considerably more to the volume taken by this 'prestige' customer. Perkins had been supplying both diesel and spark ignition engines for Caterpillar forklift trucks since the 1970s.

A new look for Quality Assurance was announced with John Lawrence heading a separate Division with responsibility for all aspects of quality worldwide for customers and suppliers. With separate managers to control Product Quality Assurance, Quality Engineering and Product Integrity, he commented 'this places more responsibility for quality of the products on the people actually making them . . . we are making sure that everyone has access to what they need to do their job properly – "no excuse" management'. There were other changes in the Peterborough Products team, with Brian Willmott taking responsibility for Production Operations, Roger Warren for Logistics, John Dobney for Site Operations and Mike Swingler for Manufacturing Engineering. In addition new Production Unit managers were appointed for each of the factory areas.

The close of the year showed a modest increase in production for the year at 131,570 engines, with much improved delivery performance with only eight engines missing their scheduled despatch date. The 4.236 family, along with the 3-cylinder, showed reasonable increases, but V8 and 4.203 volumes dropped significantly. The 4.318 sold only 1,171 engines as it headed towards phase-out, while the 6.3544 continued a slide towards the 20,000 mark. The volume of CKD kits shipped to licensees at 93,083 showed a marginal improvement. Altogether it had been a year of consolidation and preparation rather than one of great progress.

1986

The year began traditionally, with a strong presence at the Earls Court Boat Show. The new CV8 marine engine from Shrewsbury was highlighted, this being the first product to combine technical expertise from 'both sides' of the country and promised greater fuel economy than its rivals. Perkins were able to boast of an 8% rise in marine sales over the past year, and claimed around 10% of the world marine market in their power range. There was some additional pleasing publicity from an independent survey of boat owners, with Perkins scoring highly for reliability, spares and service support worldwide.

In the usual motoring press commentaries reviewing the past year there were some interesting figures on the UK vehicle market: passenger car output was 15% up on the previous year while the commercial vehicle sectors enjoyed their best sales for three years. A warning note was recorded, however, as over 36% of commercial vehicles were imported – over 100,000 units for the first time. The British Leyland Sherpa van took 15% of the van market, while at 65,000 vehicles total UK diesel car sales were 44% up on 1984: good news for the Perkins 'Prima' prospects!

There was sadness at the news of the death of Joe Hind at 69 during the Christmas holiday: he had worked for ten years at Perkins, first as Director of Product Reliability before becoming Engineering Director and then Assistant Executive Vice-President in 1975. Following his retirement in March 1978 he was active in assisting local small businesses as well as advising the Peterborough Development Corporation.

Perkins expertise was in the news regarding alternative fuels as research engineer Ian Moncrieff assisted the New Zealand Liquid Fuels Trust Board with advice and field trials of processed lamb tallow as a diesel fuel. He had also been involved in trials using ethanol in Malawi. Through the pool of expertise in their Advanced Engineering Department, Perkins was becoming recognised as one of the most active companies in the alternative fuels field.

A 32.9% increase in Cambridgeshire local rates was declared in February, bringing an angry reaction from John Towers as he declared that the change made nonsense of the recent investments to improve the efficiency of factory operations. He went on to note that a rise of more than six times the rate of inflation was forcing Perkins to consider whether Peterborough could remain the focus of future operations if competitiveness was to be maintained. The decision had already been reached to shut down the Fletton V8 facility and this latest cost increase, over which Perkins had no control, was excellent further justification for the closure!

News from the motor industry showed that during 1985 the Austin Rover Group were the largest UK motor manufacturer with 450,000 cars versus Ford with 317,000, but during January overall car and commercial vehicle production dropped considerably. The financial results for Cummins showed that their profits in 1985 dropped from $187.9 million to $50.4 million, indicative of continuing market depression. MF revealed that the MF290 tractor (4.248 engine) was the best-selling UK tractor with 5.7% of a market which itself dropped by 2.3% in the year: MF held 21.7% of the total UK tractor market.

Perkins showed an aggressive stance in producing new models, with the release of two new Electropak generator set engines in the C6.240G and CV8.320G from PESL, adding 300 and 400kVA ratings to the range. In Peterborough the introduction of a new fast engine delivery scheme – known as UQD (Ultra Quick Delivery) – used a new 'Custom' computer system, pre-planned core engine availability and a scaled-down range of options to enable despatch of generating set engines within 14 days of an order being received.

Launch of Phaser and 1000 Series

March brought the most significant engine launch in Peterborough for many years as the successor to the 4.236 and 6.3544 families was unveiled to the world. A highly sophisticated presentation of the new Phaser (vehicle) and 1000 series (industrial and agricultural) ranges of 4- and 6-cylinder engines was made to industry, customer, press and employee audiences at the Moat House Hotel to the west of Peterborough. Using all possible multimedia devices the 'razzamatazz' launch made an impact on all who saw it, persuading them that this was indeed the most important engine family in decades! The engines covered a range from 90 to 180bhp, using both naturally-aspirated and turbocharged versions, with charge-cooling for the most powerful engines. For many years the product life of both the 6.354 and the 4.236 ought to have been over, but it was only with the increasing importance of emissions and noise that the successors finally appeared, the results of major investment in design and research. A new combustion chamber design, called Quadram, was a key ingredient in the new models, providing improved emissions, smoke and noise characteristics, along with better fuel consumption. The many mechanical design improvements promised better engine life and durability and the engines were fully metric!

Although exhaustive testing of all aspects of the new engines had been carried out over the previous five years, the production introduction process would, of necessity, prove lengthy and complex. There was a large number of customer applications to be switched, each needing individual parts listing, prototype engines and sign-off procedures – and inevitably protracted negotiations over pricing, delivery dates, etc. The changeover became the biggest product headache Perkins had ever experienced, not because of product problems but simply because of the scale! An additional factor was the reluctance of some customers, including parent Massey Ferguson, to change because legislative pressures did not extend to every application and territory.

At almost the same moment as this launch was taking place, another new product was being launched with Renault Trucks in England, featuring the new T4.38(V) in the Dodge 50 Series light truck. This engine was a development of the T4.236, but much modified to suit the needs of vehicle operating conditions and needs. The engine was fitted with an air compressor to power the braking system and had been the subject of considerable test bed work as well as a 32-vehicle evaluation programme running over 1.5 million miles under differing and exacting conditions. At the same time it was announced that Renault Agriculture, the largest tractor manufacturer in France was to fit the 4.236 in their largest tractor.

Improvement Teams across the Peterborough plants totalled 15 in April, tackling not only working conditions and environmental issues but also quality issues such as reduction of scrap material. One team, the WASPS from Fletton factory, made a presentation to the National Society of Quality Circles at Warwick University while another group of sixty employees from Factory Two visited the new Caterpillar plant at Desford, near Leicester, one evening to see the machines using the 4.236 engines and see the 'Just In Time' philosophy working in practice. They were impressed to see how the Perkins 'guaranteed delivery' agreement meant that only a handful of engines were on the Caterpillar factory floor at any one time, meeting the low inventory concept.

Further management changes were announced during April as Paul Jobson left Peterborough to become Purchase Director for MF Tractor Division: his Product Planning responsibilities were devolved to David Cowcill in Peterborough and Peter Crowther in Shrewsbury, each reporting to the respective General Manager. John Devaney announced the formation of a new Business Planning Unit reporting to him and with responsibility for strategic thinking ten years ahead.

A new training initiative was announced as evening classes began in the Eastfield Training block, concentrating on self-development opportunities. Courses as varied as plumbing, car maintenance, basic electrics and electronics and computer skills were offered, each eight-week 'open learning' module giving all employees a chance to learn a

new skill. There were 400 applications for the first 50 places, demonstrating the popularity of the programme pioneered by Terry Norman, the Plant Personnel and Employee Development Manager.

Purchase of L. Gardner and Sons Limited

In May the Company announced the decision to acquire the firm of L. Gardner and Sons Limited from the Hawker Siddeley Group. The plant at Eccles, Manchester was the producer of diesel engines famed for their durability and economy, popular in bus, truck and marine applications. John Devaney noted that: 'This acquisition is part of our on-going strategy to look at the long-term future of the Perkins Group and to ensure our product offering meets the widespread needs of our customers, both within the UK and around the world. This latest move allows us to become a major marketer to the European bus and coach industry.' Gardner was founded in 1868, started producing diesel engines in the early part of the 20th century and had developed traditions for quality and durability, with engines built to a high standard and providing the best fuel economy in the market. Under close family control the company remained ultra-conservative and resisted some modern trends, in particular the growing movement towards turbocharging, with a resulting loss of sales in the face of cheaper and more aggressive competition. The takeover by Hawker Siddeley in 1977 had brought much-needed investment with some new product launches in 1985 plus some modern machining capability. Over 75% of the UK proprietary buses were Gardner-powered, and there was a significant presence in the heavy truck market too. Marine and industrial engines were in service worldwide, with an outstanding reputation for durability and fuel economy, especially with operators who valued the Gardner philosophy. There was some small synergy between Perkins and Gardner, in that all engines were water cooled, but one attraction left unsaid at the time by Perkins was the excellent opportunity for continuing spare parts sales to the large and loyal band of operators to whom 'Gardner' was a venerated name! The Gardner 6LXB and 6LXCT were still the engines of choice for the British double-decker bus market, while the new 6LYT engine was in favour with German luxury coach builder Neoplan.

'Varity' is born

Massey Ferguson Limited announced in May the decision to change their name to Varity Corporation. The name was derived from the Verity Plow Works of Exeter, Ontario, which had been taken over by Massey-Harris Limited in 1892. 'We changed a letter in that fine old name to make it easier to register internationally,' claimed President V.A. Rice, making no reference to the close similarity between his own name and that of the 'new' corporation – although the cynics quickly made the connection! The MF earnings for the year ended 31 January 1986 were only $3.9 million on $1,288 million sales, after deduction of reorganisation costs of $17.6 million, loss of $20 million on discontinued operations and a $7.7 million loss on exchange. In the last quarter of the year earnings were $3.3 million on $351 million sales. A few details were given of Perkins engine sales, with a 4% gain to a total of $327 million for the year: industrial machinery sales increased by 9% to $101 million, but tractors and farm machinery sales were stagnated at $804 million, close to the 1984 figure.

A trend highlighted in the Echo was the growth in use of electronic mail systems, with wider application of the MF Group's 'FAME' system (Filing And Mailing Electronically) using computer and satellite communications worldwide. It was possible to send messages from a linked VDU at the touch of a button instantly, quicker and cheaper than telephone. The FAME system was based upon IBM and Pan American technology and was then a leading example of computer usage. A further extension of the system by Perkins was the introduction of 'Powerlink', a means of linking electronically to major customers and suppliers – including ARG, Caterpillar and Hyster – for messages and schedules. This used a European electronic messaging standard – ODETTE – through the Geisco Company's Motornet computer clearing centre, providing a major saving over traditional paperwork, typically reducing four days' processing to one.

Seddon announced their first trucks with the Phaser 160T and 180Ti models in the new 16-tonne 2-11 range. They hoped to sell 500 trucks in the first year, expecting success for the most powerful and luxurious truck in its class. Three of the new vehicles were displayed in the Perkins car park for the workforce.

An unusual situation arose in June when world oil prices dropped, adversely affecting diesel engine sales, already hit by major industry over-capacity (9 million capacity versus 6 million demand worldwide). The lack of cash in the oil-based economies of the Middle East and Mexico was claimed to be reducing engine sales. For Perkins, John Devaney commented that the major new product launches would not immediately increase sales revenue: continued attention to product development, acquiring new customers and continued cost reduction were essential to future prosperity.

A unique event took place in Shrewsbury on 27 June as the plant management, led by David Ford, and the local trades unions, together with other local companies took part in a sponsored run to raise money for the Shrewsbury Hospice Appeal. £2,300 was raised as the runners traced a seven-mile course crossing each of the nine bridges, cementing a new spirit of cooperation for the future. Other local events included the achievement of the Perkins football team in winning the Peterborough Premier Division title, finally lifting the cup donated by Frank Perkins for the winners in 1949, which had eluded the team for years.

In the series on leading customers, the Echo profiled French boat-builders Jeanneau who used the 4.108, 4.154 and 4.236 marine engines in many of their luxury pleasure cruisers and yachts. With a total output exceeding 5,000 craft each year, their most successful model was the 41ft Legende 41, standardised on the 4.108(M).

Launch of the Prima engine

In July, Perkins and Austin Rover formally unveiled the new Prima engine, to be offered in the Maestro van initially, followed by the Maestro and Montego cars in 1987. Hailed as the world's first direct-injection car engine, the two-litre ran at 4,500rpm and offered around 40% improvement in fuel consumption compared to an equivalent petrol engine and around 15% improvement over existing indirect injection diesels. The naturally-aspirated Prima 65 developed 62bhp and the turbocharged Prima 80T was rated at 80bhp. Industrial and marine versions would be marketed alongside the vehicle engine and all would feature extended servicing intervals (up to 300 hours) as well as an expected 2,500 hours, or 100,000 miles, life to overhaul. Some of the importance of the launch was stolen, however, by the Italian Fiat company who actually announced their own DI diesel slightly ahead of the Prima. John Devaney spoke at the launch of Prima of 'this triumph of British Engineering' and the importance of ARG and the Department of Trade and Industry in assisting the funding of the development.

A centre-page spread in the Echo gave further details of the engine, its 80,000 hours and one million miles of testing: the technical features highlighted included the aluminium cylinder head, the 'instant' glow-plug heaters and the highly sophisticated fuel injection pump with self-venting and priming features. The manufacturing investment of £15 million, added to £12 million development costs, confirmed the commitment to the new product.

The Phaser engine also continued to attract good publicity in the technical press, with driving impressions lauding its quiet operation

and excellent driving characteristics and heralding the 'new generation' of diesel technology. One new manufacturer hoping to use the engine was Reynolds Boughton, who fitted the Phaser 110T in their prototype four-wheel-drive truck contending for a new British Army contract.

It seemed to be impossible to keep railway stories out of the Echo for too long, the latest news covering the use of Shrewsbury C6 350R engines in two new Hunslet locomotives on the Snowdon Mountain Railway. Yeti and Ninian were the first diesel locos to be used on the line, and were expected to offer 'instant' availability and profitability as passenger numbers soared and the problems of keeping the 60- to 90-year-old steam engines running increased. It was emphasised, however, that this did not mean the elimination of steam from the tourist attraction!

In August there was a further change in management as John Towers was promoted to Vice President, Varity International Services in Toronto. His previous position as General Manager, Peterborough Products, was assumed by Richard Allen, formerly Finance Director.

Another sporting success came to Perkins products in September when racing driver Mel Lindsey won the 1986 Euro Truck Racing Championship for the Racing Eagles team, driving his Leyland vehicle. He also won the 300bhp class and helped Leyland to win the Championship for the second successive year, with his Eagle 300ti supported by the willing Perkins service crew.

Another French manufacturer featured in the 'customer profile' as Manitou took pride of place. They used around 1,000 engines a year, including D3.152, 4.108, 4.236, 4.248, T6.3544 and TV8.540 in a range of specialist industrial equipment including telescopic handlers and fork lift trucks, as well as the 'Termit' range of logging and forestry equipment.

A further revision of the Perkins 'Business Unit' structure was announced by John Devaney in early November. The changes were aimed at encouraging better identification for employees within their own business unit, as well as strengthening the base business and moving forward 'in such a way as to place even more emphasis on the needs of our many and varied customers throughout the world'. The positions of Directors were confirmed as:

General Manager, Peterborough Products, Richard Allen

General Manager, Shrewsbury Products, David Ford

General Manager, L. Gardner and Son   Brian Davies

Aftermarket Products, Peter Jackson

Product Engineering, Tony Downes

Defence Sales, Barry Parsisson

Perkins International Sales, Peter Baker

Perkins North America, Roger Howsman

Special Projects, Brian Weedon

Strategic Purchase, Ron Hadnam

Business Ventures, Ray Carrell

Group Finance, Raj Shah

Group Services, David Bonner

Group Personnel, Clive Francis

John Devaney confirmed that each Business Unit would be responsible for its own profitability, with support from the group areas as applicable. He noted that there was a strong customer base, in spite of the uncertainties of the diesel engine market in recent times, and that Perkins must continue to be profitable in all areas to ensure investment in the future. There had been disappointments during the year, with expected volume Phaser business with Bedford Trucks failing to materialise, while CKD kit exports showed little recovery. Some short time working and a significant reduction of manpower had been necessary in order to balance the operations. The Product Engineering BU was an area of strength, which would be encouraged to do external work on a commercial basis while supporting Group activities.

The understated enforced manpower reductions had been a traumatic period for many personnel and not least for managers, who had been forced to review all employees in their departments, declare over-manning and pick those to be made redundant. The choosing process had to be done as fairly as possible, using a simplified scoring procedure, assessing the value of each employee against a set of criteria. Perversely the whole exercise regained, for those fortunate to retain their jobs, some of the team spirit that had been affected by the difficult past months. The Company set up a specialist 'job shop', staffed by UK Redeployment Services Limited, which found new jobs for more than fifty displaced staff; others were matched against job vacancies and opportunities created internally by employees volunteering for redundancy in areas where a reduction in numbers was not sought. 'Job Matching' became a new phrase in common currency. This was the first redundancy process for Perkins that had not been met wholly through volunteers alone, and was very much a sign of the times as other industries experienced the same trauma.

While these internal issues were being addressed, the potential of the Prima engine was being publicised. The launch of both the ARG Maestro van and the Freight Rover Sherpa van received good coverage by the national press. Some economy trials were conducted which backed up the goods results obtained by the Engineering Departments of the OEMs. Freight Rover produced figures of 39.4mpg for the Prima in a fully laden van, against the 28.5 of the previous 1.8 litre IDI diesel, plus a top speed of 74mph versus the previous 68mph. A Commercial Motor road test of the Maestro van returned nearly 50mpg, well ahead of the competition. An economy competition for journalists produced a win for Stuart Bladon of the BBC at 92.9mpg in a Maestro van, with six results better than 80mpg and the worst of 24 attempts at 72.5mpg! As a part of the ARG 'Track Test 86' days held at various motor racing tracks around the country, a diesel Maestro van was used for a competition linking fastest lap with best fuel economy – even racing driver Tiff Needell, not famed for his light right foot, achieved 61.6mph and 45.8mpg! By the end of the year the first big order for 100 of the new vans was received from the GPO.

Press and consumer comments were very positive, apart from some reservations about the engine noise level, and the successful collaboration between the Perkins, ARG and FR engineers was highlighted. Overall Perkins could be delighted with the positive early acceptance of the new product.

Another launch in December added to the good news as the new marine version of Prima was displayed on the Thames, using a Jeanneau 6.3m boat. Journalists watched from a river bus as the turbocharged Prima 80T went through its paces at up to 21 knots. The naturally aspirated versions at 59 and 49bhp were announced at the same time, and the Jeanneau craft was quickly transported to France for their own 'unveiling'.

There were other accolades for the Company too, first from the BBC Ideas Unlimited programme when the Perkins Suggestion Scheme won the Pilkington Glass Award for the best company suggestion scheme. 'The competition was very stiff,' said Scheme Chairman Roger Burrows. 'The key influencing factor was that we maintained and improved our level of enthusiasm and participation.' Another award was received from the Institute of Transport managers at the Motor Show, with the Phaser winning their 'Engine Excellence' award for advances in power and economy.

Varity Corporation announced their decision to acquire Dayton Walther Corporation of Ohio: they were a supplier to the automotive industry of wheels, brakes and other components, as well as being producers of consumer items such as plumbing, door and window furniture as well as solar-powered refrigerators. They employed 3,000 people at 26 plants spread across eight states, and thus added significantly to the Varity portfolio. There was also a major breakthrough for the MF tractor business, with a £5 million order for MF 300 and MF 3000 tractors for Japan. This was hailed as a significant conquest sale into a traditionally 'closed' market: the new MF 3000 tractor models were very advanced and included computer control for some operational features.

Paralleling the problems that had beset Perkins in 1986, competitor Cummins announced that they were to shed hundreds of jobs, as well as shutting their distribution centre in Darlington: their losses in the third quarter of 1986 exceeded £82 million.

In the Christmas issue of the Echo, Messrs Allen, Ford and Jackson identified their intentions for the new organisation to move forward on quality, profitability and personal accountability in 1987. There was obviously room for improvement: Peterborough production for 1986 dropped to only 124,344 engines, including 3,623 Prima/500 Series and 423 Phaser/1000 Series. There was a significant improvement in CKD sales, with 120,941 kits shipped, however. The results from Shrewsbury were also disappointing, with only 2,000 engines sold. The new 'slimmed-down' organisation looked forward to a better new year, with some guarded optimism in view of the good response to the new products.

1987

The year began with news of another collaboration as Japanese tractor manufacturer Ishikawajima-Shibaura-Machinery Company (ISM), based at Matsimoto, about 200 miles north-west of Tokyo, was announced as a new partner. ISM was about half the size of Perkins, making about 30,000 tractors each year. They produced their own small diesels to power the tractors and it was these that attracted Perkins, with the rights to sell the engines worldwide as the 100 Series. With powers between 10 and 44bhp from the two-, three- and four-cylinder units, Perkins anticipated new industrial, marine and agricultural business for a new division to be known as Compact Engines.

In exchange, ISM would buy 1000 Series engines for new larger tractors being developed for the Far East. Since the existing ISM engines used indirect injection combustion, the second intention was to use Perkins expertise to move to direct injection products. The new JV resulted from over two years of negotiations by Peter Jackson and Andrew McQuillan, following an initial agreement to sell 100 Series engines into North American industrial customers including Hobart and Lincoln Electric.

As will already be clear, long service within Perkins was already a tradition, but a new milestone was passed in January when Freddie Bedford completed 50 years' service. Bachelor Freddie had worked within the Engineering workshops all of that time. He was given special treatment for the day – chauffeured in a Rolls-Royce car into work and treated to a special luncheon with John Devaney and the directors, at which he was presented with a cheque for £500. At 64 years old, he claimed that he had worked on every new Perkins multi-cylinder product since the Second World War.

The London Boat Show proved another success for Perkins, with over £1 million in orders for the new Prima Marine engine at its debut. There was another accolade for Perkins as Prima was chosen as an example of British innovation and industrial success, highlighting the vehicle engine for achieving 40% better fuel consumption and 12,000-mile service intervals.

Perkins Shrewsbury announced the selection of the Eagle for the British Army's new DROPS (Demountable Rack Off-loading and Pick-up System) vehicles from Foden and Scammell, the £10 million order for 2,000 engines being confirmation of the pre-eminent position Perkins had achieved as supplier to the Army. The Eagle MX was supplied at a rating of 261kW (350bhp), the latest order bringing the total of Eagles in use by the Army to over 7,000. Close behind this news was another Army order for T6.3544s from Peterborough to power the Alvis Stormer chassis specified for the new Starstreak missile system: the contract was for 153 engines, plus parts.

Varity Corporation had less welcome news: MF's sales in the UK tractor market in 1986 fell to only 20% of the total 19,000 tractors – a figure that was reducing still further as the market took fewer but more powerful tractors, powers moving towards the 81 to 100bhp engine sector.

JCB's Director of Quality, Bill Hirst, presented Perkins with their 'Certificate of Quality Assurance' in February, tempering the occasion with the comment that 'You have achieved zero defects but there are still peaks and troughs in quality'! In reply, Richard Allen acknowledged that Perkins personnel were to be congratulated on a performance that had given JCB less than 1% of defects as delivered over the past year. He spoke of the need to continue the journey to zero defects consistently, to which all must strive and to which Improvement Teams were contributing. Hirst then surprised the Perkins 'ASSET' (A

Suggestion Saves Effort and Time) team by awarding them £1,000 for their work on improving crankshaft quality.

Details of the background to Phaser and 1000 Series were given to the *Echo* in a series of interviews with Roy Chowings, John Gibson and Mike English covering design, quality and assembly issues respectively. The deletion of loose washers, specific rig and test procedures to eliminate leakage, and the introduction of 'yield-tightening' for critical hardware were noted as important points in the drive for higher-quality production. The improvements given by the 'Engineered Engine Finish' were also highlighted, although the increased visibility of blemishes demanded increased care in handling and total cleanliness ahead of the finishing process.

In March there was a formal launch of the 500, 1000 and 2000 Series engines from Peterborough and Shrewsbury, covering 37 to 400bhp over the range of 46 engine models. Under the new slogan 'The Big Wheel in Diesels', the launch ceremony in the new Powerhouse facility in the old Vicarage Farm Road restaurant block was attended by specialist journalists covering the UK and European markets. There were three days of presentations and factory tours, with Perkins employees attending too. Along with over £40 million in development costs, the largest market research programme ever undertaken had consulted 400 end-users and 60 manufacturers to determine the features required. All three engine ranges featured low maintenance costs, including 400-hour filter and oil changes, equivalent to two months use for the average user.

A Financial Times feature confirmed that diesel production worldwide exceeded 12 million engines per year and was growing, due mainly to the burgeoning car business where Peugeot-Citroën had become the largest diesel producer. Industry overcapacity was estimated at 40%, encompassing 300 manufacturers, around 250 of whom were seeking third party sales. Most sales were of engines between 50 to 500bhp, the largest growth being in the 50 to 100bhp sector. The article made special comment on the price war around 70 to 400bhp, where prices had reduced by up to 30% from three years previously. Pricing pressures had seen cost cutting, plant closures and labour reductions as a result – pretty much paralleling the Perkins experience.

The launch of the Gardner 310T combined the legendary durability of the Gardner marque with Perkins turbocharging expertise.

Commenting on the survey, Tony Downes and Richard Allen noted that Perkins were one of only three manufacturers selling more engines to third parties than to their 'captive' markets, thus having a greater need to react quickly and accurately to changing market demands. With a majority of the world backhoe-loader market and almost half of the diesel forklift truck market in the USA, Perkins were a major presence in the construction and industrial market. Here over 500,000 engines a year were sold, 60% of these being 'non-captive'.

Further market intelligence suggested that truck average horsepower had increased by around 16% in recent years (larger trucks and better motorways), while the potential for passenger cars and turbocharged engines remained unrealised. As if in response, ARG announced that they expected to export 150,000 cars in 1987, looking for the Prima-powered Maestro and Montego to sell well in France, Germany and Italy. At the beginning of April the formation of Leyland-DAF was announced, the new enterprise expecting to take a larger part of the UK truck and van market. Later in the month Austin Rover Group and Honda announced a collaboration to develop a new range of cars to replace the Maestro, Rover 200 and Honda Civic.

The first public display of the new Perkins product range was at the International Construction Exhibition in the NEC at Birmingham. On top of confirmed advance orders worth £3 million, Perkins expected a further £1.5 million to be placed during the show. Johnston Sweepers won 60 orders, with a further 60 promised, for their new 1004-4 powered machines, advertised as 8dB(A) quieter than the competition and with 20% greater suction. The 500 Series appeared in their Model 200 pavement sweeper, and also featured in new machinery from F.G. Wilson, Compair and Hydrovane.

The older engine types were still in demand: 4.108s and 4.154s powered survival capsules from specialist manufacturer Whittaker Survival Systems in the USA. Over 2,000 of these were in use and were credited with 1,056 lives saved in 35 evacuations. Perkins engines were selected for their excellent worldwide service facilities and record of extreme reliability – the manufacturer commented that the one failure recorded had been due to inadequate care and maintenance by the operators.

The April Echo recorded Phaser's successes during its first year. Vehicle makers Seddon-Atkinson, Dennis Eagle and Metro-Cammell-Weymann specified the product, while seeding engines placed with fleets were returning fuel consumptions about one mile per gallon better than the T6.3544. Another benefit highlighted was the reduced engine noise level, helping to meet new European legislation, probably without the need for noise cladding on the vehicles themselves.

In June Victor Rice gave details of Varity performance over the first part of the year. A total of 1,500 jobs had been eliminated, around 8% of the total headcount, to reduce operating costs. The one-off cost of around $10 million in the first quarter of the financial year had contributed to a loss of $13.8 million on sales of $454 million. The continued problems in the agricultural sector continued to drive cost reduction actions, but Rice was confident: 'The unprecedented range of new products we have introduced to the market in recent months is repaying us with increased market penetration, but agricultural discounting and the weaker US dollar have eroded operating margins to a point where we must take resourceful measures to drive down costs,' he said, adding that the lower headcount would yield savings by year end at least equivalent to the redundancy costs.

At Eastfield the proposed sale of six acres at the north end of the site to Sainsbury's for a new supermarket was announced, subject to agreement with the Peterborough City Council. The Service Garage and Product Education Departments would be relocated, while some of the buildings to be demolished had been part of the first factory of 1947. Savings of around £160,000 a year on rates and energy were anticipated. The new supermarket was expected to create 300 new jobs in a large store offering 9,000 product lines and including a petrol station and bakery. With 500 car parking spaces, the store was expected to provide welcome services to the growing population of north-eastern Peterborough.

There was good news from a number of major customers during June. Renault Truck planned to boost UK production to 5,800 vehicles a year, many with Perkins engines, and JCB announced 1986 sales that were 17% up on 1985 with pre-tax profits increased from £24.2 million to £31.1 million. JCB were using an increasing number of 4.236 and 6.3544 engines in their machinery and claimed their productivity had risen from 9.7 machines per employee in 1979 to 19.6 in 1986, with turnover per employee around £143,000.

Prima celebrated its first production anniversary in July, with the 10,000th engine and the start of production for the marine and industrial versions. The van versions were already a clear success with 37.5% of Sherpa production now using the engine, against the 24% of the previous diesel. Maestro vans were selling 35% as diesel, major fleet users specifying the engine as the motoring press endorsed the claims for leading economy, performance and low maintenance costs.

Austin Rover Group was experiencing success with the new cars too, before the diesel was introduced, with European markets buying in record numbers. During the ARG 'Track Days', held at motor racing circuits around the country, prospective buyers were queuing to try the diesel van; the economy competition produced figures up to 121.1mpg at 33.1mph average speed.

Phaser claimed another success with export orders for International Harvester in Australia for both 160T and 180Ti engines, with the air charge-cooling of the 180Ti leading the field. The first order for 400 engines was expected to generate others as IHA standardised on the engine for their new truck range. The advantages of low noise, improved economy and reliability were the main factors highlighted. The Shrewsbury sales team also confirmed that Condor CV8 260G Electropak units had been chosen as stand-by generators for the first five Type 23 frigates for the Royal Navy.

Improvement Teams success continued with a total of 20 teams now in place and others being formed around the Eastfield production areas. Under the guidance of full-time coordinator Malcolm Storton and Production Unit Manager Ray Abell, each team had about seven members. Team efforts were directed mainly towards improvements in working practices and conditions, cutting waste and improving quality, with many ideas already implemented.

The efforts of the Massey Ferguson and Perkins employees who formed the 'Massey Lads' tractor pulling team were in the news again during August. After the success of Little Nipper with a highly modified T4.236 engine, their latest creation featured a triple-turbocharged TV8.640 engine producing 1,300bhp in another much-modified MF tractor. Perkins Express beat all comers at a competition at Silverstone sponsored by Shell, its thunderous roar and twin exhaust plumes providing a spectacular sight. Although reliability came second to sheer output, the engine ran at 5,000rpm and 100psi boost with few ill-effects, although the high operating stresses shortened the connecting rods over the season's running!

In both Eastfield and Shrewsbury production records helped satisfy customer demand. The 4.236 family boosted output by 800 engines in one month, surpassing 7,500 engines in the month for the first time in seven years, while the PESL production level of 60 engines a week compared to the 40 per week of 1986.

There were local initiatives aimed at maximising the use of facilities and expertise within Perkins. A small group of employees formed their own company, SPA, using leased space inside the walls of Factory 3, to produce 'show-finished' engines for Perkins and anyone else seeking this specialist service. The hand-fettled, smoothed, painted and chrome-plated units provided the best possible appearance for displays, with the addition of sectioning and motor-drive if requested.

Perkins Product Engineering Business Unit, under Director Tony Downes, announced their intention to seek business opportunities using the expertise and specialist equipment of the £40 million research and development facility at Peterborough. The initial plan to provide small companies with a cost-effective service would be followed by more ambitious and comprehensive services, with the expectation that ultimately the BU would derive one third of its income from external business and consultancy. The new 'Product Business Unit' organisation within Peterborough, giving individual units control of their own finances and rewarding employees according to their overall performance, was part of a new concept, where other Business Units would pay for all work done on their behalf by Product Engineering or the other 'service' business units. This approach injected a new sense of purpose into the minds of many engineers and helped to smooth out the workload fluctuations endemic within any 'research' type activity.

On the sporting front, engineer Steve Small joined an elite band of 'triathletes' competing in the Swiss Triathlon meeting in Zurich: they swam 2.5 miles, cycled 112 miles and then ran a 26.2-mile marathon! Steve finished 352nd out of the 650 competitors, recording a time of 12 hours 41 minutes. In a slightly different category was the performance of Perkins pensioner Bill Walton who completed his third London Marathon at the age of 68, having taken up running when he retired with the objective of keeping fit and losing weight. His 1987 time was an improvement on the previous year at 5 hours 18 minutes. As well as training over 45 to 70 miles a week, Bill found time to coach local youngsters – in running!

Launch of the Compact Engines Range

The public launch of the 100 Series engines in September came in two phases: the debut of the 'Perama' marine engines at the Southampton Boat Show, followed by the 100 Series industrial engines at the Royal Windsor Show. The two-, three- and four-cylinder engines produced in partnership with ISM provided an extended product range, more complete than previous attempts using factored engines. The Compact Engines Division under General Manager Andrew McQuillan was based at Peterborough; local assembly from CKD was the first stage, to be followed by introduction of local content. The engines were all water-cooled indirect injection design, appealing to potential users through their compact size, light weight and backing from Perkins' worldwide sales and service network.

The new automated 'First Stage Build' (FSB) project announced for the Eastfield plant gained funding equal to half of its £1.8 million cost through the European EUREKA incentive scheme. Minister for Trade Kenneth Clarke announced that Perkins was the only British company to be selected under the 'FAMOS' flexible automated assembly project – a statement of faith and recognition of the Company's position in the forefront of British industry. The FSB project was intended to provide 'state of the art' automatic assembly of cylinder heads for three-, four- and six-cylinder engines, using Renault Automation as the prime contractor.

The opening of the Frank Perkins Parkway, the last link in the Peterborough ring road, was celebrated with a static display of Perkins-powered equipment as well as a procession and opening ceremony. The view shows some of the machinery in front of the main office block

The range of applications covered by the Perkins diesel engine range in the 1980s is best illustrated here with the Challenger main battle tank (CV 12 engine) and the Montego car (Prima), both being used by the British armed forces

A road test conducted by Truck magazine produced another accolade for the Phaser. The comparison of an 180Ti-powered Seddon 2-11 truck with a Volvo FL6 showed the Perkins with a 2mpg advantage, translating to £1,677 saving over 80,000 miles' operation. In spite of its lower power and torque on paper, the Seddon also returned almost identical journey times and was also declared superior to both ERF F6 and Scania G82 trucks tested under similar conditions. The magazine concluded that 'If you were to base the buying decision on payload capacity and fuel economy, the Seddon Atkinson would win every time.'

In October JCB placed orders for three versions of the 1000 Series four- and six-cylinder engines for the 410, 415 and 425 models of their new wheeled loaders, selecting the engines for their high power, good low speed torque and exceptional reliability. With their lower noise level the engines were also deemed more suited to operation in built-up areas. The Industrial Sales team celebrated the achievement of over £6 million of orders for the 1000 Series since its launch six months before. There was success for the Phaser vehicle versions too as Renault Truck Industries ordered Phaser-90 and 110T engines for their revised 50 Series light trucks, the first significant sales for the four-cylinder version. RTI announced that orders were 25% up on the previous year, production was 33% up and the company had returned to profitability.

In America, the Chicago Public Works Exhibition was used to launch the 2000, 1000 and 500 Series engines in September. Johnston Sweepers, one of the first UK customers for the 1000 Series, began exporting to Canada and also displayed at Chicago. Perkins North America, already a leading supplier of engines to the industrial market, relocated from Wayne, Michigan, to Atlanta, Georgia. An opportunity for extra sales came as the Phaser 180Ti was cleared for North American sales following successful completion of the US Federal Emissions Regulations test. A Peterborough engineering team had worked for seven months to clear the project, tests at Peterborough being followed by independent tests at Southwest Research Institute in Texas. Clearance allowed the engines to be sold in 49 states for panel vans, buses and trucks up to 24 tonnes. The test used for US Federal certification required special dynamometer, computer and emissions equipment, and involved completing cycles covering different loads and speed conditions, including cold and hot starting – much more complex than the European requirements.

The October industrial news contained a worrying message for Perkins as MF slipped to third place in the UK tractor sales charts behind both Ford and Case IH. Business had been lost as MF refused to join a price war between their rivals. MF's new sophisticated range of tractors was also taking time to become established – especially in a market where price outweighed technical specification.

In the vehicle market a potential opportunity was lost when it was announced that the Bedford truck plant was to close, although it was possible that the David Brown AWD Company would take over the plant. Perkins had been in protracted negotiations with Bedford to re-power their products with Phaser engines, under a project codenamed 'Dover'. There were lingering hopes that the AWD takeover would pick up on the work already done. Indeed a conversion already undertaken on a Bedford TL 16.25 with the Phaser 160T won a trophy in the Brewery Transport Advisory Committee contest for economy, as did a Ford Cargo 7.5 tonne with a Phaser 120Ti 4-cylinder. The trucks, converted under the supervision of Perkins engineer Brian MacMurray, outperformed the Cummins-powered Bedford and Ford-engined Cargo.

The opening of the Frank Perkins Parkway in October completed the Peterborough ring road and featured a cavalcade of Perkins-powered vehicles to celebrate the event. The convoy of machinery old and new ranged from a 62-tonne Challenger tank to a little Melroe skid-steer forklift truck, while the engines ranged from P6 to CV-12. The static display at Eastfield included a 1940 Leopard restored by Dereck Lambe, along with the Perkins Express TV8.640-powered 'pulling' tractor. One of the oldest vehicles was a 1953 Seddon truck, which was driven down from Preston, Lancashire, by owner Richard Sanders who had taken four years to restore the truck.

In November the Eastfield plant produced 17,000 engines in one month, the highest total since September 1981. There was some

The range of small engines developed with ISM provided compact power units taking Perkins into a whole new market sector. Seen here is the largest four-cylinder unit

element of 'catching up' in this total as well as increased customer demand, with the high level of overtime needed underlining the reduced manning level and the difficulties associated with the completion of 'floor-stock' engines.

The Manpower Services Commission recognised the efforts of the Perkins Training Department with the presentation of a National Training Award for the 'multi-skilling' course being run for maintenance personnel. This had been started in 1983 and was scheduled to continue into the 90s as up to 200 employees were trained in the skills needed for complex equipment such as robots and the electronically controlled machine tools. As one of only 60 winners from over 1,200 entrants, the specialist trainers took pride in their achievement.

There was some news from Gardners, the 'new boys' up in Manchester. They announced new business with Neoplan 'Skyliner' coaches as Blueline Intercity Express placed a £1.25 million order for the new 330bhp 6LYT engine for their double-decker holiday market. With an average 4,000 miles a week projected, the buses needed high reliability and performance coupled to excellent fuel economy. Gardner claimed over 30,000 engines in service in the bus and coach market, with their reputation underlined by the new contract.

December closed the year on a further series of high notes. Some return business was confirmed with the Japanese ISM tractor factory as the 1000 Series was specified for their new tractors, using both four- and six-cylinder versions. Swedish distributor Malte Manson equipped a bus as a mobile showroom for the 100, 500 and 1000 Series engines and completed a 3,000-mile tour of Sweden, resulting in tenders for 1,200 engines – many with new customers whose reactions to the new products were very favourable.

The Varity financial figures for the last quarter showed a profit of $5.7 million on sales of $465 million, compared to a loss of $19.9 million on $265 million for the previous year. Perkins shipments were 21% up on the same quarter of the previous year. MD John Devaney commented, 'There have been useful volume gains at a time when the industry is fairly stagnant with pricing pressures and margins still inadequate. Financial turmoil in the USA is cause for concern, so we are conscious of the need to go on reducing our internal costs against the possibility that improved volumes may not prove sustainable in the year ahead.'

Total production of 147,493 engines was a significant improvement, despatches of Prima/500 Series (12,207) and Phaser/1000

Series (4,263) providing welcome added volume. The 4.236 family with 80,427 engines despatched was its best performance since 1981. 2,468 of the new 100 Series engines were also despatched.

1988

A new role for the Walton factory was announced with the formation of a new and separate business unit. Perkins Components Division, with 350 employees under General Manager Mike Swingler, could take on external business whilst remaining a supply source for Perkins. The facility had already supplied brackets for PESL and a first third party contract for pipes, targeted to have one third of its business for other customers within five years. The project had been approved after an external study confirmed full utilisation of the Walton capacity should ensure component supply at competitive prices. Additional machining had already been moved from the Eastfield factory, including pulleys, flywheels and aluminium parts. (The plant was sold later to the Triplex Group, who maintained supply to Perkins whilst gaining other motor industry business to fill the plant; most of the ex-Perkins personnel were re-employed by the new owners.)

The Earls Court International Boat Show in January provided a good start to the New Year. Oyster Marine of Colchester standardised on Perkins engines for their twelve-model range, including Perama, Prima and Range Four 90 (4.236). Beneteau, Jeanneau, Yachting France and G.I. Bert of France, along with Westerley, Moody and Marine Projects in the UK, all specified Prima engines in their products. Another novel marine application story was the 'Marlin' miniature submarine prototype fitted with a 3.152 engine. With a two-man crew and range of 300 miles on the surface, the craft could operate at 100 metres depth, with a safe diving limit of 360 metres. It was hoped that production craft, fitted with Prima engines, would be used for recreation, commercial and military purposes, with a selling price of £70,000.

Success continued for the Prima vehicle engine in light vans. Littlewoods Home Delivery Service ordered 1,500 diesel Sherpa vans after tests showed them to be 2–3mpg better than the Ford Transit. Sales of the Sherpa had reached 20,000 in 1987, with the Prima specified in 60% of the lighter 200 Series version, compared to only 15% for the previous diesel. Renault Truck sold 81 midi-buses with the 50-Series chassis and a further 33 to the Clydeside Scottish Omnibus Company, all with the Phaser four-cylinder engine.

Although there had been many charitable events undertaken by Perkins' employees in both Peterborough and Shrewsbury over the years, one involving six runners from both plants was especially notable. A relay run from 'Wales to the Wash' covering 250 miles over three days raised £2,500 for the 'Thomas Reidy to Hungary' Fund to benefit a three-year-old cerebral palsy victim; the runners braved sub-zero conditions, lashing rain and sore feet, starting from Barmouth to finish three days later in King's Lynn.

In February John Devaney was promoted to Vice President of Varity European Components Group: in this position he became responsible for Pacoma Hydraulics in Germany, the MF tractor axle plant in Italy and Dayton Walther operations in the UK, as well as the Perkins plants.

Another 'oddball' application story appeared in February. The Severn-Lamb business based in the Midlands produced replica locomotives, often of old-style 'Wild West' type, for theme parks all over the world. They standardised on Perkins 4.108 and 4.236 engines whenever diesel power was specified and used the same power units for 'road train' and 'Mississippi river boat' replicas. Owner Michael Severn-Lamb commended the power and reliability essential for such applications.

The Marine Sales Department announced a renamed range of engines, with the name 'Power Prestige' being adopted for leisure and light commercial use; the new Range Four offerings included the M275Ti as the range topper, with a new piston bowl giving reduced white smoke on start-up. The workboat applications were to be known as the 'HD' range.

The March edition of the Echo featured an application sector of growing importance, the generator set market. British Telecom were noted as a major user, with over 800 Perkins engines installed in their 7,000 exchanges for standby power, ranging from 15 to 650kVA output, depending upon the needs of the exchange. All the engines involved, from D3.152 to 3012TAG, had to pass stringent tests to ensure that they were 'instantly' in action when a breakdown occurred. Other manufacturers featured included Petbow, whose ultra-quiet sets used the 4.236, and Broadcrown who had installed three 3000 Series 3012TAG2 units in the Access credit card building. The appearance of Belfast-based F.G. Wilson as a customer was also of major significance: they had opted for Perkins in 1986 for their highest-powered sets and were now taking other engines, from 100 Series and 3.1524 up to 1000 Series. Perkins had just shipped the one-thousandth unit in what became a major partnership.

Venture with Detroit Diesel

In April an agreement with major American engine manufacturer Detroit Diesel Corporation was made public. The first stage of this joint venture was the amalgamation of the Perkins and DDC service and distribution networks across the USA. DDC was itself a joint venture between General Motors and Penske Corporation; when linked to Perkins their combined worldwide capacity was about 800,000 engines a year, and combined sales turnover over £1 billion a year. While DDC was strong in large and on-highway engines, Perkins' strength in smaller engines in the agricultural and industrial sectors was complementary, providing the North American market with products from 5 to over 2,000 horsepower. Later the collaboration was expected to be extended to manufacture and high technology engineering. DDC's charismatic chairman, Roger Penske, was well known in Britain for his involvement in motor racing, including Formula One and the Indy Car series. This latest move represented another attempt for Perkins to gain success in America, where initiatives over many years had failed to gain a significant foothold in the vehicle market.

In Peterborough Richard Allen reorganised manufacturing operations into three 'supply units'. Martyn Vaughan became General Manager of the 'mainline' products, covering 4.236, 6.2544, Phaser and 1000 Series; Alec Stephenson became GM of the small engines, covering Prima, Prima Marine and 500 Series; and Peter Murray was appointed GM for 'Special Products', encompassing 4.108, 3.152, 4.203 and V8s. Peterborough Components Division, headed by Mike Swingler, made up the fourth unit: each GM had full control of clearly-defined areas of cost, and was expected to maximise profitability from the assets employed.

Elsewhere the Service Garage moved to its new premises, formerly occupied by the Engineering Field Test workshops. Continuing the theme of maximising profitability and utilisation of all assets, the Garage took on servicing of vehicles from outside Perkins as well as the in-house fleet. The first such contracts were with electrical contractors C.F. Parkinson and Steer Tyres, with other business including the routine servicing, MoT testing and repair of employees' vehicles.

Another 'service arm' of Perkins operations to receive recognition was the Sports Association. The Sports Council's magazine Sport and Leisure praised the Association's success in providing a first-class sports club service when many other firms were closing their facilities, hit by hard times and falling membership. PSA General Secretary Sandy Dobson addressed the Sports Council's 'Recreation Management 1988' conference at Wembley in March, alongside Sebastian Coe and Trevor Brooking. In his presentation about the continuing success of the PSA, Sandy noted the successful policy of 'independent operation' – no Company interference but full support.

Many activities of the PSA have been mentioned briefly in this history, but its importance to the employees over the years must not be underestimated. The diverse nature of the many clubs within the Association, from the most popular to the very minor, has been a major factor in its success. The role in the social and recreational activities of those employees and their families through the years has been very important. The club facilities and bar provide a meeting point for outside-work socialising, while the sporting activities contribute to leagues and other friendly fixtures throughout the Peterborough area, their presence helping healthy competition and nurturing talent.

Another important accolade came the way of the Prima marine engine in June when Volvo Penta, a major name in the marine world, decided to market the engine as part of its product range. VP contracted to take a version of the M60 engine designated MD22, branded with the Volvo Penta name and finished in their standard green livery. Volvo Vice President and General Manager Leif Strand commented: 'Following extensive tests on different engines we found that no other unit . . . could better match our demanding requirements for a product to be included in a Volvo Penta power pack.' Richard Allen added that '. . . it is an endorsement of our belief that the Prima engine is a winner, and I have every confidence that the Prima workforce can meet the quality and delivery demands that VP place on us.'

The growing confidence in the industrial sector was confirmed at the 'Site Equipment Display' exhibition held near Whipsnade, which included more than seventy items of equipment powered by Perkins, many using 1000 Series engines one year after their first appearance. Amongst the customers exhibiting were JCB, Caterpillar, MF, Compare, Hydrovane, FDI, Manitou, Hydrema, Hymac and Matbro-Bray. The secret, according to Geoff Dunmore, Perkins Industrial General Sales Manager, was not just reliability and economy but also worldwide acceptability and service support.

In August the Defence Sales team could boast success. At the British Army Equipment Exhibition at Aldershot there were orders for Reynolds Boughton RB 44 trucks with the Phaser 110MT engine for the British Army, and eighty Alvis Scorpion light tanks for Venezuela, using the T6.3544. Interest was also being shown in the Phaser engine for re-powering Ferret scout cars, and in the PESL CV8 and CV12 engines for updating other equipment. The US Army Tactical Command showed interest in the 1,500-horsepower CV12 for main battle tanks and the Eagle MX350 for a bridge-laying vehicle.

Peter Whitaker joined Peterborough as Sales Director from Seddon Atkinson Trucks. In an interview he commented that his experience of the Phaser engine confirmed that it met all the claims made by Perkins, and that it had been the most trouble-free engine ever introduced by SA. He relished the challenge of his new job, which would take him beyond the truck market into other sectors. The personal attention given by Perkins to all customers, large and small, was another factor he believed was important to success.

At the north end of the Peterborough site clearance work had started ready for the Sainsbury's store, scheduled for September 1989 opening. An application for planning permission was made for about 18 acres behind the factory, including a part of the sports field, the area designated to be for 'mixed commercial and industrial use'. This sale would require relocation of some working areas, and there were implications for the Sports Association. As an indication of the Company's intent to profit from assets no longer seen as necessary, the news was received with mixed feelings, especially since the intended sale would split the playing field area in two.

More details were given about the DDC/Perkins Agreement. A doubling of sales to North America in four years was confidently forecast,

with vehicle engine sales adding to the 25,000 engines a year delivered to the existing industrial and marine customers. The six-cylinder Phaser was expected to be sold into the American Class 3 to 7 truck market. More details were given of Roger Penske's background and business interests: he held 80% of DDC stock in his Transportation Services Division, which also included truck leasing, operating over 40,000 vehicles from 270 locations. In addition to his motor racing interests, Penske owned various car sales franchises. During a visit to Peterborough he spoke to the senior managers and his personal charisma and business acumen were very apparent.

A further change of management was announced in September when John Devaney was appointed Group Vice-President of Varity Corporation North American Enterprises, including Dayton Walther, retail financial operations and a venture capital portfolio. Devaney had been MD of Perkins Engines Group for five years, presiding over a difficult period of the Company's history.

Confirmation of the new role to be taken by the Engineering side of the operations came with the announcement of the formation of 'Perkins Technology' as an independent business. The 14 September 'Press Day' launch to around forty journalists demonstrated the intention to win a significant part of the yearly £400 million spent worldwide on diesel research and development. In addition to 'in-house' work for PEPL, PESL and Gardner products, the new company would seek new third-party business to utilise fully the complex of 90 test beds, noise and climate cells, workshops, design, computer and CAD facilities.

The drive for improved quality included a special campaign using an external consultancy. The QED (Quality Every Day) approach resulted in over 1,000 money-saving ideas being submitted through September, with many implemented for immediate savings. A special quality drive – 'Prima Perfection' – came ahead of the release of the engine in the Austin Rover cars, to ensure further improvements in the already high production standard.

Another new production facility was commissioned, again with quality very much in mind. A new six-cell automated production test area in Bay 10 of Factory 1 was intended to test up to 40 engines per hour on shorter test cycles, with pre-rigging, computer monitoring and automatic logging of many parameters.

Turbocharged Prima

The biggest event of the year for many at Perkins was the launch of the turbocharged version of Prima in the Austin Rover Montego passenger car at the International Motor Show in Birmingham during October. There was tremendous interest, with coverage by national and local media, including TV and radio interviews with Product Manager Gordon Mitchell and the two-litre General Manager Alex Stephenson. The first fleet order came from Perkins for a total of 37 cars, needed to replace the existing vehicles used for service engineers and general transport. The Prima 80T was already being produced at about 250 a week and one car had been used to set a 'double century' record as it achieved a top speed of 102mph and a consumption of 110mpg at an average of 31.4mph over 19.4 miles on the MIRA proving circuit at Nuneaton under RAC supervision. This was believed to be a first for a car of its size and allowed some interesting advertising! There were many good comments in the motoring press; perhaps one of the most telling was the assertion that the diesel was no noisier than the petrol-powered car.

Manchester-based Gardner was not to be left out, launching the turbocharged version of their 12.7-litre engine as the 310T. Developed at Patricroft with assistance and support from Peterborough, this engine was scheduled for 1989 production and was expected to provide increased performance whilst retaining the legendary Gardner

The Eastfield site changed during the 1990s. This view from 1994 shows the factory from the north, with the Frank Perkins Parkway and the Sainsbury's store built on the area formerly occupied by part of the original factory

fuel economy. Extended trials of a prototype engine in a Foden tanker owned by Tilcon Special Products Division with 20-tonne payloads produced average fuel consumption of 8.8mpg – the best of their fleet. Meanwhile, just down the road at Shrewsbury, PESL announced their 'concept' Eagle engine for 38-tonne trucks. Rated at 430bhp, the engine was claimed to be ahead of all its competitors and a force for the future.

The steady stream of good publicity continued in November with a collaborative agreement with Komatsu UK, based at Birtley near Durham, for the supply of engines for their construction equipment. Starting with 125 and 155bhp versions of the 1006-6T engine for the PC210 and PC 240 excavators, the joint programme produced engines 'specifically tailored to the Komatsu requirements' – a claim that could be made by all the major equipment manufacturers who worked closely with the Perkins applications engineers! Prototype testing had confirmed the acceptability of engine performance, durability and fuel economy against the exacting Komatsu demands. With the other agreements featuring DDC, ISM, Volvo Penta and of course Austin Rover, the worldwide total of individual original equipment applications now exceeded 2,000.

On the factory front, Perkins people met the Secretary of State for Employment, Norman Fowler MP, when he opened the new Powerhouse Training Centre as part of a £2 million investment in multiskilling and apprentice training. Outline planning permission was received for mixed industrial and residential development on the site behind the factory, allowing plans to go ahead to vacate and prepare the site for sale by tender.

In December the vacancy at the top of the Perkins Group was filled by Michael Bird when he took temporary charge as Group Vice-President. A long-serving MF man, he had occupied various senior positions since 1955, and had been a Board member since 1988. He maintained his previous roles as Chairman of Varity Holdings and Chairman of Varity's European Companies. There were other senior position changes too as Barry Parsisson became General Manager and Director of Perkins International operations, his previous role as Director and General Manager of Defence Sales being assumed by Peter Baker.

Another of the longest-serving employees retired in December after 48 years' service. R.G. (Ron) Hadnam had started as an office boy in 1940 at the age of 17, gradually moving through the ranks in the purchase and supply area, to become Director, Purchasing and Supply in 1979. It was reckoned that he had probably been responsible for £3 billion of purchasing over the years, as well as assisting the setting-up of purchase departments overseas. Ron's many other interests included the Sports Association and the Footlights Club, producing shows and pantomimes for the city. In more recent years he had been involved in fund-raising events for the Macmillan Nurses Cancer Relief charity and was on the Board of Westcombe Industries, which employed eighty disabled workers.

The close of the year brought satisfaction as Peterborough production rose to 178,270 engines. Prima volume at 22,665 and Phaser/1000 series at 19,557 were high spots, with both 4.236 (83,073) and 6.3544 (19,347) also healthy trends. 100 Series production reached 9,305 en-

As part of the launch of the Prima engine in the Austin Rover Montego car, an early vehicle was driven to Moscow as a repeat of the 1934 journey and is seen here in Red Square

gines as the smallest range began to gain acceptance in its market. In Shrewsbury the trend was also modestly upwards as 3,008 engines were despatched. The one disappointment was the CKD shipments, where the total of 57,325 kits was the poorest for five years.

1989

In January Perkins took delivery of the first twenty new Montego cars, with turbocharged Prima engines, as replacement fleet vehicles. There had been an excellent road test report in Diesel Car magazine: 'Rover's brave new venture has paid off with a combination of performance no-one else can match . . . as an overall package the Montego turbo is attractive and likeable. It stands comparison with the French opposition, is miles better than the Sierra and deserves to sell by the thousand.' A few weeks later the diesel Montego won the 'Golden Klaxon' award from the Belgian Auto and Sport magazine – awarded by a panel of Flemish journalists for the most remarkable technical innovation of the year. The accolades continued with a good report in the Autocar and Motor road test extolling the 55.8mpg touring fuel consumption and suggesting: 'The diesel has it all. If you are looking for an oil-burner [OUCH!] take a long hard look at the Montego.' To round off fantastic press coverage, Fleet News described the engine as 'a revelation' and stated: 'You wouldn't believe that a DI engine could be so good. It is refined and rapid. The Montego stands alone in the economy stakes and doesn't it look good value for money?'

Arrival of Tony Gilroy

The new Managing Director of Perkins was appointed in January, allowing Michael Bird to stand down. Fifty-two year old Mr J.A. (Tony) Gilroy was previously the MD of Land Rover Group and had held positions with Ford and British Leyland before heading up Freight Rover and Land Rover. After the previous MDs, where Peter Wright had a sales background, Jim Felker was from finance and John Devaney from manufacturing, Gilroy quickly demonstrated his open-minded approach to the business. In his first few months he took a particular interest in quality issues, beginning a major exercise on product quality, looking to instil new attitudes across all areas of the Company. He instigated a survey to identify the true 'cost of quality' – perhaps better defined as the actual cost of poor quality – and the areas where lack of attention was increasing non-productive decision costs. It was a new approach and focused attention on individual responsibilities.

Perkins Technology signed a contract in February with Bulgarian manufacturer VAMO to assist them with noise, emissions and fuel consumption improvements to support Balkankar forklift trucks for the 90s. This was the first Eastern European contract following the launch of PTech, although connections with Bulgaria dated back to the 60s. Later came agreement to build a technical centre in Varna, to be manned by PTech and Vamo personnel, able to draw on the expertise of 800 specialist engineers. Joint sales teams were already in contact with potential customers in Czechoslovakia, East Germany and Poland (see Chapter 20 for more details).

The Works Fire Brigade celebrated its 50th Anniversary with a history researched and written for the Echo by fireman Peter Ashpool. The idea of an in-house brigade had been triggered by a Ministry of Defence visit to Frank Perkins in 1939, when they suggested the formation of a 'fire squad' to deal with local fires and the effects of bombing. The job was given to Bert Harris, who started with six volunteers – Ernie Vinter, Alf Moulds, Ted Sells, Bill Carter, Bill Baxter and Bob Storey. Their initial equipment included reinforced bowler hats until tin helmets became available! On 8 June 1940 they dealt with forty incendiary bombs dropped on the Queen Street and Wood Street area. The present-day equipment was much more modern, including self-breathing sets and a thermal-imaging camera.

New product announcements included the new Tx version of the Shrewsbury Eagle engine, producing up to 375bhp and with better low-speed torque to improve driveability and lugging performance over tough terrain. ERF were the first truck manufacturer to offer the engine in their 'E' series vehicle, claiming outstanding performance coupled with low weight and competitive pricing. Another important event was the despatch of the first engines to Komatsu in Durham, while in the BAUMA fair in Munich the eight engines displayed on the Perkins stand were supplemented by no fewer than 162 Perkins-powered machines exhibited by 42 manufacturers, including JCB, MF, Komatsu, Caterpillar, Clark, Hyster, Linde and Hanomag.

In Russia, teams from TV and the press gathered in Moscow's Red Square to meet a Montego Turbo diesel car driven for five days overland by Perkins' service engineer John Burgess and Diesel Car editor Jon Kerswill. In repeating the historic drive of the 'Wolf'-powered Hillman car over 50 years before, the modern vehicle achieved an average of 49.5mpg and gave 'a comfortable and relaxing ride'. The drive was timed to coincide with British–Soviet Month and Trade Fair; the car joined an exhibition of Prima, Phaser and Eagle engines on the Perkins stand.

In July the long-running Echo changed its format from newspaper format to an A4-sized colour magazine. Although still intended to cover the full spectrum of interests in people, places, events and Company news the new publication would be published bi-monthly.

German customer Linde used the Perkins 'Powerhouse' facility to launch their new range of H 35, 40 and 45 forklift trucks fitted with 1000 Series engines to their UK distributors and customers, who took the opportunity to tour the factory and see the 1004-4 engines being built.

True to the promise of improved coverage, the new Echo articles featured eight production managers from Eastfield spending a weekend on an outward bound course for the over-40s in snowy Northumberland, community help to Eastholm School in Peterborough, and the Elfred Williams Memorial Fund in Shrewsbury helping local handicapped children. Succeeding months saw many other stories.

The launch of Phaser in Turkey was attended by British Consul-General Michael Collins, who heard of Turkish success over 26 years for Perkins-powered equipment, now totalling over 300,000 units. The new Chrysler Kamyon AS900 with the Phaser 160T engine would join the 65,000 locally-produced trucks already in service, with orders for 2,000 CKD sets for the next twelve months to meet demand. Other overseas news concerned the move of Perkins' Latin-American Operations from Miami to Atlanta, whilst a visit by General Manager Hector Garcia from MODASA Peru confirmed that CKD orders were continuing despite economic difficulties in that country.

The success of the Prima was celebrated in June with the build of the 50,000th engine and the introduction of a night shift to cope with the increasing demand. An order for 1,600 diesel Montegos from the Ministry of Defence confirmed its growing popularity in fleet use.

As a direct contrast, the tractor pulling team of 'The Massey Lads' (including Perkins application engineer Terry Sidwell) celebrated national and international successes in a very specialist sport. The highly-modified TV8-powered MF 2775 named Perkoil Express notched up a series of successes in the 3,400 and 4,400kg categories. With three first places and eight seconds in twenty-five competitions since 1987, the team finished 1989 as UK Champions in the 3,400kg class.

In July Perkins hosted the finals of the competition for the Perkins Award to the National Society of Quality Circles (NSQC) at the Power Centre. The award for achievement was contested by six finalists, and after their presentations to five judges, the winner was Michelin Tyres from Stoke-on-Trent. In presenting the award, Tony Gilroy emphasised the role of Quality Circles in harnessing the talents of employees effectively and commended all the finalists.

The Varity head office in Canada featured in the Echo. The office was situated on the ninth floor of the 'Atrium on Bay' building in Toronto, with seventy people supporting President Victor Rice. With no end product made there, the most important connection was with the 87,000 investors in the $2.3 billion Corporation – nearly six times the total Varity worldwide labour force. Varity's diversification continued with the addition of Kelsey Hayes to the Group, joining Perkins, Massey Ferguson and Dayton Walther in making Varity one of the top ten Canadian Companies.

In October Perkins and DDC ran a presentation in Detroit, aptly named 'Team-Up', to introduce the collaboration in the American market between the two companies, including sales and service. There was an associated promotion in Peterborough when Gilroy picked Michel Eschalier to be General Vehicle Project Manager – heading a team tasked specifically with penetration of the American vehicle market for the 1991 Model Year with the Phaser engines.

At the end of November, the annual Perkins Teamwork Awards were presented. Peter Murray commented that during the six years the awards had been running the company had come out of the worst recession in its history and had recovered from 500 to over 850 engines per day. Managing Director Tony Gilroy presented the certificates to the winning teams and commented: 'Each team has approached its problems in a different way, but you can tell that every team member gets more out of it than just a job.' He likened the teams to missionaries to the rest of the employees, adding: 'If we could all approach our work in the way these teams have, there would be nothing stopping us – keep up the good work!' One of the teams rewarded was the 'Mo Mechs' from the Service Garage, who had seen their business turnover rise from £123,000 in 1988 to over £400,000 in 1989.

The end of the year showed 189,437 engines despatched from Peterborough – only 6% above the previous year but the best result since 1980. The new engine types showed significant increases, with 36,094 Prima/500 Series and 28,576 Phaser/1000 Series promising much for the future. Of the older engine types, the 4.236 and 6.3544 families continued at high volume, while the 4.108 and 3.152 were still maintaining a presence. Sales of the ISM 100 Series dropped to only 6,496 units, while Shrewsbury sales topped 4,000, the best figure since the Perkins takeover. Despatches of CKD kits totalled 58,877, marginally up on the previous year, although total production in all licensees and associates topped 229,000. Taken in the context of the economic situation and some industrial unrest, the results were acceptable, if not quite as expected.

1990

The year started well for the 'Third Party' side of Perkins Technology who claimed over 150 clients spread around the world, from the USA to Eastern Europe and Japan, as well as EEC countries and the UK. Stephen Parker, their head of Business Development commented that: 'The fact that we can supply engine manufacturers with a complete service from design to manufacture has been well received.' Amongst those visiting the PTech stand at the Autotech exhibition was Minister of Transport Michael Portillo, who expressed interest in the QHV90 exhibit – a 'quiet vehicle' project offering advances in environmental and emissions technology. PTech also announced the appointment of Ken Galloway to be the first head of the Bulgarian 'Intertech' Consultancy Centre being established as a joint venture.

Environmental issues were also the concern of an employee initiative to develop a 'wildlife haven' on an acre of garden outside the Technology offices. A team of volunteers gradually transformed the lawn and shrub area into a sanctuary for birds and other wildlife. Their plans included a beehive, pond and wild flowers, and were supported by the Nature Conservancy Council through a grant and advice. (The area flourished well beyond 2000, with an increasing wildlife population which at one point even included a visiting deer and a marauding sparrowhawk!)

In March, Tony Gilroy introduced a new level of employee participation with the publication of 'Viewpoint 90', a survey seeking the views of every UK employee on the company as a business and employer, and how its effectiveness could be improved. This was the first of a series of such surveys; along with the emphasis on quality issues they characterised Gilroy's intention to develop a more open relationship between management and the workforce – a culture change needed for the new decade. At about the same time a monthly 'Team Brief' was started, tailored for each area of the operation and designed to give additional, focused, information to the workforce. It was interesting to note that the 'teamwork' methods at Peterborough encouraged a visit from the Docklands Light Railway early in 1990; a team anxious to see how they could apply the Perkins methods of training to improving customer satisfaction and quality in their business.

Following the sale of land at Eastfield for development, in Shrewsbury plans were laid to extend the west factory, build new offices and sell off the old east factory site – originally the home of the Sentinel steam wagons – for commercial development. The plans were approved by the local council and the £5 million programme got underway in June, scheduled for completion by the end of the year. Ultimately a new Morrison's supermarket was built on the old site, almost exactly duplicating the changes at the north end of the Peterborough site.

The Prima engine won perhaps its greatest accolade in April – the Queen's Award for Technological Achievement. The citation noted that the combination of the Montego and Prima was unique in achieving 100mpg and 100mph for a family-sized car and that its fuel consumption was 40% better than an equivalent-sized petrol engine. Tony Gilroy expressed his delight at winning the award which recognised achievements at the threshold of new technology, made more important by growing concern over environmental issues. Later in the year all employees were presented with a specially-minted commemorative medal. When the award was presented to Tony Gilroy by the Lord Lieutenant of Cambridgeshire at a ceremony attended by most of the workforce, he said: 'This is the one of the proudest moments in our history. Winning this – Britain's top accolade – is a tremendous achievement for it represents the successful outcome of what was for all involved an enormous challenge.' At about the same time, ARG announced a new model of the Maestro hatchback, fitted with the naturally aspirated version of the Prima, giving a top speed of 93mph and fuel consumption of 64.5mpg at 56mph.

In midsummer Perkins service engineers provided support for the re-enactment of the Dunkirk evacuation. Amongst the boats taking part were 21 which had been fitted with Perkins engines and a further four with Gardner units. Special thanks were given for their help at Dover which helped ensure a safe passage for the many veteran 'little ships'.

Announcement of Navistar Collaboration

Another agreement was signed in July, this time with US diesel manufacturer Navistar International Transport Corporation to market and sell the six-cylinder 6.7-litre and 7.6-litre Navistar engines to Perkins customers worldwide. DDC would take on the marketing for off-highway use on the USA, identifying the engine as 'Series 40'. The tie-up resulted from a 'cold call' by Product Planning Director Brian Weedon; after discussions it was agreed that mutual benefit could be realised. Navistar would provide the base engines, with Perkins designing and producing any new dress options that might be needed. It is interesting to note that, as International Harvester Corporation, Navistar had been a very early customer for Perkins with the 6.354 actually badged 'IHC' on the exhaust manifold. Tony Gilroy commented that this addition to the Perkins range made it even more complete from 5 to 1,500bhp across all market sectors, and added to the series of mutually beneficial ventures announced in recent months. The initial engines would have a limited sales life, since Navistar were in the process of developing a new version, known as NGD – New Generation Diesel, scheduled for production in the mid-90s.

There was a small celebration in Factory 2 when the block line produced its two millionth four-cylinder block after 25 years of operation. Seven operatives could claim to have been on the line since the first component was produced in 1965 and had seen every change through to the 1004-4 series.

In October the next stage of Tony Gilroy's quality initiative was announced. Following the analysis of the feedback from the 'Viewpoint 90' questionnaire returned by employees, and the previous 'Cost of Quality' survey, Quality Manager Dick Yates explained the next moves. With the assistance of Quest Quality Consultancy, the planning process would be followed by a company-wide training programme starting in early 1991, which would teach the principles of 'Total Quality'.

As the end of the year approached, there was further evidence of growing success for the Prima engine in passenger cars. The Maestro and Montego diesel cars were placed fourth and fifth in the August sales of diesel vehicles, which now represented over 6.5% of total car sales in the UK. This growth, from 6,000 in 1980 to 123,000 in 1989, proved that the public were at last appreciating the merits of diesel motoring, although many sales were for high-mileage fleet use. The van market continued to grow, with Royal Mail Letters placing a £12 million order.

Other new products included the announcement of the Gardner LG 1200 series: an eight-model range of their 12.7-litre automotive range offering 210 to 350bhp in a durable but lightweight package – further fruits of the Perkins takeover. Meanwhile the Eagle Tx was taking 25.5% of the optional engine market in the 350 to 375bhp range, in spite of depressed market conditions. To round off the good news, the Compact Engines Division sales topped 20,000 to date, with turnover 200% up on 1987.

The year-end statistics showed a total of 170,748 engines, a disappointing figure in view of the efforts on all sides, and almost 19,000 down on 1989. Even the Prima volume had dropped by 4,800 units. The only bright spots were the growing sales of the six-cylinder 1000 Series and the recovery of CKD kits despatches to 139,314 – a massive improvement on the previous year.

f the Engineering Division had felt busy during the late 1970s, this proved to be just a mild introduction to the decade to come. While the work on alternative fuels was to prove to be largely wasted, the pioneering work on high speed direct injection and research into the combustion process was to prove critical to engine developments in the 80s. The growing importance of computers as an essential tool in every aspect of engine design, development and research was appreciated by Perkins, although the primary Corporate interest was the use of the computer as a business aid rather than a technical device. Massey Ferguson had appreciated the potential of a linked computer and communication network much earlier than many enterprises, so that the use of satellites and an electronic mail system meant that many employees were conversant long before the internet and email became commonplace.

Within the Engineering Division in Peterborough it had been realised that engine durability and reliability were steadily improving, as were the expectations of the end-users. The traditional engine validation approach via exhaustive test bed running was also becoming more and more expensive. A new approach was needed. A vigorous programme of software development began, initiated and guided by Roland Bertodo, with the aim of predicting the performance of engine components before they were made and tested. This included prediction of noise from engines, a tool that Perkins was the first to introduce, using technologies in which Perkins was a world leader. Alongside this work was the Basic Design Team, led by David Larkinson, responsible for the initial basic calculation and design scheming which led to project proposals and, upon agreement, the beginning of detail design work.

While the use of mainframe computers for technical calculations was now well established, the extension to encompass electronic draughting became the initial concern of a small group of designers under John Brentnall in the late 1970s, as mentioned in an earlier chapter. The first experiments were rather slow and painful as both the understanding of the design staff and the capability of the Computer Aided Design equipment (CAD) developed. It was quickly apparent that the new processes needed a large library of detail drawings in digitised, electronic format before much use could be made of the potential for increased productivity, especially in the production of layouts and scheme drawings. Committed training of personnel began against a background of trade union disquiet – the potential of the new equipment ringing alarm bells in the minds of many TASS members who saw a future with smaller numbers of design staff doing the work previously carried out by many. There were months of increasingly acrimonious negotiations culminating in a withdrawal of labour, in effect a 'sit-in', by many of the draughting team plus the 'blacking' of CAD-produced drawings. Eventually a way forward was found, inevitably through a package of revisions to salary scales. Peace at a price was the result and Perkins began to move into a new era where computer-produced drawings became the norm, and electronic transmittal of information between companies across continents and oceans revolutionised the 1980s.

In parallel with the difficulties in producing drawings came other similar 'new technology' problems, notably in the support areas where the parts listing and design change personnel realised that there was now an increased 'technical' content to their work as opposed to what had been a mainly clerical function. The clerical staff unions looked for, and eventually received, upgraded pay scales as a quid pro quo for their members' changing workload.

These changes formed the background as the Engineering Division came to grips with the immense impact of the series of new engine

programmes. The programme for the larger engine known as the Q14 has already been mentioned. This was soon joined by the Q20, the upgrading of the medium-sized products that had been the mainstay of Eastfield's production since the 60s. In truth this was an oft-delayed and overdue programme, needing much engineering effort as well as impacting on every other area of the company. The push to address this issue came from Product Planning Director Brian Weedon, who was concerned that arch-rival Cummins would take a large proportion of the existing Perkins medium engines business with their new 'B' series product. He convinced MD Jim Felker that the new engine range was essential. Alongside these two programmes were the various joint ventures with the old British Leyland companies as well as other initiatives – of which more later.

The Q20 programme entailed the complete replacement of the 6.3544 and 4.236 engine families by state-of-the-art products capable of meeting all impending legislation and able to compete on the world market for the remainder of the 20th century. This task was daunting, with the number of active customer lists running into hundreds, the total volume of engines exceeding 100,000 a year for Peterborough alone, to say nothing of the major licensee usage and of course the re-working of the highest volume machining lines at Eastfield. The total expenditure represented a huge commitment for the MF Group.

The initial team entrusted with the task under Chief Engineer Alec Osborn included Project Manager Roy Chowings and Design Supervisor Ken Osborne, with major input from David Cowcill, David Kempton and Brian Willett in Product Planning. As the programme developed and its complexity grew, further management effort was needed, with Roger Adams taking over as Project Manager for the applications side while Roy Chowings concentrated on the 'core' engine.

The new engine designs could not be done as a 'clean sheet of paper' – on the contrary, to hold capital expenditure within sensible limits the design had to remain within clear physical boundaries. Thus the engine cylinder blocks, cylinder heads and crankshafts had to stay broadly identical to the dimensions of the existing volume products to ensure that the existing transfer machinery could be modified to handle the new product – so compromise was the name of the game before pencil was laid to paper.

However, since the new combustion system allowed retarded injection timing, and hence lower cylinder pressures compared to the old engines, it was apparent that the existing crankshaft designs remained suitable for both 4- and 6-cylinder versions of the Q20, thus saving major tooling costs. (This also effectively killed the latest in a series of projects looking at producing a stronger crankshaft for the 6.3544 family – the so-called 'big bottom end'. Project 'Mercury' took its name from Freddie Mercury after the Queen song entitled 'Fat Bottomed Girls' . . .)

The original design scheme for the 6-cylinder block incorporated oil and water drillings within the casting to connect an integral oil cooler. This was rejected as being too costly, so that a compromise arrangement was designed to allow a block-mounted cooler to receive water from the jacket but with the oil supplied through external pipes from the filter head pad. The final approved scheme looked acceptable but became the cause of considerable warranty costs and additional expense, due to the tight geometric tolerances necessary and the consequential stresses unwittingly forced upon a percentage of the oil pipes during assembly.

There were other issues addressed by the new design. The use of modern techniques such as finite element analysis ensured that the cylinder block designs were more stable and did not suffer from the

The introduction of computer aided design revolutionised the design process for Perkins Technology in the 1980s

distortion problems which had always plagued the 4.236 and 6.354 families. Thus the cylinder bores stayed round and allowed the improvements in oil control necessary – in addition a switch to silicon carbide honing stones in place of the double diamond honing process gave better bore finish, cleaner cut and less vulnerability to the outbreaks of ring and bore scuffing suffered throughout the lives of the earlier engines. (The resulting improvements in oil control and cylinder component life put the Q20 engines well within industry standards for modern products.)

In the quest to improve overall engine sealing and eliminate a major issue with the old engines, Perkins Technology developed new gaskets and joints using the latest technology in conjunction with their suppliers; this coincided with the elimination of asbestos as a constituent material, in line with worldwide concerns over the health issues arising from asbestos use in many applications. Naturally the Q20 engines were to be all-metric as far as components were concerned; not only were all fasteners to ISO standards, but of course all drawings used metric dimensions.

The coming of 'Quadram'

The major change as far as performance was concerned was the introduction of a new combustion chamber shape, together with porting changes and new fuel injection equipment, following from the painstaking performance development work undertaken by the research engineers over the previous decade. The new patented combustion bowl shape was known as 'Quadram', and quite by chance the shape almost mimicked the Perkins trademark symbol, since it had four equispaced circular cut-outs around the circular bowl. This more elaborate shape was found to give better overall performance for gaseous emis-

sions and smoke, and coupled with the retarded injection timing provided benefits in noise terms too.

In the spirit of metrication, the new engines were given new nomenclature, following the old pattern of cylinder numbers plus swept volume, but this time in litres, or more exactly decilitres. Thus the six became the 6.60 and the four became the 4.40, reflecting the slightly greater swept volume of one litre per cylinder. In due course additional complexity was added for marketing and sales purposes, as the new

Powerful computer programs aided the research engineers in their quest for improvements in the combustion process, supporting Perkins' actions to meet new legislation on noise and emissions

Prior to its cancellation from the company forward programme, prototypes of the Q14 engine were produced for customer trials, including this turbocharged six-cylinder destined for a Ford LT8000 truck

range was named 'Phaser' for vehicle applications and '1000 Series' for industrial, agricultural and marine use. To add even more complexity, the four and six were given additional identifiers, so that the vehicle engines became Phaser 90, Phaser 100T, Phaser 135, Phaser 160T, Phaser 180Ti, etc., and the 1000 Series was graced by nomenclature starting simply with 104-4 or 1006-6, but adding Ts and other identifiers for charge-cooling, generator set applications, etc. All very complex – but with engineers being of a more direct and simple persuasion the engines tended to be known internally as 4.40, T4.40, etc., or even remain as Q20!

It soon became clear that this new engine range would take priority for engineering effort, since the 'one litre per cylinder' size was going to continue to be the most important and versatile offering for the marketplace. The 4.236 and 6.354 families had provided the overall workhorse range since the 1960s; their replacements were essential and must satisfy all impending legislation and be produced in at least the same volumes. The problem would become twofold – not just switching over the customers already champing at the bit to have the new engines, but also persuading the other customers not affected by legislation to make the switch when Perkins needed it. In the event the persuasion was inadequate: the 6.354 and 4.236 hung on for far too long, albeit with steadily reducing volumes, so that the production areas were forced to produce the old and new ranges side by side, resulting in considerable inefficiency and complexity well into the 90s.

The 'larger engine' project is dropped

Meanwhile the Q14 engine range, under Ron Macintosh as Project Manager had proceeded through development and field testing to the point where production tooling was being discussed, and indeed the engine was exhibited and given advance publicity including the issue of a brochure detailing its background, technical content and performance. The six-cylinder engines, of both naturally aspirated and turbocharged configurations, promised to be class-leading products, with good performance including excellent fuel economy, low noise and emission levels well inside impending legislation. However, a

review of the changing market needs in about 1983 suggested that in reality there was insufficient demand and probable volume to justify proceeding. The lack of a committed lead customer or partner must also have been a factor, making one wonder why the company had proceeded so far without some guarantee of initial sales. The project was cancelled after considerable expense, so that the engineering resources freed off could be applied to the Q20 and smaller engine ranges.

Major efforts on smaller 'joint venture' engines

The other major effort during the 1980s was the work on what was known within Perkins as 'Small Engines', although some in fact were quite large! The real common denominator was that all the engines involved were derived from existing spark-ignition products of various other companies – and the intention was to produce diesel versions for cars and light trucks, with probable spin-off use by Perkins for other applications. All of the projects were joint ventures and all rejoiced in a variety of code names in at least their early days. 'Iceberg' and 'Ferret' were JVs with the Austin Rover Group, whilst 'Squirrel' was with Chrysler Corporation in the USA and 'Freezer' was a venture with Ford Motor Company, also in the USA. All of these projects began through visits and proposals between the prospective customers and the Perkins Product Planning Department, involving the late Brian Weedon with John Baxter and Gordon Mitchell – although the early discussions with ARG also involved David Hodkin, who had moved to the Group from Perkins. The Chief Engineer for these projects was Mike Hawkins, who had come to prominence with work on the 'high-speed diesel engine' in the late 1970s, including the 4.22X derivative of the 4.236 family.

There were other projects which did not get beyond the discussion stage. One of these with a Russian vehicle manufacturer was stopped by Perkins when it was realised that the engineering resources were already over-stretched without another major involvement! In most instances Perkins received considerable support from the Department of Trade and Industry, for whom the attraction of more overseas business, even for expertise rather than hardware, was highly desirable in the difficult economic conditions prevailing in the early 80s.

Let's start with the smallest of the JV engines: the Ferret or, as it later became, the Prima (vehicle and marine) and 500 Series (industrial). The proposition arrived at between Perkins and British Leyland (later Austin Rover Group) was to take the 'O' Series petrol engine – a two-litre four-cylinder overhead camshaft unit used in vehicles like the 70s Princess – and convert it to a direct injection diesel. This was a brave move, since nobody had produced a DI small engine quiet enough to fit into a passenger car where noise and refinement were important. A number of modern indirect injection engines were of course already in production, notably with French and German manufacturers, while several other companies were known to be working on DI units. The common problem with DI units was the difficulty of running up to the high speeds needed for passenger car use – at least 4,000rpm – while ensuring good combustion, and therefore emissions and smoke within legislative levels. Perkins' experience with the 4.22X and Q16 proved that this was possible but that combustion noise remained a challenge, even with new combustion chamber development and the latest fuel injection pumps from CAV and Bosch. (It must be remembered that this was all well before electronic controls and developments such as the 'common rail' system.)

The agreement with ARG was for Perkins to provide the diesel expertise and carry out engine development, in close liaison with ARG engineers; Rover would produce the major components from their existing machining lines, with Perkins carrying out the assembly, test and finishing of the engines. Funding for the development phase was shared between Government (50%) and Perkins/Austin Rover. Complex negotiations over the legal agreements lasted many months, during which time a start was made on the detailed engineering work. The agreement was to run for ten years, with supply to ARG for three car models, plus van derivatives, leaving Perkins to use the basic engine for third party industrial and marine applications. The author was the first Project Manager on this project, giving way to Alex Stephenson after the first year.

Initial design and development work proved the diesel engine was feasible, although there were teething problems with cylinder block and camshaft. The use of a 'cog belt' drive for camshaft and fuel injection pump provided an initial challenge for the belt manufacturers, since the fluctuations of load were high. The cylinder head was an aluminium casting, a novelty to Perkins, and was eventually produced using a high-pressure system pioneered by Cosworth Engineering. A plan to use hydraulic tappets was eventually dropped due to cost, and other components were closely scrutinised by Product Cost personnel in both companies to ensure that engineering thinking did not result in unacceptable economics. The decision to proceed with a linerless cylinder block was also a novelty for Perkins, but concerns about acceptability of the parent metal of the cylinder block as a suitable running surface proved groundless. Cost targets were established for every part and close liaison kept both sides aware of all adverse impacts.

Test bed and then initial road running with prototypes proved that the engine in naturally aspirated form was feasible, but noisy. Development of the combustion and fuel injection systems did not produce the desired result until CAV came up with an injector giving 'two-stage' injection – an initial small amount of fuel starting pilot combustion in the chamber, with the main fuel quantity injected microseconds later into the already-ignited charge. This 'softened' the harsh quality of the engine noise signature. Cold starting, a problem with diesels in cold weather where customers expect the same immediate start-and-run characteristics as the modern petrol unit, was resolved easily by the use of fast-acting glow plugs fitted into the cylinder head and acting

directly in the combustion chamber. This chamber was a patented feature, of re-entrant form with an anodised ring around the piston bowl rim to give protection against thermal fatigue damage.

It was always envisaged that there would be a turbocharged version of the engine for higher performance car models and this engine proved highly successful. The 'packaging' needs for the additional components were resolved and the performance characteristics showed good driveability and promising fuel economy. This latter feature had always been a contentious point, with the Project Team under pressure from very early in the development programme to forecast likely on-the-road consumption figures. The accuracy of any forecast – at a time when vehicle weights, frontal area and coefficient of drag had not been defined, and when engine fuel consumption maps were as yet unexplored – was likely to be suspect, but demands were made, and reluctance to guess the answer not accepted! The eventual posting of 100mpg (at about 30mph) and 100mph maximum speed for the Montego saloon under RAC-observed test track conditions was a boost for publicity – and in service 'real life' average consumptions in excess of 65mpg proved the wisdom of the decision to go to direct injection. One disappointment, however, was the cancellation of the intention to put the diesel into the larger Austin Rover luxury saloon known initially as Project 'XX'. This car was originally intended to be a light executive vehicle but eventually grew in size and weight to the point where the engine could not provide enough power. (As the Sterling or Rover 800 Saloon the car did find a market, but never in the original forecast quantities.)

Although there were some delays to the project, the joint programme resulted in a well-proven engine (known as the Mdi within Austin Rover) and excellent installation in the vehicles, starting with the naturally-aspirated engine in the Maestro and Freight Rover Sherpa vans. These launches gave the production processes time to settle in, and for the few technical 'bugs' to be sorted before release of the more critical car engines in turbocharged and naturally aspirated forms. Excellent working relationships were developed between Perkins and AGR staff which aided fast resolution of problems, even including the inevitable arguments about costs. Perkins found a few customers for the engine, the most important being Volvo Penta who adopted a marine version as part of their product range, branded and painted as a Volvo product. The production life of this engine was longer than the vehicle version, being finally phased out in the 2000s when continuation became problematic due to small volume and reliance on Austin Rover for the major cast components and machining.

Iceberg, the second JV, with the Land Rover branch of British Leyland, was the conversion of the Rover V8 engine, which began life as a Buick-designed unit of 3.5 litres with aluminium block and cylinder heads. The plan was to adapt the engine to an indirect injection diesel and add turbocharging to produce around 125bhp at 4,000rpm for use in the Range Rover. Perkins hoped to use the engine in small volumes for industrial and marine purposes, and there were hopes of selling engines to other vehicle manufacturers such as Jaguar. Alex Stephenson started as the Project Manager for this venture, handing over to Bob Dawson later in its development life. From the beginning there were problems with the strength of the cylinder block, and with the fuel injection equipment, although the engine showed some promise both on the test bed and in initial vehicle running. As with the 'Ferret' programme, there was close and constant liaison with the Land Rover engineers as the design and test experience progressed. The design process owed much to the experience gained by Perkins in other projects, and especially to the predictive computer-based processes developed through the 1970s. Compared to the original petrol engine design, the diesel had significant changes to fit the fuel injection pump and turbocharger in the vee of the block to keep the profile compact, while the timing drive became a cog-belt in place of the original chain system. There were changes to the block casting to increase bottom end strength, plus the introduction of cross bolts to anchor the main bearing caps into the block sidewalls to enable it to sustain the higher stresses associated with diesel combustion characteristics. Perkins had sufficient confidence in the engine to exhibit a prototype at the Paris Motor Show in October 1982 and to provide preliminary advertising literature.

Unfortunately the mutual confidence in the programme reduced as the cylinder block problems did not respond to development efforts, the final decision to cancel the project coming when Perkins proposed block modifications which would have increased the capital investment considerably. Since there were also problems with the fuel injection equipment, and especially the CAV 'micro-injector' needed to fit in the limited space in the new cylinder head with its Ricardo combustion chamber, Land Rover decided to go with the alternative engine, a proven in-line diesel made by Italian manufacturer VM. As an exercise the engine design was successful: the problems were probably resolvable given more time and investment, commodities which at the time did not exist. Some of the design changes and lessons learnt were incorporated in a special dry sump version of the petrol V8, which was used very successfully in the mid-engined Metro racing cars sponsored by the Royal Mail in the 1980s.

The third project was Squirrel, a venture with Chrysler Corporation to provide a 2.2-litre four-cylinder diesel version of their slant-six engine used in many cars. Providing 65bhp from the naturally aspirated engine, it was also planned to make a 75/85bhp turbocharged version. The proposal was to convert a plant in Windsor, Ontario, to manufacture the engine in large volume as an urgent response to the General Motors V8 diesel to avoid losing market share. Funding for the development phase would have been 75% Canadian Government (incentive to assist local employment) and 25% between Perkins and Chrysler, while for the production plant the Canadian Government would have provided 10% with the rest of the cost shared between the two partners. Although Chrysler started too late, their enthusiasm was considerable, with a strong team of experienced engineers working alongside Perkins and pressing for urgent action with an original target of production in 1983. The initial design work was completed and a feasible proposal put forward for an indirect injection engine, but the whole project was cancelled overnight when the GM Oldsmobile V8 engine attracted extremely adverse publicity due to its poor performance in customers' hands. All of a sudden the word 'diesel' was anathema as far as the American public was concerned, killing not only this project but others too (see below). Even the imported diesel cars from Mercedes-Benz and Volkswagen were affected adversely, and of course lessening global concern over crude oil availability was another influencing factor.

The last major project was Freezer, a project with Ford Motor Company to produce a diesel version of one of their V8s. The 429 cubic inch displacement engine was a heavy-duty gasoline unit and the proposal was to create a diesel engine, or even range of engines, which could be built largely on existing tooling and assembly facilities. The approach would have given Ford a competitive mid-range diesel product for the mid-1980s, with minimum investment and flexibility of mix between gasoline and diesel derivatives. Since the whole production operation was to be in-house at Ford, they would have retained control of the after-market too. The Perkins proposal was to make the engine a direct injection unit, using proven 'squish lip' technology. With limited time available for the project it was decided to run what was known as a 'hash' programme – using an engine with minimum changes to confirm the basic concepts and give an indication of the probable achievements for a fully-engineered version. Some vulnerability was expected in certain components but with the power of the Perkins predictive engineering techniques in support, it was expected that such mechanical issues could be resolved once basic parameters

had been confirmed.

Starting in June 1981, various aspects of the design work began in parallel, along with rig tests and analysis. The 'hash' engine programme used a Stanadyne DM4 rotary fuel injection pump and pencil injectors in a modified cylinder head, with Mahle pistons and a new cylinder head gasket from McCord, and was run in naturally aspirated and also turbocharged form. The first engine was built on 23 October and the test programme was complete by 24 December, a considerable achievement. The engines demonstrated the capability to meet if not exceed the initial power target of 145bhp at 3,600rpm with promising emissions and smoke levels. Noise was higher than the optimistic Ford target although not outside Perkins expectations. Overall the tests met the preliminary stage requirements and a second phase was started, this time funded by Perkins rather than as a joint programme. The second stage saw objectives modified in view of impending emissions legislation and a change by Ford to encompass not just passenger car application but also light commercial vehicles up to 8,500lb gross weight. Perkins envisaged extension to include a V6 engine too for smaller vehicles. However, the whole programme was cancelled. Although the real reasons are not recorded, it is believed that this too was connected with the debacle of the GM car diesel introduction. (One of the prototype Freezer engines is believed to have been donated to the Perkins gliding club, where it powered the launching winch for some time.)

'Product maintenance' requirements

While all this new engine work was proceeding, there was also activity on the existing engine types. A small team made improvements to the D3.152, D4.203 and 4.318 engines, updating their combustion and injection systems to improve overall performance and especially emission levels, creating the 3.1522, 4.2032 and 4.3182 derivatives. Part of the team's efforts was directed at a long overdue detail design appraisal to reduce fluid leaks in response to customer demands for a cleaner product.

On the 6.354 team, work was carried out to develop an engine to be compliant with USA emissions legislation while on the V8 team the development of marine versions was also aimed at the North American market. The 4.236 team was also busy with the development of a vehicle turbocharged version, in particular to meet a requirement for Renault Truck. The available Engineering personnel and facilities were stretched in all directions, with support to overseas operations also a factor.

The purchase of the Rolls-Royce plant at Shrewsbury brought additional pressure upon the Engineering staff of both plants as the 'getting to know you' process began, with considerable discussion around common requirements and standards. Since the products were different in many ways some of the engineering procedures remained separated, although switching of staff between the two plants brought useful cross-fertilisation and the opportunity to give individuals new challenges. The same thing applied to a lesser degree with the Gardner plant in Manchester. In both the new acquisitions there was close evaluation of their products, which were reckoned to be conservatively rated by the Peterborough management, to see what opportunities there were to stretch them to higher powers or additional applications. The traditional Perkins approach regarding cost control was also applied to the two larger product ranges, although the much lower production volumes did not provide the same opportunities for major cost savings.

In the mid-80s the equipment and technology being explored at that time eventually developed into the 'common rail' injection system now used on many modern diesels. Perkins research engineers were also in the forefront of investigation into the potential of digital electronic engine control systems: an Electronics Control Systems team was set up under John Kaliski who was recruited from CAV Limited.

Generating 'Third party' business

There were other complications during this period for the overall Engineering operations. There had been a number of early retirements in 1980, including some senior management. While this gave an opportunity for younger replacements to be grown into the vacated positions, it had to be done at a time of heavy workload and therefore added stress. There were further redundancies, both voluntary and forced, later in the early 80s as the Division felt the same pressures as the rest of the Group in reducing headcount. This inevitably led to the removal of the poorer performers, together with a hard look at every aspect of the normal operations to eliminate, combine or streamline wherever possible. In view of the considerable manpower reduction achieved, it was not surprising that the settling-down period was traumatic, but the continued pace of work and achievement were a tribute to the professionalism of the remaining workforce.

There was also considerable pressure from the Managing Director, John Devaney, to utilise the available talents and facilities of the Engineering personnel to the full, or instead be forced into a greater number of enforced redundancies. To meet this challenge a new department was created to handle 'Third Party' business outside the normal relationships with OEM customers, where the expertise of many specialist engineers could generate much-needed additional revenue, in direct competition with established independent research companies such as Ricardo and AVL. The creation of the new 'branch' company resulted in contracts being undertaken with many new customers, even including direct competitors! Confidentiality was ensured by divorcing this sensitive work from the other workload. (For personnel already experienced in keeping a careful dividing line between MF and their competitors in the agricultural and industrial fields, this was not too hard a task.) Over the next years the reputation and professionalism of Perkins Technology Limited grew, with a considerable number of lucrative contracts being worked on where the expertise of the Peterborough engineers supplemented that of the third parties.

Liaison roles

Little has been written about the role of the Applications Engineering Department which had always been a major interface between Engineering, Sales and the major customers. After a period in the 1970s when there had been a split of responsibilities for the UK and Group sales areas, the applications engineers were once again brought together, leaving only small specialist functions in the French, German, Italian and American regions. For the major OEM customers such as MF, JCB and the UK truck manufacturers, individual engineers performed a specialist service looking after all their needs. Other engineers took responsibility for the different sectors such as industrial and marine where common expertise could support a number of smaller equipment manufacturers. The role for smaller businesses was often more exacting, since the Perkins engineer would carry out machine appraisals on behalf of the customer while the larger concerns would employ their own engineers in liaison with the engine men. Where customers were international the Perkins personnel often made extended overseas trips to carry out work.

From the early 80s a move was made to hand responsibility for some of the everyday processes (such as design change, licensee contact and liaison with production and other departments) to small 'Product Support' teams. These were formed under three experienced engineers – Barrie Allen (small engines), Neil Murray (medium) and Aubrey Southgate (large) – who took over much of the essential but routine workload, allowing Project Managers to concentrate on their main responsibilities. In addition it was at last recognised that the average Perkins engine was far from acceptable in terms of leaks: new materials and techniques were pursued to improve a growing concern with customers.

At the close of the 80s a number of things were becoming clearer.

The impending legislation on emissions, smoke and noise was forcing the pace of change, so that new generations of engines would need to be developed more quickly. In addition the projected upgrading of legislative levels would force more frequent model changes. It was fortunate that Perkins Technology had placed itself in an advantageous position with the development of the new computer-based techniques allowing the creation of an engine 'on paper' ahead of cutting metal.

1990s

A number of new products appeared on the design sections in the 1990s as the first attack on the new legislative levels began. The replacement for the 1000 Series, under Project Darwin, began its path through the Engineering areas, with considerable resource commitment. Eventually Roger Warren was moved into the role of Project Director, coordinating the efforts of all sectors of the Company and ensuring the 'simultaneous engineering' remained on path to meet challenging targets for delivery of prototype engines to customers. Although the engines were visually not too different from their immediate precursors (as the eventual designation as 'New 1000 Series' suggests), the technology strides to improve emissions, reduce noise and control costs challenged the engineers on every side. The use of different materials, notably the introduction of plastics for components such as water outlet connections and top covers, needed a fresh approach to purchasing and technical liaison with a new group of suppliers.

The birth of the 900 Series, a linear descendant of the original P3, was an interesting process as the tried and proven parts were amalgamated with new technology to provide an engine able to meet the Stage 1 off-highway legislative levels needed for 1999. Incorporation of the 'Fastram' combustion system with latest injection pump and five-hole injectors gave the gaseous emission levels needed, along with low smoke and a reduction in noise level due to the more retarded injection timing inherent with the system. With a new cylinder head incorporating helical ports and changes providing single-sided servicing, considerable benefits were incorporated in a base engine design already over 40 years old. With a turbocharged version the engine gave powers up to 48kW (64bhp).

The other new engine types, 700 Series and 100 Series, were two entirely fresh designs to Perkins, with close liaison with the Japanese partners as the engines were proven for Peterborough production. The Iseki design which was evolved into the 700 Series provided two engines from the basic scantlings: the 2.6-litre indirect injection version provided a low noise, low emission engine for forklift truck and similar applications, while the 3.0-litre direct injection version provided higher power and better torque characteristics for other agricultural and industrial machinery. The 100 Series, initially imported from ISM before completion of Factory 4 to produce it, was a range of 2-, 3- and 4-cylinder engines ranging form the 102-05 at only 0.451 litre to the 104-22 at 2.2 litres. Providing outputs between 8.2 and 37kW at speeds up to 3,600rpm, these indirect injection engines provided clean, quiet and cost-effective power for a wide variety of equipment. Both the 100 and 700 series engines used Zexel in-line fuel injection pumps and were fully adaptable to any application.

It is possibly worth a digression to cover the technicalities of the new emission regulations to understand the challenges facing Perkins engineers. There are two sets of regulations for the EU and the USA; although slightly different the basic demands of each set are the same – a gradually tightening level of emissions over a period from 1996 through to 2015. Since the detail requirements and limits change depending upon engine power, I will limit the tabulation of the regulations to a sample size of engine – namely powers between 75 to 130kW (c. 100 to 175bhp).

All figures given below are expressed in grams per kilowatt hour (gm/kW/hr)

Model	Year	Combined NOx/HC	Oxides of Nitrogen	Hydro- carbons	Carbon monoxide	Particulates
USA						
Tier 1	1997	9.2	-	-	-	-
Tier 2	2003	6.6	-	-	5.0	0.3
Tier 3	2007	4.0	-	-	5.0	0.3
Tier 4A	2012	-	3.4	0.19	5.0	0.02
Tier 4B	2015	-	0.4	0.19	5.0	0.02
Europe						
Stage 1	1999	-	9.2	1.3	5.0	0.7
Stage 2	2003	1.0	6.0	1.0	5.0	0.3
Stage 3A	2007	4.0	-	-	5.0	0.3
Stage 3B	2012	-	3.3	0.19	5.0	0.025
Stage 4	2014	-	0.4	0.19	3.5	0.025

With the wealth of experience and research tools available, Perkins' engineers were able to achieve excellent results without resorting to full electronic fuel pump control in the early stages of legislative demands.

The development of the engines needed for 2003 and beyond, however, were found to be more demanding, with extra sophistication, electronics and – inevitably – higher costs becoming mandatory. It is not in the remit of this chapter to cover the development of the 1100 Series engines as replacements for the 1000 and 900 Series, or the changes needed for the 100 series in becoming the 400 Series, and the 700 Series in becoming the 800 Series. Suffice it to say that the technical expertise available has proved the equal of the very searching standards required.

The decision for Perkins to drop all programmes for on-highway vehicles and concentrate on the off- highway markets may seem a sad situation for a company which started life concentrating on converting road transport to diesel. It is a fact of modern life that pure economics must overcome desire and emotion – the remaining market for vehicle engines was too small to justify the expense of continuing on two fronts, so the difficult decision was inevitable. With increasing attention being paid to some industrial sectors, especially the generating set market and the Caterpillar business, the workload overall did not reduce but could become more concentrated.

Chapter 25: Change, Change & More Change (the 1990s)

The beginning of 1991 was dominated within Perkins by the impending Total Quality training programme. The process envisaged around 11,000 total hours of training by internal teams, with 12 personnel at a time taken through the course of presentations and group discussions. After some initial problems in start-up, the enthusiasm of all concerned and the quality of the training material proved very successful, making TQ real to all.

While TQ proceeded, concern grew as the first Gulf War began to involve British forces, including Shrewsbury-built engines in the Challenger I tanks and Warrior armoured vehicles. A team of three PESL engineers was deployed into the Gulf extremely successfully. After assisting REME to set up workshops to handle the CV8 550 TCA engines from the Warrior only 16 of the 47 engines overhauled had to be returned to Shrewsbury – whereas without the team all would have been shipped. Support to the V12s in Challengers included updating to suit desert conditions, by modifications to air filtration and air conditioning. At the end of the year an OBE was awarded to Peter Baker in recognition of the support given by Perkins during the hostilities.

In June the new factory extensions at Shrewsbury were opened by Victor Rice, comprising 75,000 sq ft of workshops and 22,000 sq ft of offices. The closure of the old factory would cut ties with Sentinel, the most prolific producer of steam wagons, dating from 1915 up to its purchase by Rolls-Royce in 1956. The new facility would build all the Shrewsbury range, including the Condor CV12 which had been picked as the power unit for the Challenger II tanks (scheduled as replacements for the ageing Chieftain). The launch of the V8 3000 Series engine in spark ignition form was announced, designed to run on methane gas from landfill sites and for co-generation ('total heat') projects where exceptional life on round-the-clock operation was expected.

In the same month the death of Sir Monty Prichard was announced at the age of 75; his influence and drive had been of immense importance in the 50s and 60s, with the continued worldwide success of the Perkins products serving as his legacy. A few months later Michael Bird died after a long illness: he had been Chairman of Varity Holdings, a member of the Varity Board and remembered in Peterborough for his caretaking role during 1988/9.

During August PESL announced that they were donating six engines to the Sir Henry Royce Memorial Foundation at Paulerspury, Northamptonshire, along with 20,000 photographic negatives. The engines

included prototypes of the CV12 tank power unit, the CV8 and LDV8, plus an early C65FL six-cylinder and D range 600G. The last unit was a 'Meteor' V12 petrol engine, a tank engine based on the Merlin. In Peterborough, plans were announced to move the whole Sports Association to the newly-purchased Alma Road sports ground vacated by Baker Perkins, with planning permission being sought to enable the move after January 1992. (Eventually the whole proposal foundered and the Club facilities remained at Eastfield.)

While the standard Phaser and Eagle engines were receiving more press from Motor Transport and Commercial Motor magazines, a new project, code-named 'Policeman', was launched to produce a new version of Phaser to meet US Federal and Californian emissions regulations. Under Project Leader Michel Eschalier, the project team drew upon simultaneous engineering processes to develop the engine, which incorporated the new 'Fastram' combustion system. Varity Corporation shifted their headquarters from Toronto to Buffalo in New York State during 1991, ceasing to be a Canadian Corporation as Victor Rice looked to diversify away from farm machinery.

The end of the year showed a very poor picture. Total production was only 135,975 engines, with virtually every type showing substantial reductions on the previous year. CKD volume was also much reduced at only 51,449 kits. Only the increased despatches of 100 Series by Compact Engines Division lightened the gloomy picture.

1992

In early 1992 a £1 billion order for engines for industrial and construction equipment from Caterpillar brought attention from the press, TV and radio. The order covered a ten-year period and was for 1000 Series products to support Caterpillar's requirements worldwide. The deal included branding the engines to Caterpillar specifications.

The progress of the TQ training programme continued to generate interest and comment. With over 200 active projects across the sites, the diverse topics included reduction of paperwork, reorganisation of working layouts in the Shrewsbury factory, weight reduction of Gardner engines and improved publicity for the Perkins 'Power Collection' clothing.

A strange event was noticed in Peterborough in the small hours of 17 February when the city was struck by an earthquake measured at 3.3 on the Richter scale. Lasting for just under a minute, the tremor woke residents with a sound like an underground train passing below the city, apparently centred deep under the Ferry Meadows Country Park. Little damage was reported but it was a talking point for a few days.

The 60th Anniversary of the founding of Perkins was celebrated in September with Open Days at the main sites; families watched demonstrations of customer equipment, examined many examples of Perkins-powered machinery and visited the modernised production areas, while the Echo produced an article recording the highlights of those 60 years.

During the year special tributes were paid to the reliability of the modern engines. A Montego hire car clocked up 258,000 miles: the Prima engine was returned to Peterborough for close examination and the operator given a new replacement. On the Channel Tunnel site at Crediton, Kent, eight Perkins-powered F.G. Wilson generating sets ran a total of 120,000 hours, with two engines each completing over 22,000 hours with only regular maintenance. The engines had provided all non-mains electrical power for offices, stores, canteen and other services since 1989.

At the Earls Court International Boat Show in December, Perkins

The acquisition of the Dorman factory at Stafford increased the power range of the Perkins products significantly, up to the V16 version of the 4000 series engine shown here

announced a new generation of marine engines, produced in collaboration with Sabre Marine of Ferndown, Dorset. The first offering was the Perkins Sabre M225Ti, based on a 1000 series 6-cylinder turbocharged core unit with marinising engineered by Sabre. Over 60 of the engines were ordered during the Show.

At the close of the year there were signs of a slight improvement as the total Peterborough volume increased to 141,827 engines, plus 14,951 units of the ISM 100 Series. The V8 series engines were phased out during the year, along with the 4.108, although a batch of the latter was built as CKD by distributors Talbot Diesel to meet an MoD requirement for auxiliary power units to fit in tank air-conditioning packs. Renewed attempts to phase out the 6.3544 and 4.236 families were thwarted by customer demands to retain the older, cheaper, engines where tighter legislative levels were not yet required.

1993

At the start of 1993 Perkins received a local honour by being named 'Mid-Anglia Business of the Year' in a competition organised by Business Week, beating over 50 other local companies judged on quality of management, profitability, innovation and ability to win new orders. Tony Gilroy received the award at a ceremony in Cambridge. A few weeks later Perkins received BS5750 quality accreditation from Lloyd's Registry QA, a key milestone in the Total Quality process for the PEPL, PESL and PTech businesses.

During March, Caterpillar launched their new 'Olympian' range of generator sets, using the 1000 series engines: these were built for Caterpillar by F.G. Wilson in Belfast, fast becoming a world leader in generator sets and an increasingly important customer for Peterborough. Cat dealers ordered 150 units during the launch in Malaga. At the SIMA agricultural exposition held later in the month, Perkins announced the 'Dual Zone Torque' version of the 1000 Series, with MF the first customer in a new tractor model. There was another important launch in April, when Perkins released the 'Peregrine' vehicle engine: this was the Perkins-branded version of the Navistar 6-cylinder engine, available in 6.7, 7.6 and 8.7 litre versions. Dennis Eagle adopted the engine for their 'Elite' municipal vehicles.

During the early part of the year there were a series of new appointments: Colin Ingram took the position of Managing Director of Perkins Technology, with Tony Downes moving to a new position covering the increasingly important environmental issues. Mike Hawkins became PEPL's Technical Manager and Simon Roberts the Manufacturing Engineering Manager for PEPL, reporting to Richard Allen. New premises were opened for the Perkins Aftermarket business: the purpose-built Distribution Centre at Irlam replaced the old facility at Urmston, Manchester, shared with MF. The new self-contained plant was designed to handle all parts for Perkins engines with quick response intended to increase customer satisfaction by filling and despatching orders faster. Sophisticated computer links and 24-hour manning of a 'help desk' were integral parts of the improved operations.

A heritage story close to home came to light when Paul Cousins of the Service Garage unveiled his restored Seddon 5L truck. This lorry, powered by a P6, had been owned by F. Perkins Limited in 1947 and had been discovered in a very dilapidated state in a Bedfordshire farm-

The 700 Series engine developed in conjuction with Iseki is seen here in three-litre form

The company-wide activities to improve quality in every possible manner were celebrated each year with exhibitions covering a multitude of projects across all sites

yard. The major restoration, back to full Perkins livery of the time, had been lovingly undertaken by Paul, his family and friends, including John Guy, who had worked on the truck while it was in the Perkins fleet.

Late in the year the progress in Total Quality and teamwork was celebrated with an exhibition at Eastfield and a dinner at the Moat House Hotel in Peterborough, where celebrated mountaineer Chris Bonington addressed the assembled guests. He had a recent connection with Perkins, as he had sailed to Greenland (to conquer the Cathedral Peak) aboard Robin Knox-Johnston's yacht Suhaili, fitted with a Prima M50 auxiliary engine. A similar event was also staged at Shrewsbury.

Another small improvement in production was recorded at the end of the year, with the total volume of 144,324 engines supplemented by 13,959 100 Series and 2,375 of the new Peregrine/1300 Series products. The venerable P4 engine was nearing the end of a long production run in its final guise of 4.2032, while the combined total of 1000 Series/Phaser engines passed the combined totals for 4.236 and 6.3544.

1994

Early 1994 brought special recognition and a visit by Prime Minister John Major when he presented the ISO 9000 quality award to the Managing Directors of all five Perkins businesses. He toured the factory with local MP Brian Mawhinney, meeting production line workers and staff.

In February Perkins gained the much-coveted US Certification for the Phaser 180Ti engine. Heralded as possibly the most technically advanced European engine, the engine soon gained its first sales success with Chrysler in Mexico for their 8-tonne PD600 truck. Perkins now set its sights on achieving compliance with the impending European 1996 emission regulations.

In May Perkins signed another ten-year, $1 billion deal, this time with Belfast's F.G. Wilson, the fastest-growing generator set manufacturer in the world. From a start in 1986, their growth had been astonishing, increasing four-fold in the previous four years. Managing Director Tom Wilson said: 'Perkins offers us a complete range of engines dedicated to our sector, backed by excellent levels of product development and engineering support. We have strong growth and need strongly-established partners to sustain our plans. Perkins is recognised for its quality and reliability; it is to our benefit that many customers specify Perkins.'

Further deals followed, first for engines worth £15 million to power five new machine models for German manufacturer Hanomag, and secondly with Tianjin Engine Works in recording the first-ever agreement with a Chinese enterprise (see also Chapter 20). The Echo pictured the first activity of this agreement – the despatch of a large packing case containing the technical documentation. With 1000 Series production in China projected to reach 170,000 engines a year, Tony Gilroy heralded the deal as 'a very important step in developing our presence in China'.

The middle of 1994 turned out to be an exceptionally important period. Victor Rice joined Tony Gilroy in signing an alliance with Japanese engine manufacturer Iseki. The agreement was to develop a new range of low emission diesels to be built in Peterborough. To be designated 700 Series, the 4-cylinder, 3-litre engines would provide power in the range of 50 to 75bhp, and would be available from 1995, two years ahead of the next level of impending legislation. The initial $30 million investment would cover the manufacturing base for engines aimed at the light off-highway markets – such as forklift trucks, light tractors and compressors. Iseki would also become the distributor for Perkins products in Japan.

Dorman Diesels join the Perkins Group

That was not the end of major events in June, however! An investigation under the code name 'Bouncer' led to the acquisition of Dorman Diesels Limited of Stafford. Tony Gilroy was enthusiastic about joining together two of the foremost names in the British engine industry. His announcement stated: 'Customers of both companies will benefit from a wider product range and Perkins' commitment to Total Quality, customer satisfaction and continuous improvement.' Dorman was a company with a history stretching back to 1870 and had started producing diesel engines in the 1930s, even ahead of Perkins. Although there had been some products of similar size and power to the Perkins range, it was in rather larger engines that their reputation had been established. In 1966 Dorman had acquired the Ruston Group and their site at Lincoln. Although once a part of the GEC Group, Dorman had become part of the Broadcrown Group and was at the forefront of natural gas engine technology and a leading supplier of high-horsepower engines.

Perkins had identified power generation and gas engines as key growth areas, making Dorman a perfect complement to their existing range of products. It was announced that Brian Willmott, Managing Director of PESL at Shrewsbury, would also assume responsibility for the Dorman plants in Stafford and Lincoln. A few weeks later the 'Minnox' range of Stafford engines gained The Queen's Award for Environmental Achievement, following the achievement of ultra low

levels of nitrogen oxides by the use of catalyst technology.

Varity cut the long-standing ties to Massey Ferguson when the whole farm machinery business was sold to the American AGCO Corporation, who would continue to use the name for the line of tractors and continue the connection with Perkins in buying engines to power them.

Recruitment of 66 new employees at Peterborough in October, adding to the 50 recruits earlier in the year, was an expression of the confidence stemming from the improved level of business. Further confidence was expressed in the same month when the creation of a new joint venture with ISM was announced. The new company, named Perkins Shibaura Engines Limited, would manufacture new low-emission engines in Peterborough in the 5 to 50bhp range, following on from marketing of the ISM products as the 100 Series in the previous seven years.

In December Perkins announced the new 900 Series 3-cylinder engine, a further and final derivative of the original P3 engine. This variant had been developed quickly through the application of 'simultaneous engineering' techniques by Perkins Technology and offered reduced emissions and noise levels through the latest combustion technology and more sophisticated fuel injection equipment. The new model was expected to achieve volumes of 25,000 engines a year at Peterborough alone, with the first users to include Linde for their latest forklift trucks.

Peterborough production for 1994 was 173,270 engines, a substantial increase on the previous year, with 1000 Series volumes moving ahead strongly, although the 500 Series/Prima had begun to drop. The 4.236 family, however, showed a resurgence of sales to over 113,000. The 100 Series production increased slightly but total CKD despatches dropped to only 33,760 kits, the lowest for over 25 years.

The factory purchased from Dorman Diesels occupies a prime site close to the centre of Stafford and provided an important addition to the Perkins production capability

The venture with Sabre Marine to produce marine version of the latest model Perkins engines successfully launched a number of products including this Compact version

The Impact of Total Quality

It is perhaps worth pausing in the chronology to consider the overall impact of the most intensive training process ever undertaken by Perkins, the reasoning and the resulting changes.

During the 60s and 70s Perkins were driven by the need to produce more and more engines for a seemingly insatiable market. With production as the driver, insufficient attention was paid to quality problems, to the frustration of those wishing to raise standards. When the 80s brought crisis after crisis and the need to retrench and fight for survival, the driving force became cost-saving and contraction to minimum facilities and staffing level. Increased attention to quality issues was essential as customers started to become more particular and as Japanese practices became known, although not really understood, in British industry.

A number of initiatives were started to drive improvements, usually involving outside consultants, but these, almost without exception, failed to reach fruition. Attempts to achieve 'just in time' material handling were stymied by suppliers failing to deliver parts either in time or to the right quality, whilst other attempts to introduce value analysis and profit improvement disciplines failed to gain adequate support.

The arrival of Tony Gilroy and his intent to improve quality within the Perkins operations marked a major change in attitudes and motivation, although it took some time to show. After a gentle introduction through the 'cost of quality' awareness exercise the move towards Total Quality training, and especially the involvement of every employ-

ee, was a turning point. It was perhaps fortuitous that the 'them and us' attitudes of shop-floor workers towards management and supervision, exacerbated by trades union demarcations, had been diluted by the years of industry shrinkage under the Thatcher regime. Faced with the opportunity to become involved in changing operating conditions and practices within their own areas, many workers grasped the chance and showed themselves capable of innovative thinking and persuasive arguing. It is not the purpose of this history to chart any of the many projects that were proposed and run to fruition; after gaining many detail improvements for their own working conditions, the workers displayed teamworking of the highest degree in tackling major issues which saved costs and improved quality in many unexpected ways.

Nor was this restricted to shop floor areas: many projects were actioned in offices and within management areas, often tackling fundamental issues. There were teams that took members from diverse departments, producing strong relationships and blending talents to good effect. Ideas across the sites looked at, for instance, savings in paperwork, re-use and refurbishment of tooling, whole procedures affecting many departments across the company, the processes needed to take on board new recruits and even to ease the retirement process for retiring employees.

The level of encouragement generated by the company of course helped to foster the feeling of achievement and worth experienced by all team members, proving that there is nothing like empowerment and reward, plus an element of competition, to ensure motivation. The introduction of quarterly award ceremonies and the yearly exhibi-

The importance of the Shrewsbury products to the British Army during the Desert Storm operations cannot be overestimated. Here Warrior vehicles are seen operating in typical desert conditions

tions held at all sites, together with the wider publicity given to the TQ process countrywide – with Perkins sponsoring national competitions and awards – all helped to demonstrate that here was an enterprise thinking on its feet, involving, teaching and rewarding employees. Even the most cynical had to applaud an initiative that generated visible success and pride.

For any past employee walking round the Eastfield factory a couple of years after the TQ process began, the change in its appearance was startling and always generated comments. The whole place was clean and tidy, with pristine paint and floors; engines in progress were handled carefully and stored neatly. The atmosphere was clean, the lighting improved and everywhere there were neat charts and information about targets and achievements. Above all the attitudes and enthusiasm of the people were clear to see as they went about their tasks.

1995

The beginning of 1995 brought a further reorganisation as two new Business Units were created: Perkins International Limited with Allan Arnott as MD was formed to handle engine supply, sales and distribution worldwide, while Perkins Parts Limited under Chris Dunn would look after marketing and distribution of the aftermarket parts business and direct parts sales to OEMs. Sales of engines from the UK to major OEM customers would remain with the individual product Business Units.

The introduction of the Margin Enhancement programme at Peterborough generated more than 3,000 ideas in its first six months, with savings of over £125,000 in each of the last two quarters of 1994. Projected savings of over £1 million had been identified for implementation in the New Year.

A change of Managing Director was announced in April as Tony Gilroy moved to Varity headquarters in Buffalo. M.J. Baunton was appointed to succeed him, and gave a first interview to the Echo in which he outlined his work philosophy and beliefs. Mike Baunton came from a mechanical engineering background, and had worked in turn for Automotive Products, Mars Confectionery, Quinton Hazell

and Tenneco in Europe, Australia and the USA. He affirmed his view that the workforce was the most important asset of the company, and his enthusiastic support for the TQ programme as the way forward. 'The real strength of TQ is the ability to harness individual talents in a win-win combination to benefit the employee by increasing job satisfaction while benefiting the organisation through continuous improvement,' he said. He noted the recent joint ventures with Iseki and ISM as part of a major investment programme but injected an element of caution with regard to the market. Times were tough, with suppliers looking for better pricing and customers expecting more – the need to 'delight' rather than merely 'satisfy' had to be the way forward.

Mike Baunton was soon closely involved in new business opportunities as he joined a 100-strong mission to the Beijing International Construction Exhibition and Seminar in May. The UK team also included Michael Heseltine MP and Sir Anthony Bamford. The exhibition was Perkins' first major presence in China, giving Mike an opportunity to meet the Tianjin Engine Works partners as well as Chinese government and industry leaders.

The Varity Global Share Plan was announced in August, giving every employee the opportunity to hold a stake in their own company and benefit from Varity's worldwide growth and expansion, with incentives also in the form of bonus shares. Varity announced record income for the second quarter, ended 31 July. At $32.7 million this was 56% up on the previous year as sales in the same period rose to $572 million. Victor Rice commented upon the excellent results, driven by strong Perkins sales and Kelsey Hayes' growing anti-lock braking business.

Another new face appeared in Perkins as Brian Amey took the position of MD of Perkins Engines (Peterborough) Limited, vacated when Richard Allen moved to a post with Varity in Buffalo. Brian had held positions in Ford, British Leyland and Chrysler before joining the Weir Group and BSG International. Tony Downes became Group Director, Environmental Engineering, a change demonstrating Perkins' commitment to its environmental strategy and the growing importance of such issues on the world stage. This was followed in November by publication of a new Environmental Policy, laying down a series of commitments to environmental issues to be followed by all employees, and encouraged with suppliers, customers and the community.

The venture with ISM was confirmed with the formation in September of Perkins Shibaura Engines Ltd, occupying a part of Factory 4 at the rear of the Peterborough site. The new $19 million facility was scheduled to begin production of 100 series engines in 1996, with volumes expected to reach 50,000 units a year by 2000. The products were being developed to meet all projected emissions legislation and would ensure the continuing production of 100 Series, already in use by some 300 manufacturers of small mobile equipment worldwide.

In parallel with the internal TQ programme, Perkins supported local schools through the creation of Perkins Teamwork Awards, supported by English Nature and the Cambridgeshire County Council. A similar scheme was instituted in Shrewsbury with local support.

In November a contract was announced with Simpson and Co. Ltd in India to build up to 10,000 4-cylinder 1000 Series engines a year for use in local production by Escort Ltd (JCB machines), Hindustan Motors (Fermec backhoe loaders) and TAFE (MF tractors).

At the end of 1995 production from Peterborough rose to 187,463 engines, with the 1000 Series accounting for almost 84,500. Although the 4.236 family remained strong, 6.3544 volumes were dropping and the phase-out of Prima by Austin Rover meant that fewer than 6,000 were built to satisfy industrial and marine customers. Some weeks later, Victor Rice confirmed that Varity Perkins had achieved the magic $1 billion sales for the first time, with a target of $2 billion by 2000.

1996

The London Boat Show was the venue for the unveiling of the latest Perkins Sabre engine, the M300Ti, which was rated at 300bhp at 2,500rpm. This was the eighth model produced by the partnership in three years, a highly successful arrangement taking basic engines from Peterborough and finishing them to a series of marine options at Sabre: although most versions were for propulsion, there were also on-board generator sets. A novel yacht race format reaching the final planning stages was also to feature Perkins products: the Global World Challenge would use 14 identical steel-hulled yachts, 67 feet long. Each would be fitted with a Perkins Sabre M135 main engine plus a 28bhp 3-cylinder 103.10 as auxiliary to power the electrics and fresh water distillation plant. Engine performance would be monitored through the same satellite links used to track the progress of the yachts, which would feature state-of-the-art global positioning and communications equipment. Each yacht would have a professional skipper but a crew of volunteers paying to take part in one or more of the race legs around the world.

Another ten-year agreement for engine supply was signed, this time with Fermec, who had taken over the industrial tractor and machine business previously owned by MF, and whose MD happened to be an ex-Perkins manager, Richard Robson. The deal was for 1000 Series 4-

The launch of the innovative JCB 'Fastrac' agricultural tractor, powered by various versions of the six-cylinder Perkins 1000 Series engine, brought a new versatility to the farm tractor, being capable of undertaking traditional tasks while providing fast road speeds for trailer operations

The major refurbishment of Factory 2 resulted in a modern assembly hall with state-of-the art automation. This picture shows a small part of the new assembly track, emphasising the clean and light operating conditions

cylinder engines and was hailed by Mike Baunton as another case of 'winning with winners'.

The first Peterborough-built 100 Series engine went on test on 1 February, in the new test shop in Bay 27 of Factory 4. The test area was acoustically treated to ensure comfort for the operators, and the whole plant was designed to be environmentally friendly, including quiet electrical power tools rather than the old pneumatic guns.

On 26 February Victor Rice and members of the Varity head office team attended a conference with Peterborough senior management to review the business plans and targets for 1996. The day was highly successful in terms of team building and in furthering understanding of the management strategies. In the course of his closing speech, Victor stated that there was no intention within Varity to divest the Group of the Perkins companies: his audience would have cause to recall his words within two years!

In March all the Varity Group companies were renamed as part of a move to enhance business recognition: 'VarityPerkins' became the new Group name, although the individual companies were to retain their existing names and identities, such as Perkins Engines (Peterborough) Limited, and all product identification would remain as before, along with show stands, literature etc. After commenting on the new identification, Victor Rice noted that the Varity commitment was to achieve worldwide sales of $10 billion by 2005, with 40% coming from Asia. He claimed the power of the Varity 'umbrella' was needed for member companies to achieve that vision.

Later in the spring, Stafford launched the new Perkins 4000 Series engines, a range of diesel and gas engines featuring the latest technology. The diesel versions were turbocharged and charge-cooled, using four valves per cylinder and unit injectors. The use of electronic governing completed a package giving more complete combustion and high output, coupled with low emissions and excellent fuel economy. The gas versions used Minnox ultra low emission technology, and a closed loop management system: the engines gave low emissions of nitrogen oxides and operated at very precise air–fuel ratios. With in-line 6- and 8-cylinder, plus V12 and V16 versions, there were a total of 15 diesel and 12 gas models with ratings up to 1879kW.

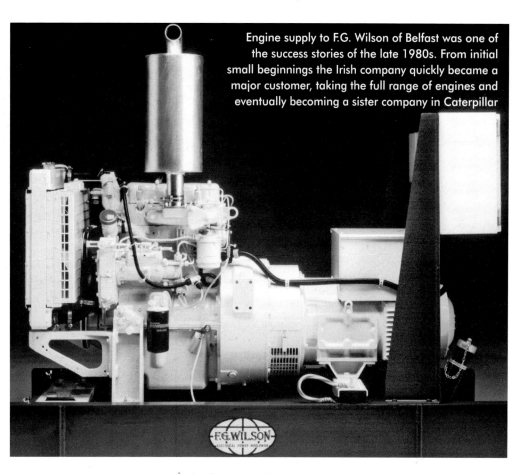

Engine supply to F.G. Wilson of Belfast was one of the success stories of the late 1980s. From initial small beginnings the Irish company quickly became a major customer, taking the full range of engines and eventually becoming a sister company in Caterpillar

Stafford announced a £1.2 million contract with Japanese CHP packager Shinko Engineering Company for twenty of the new engines, these being repeat orders after three years of sales. Less satisfactory was the announcement that the Lincoln site would be closed, with its machining activities transferred to Stafford, and the parts business moved to Manchester by the end of the year. Assistance was given to those made redundant to find new employment.

The new 700 series engines were announced in Munich during March. The presentations were attended by 75 journalists from 11 countries, the format allowing detailed question and answer sessions. The two models were a 3-litre with direct injection intended for general agricultural and industrial use, and a 2.6-litre indirect injection version aimed specifically at material handling equipment. Perkins expected to sell up to 50,000 units a year in a sector expected to grow to around 160,000 engines annually by 2000.

In April the activities of the Margin Enhancement and Cost Reduction Teams were reported to have saved £2.6 million, all adding to an 'Economic Value Added' parameter introduced to track improvements. 'Teardown' exercises were being mounted on each engine type to allow engineers from around the company to contribute ideas for improvements and savings.

LucasVarity

On 31 May the Boards of Varity Corporation and Lucas Industries plc agreed on a merger into a new UK holding company, subject to Government approval. The new enterprise would be called LucasVarity plc, with Victor Rice as Chief Executive officer and Sir Brian Pearse, the then Lucas Chairman, as non-executive Chairman of the Board. The new Company would have sales of around £6.7 billion with a share capital of £3.2 billion ($4.9 billion). LucasVarity would be headquartered in England with the American HQ at Buffalo. It was envisaged that VarityPerkins and Lucas Diesel Systems would continue to be managed separately but with increased opportunity for operating synergies. All constituent companies were seen as leaders in their respective fields, covering brakes, anti-lock braking systems, aerospace and diesel engines. The pace of change was increasing and employees struggled to understand the full implications of the new situation. The proposed merger was given approval by the European Commission in August, followed by UK High Court approval and full shareholder approval on both sides, allowing the arrangements to proceed. The new company became one of the top ten automotive component suppliers in the world.

Further sales successes were announced during the summer, with the Chinese launch of the Phaser in Chang Jing coaches and Luizhou trucks an indication of growing business in China. In the UK a $150 million deal with J.I. Case to supply 1000 series and 900 Series engines for their UK-built tractors was announced, the engines to be fitted from 1997. In Stafford the company proudly pointed to a 250% increase in sales in the past two years, plus major investments for a new production test facility, as well as TQ training for all employees.

In support of the VP Environmental Policy, TQ Team 'War on Waste' targeted factory scrap of all kinds, aiming to maximise recycling and minimise material consigned to landfill. Another TQ team – 'Burnout', formed from the medical departments – sought to publicise and combat stress in the workplace. Later in the autumn an environmental conference at Eastfield was attended by local government representatives from Peterborough and Cambridgeshire: the central theme was individual and collective responsibility for the environment in order to safeguard the future for the generations to come.

As the BT 'Global Challenge' yacht race neared its start, skipper Boris Webber from the Courtaulds boat visited Eastfield and discussed the thinking behind the 10-month, 30,000-mile voyage. Each novice

The transfer of the spare parts operation from the facility shared with MF at Urmston to the purpose-built Distribution Centre in Irlam transformed the Perkins Aftermarket business. Round the clock operation and computer systems helped fill customer needs

crew member was paying £18,000 for the privilege of facing the arduous and uncomfortable conditions; most had never sailed before but had quickly become a team during the shake-down trials. Key members of each crew had attended courses at the Perkins Training Centre to learn about the M130C and 103-10 engines on which their lives might depend. Perkins was committed to this and other events, reinforcing the name and reputation of the Perkins Sabre products throughout the sailing world.

LucasVarity confirmed the names of key personnel during October. CEO Victor Rice named Tony Gilroy as President, Transition Operations, with Mike Baunton as Divisional MD, Diesel Engines and Dominique Chauvin as Divisional MD, Diesel Systems. It was announced that LV would be a quoted company on the London Stock Market in the FTSE 100 index.

As one new enterprise took shape, another initiative was discontinued: the DDC/Perkins collaboration of the past eight years would finish at the end of December, with VarityPerkins re-establishing a more direct distribution structure for North American sales and service. Better control of the business was expected to double sales by 2000. There would be seven American and three Canadian 'master distributors' in the new network arrangement, starting on 31 December – with appointment of 2,000 parts and service outlets to follow, covering every state and province.

On 3 October, local MP Dr Brian Mawhinney formally opened the new premises of Perkins Shibaura Engines Limited in Factory 4: he also presented the new company with their 'Investors in People' award. The total employment was 120 personnel with a projected output to reach 50,000 engines a year, replacing the previous sales of Japanese-built engines ex-ISM which had been operating since 1987. The new factory would shorten lead times for despatch of engines to European and North American markets substantially, while increasing flexibility.

In December the North American market was the first to see the launch of the New 1000 series products. Under Project 'Darwin', the new range of engines provided an upgrade of the previous models, meeting Stage 1 off-highway emission regulations. The product offering was tailored to meet changing market needs, being quieter, more fuel efficient, more versatile and more reliable. The European launch was planned for late February 1997.

At about the same time, the new CV6 engine was announced from Shrewsbury. Rated at 400 to 700bhp, the engine was developed for both military and commercial markets, its small envelope allowing easier installation in the latest tracked and wheeled armoured and logistic vehicles. The first sales success was for main propulsion in the US Marines Advanced Amphibious Assault Vehicle (AAAV).

The production figures for 1996 showed another small increase to a total of 189,547 engines, the highest total since 1980. Once again 4.40 and 4.236 family volumes were predominant, with the new 700 Series starting to grow. The 6.354 family was finally phased out during the year, after over 35 years, while the Prima/500 Series reduced to under 3,000 units.

1997

Another tool in the continued drive for cost reduction was displayed as the first 'Added Value In Design' (AVID) engine teardown on the New 1000 Series took team members from around Eastfield. The day-long workshop identified potential savings of £7 million as over 400 ideas were put forward. LucasVarity Board members visiting Peterborough also attended the event.

In a move to offload some of his day-to-day activities, Victor Rice appointed Tony Gilroy as CEO of LV, directing the activities of the seven operating divisions alongside his tasks managing 'transition operations' and the SE Asia expansion plans. A further LV announcement covered the impending sale of 13 smaller businesses around the world.

A progress report on the BT Global Challenge, with the fleet en route from Rio de Janeiro to Auckland, spoke of the dismasting of Concert in a storm, necessitating the use of the M135C main engine for 2,000 miles and the transfer of fuel between the yachts in severe weather conditions. All reached Auckland ready for the next leg starting on 9 February.

Brian Amey was appointed Director and General Manager of PESL and PESTL, working with Brian Wilmott until the latter's retirement. Brian retained his Peterborough position as Divisional Director, Product Supply, while his successor as General Manager, PEPL was not identified.

In June the JV agreement with the Chinese Tianjin Engine Works (TEW) was signed. With 60% shareholding by VP and an initial investment of £18 million, the new plant was planned to be one of the most modern in the world and would be producing 50,000 Phaser and 1000 Series engines from CKD parts each year by 2001, rising to 120,000 a year. TEW was founded in 1935 and employed around 7,000 personnel, supplying engines from 70 to 500bhp to all market sectors. In another deal with NACCO Materials Handling Group, makers of Hyster and Yale forklift trucks, VP agreed to supply 700 Series engines to the Craigavon plant in Northern Ireland from early 1998. This £80 million contract added to the existing supply of 1000 and 2000 Series engines.

Perkins Technology broke new ground with the unveiling of a 3-litre V6 engine, featuring high-speed direct injection. The project, code-named 'Sunshine', was designed for large passenger cars, with PTL looking for a group of car makers needing a diesel engine for executive car applications, based on the premise that such vehicles would be in a relatively low volume 'niche' market. The 170bhp prototype was an advanced design, with twin overhead camshafts on each cylinder bank and four valves per cylinder. The engine pushed the boundaries of fuel management and NVH (noise, vibration, harshness) control in the belief that drivers of premium cars would expect driver comfort, while potential OEMs would demand fuel economy, performance, good power density and fast time to market. As it transpired there was initial interest from a number of companies, especially Renault. A prototype was installed in a Safrane car and provided a good driving experience, although its most famous moment came when the car and the trailer carrying it were stolen from a motorway service area – giving unwelcome national publicity about 'a secret £250,000 engine being pinched while the drivers took a break'. The car was recovered undamaged, and the thieves took just the trailer! After considerable expenditure no serious commercial interest was shown in the engine and the project was shelved. (In view of the production success for a number of larger diesels in executive cars in the early 2000s it could be suggested that Perkins had been on the right track!)

The 14 competing yachts in the BT Global Challenge all completed the voyage, being given a tremendous welcome on their arrival at Southampton. VP featured strongly in the festivities and was well pleased with the outstanding performance of all the engines; the information obtained during the voyage was expected to give pointers for further service improvements.

The first financial results from the LucasVarity merger showed a healthy rise in profits compared to the combined results of previous years. Victor Rice presided at the announcement to analysts in London commenting: 'The speed at which we have become one company, sharing common objectives and transferring best practices among our businesses has surprised even me.' LucasVarity ranked within the '100 Best Companies to work for' in the UK listing. VarityPerkins sales increased by 2.3% to £655 million, with operating profits up by 7.3% to £59 million.

In September the annual TQ celebrations and exhibitions at Peterborough, Shrewsbury and Irlam demonstrated not just what had been done but what else was possible as opportunities for improvement were identified. What was becoming identified as 'the never-ending journey of continuous change and improvement' was proving to be a marathon essential to combat competition.

October and November brought news of more changes. Tony Downes announced his retirement from February 1998 although he would retain contact with Perkins through consultancy on legislation, emissions and some governmental matters as well as standing on industry committees. He was awarded the MBE for services to industry. There were significant new appointments with Hans Haefeli named as the new Finance Director and Graham Maundrell as Director, Human Resources for VP, while Tom Nottidge joined PESL and PESTL as Quality Manager from Lucas Diesel Systems. Roy Chowings became Project Director for Stage II products (the next generation of the 1 litre/cylinder engines, given the code name 'Vista'), with Roger Warren appointed to Business and Product Planning Director in addition to his responsibilities for the New 1000 Series.

There was good news on the product front as the new Case/IH tractors were launched with the 900 series and New 1000 Series engines, covering a range from 50 to 100bhp. Claas also announced their new 'Xerion' multi-purpose tractor fitted with the 1300 Series engine. In Shrewsbury a field trial of ten Eagle TxSI natural gas engines was publicised: these would be used in ERF tractor units in partnership with BOC Distribution Services, handling London store distribution for Marks and Spencer. The engines were fitted with an electronic 'drive by wire' system and offered quiet, low emission operation on LNG (liquid natural gas).

Caterpillar makes a bid

Perhaps the most important announcement in the history of Perkins was reserved for December when Victor Rice announced a conditional agreement for Caterpillar Inc to acquire VarityPerkins for $1.325 billion (£803 million). The negotiations were subject to LucasVarity shareholder agreement at an extraordinary general meeting to be held in late January 1998, and to clearance by various Government bodies. Statements from Mike Baunton and Caterpillar Group President Rich Thompson said that the Perkins name would continue and that there should be no employment impact. Caterpillar was the largest Perkins customer when their F.G. Wilson interests were included, as well as being a major customer of Perkins Technology Limited for their own engine development.

Mike Baunton went on to express his pride that Caterpillar viewed VarityPerkins as impressive on performance and reputation and had decided to make them part of the Caterpillar family – put together the two companies would become the biggest manufacturer of diesel engines in the world. He did not anticipate major issues with current customers and partners, whose initial reaction had been positive. Caterpillar was committed to the investment needed to meet emissions legislation as off-highway and on-highway requirements converged. He concluded 'The future is bright for Perkins!'

Victor Rice commented: 'We have secured a full and fair price for VarityPerkins, which reflects the excellent fit between the two businesses.' He noted that Perkins did not have a major presence in on-highway applications and that development on that side was not economically viable for LV; however, Caterpillar was a full-line engine producer committed to development of small and medium engines which was where Perkins' strength lay.

Donald Fites, Chairman and CEO of Caterpillar, said: 'The combination of Caterpillar and Perkins enhances our strategic position in the worldwide engine business. Excellent strategic fit between the companies makes this a natural extension of our strategy to be a global leader through select investments in or near our core business.'

Although there was some uncertainty involved, overall the employees saw the prospect as good news, and, added to the good results for the year as production passed 200,000 engines for the first time since 1980, it promised much for the New Year.

1998

Agreement to the sale was soon received from the LucasVarity shareholders, and by March the deal had been accepted by both the European Union through the Merger Task Force and by the US Federal Trade Commission. Michael Baunton in a statement allayed fears over job losses and terms and conditions, noting that bonus arrangements would continue into 1998 and that share plan options changes would be addressed in due course. In confirming that the company name would be carried forward, as 'Perkins Engines Company Limited', he noted that there would be subtle changes to the company logo itself, while the blue used for a number of years would change to a slightly darker hue. Other signs of change were soon visible on vehicle badging and on the five-storey offices where the Perkins sign reappeared.

On his last visit to Eastfield as Chairman of LucasVarity, Victor Rice unveiled a new bronze bust of Frank Perkins in the office foyer. There was some sadness at the same time with the death of Norman Collins at the age of 100, one of the longest-living members of the extended Perkins 'family' and also one of the few remaining veterans of the First World War: some time after his death a book was published recounting his memories of that traumatic time.

On the product front the new Track 4 was being completed to produce the new 1004-42 engine as a replacement for the 4.236, 4.41 and 1004.4: the new assembly area, also dubbed '4c' or 'Foresee', was a state-of-the-art facility with equipment installed by Renault Automation providing major improvements over the previous area. With many automatic assembly and checking fixtures the line would increase production of the important 4-cylinder engine while providing market leading levels of quality. The new engine was part of Project Darwin, which had brought the engine into production in about 19 months, an indication of the power of both the new product introduction and simultaneous engineering processes.

In March JCB gave the new partnership a vote of confidence in signing a new five-year deal with Perkins for the supply of 100 Series engines at 25,000 a year. The deal was signed by Sir Anthony Bamford, Michael Baunton and Don Fites, Chairman and CEO of Caterpillar on his first visit to Peterborough: it was noted that JCB would shortly be supplied with their 250,000th engine after around 30 years of partnership.

During the year the Total Quality processes continued around all the factories, with more projects raised and keen interest being taken by many employees. In July the Peterborough plant was awarded BS14001 accreditation for environmental processes. A new level of customer satisfaction was demonstrated by the PDC facility at Irlam

when they announced a new record of 96% first fill against 'vehicle off road' orders and 95% for routine orders; although this was declared a world class performance the PDC personnel declared their target to be 100% for the near future.

Another major project affecting all computer operations was put in place as concern over the 'Millennium bug' was addressed: ensuring that the change to '2000' would not wreck all programs overnight was a concern not just in Perkins but worldwide – the 'shorthand' use of the last two digits of the year in many programs needed to be tackled fast and efficiently to avoid problems!

The promised connection to the Caterpillar shareholder scheme arrived in September with the Employee Investment Plan, allowing any employee to make voluntary contributions direct from their monthly salary: the encouragement of participation was assured by offering bonus shares, including special arrangements for long-serving personnel.

By the end of the year Michael Baunton had been appointed a Vice President of Caterpillar Inc., as well as President of Perkins, confirming the Company's place as a stand-alone division alongside the others within the Caterpillar enterprise. Awards to a number of Perkins entrants in the 'Caterpillar Pollution Prevention' competition confirmed the active role already being played across all parts of Perkins.

Perkins was also recognised as a caring and sharing organisation by Alan Beale MP, Under Secretary of State for the Environment, when he visited Eastfield to present the BS14001 certificate. He praised the many activities ongoing to address environment, quality, health and safety issues. Perkins was participating actively, committing itself to identifying and setting targets for continuous improvement while encouraging its employees, customers, suppliers and the wider community.

1999

Richard Noble's Thrust SSC Land Speed Record-breaking car was in the news, with little attention, not surprisingly, paid to the support vehicle loaned by Merlo UK. This was a 60.6 EVS telescopic handler fitted with a 114bhp turbocharged Perkins engine – although only capable of 35kph against Thrust's 1227.72 kph, this machine proved very useful as forklift, tug, camera dolly and crane in assisting the team to achieve their goal.

With the TQ processes well absorbed into everyday working practices, Mike Baunton announced a new stage in continuous improvement with the creation of the 'Vital Few' initiative, intended to concentrate efforts towards particular concerns in every operations area. He reminded all employees that any world class company could not afford to rest on its laurels even for a moment since those at the leading edge would move on – only by continuing to seek improvements and extending capabilities would Perkins remain competitive. New Quality Director, George Hadley, and John Sewell, Director and General Manager of Corporate Sales, reinforced the message and commended Vital Few as the driving force for the new phase. Later in the year Hadley declared a new slogan – 'Dependable Quality is Everybody's Business' – and announced some of the new measures being put in place. These included a daily engine quality assessment with results clearly identified and remedial actions highlighted, plus a Lotus Notes-based Perkins Business Quality System connecting plants, suppliers and customers to allow tracking of all quality concerns. Links to Total Quality Cost measures would follow. The Vital Few featured in the annual TQ Experience exhibitions, covering the resetting of expectations, use of standard operations in the factory areas, elimination of leaks and fuel injection equipment defects, and the introduction of rapid problem solving as plans were put in motion to achieve QS9000 Quality System status.

Change, Change & More Change

Earlier in the year Perkins had paid tribute to another 'vital few' when special awards and a luncheon were given to twenty long-serving retired employees who had reached their 80th birthdays. The Long Service Club made all the members Honorary Life Members, and they were shown round the factory after meeting with Mike Baunton and other directors. Pride of place went to Bill Baxter MBE, in his 93rd year and Frances Atkins, the same age, whose service included working on the machining areas during WW2 and up to her retirement in 1967.

At the end of the year Colin Ingram, Director of Perkins Technology, commented on the technical challenges being faced with the new legislation to meet Stage 2 emissions for 2000, Stage 3 in 2007 and Stage 4 in 2010. The massive workload would see engine design and equipment change radically as pollution levels would be reduced to only 1% of levels from unregulated engines such as the 6.354 and 4.236. The use of electronics for engine control and exhaust after-treatment such as catalysts would become essential as millions of pounds and thousands of man-hours were expended in achieving, and exceeding, the exacting new standards.

When the author started this history, it was always the intention to stop somewhere short of the year of publication – the year 2000 has been chosen as a 'natural break' point since it encompasses the first period of Caterpillar's ownership, was the year of the author's retirement and was the end of the 20th century. Recent history is problematical since it is too recent to have a settled 'shape' and too many people have divergent memories and views!

I hope that in future years someone will write the continuation of this story, covering the future events, the products and the people that make Perkins what it was, is and hopefully will be. I wish that future author well, and that he finds the task as stimulating and enjoyable as I have. The temptation is too great, however, to leave it there: I am offering in this closing chapter just a few brief notes on things I have noted over the past six years.

After the sale of both Massey Ferguson and Perkins the USA-based TRW Inc purchased Lucas Varity in 1999 and later sold Lucas Diesel Systems to Delphi Inc. and then Lucas Aerospace (by then TRW Aeronautical Systems) to Goodrich Inc.

Within the Perkins plants, the culture change started by the TQ training extended to all aspects of the business including the environmental side. Many TQ projects contained elements of environmental improvement, benefiting the company and employees as waste in many forms was driven out. Continued support for schools was a feature of Perkins' involvement in the community, with a yearly competition, 'The Eco Challenge', linked to the environment. Later that support to education became more direct with sponsorship along with the City and DfES of the Thomas Deacon Academy, a new school complex built adjacent to Deacon's School to draw pupils from three of the Peterborough senior schools. The appointment of Allan Arnott, a Perkins director, as a sponsor Director on the board of the Academy gave a new link between industry and education, in line with similar enterprises around the country.

On a wider city front, the creation of a wildlife haven and environmental centre alongside the 'Rail World' area on the banks of the River Nene close to Peterborough city centre came about through the dedicated efforts of Brian Pearce. He exhibited a level of commitment and persistence that was an example to others, and a genius for persuading other companies to help.

In the City itself, Perkins' influence was positive with collaboration on an energy audit across the community, and a commitment to spread the message regarding actions to save energy, recycle wherever possible and, above all, encourage teamwork to resolve problems. On the entertainment side, the Perkins Concert in association with the City Council, already an annual institution after 36 years of sponsorship, ventured outside to become part of the city's summer festival.

The substantial benefits associated with Caterpillar ownership took many shapes. Caterpillar Logistics had already taken over the operational aspects of the parts operation at Irlam, as well as engine despatch and CKD packing at Eastfield. The use of subcontractors had increased over recent years, with the restaurant and catering side as the start point. Later international facilities management companies took over the running of the facilities for all three sites, covering security and all of the day-to-day services supporting the plant operations.

For the personnel within Perkins there were tremendous opportunities for personal advancement as the culture and philosophy of the Caterpillar corporation began to be appreciated. The movement of personnel at all levels soon became a part of the everyday experience, with Caterpillar staff being transferred from other plants into

Michael Baunton was Managing Director at the time of the Caterpillar takeover, later moving to a post in Caterpillar Europe

Hans Haefeli succeeded Michael Baunton as Managing Director of Perkins and will preside over the celebrations for the 75th Anniversary

Peterborough on assignments of varying duration, while a number of Perkins employees transferred similarly to posts in Europe and the USA. Hans Haefeli was one executive who found himself on the move to run a Cat plant in the USA, only to be recalled very quickly to England to take over at Perkins when Mike Baunton was promoted into a job in Switzerland.

The reorganisation of Perkins was gradual. Close working relationships included amalgamation of a number of areas into Cat global operations, including Engineering, Purchase and in part Sales, while a 'Shared Services' office at the Vicarage Farm Road offices was created to look after pensions etc. for the UK Caterpillar plants as well as Perkins.

The emphasis on quality remained. Following the TQ and Vital Few initiatives the most sweeping programme of all, '6 Sigma', had been rolled out within Perkins and across all Caterpillar plants worldwide. The author was privileged to be present at a dinner in June 2000 with the Caterpillar European Quality Council at The George Hotel in Stamford when Pierre Pellerin of GE Capital Europe gave a presentation on this process and the way in which GE had embarked on their 6 Sigma journey. From this initial glimpse the programme was developed and the impacts on personal and corporate activities are clear to see.

The already-changing environment in the Eastfield, Shrewsbury and Stafford factories continued to undergo tremendous improvements to working conditions and plant as upgrading of every part of the facilities was undertaken. Any past factory worker visiting his old place of work will be astonished by the scale of change: the machining, assembly, test, and paint facilities in Factory 1 and 2 at Peterborough have undergone total remodelling with cleanliness and quality the watchword. Similarly, the changes at Shrewsbury and Stafford have been considerable.

Production of 2000 and 3000 Series engines at Shrewsbury was phased out gradually up to 2004. As a consequence, the Shrewsbury plant was turned over to a remanufacturing role for all diesels, with a special responsibility for the military versions of the V12 and V8 engines for the various armed forces using them.

In Peterborough the steady march of emissions legislation ensured that the engineering staff were fully occupied in developing the replacements for New 1000 Series, 900 Series, 700 Series and 100 Series. The new 1100 Series provided replacements for the first two – finally phasing out the P3 and its linear descendants after over 50 years of production – while the 800 and 400 series replaced the smaller engine ranges. Use of the Navistar 1300 series continued as a factored engine, providing a gap-filler in its horsepower range enhanced by the new electronic version using Caterpillar fuel injection technology. The demands of the successively tighter emissions legislation and tight timescales have been, and will continue to be, a major drain on resources. The changes incorporated in the latest engines include four valves per cylinder with centrally-placed injectors to optimise the in-cylinder conditions.

The trade-off and compromise required to turn a collection of numbers into actual complying engines is difficult for many to grasp – to say that costs of development rise almost exponentially as technology

New engine models have to be introduced to meet the demands of new emissions legislation. The 1103-33 is the smallest of the new 1100 Series products; its introduction heralded the final demise of the three cylinder engines based upon the 'P' series engines of the 1930s

is stretched to its limits perhaps sums up the situation. It is said that already in some city areas the most modern diesel engines actually exhaust cleaner air than they take in . . .

The production facilities in Peterborough began to change significantly too, not least when the Factory 2 dedicated machining lines were decommissioned in 2005. Other areas of the plant saw major changes as old machine lines and assembly areas gave way to state-of-the-art facilities, continuing a process started with the introduction of the Factory 4 computer-controlled machining centres for the 700 Series and the Foresee assembly hall, test shop and paint processes. Many areas of the old, northern, end of the factory now contain store areas while the outside of the entire factory has been given a modern look with metal wall cladding and window renewal.

Although the associate and licensee operations have faded from their previous importance, Perkins has a new presence in Brazil with the opening of a plant in Curitiba, and a new facility in the USA in the manufacturing plant at Griffin, Georgia producing 400 Series engines. Globalisation has ensured that worldwide supply and procurement are a reality for many manufacturing operations; clearly Perkins has grasped this as a routine part of its activities. Although overall the company now has only around 4,500 employees in total, production volume is higher than at any other time in its history and its customer base remains wide, encompassing both large OEMs and small specialist manufacturers. Aftermarket care, the prompt availability and supply of parts, advice and training to customers around the world receive the priority needed to remain competitive. This ensures the reputation of Perkins in product support excellence grows as electronic engine control comes to the fore.

As Perkins moves towards its 75th anniversary there is a clear indication that, under its new owners, the words incised above the North Offices by its founder are being well respected. There is vision, there is a future, the workforce is enthusiastic and the Perkins name is stronger than ever. It has been my privilege to give you a taste of the rich and sometimes turbulent past – I believe that the Company is well aligned to the needs of the 21st century as it moves confidently towards its own centenary.

Francis Arthur Perkins (1889–1967)

Francis Arthur Perkins, better known as Frank, was born on 26 February 1889, the elder son of John Edward S. Perkins and his wife Charlotte, née Long. Their home was Clifton Villa on Park Road, Peterborough.

J.E.S. Perkins had joined the family business, Barford and Perkins in 1884 after graduating from King's College London. The firm were agricultural engineers and iron founders with a works in Queen Street, Peterborough and had been Amies, Barford and Co. until 1872. Frank's grandfather Thomas Perkins had joined them in 1865, moving from the business he had started as an ironmonger and agricultural machine maker in Hitchin, Hertfordshire. Thomas became head of the company in 1898 on the death of William Barford. J.E.S. Perkins later became joint managing director of Barford and Perkins, the company having branched out from making all manner of farming equipment into producing small rollers, some fitted with petrol engines.

Frank was educated briefly at the King's School, Peterborough, but at the age of ten went as a boarder to Lindley Lodge Preparatory School in Staffordshire before entering Rugby School at thirteen. After one year he was removed due to health problems – perhaps brought about by Rugby's spartan regime – and was sent to join his younger brother Christopher at Gresham's School, Holt in Norfolk.

In 1907 Frank went up to Emmanuel College, Cambridge, graduating in 1910 with a third class degree in engineering. He then went into farming, taking a rented farm in Hertfordshire, but this career was interrupted by the First World War. He volunteered in 1914, was commissioned in the army and served with the Royal Engineers in the Dardanelles, Palestine and Egypt up to his demobilisation in 1918 with the rank of Major.

Frank then ran a 400-acre farm at Leintwardine in Herefordshire but after a few years moved with his wife Gwyneth (married in 1915) and two young children to Peterborough after concerns about the family business; he joined his father at the Queen Street Iron Works, where he went through the works to learn the business. He developed some dairy machinery for farmers and also sterilising equipment to assist bulb growers. Barford and Perkins had become a small part of the Agricultural and General Engineers (AGE) group and by 1929 Frank was works director of Aveling and Porter at Rochester, another part of AGE. It was here that he came to know Charles Chapman and the history in this book started from there.

Alongside his professional career, Frank Perkins was deeply involved in the Peterborough Council of Boys' Clubs, for whom he did much good work, and with other bodies such as Peterborough District Savings Committee, Peterborough Cathedral and Alwalton Parish Church (the family purchased and lived in Alwalton Hall). He was made an honorary freeman of the city in 1962 and also served as High Sheriff of Cambridgeshire and Huntingdonshire. He retained an interest in farming throughout his life, running a small arable farm, and was President of Peterborough Agricultural Society in 1965. He enjoyed shooting and fishing, and took up sailing in his later years, keeping a small yacht on the River Orwell in Suffolk. He had three daughters and a son with his first wife, Gwyneth, and after her death in 1961 remarried in 1965 to a widow, Maud Dixon. He died on 15 October, 1967.

Charles Wallace Chapman (1897–1979)

Charles Chapman was born in Lancaster and after local education including Barrow-in-Furness Technical School was apprenticed to Vickers at Barrow and was engaged in sea trials before he went to Liverpool University. This was cut short by the First World War in which he served as a lieutenant in the Royal Navy Volunteer Reserve, engaged in anti-submarine work around the British and French coasts on the 'Dover Patrol'.

He returned to Liverpool University to complete his engineering degree and then looked for his first job. He obtained a post with Beardsmores and leant a great deal from working with Alan Chorlton for some two years, developing a semi-diesel engine for trawlers. The job folded, however, during the period of the Depression, and he obtained work with Vickers-Petters Limited at Ipswich, Suffolk, who were developing two-stroke diesels running on heavy oil: this job too came to an abrupt end in 1930 at which time Chapman was personal assistant to Sir Frank Petter.

The next move was to the Agricultural and General Engineering Group at Rochester, where he became chief engineer of the Aveling and Porter diesel engine department, working to develop a diesel engine for sister company Garrett and Co. of Leiston. The outcome of the bankruptcy of yet another company and the ensuing creation of F. Perkins Limited is covered in this book.

In the early 1940s, after Chapman's disagreement over the T12 engine led to his resignation, he rejoined the RNVR as Commander (Engineering) and was stationed at the Admiralty for the rest of the war period. When hostilities ended, he built his own laboratory in the grounds of his house in Sussex, going into consultancy on engines and couplings: his work on the latter resulted in his abandoning work on engines to concentrate on production of couplings used on many different applications. He also found time to write a three-volume work for Caxton's entitled Modern High Speed Oil Engines, which became a reference work after its publication in 1949.

Later he sold his interest in the coupling company and became a consultant on engine design for Perkins and Ford Motor Company, working from home with visiting design staff. He only rarely visited Perkins, even after he had become reconciled with the company, and wrote a draft history for Monty Prichard, which was never published. He also wrote a novel, The Director's Dinner, apparently based on his experiences at Perkins! He did, however, visit an exhibition portraying the history of the company at the Peterborough Museum in company with Joe Hind, and pictures taken at that time are the best available of the very shy individual who had shunned the limelight throughout his career.

Charles Chapman died quietly at his home at the age of 82.

APPENDIX 1: ENGINE SPECIFICATIONS
1.1 VIXEN, FOX, WOLF, LEOPARD I & LEOPARD II

The first engines were based around a common design, with a maximum commonality of parts. The Vixen and Fox were short-lived in production and differed from the Wolf only in their cylinder bore dimension. The Leopard engines were slightly longer than the Wolf to accommodate the bigger cylinder bore dimension and the increased stroke. (It is interesting to note that these 1930s engines had identical stroke and bore dimensions to the 1000 Series of some 50 years later!) Fuelling settings were of course different to suit the power outputs.

Cylinder Block/Crankcase

One piece casting of high-duty chromium cast iron alloy, deeply-skirted and very rigid, with siamesed cylinder barrels to ensure minimum engine length. All facings for accessories and brackets cast integrally, with the rear face adapted to suit various bell housings. Cylinder bores finished to fine limits with ample metal for re-boring. The high camshaft position eliminated the need for push rods and was the subject of British patent 404943.

Crankshaft

Machined from highest-grade nickel-chrome molybdenum steel, extremely rigid and supported in five bearings. Each shaft statically and dynamically balanced. Main and big end bearings of lead bronze material generously proportioned to ensure long life and minimum wear, although early engines had white metal bearings which had to be scraped by hand to fit. Main bearing caps were of steel, with lined steel shells for ease of renewal. Flywheel secured to the crankshaft rear end using a flange formed integrally with the crankshaft.

Cylinder Head

A one-piece chromium iron casting of exceptional depth, bolted to the cylinder block by through studs with a special flame-resisting gasket. The design was covered by British Patent 401703 and carries the rockers and rocker gear for valve operation. The atomisers and combustion chamber caps were located in the head and easily removed for maintenance. The valve gear was covered by an aluminium alloy cover, which featured an integral induction manifold.

Connecting Rods

Made from light 'H' section chrome-molybdenum steel stampings. Bearing caps secured by two bolts. Small end bearings of fully-floating bronze material. Forced lubrication to both small and big ends.

Piston Assemblies

Pistons of special light aluminium alloy with crowns thick enough to resist heat of combustion. Fitted with three compression rings and one oil control ring above the gudgeon pin, and one oil ring below.

Valves

All valves of special alloy steel and generously sized in relation to the engine swept volume. Inlet valves of simple design without masks or deflectors.

Timing Gear

Camshaft, fuel pump and idling governor driven by one continuous triple roller chain running within an aluminium alloy case at the front of the cylinder block. Chain provided with an automatic tensioner and dampers to obviate whip: chain designed to require no attention during the life of the engine and provide silent running.

Fuel System

Bosch unit type injection pump fitted on left side of engine on a slightly-inclined platform with ready access. High pressure pipes of equal length feed each injector mounted in the cylinder head, using the Perkins patented combustion system. Two fuel filters fitted.

Cooling

Cooling using pump circulation with ample cooling surfaces in both head and block, with large passages connecting the two. The circulating pump was fitted on the timing case, belt-driven from the camshaft. A belt-driven cooling fan was provided.

Lubrication System

The high-pressure lubrication system was fed by a fully-submerged pump within the oil sump, feeding oil to all parts of the engine. The system featured a large suction strainer and a pressure oil cleaner.

Exhaust Manifold

Cast iron, fully-ribbed to dissipate heat. Designed to suit front or rear outlet by turning the manifold over.

Self-contained Starting Handle

Each engine supplied with a starting handle, carried in a nose-piece bolted to the front end of the timing case. Extension spindle also available to suit installation requirements.

Accessories

The engines featured a clean right-hand side, all accessories being fitted to the left-hand side.

Engine 'suspension' possible from facings on each side of the cylinder block sides with four studs on each, plus a steel banjo secured by a ring of bolts round the rear main bearing. (an alternative three point suspension embraced the starting handle bracket).

Electric starter motor and dynamo from Bosch were available as extras, as were various flywheels and clutchs, fuel transfer pump, exhauster and fans.

Comments

The contemporary advertising literature of the late 1930s makes considerable play of the advantages of the Perkins engines in terms of compactness and weight, cost and economy. Comparison with petrol engines and competitive diesels stresses the benefits obtainable by using the Perkins engines in smaller vehicles than had hitherto been possible.

Technical Details:

	Vixen	Fox	Wolf	Lynx	Leopard	Leopard II
Bore (mm)	75.0	80.0	85.0	100.0	100.0	105.0
Stroke (mm)	120.6	120.6	120.6	127.0	127.0	127.0
Number of cylinders	4	4	4	4	4	4
Swept volume (litres)			2.75	4.0	4.0	4.4
Power output (BHP):						
@1000 RPM			21	27.5	30	35
@1500 RPM			31	41	45	54
@2000 RPM			40	51.5	56	68.5
@2400 RPM			43.5	55	60	75
@2500 RPM			45	-	-	-
BMEP (lbs/sq in):						
@1000 RPM			99	90	97	103
@1500 RPM			100	89	97	106
@2000 RPM			96	83	91	101
@2400 RPM			86	75	91	92.5
@2500 RPM			85	-	-	-
Useful Torque (lb.ft):						
@1000 RPM			110	145	158	186
@1500 RPM			111	143	158	190
@2000 RPM			105	135	147.5	181
@2400 RPM			95	120	133	166
@2500 RPM			94	-	-	-
R.A.C Rating			17.9	24.8	24.8	27.34
Spec Fuel Cons (pt/BHP hr)			0.39	0.37	0.36	0.36
Bare weight (lbs)			532	608	608	603
Standard flywheel (lbs)			76	76	100	112
Electrical equipment (lbs)			56	56	56	56
Governed engine speed (RPM)			2500	2400	2400	2400

N.B. All the above data taken from advertising literature of the time

Basic Dimensions

(inches)	Vixen/Fox/Wolf	Leopard I & II
Height (crank centreline to top cover)	22.125	22.625
Length (timing case to block rear face)	28.156	32.906
Width (max starter motor to exhaust manifold)	19.249	19.418
Depth (typical, crank centreline to sump plug)	11.125	11.125

(It is interesting to note that, from the earliest brochures, dimensions were given in metric as well as imperial measure.)

The famous 'P Series' engines were introduced at the Commercial Vehicle Exhibition in 1937 as 6-, 4- and 3-cylinder versions. In fact the 3-cylinder did not see production until after World War II but the 6-cylinder, followed soon by the 4, were the real foundation of Perkins business. The use of names, as shown above, was soon discontinued after objections by the motorcycle company Phelon and Moore who produced the Panther motorcycle with engines of their own design. Maximum component commonality was designed into the three versions, with the same stroke as the Leopard engine but a smaller bore size to allow a shorter, lighter, engine.

During the late 1950s and early 1960s variants of the original engines were produced, introducing increased swept volume through the use of a 3.6-inch bore in place of the original 3.5-inch. The second change was the development of direct injection versions of the 3- and 4-cylinder engines, necessitating new cylinder heads and piston assemblies, plus the adoption of the CAV DPA distributor type fuel injection pump on all three versions.

Cylinder Block/Crankcase

One piece casting of high-duty chrome cast-iron alloy, ribbed for stiffness whilst minimising weight. Featured main bearings each side of all cylinders, with the block skirt extending to the crankshaft splitline. Cylinder barrels had water passages right round, as opposed to the Wolf siamesed design, although the $1/8$-inch thick sand cores frequently broke so that this feature was at best inconsistent! The camshaft again was carried high on the right side of the block. Steel forged main bearing caps dowelled to block.

Crankshaft

An extremely rigid nickel chrome molybdenum steel forging, statically and dynamically balanced. Integral flange at the rear to mount the flywheel, with a threaded nose to accept a starter dog at the front end. Main and big end bearings featured steel shells with white metal linings in the top halves and lead bronze in the cap halves; later all engines had copper lead bearings throughout.

Connecting Rods

Light 'H' section forgings of chrome molybdenum steel, with caps split from the same forging as the rod and secured by high tensile bolts. Bronze full-floating gudgeon pins of large diameter.

Timing Gear

Camshaft and fuel pump shaft driven through a triple roller chain enclosed in an aluminium timing case on the front of the engine, with a pressed steel cover. Chain whip and tension controlled by dampers and an automatic tensioner, removing the need for attention during engine life to overhaul. In the late 1950s gear-driven versions were developed and introduced for the three and four cylinder engines, and in France only (designated 6PF) for the P6 too.

Pistons

Made from special aluminium alloy, ribbed to take loads to the gudgeon pin direct and not through the piston skirt. Three compression rings and two oil rings fitted to ensure adequate control of lubrication. (Early industrial engines rated at lower speeds were fitted with cast iron pistons.)

Lubrication System

High-pressure system supplied by an oil pump driven through spiral gears from the fuel pump drive shaft, bolted to the cylinder block between the front two cylinders and submerged in the oil in the sump, eliminating the need for long suction pipes. Oil drawn through a large and readily detachable suction strained and pumped through an efficient pressure-type cleaner, located accessibly on the left side of the engine, to a cast-in pressure rail and thence to individual drillings feeding all bearings, camshaft, overhead rocker gear and timing gears.

Crankcase Ventilation

A new continuous suction system was featured, ensuring that filtered air was continuously drawn through the engine at all operating speeds, carrying away any blowby or water vapour which might otherwise lead to sludging of the oil and wear of the working parts. With the crankcase always under a slight vacuum it was impossible for fumes to collect in the engine compartment and find their way into the cab.

Cylinder Head

A one piece chromium-iron casting, secured to the cylinder block by a large number of through studs, sealing via a copper-asbestos head gasket. Valves and tappets carried directly in the head, with the rocker shaft assembly mounted on top and enclosed by a light steel pressing. Special attention to the fastenings allowed them to be tightened without removing the rocker gear. The cross flow design featured an induction manifold formed in the right side of the head and closed by an aluminium manifold cover. Individual exhaust ports for each cylinder fed to the cast iron manifold on the left side of the engine. The patented indirect 'Aeroflow' combustion chambers were partly formed in the head and closed by separate steel caps.

Fuel Injection System

The Bosch unit type fuel injection pump mounted on the left side of the block and driven through a coupling from an alloy cast housing fitted to the back of the timing case. A Bosch pneumatic governor was fitted, controlled through a venturi fitted to the induction manifold. The atomisers were fitted vertically into the cylinder head, with fuel being sprayed into the combustion chamber sphere and into the port itself to assist starting. Control of the engine was through a throttle lever on the intake venturi and a stop control on the injection pump.

To assist cold starting a heating system was fitted, consisting of glow plugs and a Ki-gas pump. Later engines used the CAV in-line injection pump, to be superseded in the late 1950s/early 60s on later engines by the CAV distributor type pump.

Cooling System

A coolant pump was fitted on the front of the cylinder head and driven by a vee belt from the crankshaft at $1\frac{1}{3}$ times engine speed. The pump incorporated a thermostat and the outlet connection from the cylinder head. A combination of forced circulation to the head and thermo-syphon cooling for the block via cast passages ensured rapid engine warm-up with elimination of any possibility of overheating of the injectors.

Electrical Equipment

12-volt Bosch starter motor and CAV or Lucas dynamo were available as extras.

(The engine could be hand-cranked for starting, giving some indication of the expectations at the time, as well as the low compression pressures typical of the 'Aeroflow' combustion system – although the compression ratio was nominally 16:1.)

Other Equipment

'Extras' offered included mounting feet, flywheel and starter ring, flywheel bell housing or adaptor to suit various conversions.

Technical Details

For the 3.152, 4.203 and 6.305 the cylinder bore was increased to 3.6 inches, giving capacities of 152.7 cu ins (2.5 litres), 203.5 (3,33) and 305 (5.0) respectively. The direct injection versions of the three and four cylinder engines were designated D3.152 and D4.203 respectively.

	P6 (Panther)	P4 (Puma)	(Python)
Bore (inches/mm)	3.5 / 88.9	3.5 / 88.9	3.5 / 88.9
Stroke (inches/(mm)	5.0 / 127	5.0 / 127	5.0 / 127
Cylinders	6	4	3
Swept Volume (cu ins/litres)	288 / 4.73	192 / 3.15	144 / 2.36
Power Output (BHP)			
@ 1000 RPM	36	25	18.5
@ 1500 RPM	55	38.5	28.5
@ 2000 RPM	71	48.5	36.5
@ 2600 RPM	85	56	42
Maximum BMEP (lbs/sq in)	100	106	104
Maximum Torque (lbf ft)	170/193	135	100
R.A.C. Rating (hp)	29.4	19.6	14.7
Spec fuel cons (pts/BHP hr)	0.36	0.36	0.37
Firing order	1,5,3,6,2,4	1,3,4,2	1,3,2
Bare engine weight (lbs)	608	406	350
Typical installation weight (lbs) (including fan, electrics, flywheel, housing and filters)	712	578	522

The design of the T-12 engine was started in 1939 as a result of an Air Ministry request, following the development contract placed in 1938 to explore the possibility of a diesel engine using the Perkins 'Aeroflow' combustion chamber for aircraft use. The proposal was to use the engine as a replacement for various petrol engines, up to and including the Rolls-Royce Merlin, for powering large high-speed marine craft used off-shore for air-sea rescue and other work. Other potential use was to power motor launches and fighting craft such as Motor Torpedo Boats and Motor Gun Boats.

This engine was to become the largest ever designed and built in Peterborough, and of course the most powerful, since the Ministry requirement was for at least 1,000bhp.

(It is interesting to note that although the letter 'T' was logical, following on behind the 'S6', Charles Chapman comments that it was named for Mr Tweedie, who was its mentor in the Air Ministry!)

The earlier work had been on a single-cylinder research engine with bore and stroke of 6 inches with separate supercharging, so it was natural to read across the promising results of the work done on this to design a 12-cylinder engine with the same bore and stroke, giving a swept volume of 33.3 litres. Charles Chapman decided to use a 55 degree vee configuration, with the two banks of six cylinders arranged to be capable of running independently through the provision of separate fuel injection pumps, oil pumps and water pumps – with interconnection and non-return valves as appropriate. In this way a measure of fail-safe was incorporated into an engine likely to operate at sea and in war conditions.

Basic Structure

A cast iron bedplate formed in an open box shape was the backbone of the engine, supporting a six-throw crankshaft in seven forged steel main bearing caps bolted on to the top of the bedplate: the bedplate was hollow and carried cooling water to dissipate heat from the area of the mains and from the bolted on lube oil sump. A crankcase of aluminium was bolted on to the bedplate, bored to carry the individual cast iron cylinder liners spigotted into the aluminium casting. Each liner was surrounded by a fabricated spun steel water jacket, sealed with a gasket to the base of each liner.

Individual cylinder heads of cast iron were in turn spigotted to the top of the cylinder liners with a solid copper seal, each carried a triple 'O'-ring seal to the top of the water jacket. The clamping arrangements for this assembly were understandably complex, with through bolts holding the cylinder heads to the bedplate and providing considerable stress-relief to the light alloy crankcase. A row of seven hollow bolts passed vertically through the casting served the dual function of clamping and providing oil feed to the main bearings. Side rails were attached to the bedplate and provided both additional longitudinal stiffness as well as attachment for the engine to test bed or mounting in the application.

Each cylinder head assembly was made up of three parts. The cast iron head itself contained the Aeroflow combustion chamber (with a bolted-on cap completing the spherical chamber shape), three valves and the two-hole injector, set at 120 atmospheres breaking pressure. The two inlet valves were fed from a manifold running down the outside of the cylinder bank, with the single exhaust valve feeding a common exhaust manifold running down the inside of the vee. The second part of the assembly was the light alloy cast rocker box, topped by the third portion, a cover plate also in light alloy. The rocker gear for each cylinder consisted of individual steel stamped rocker levers actuated by hollow tappets mounted in bores in the head casting and running on one of the pair of camshafts mounted high in the vee, one for each bank. Valve clearance adjustment was provided by adjusting screws at the valve end of each rocker. The twin inlet valves had hollow stems, with the 45-degrees seat sealing directly on to the cylinder head casting. In the case of the exhaust valve, also 45-degree, both valve and head faces were stellited and the valve stem was sodium filled for additional heat dissipation.

Drive Arrangement

One of the most novel parts of the engine design was to be found at the front of the engine, comprising the drive arrangement for the camshafts, fuel pumps and other auxiliaries. A complex aluminium cast housing was centered around a spiral bevel gear bolted to the front of the crankshaft. From this gear, meshing pinions take drives in four directions:

1 – upwards at a slight angle to the vertical, meshing with a bevel gear on the portside camshaft. A pair of gears then provided the drive to the starboard shaft.

2 and 3 – to each side to drive jackshafts for the in-line fuel pumps mounted on the side of each bank. Drive from behind the fuel pumps was possible for other auxiliaries.

4 – vertically downwards to a cross-shaft which drives port and starboard oil and water pumps.

The shafts were all carried in caged ball bearings, with considerable commonality between most parts for ease of production assembly and service replacement. The reduction needed to provide the half engine speed drive for fuel pumps and camshafts was obtained in two stages at the crankshaft interface and the respective drive ends.

The cylinder components also displayed some novelty for a Perkins design, although following vee-engine practices of the time. The connecting rods for each pair of opposing cylinders were of fork and blade configuration, with the forked rod being positioned in the starboard bank. The forked rod big end featured four bolt securing for the big end cap, whilst that of the blade rod had two securing bolts: the copper-lead lined bearings for the forked rod were held in a carrier assembly, on the outside of which a chrome-plated surface formed the running surface for the blade rod bearing. The flat-topped aluminium pistons carried three plain cast iron compression rings (the upper two being keystone section and the third downward-scrapping) and one slotted oil scraper ring, all above the gudgeon pin, which was of fully floating design secured by circlips. The cylinder liners were chrome-plated by the Van Der Horst process for durability, being etched to improve lubrication.

The gearbox drive from the rear end of the crankshaft was taken through a built-up flywheel assembly comprising a rubber-bonded torsional damper, a three-plate flexible coupling and a light flywheel carrying the starter ring gear. Thus the engine torsional vibrations were effectively isolated from the gearbox. Twin starter motors engage with the starter ring from their positions on each side of the crankcase.

Cooling System

The cooling system used a combination of fresh and raw water, with a closed fresh water circuit feeding the cylinder heads and water jackets, a combination of convection and force feed being employed. A second circuit fed raw water to the bedplate for main bearing cooling, the supercharger and air intercoolers plus the exhaust manifold jacket.

Supercharger

The centrifugal supercharger was driven direct from the crankshaft nose through step-up gearing incorporating centrifugal clutches; at 2,300 engine rpm the supercharger ran at 21,100rpm and delivered 2,400 cubic feet of free air per minute at 8.9psi. The power requirement of the supercharger at 850bhp rating was quoted at 115bhp!

The air intake to the supercharger was protected by a gauze filter and directed air into the forged aluminium rotor from which it was directed outwards into a plain annular diffuser through guide vanes into a volute: here the compressed air was divided and directed through twin water-cooled heat exchangers and thence into the manifolds running along the outside of each cylinder bank. The heat exchanger tube stacks were of cupro-nickel, the water being passed through the tubes with air directed around them.

Fuel Injection System

The CAV monobloc six element fuel pumps, one on each bank, were of conventional type, driven through vernier couplings with fuel fed via filters and transfer pump. Each pump had a three-weight mechanical governor, connected together via a hydraulic relay system designed by Perkins, using oil pressure from the main engine system. The system could be balanced bank-to-bank and allowed single lever control.

A mechanical stop control linkage was fitted to move each control rack to the 'no-fuel' position.

Cold Starting System

Each induction manifold was equipped with twin 12-volt hot wire heating plugs, connected in series and taking 30 amps of current, with a heating time of around 15 seconds. A 'Ki-gas' pump was used to deliver fuel oil to two sprayers in each manifold, delivering a fuel mist to each incandescent heating element: ignition of this spray with the twin starter motors actuated fed hot air to the cylinders. With the engine warm, no starting aid was necessary for a restart.

Lubrication System

Oil from the 9.5-gallon wet sump was drawn by the gear-type pumps through a gauze strainer and fed under pressure through a twin-element filter and cooler to a high pressure rail located above the camshaft tunnel and running the length of the engine. From this rail high pressure oil was directed to the main-bearing caps to feed main and big-end bearings: splash lubrication of pistons and gudgeon pins was augmented by a jet spray to the cylinder liners. The camshaft bearings and the hydraulic governor were also fed full pressure oil, whilst oil fed through a pressure-reducing valve went to the overhead valve gear and the supercharger gearbox. A pressure feed to the front case provided lubrication to the complex gear train.

(To present-day engineers the plethora of pipes and connections involved in this system will look uninviting; the potential for leaks and weeps of lubricant is readily apparent!)

Dimensions and Performance

Overall length (including gearbox)	9ft 6.875 in	(2,918 m)
Overall height	4ft 5 in	(1,340m)
Overall width	3ft 7.75 in	(1,112m)
Crankshaft centre to highest point	2ft 9.75 in	(0,857 m)
Crankshaft centre to lowest point	1ft 7.25 in	(0,489 m)

Weight, including auxiliaries, side rails, gearbox and dynamo   4750 lbs

Maximum Military Rating	1000 BHP at 2300 RPM
Emergency Rating	850 BHP at 2300 RPM
Maximum Continuous Rating	643 BHP at 2000 RPM
Cruise	492 BHP at 1750 RPM
B.S.F.C.	0.375 lbs/BHP/hr

After the end of the war, there were thoughts of marketing this engine for rail traction and other high-power applications, or for generator sets. There was some low-key advertising and an article which appeared in The Oil Engine of May 1946. In the event, no engines were sold and the only engines kept were installed in a power house at the Eastfield Factory as emergency generator sets, where they remained until the 1980s, when that area of the site was demolished, having been sold off to Sainsbury's for a supermarket. The engines were sold for scrap; the only one now remaining is a carcase, no longer capable of running.

As an example of what could be done under wartime conditions, this virtually unknown engine is a fine demonstration. Although various comments over the years have suggested that this engine remained on the secret list until well after the war, this was not actually the case. Certainly during the war years its existence, and intended use, was carefully concealed just in case word should somehow leak out and attract hostile action.

This engine was developed in 1938 in response to a request from the Air Ministry for an engine with greater power than the P6, which had been accepted for marine applications for the Services. From the start of design to first engine running on Test took less than six months, with the engine being designated 'S' to signify its origin for 'Service' use. The need was for a compact engine producing around 120bhp; this was achieved by stretching the cylinder bore to 4.375 inches while retaining the 5-inch stroke of the 'P' series engines.

Cylinder Block/Crankcase

Formed of a very rigid one-piece casting, produced in chromium-iron alloy. As with the P6, this block extended to the centre-line of the crankshaft, with water-cooling to the main bearing scantlings.

Crankshaft

A fully-balanced crankshaft with integral balance weights, forged from nickel chrome molybdenum steel with bearing surfaces hardened by the 'Tocco' process. Supported in the crankcase in seven steel bearing caps. The steel shell bearings were lined with lead-bronze material. The crankshaft was fully drilled for lubrication to main and big-end bearings, fed via drillings in the cylinder block.

Camshaft

Carried high up on the right-hand side of the cylinder block casting, supported in four bearings and running partially submerged in lubricating oil.

Cylinder Heads

Two cylinder heads were used, each being a one-piece casting of chromium cast iron catering for three cylinders. Two valves per cylinder were used, with tappets located in bores in the head, actuating the valves via rocker levers. The valve gear was the subject of British Patent 404943, whilst the modified 'Aeroflow' combustion system was the subject of Patent 486208.

Connecting Rods

High duty alloy steel 'H' section rods used, similar to the P series.

Piston Assemblies

Flat-topped cast aluminium pistons were used, with fully-floating gudgeon pins secured by circlips. Three compression rings were fitted, with two oil scraper rings, one above and one below the gudgeon pin.

Fuel Injection Equipment

A CAV injection pump of in-line type was fitted, with a pneumatic governor connected to the intake manifold venturi. The CAV injectors were mounted vertically in the cylinder head, and were of the two-hole type.

Lubrication System

A high-pressure pump provided lubrication, driven through spiral gears from the fuel pump drive shaft. The system featured a pressure relief valve and a high capacity full-flow filter, mounted accessibly on the engine.

Timing Gear

The drive to camshaft and fuel pump shaft was via a triple roller chain, mounted at the front of the engine and driven from a sprocket on the crankshaft nose. An automatic chain tensioning device was fitted. The drive was enclosed in an oil-tight housing, with the fuel pump drive taken through an adaptor fitted at the rear of the casing on the left side.

Manifolding

Common intake and exhaust manifolds were mounted on the right side of the cylinder heads, with water-cooling of the latter for marine use.

Auxiliary Drive

A fully enclosed drive was provided for the dynamo and gear-type water pump.

Flywheel and Starter Motor

The flywheel was mounted at the front of the engine, to allow the engine to be placed low in the boat. The 24-volt CAV starter motor was fitted on the right side, engaging with the starter ring on the flywheel.

Other Features

The engine was fitted with an oil cooler at the rear of the engine. For marine use an epicyclic gearbox for forward and reverse was fitted, featuring a multi-plate clutch and optional reduction gear: this gearbox was bolted to the rear of the engine sump and force-lubricated using the engine oil system.

Brief Technical Data

Bore:	4.375 inches	(111mm)
Stroke:	5.000 inches	(127mm)
Swept volume:	7.35 litres	

Rating:130 BHP at 2,250 RPM (for 2 hours maximum 'overload')

100 BHP at 2,000 RPM (continuous cruising)

Weight:	1,250lbs	(570kg)
Overall length:	65.625 inches	
Overall height:	40.813 inches	
Overall width:	28.500 inches	

These dimensions are quoted as typical, since they varied with specifications and build date.

1.5 THE R6 ENGINE

The R6 came into production in 1953 as the answer to the demand for more power for truck applications. The early advertising literature extolled its virtues as simplicity, accessibility and ease of maintenance along with reliability, economy and ease of starting. After the problems experienced (see book text) the engine was modified and relaunched as the R6 Mark 2, and eventually renamed the Six 340. With the failure of the product to recapture the market, the opportunity of another market in Brazil was taken and the whole production facility exported where the engine was eventually modified to become the 6.357, and later 6.3572, and established a good reputation in line with the original concept.

Cylinder block/crankcase

A monoblock iron casting of high rigidity and strength with a skirt extended to below main bearing cap level. Plain iron dry cylinder liners are fitted and seven main bearing caps are fitted snugly into the crankcase, each being secured by two setscrews.

Cylinder Head

A one-piece alloy iron casting of cross-flow design, incorporating 'Aeroflow' combustion chambers and two valves per cylinder, is clamped to the cylinder block by well-spaced studs. The combustion chambers are closed by detachable caps containing the outer portion of the spherical chamber. A one-piece rocker shaft is mounted on the top of the head with rocker levers actuated by mushroom-headed tappets and short push rods.

Crankshaft

Alloy chrome molybdenum steel forging with seven main bearings, hardened main and big end journals. Shaft statically and dynamically balanced with a rear-end flange for flywheel fixing using six fasteners. End thrust taken up by thrust washers fitted to rear main bearing cap.

Camshaft

As with P-series engines, the camshaft is carried high up on the right-hand side of the engine and supported on four bearing surfaces of generous proportions.

Timing Gear

The camshaft and fuel pump shaft are driven by a triple roller chain from the crankshaft. The drive is fitted with damper pads and an automatic chain tension, and runs in a totally enclosed timing case at the front of the engine. Close adjustment of the camshaft timing is provided for on the camshaft sprocket.

Although the above arrangement applied to the R6 in both marks and to the 6.340, the engine was modified in Brazil to use gear drive for the 6.357 and 6.3572.

Connecting Rods

Light 'H' section nickel chrome molybdenum steel forgings with serrations for location at the split-line. Fitted with thin-wall shells of anti-friction material for the big ends and bronze bushing for the small end.

Pistons

Formed of die-cast aluminium alloy with three compression and one oil ring above the gudgeon pin and one oil control ring below. The fully floating gudgeon pin is retained by circlips.

Lubrication System

High pressure forced lubrication is provided to the main and big end bearings through block and crankshaft drillings, supplied by a gear-type oil pump driven by spur gears from the front of the crankshaft. Lower pressure oil is supplied to the valve gear, rocker shaft and timing chain. The suction pipe picks oil up from the sump through a fine mesh gauze strainer. A full-flow filter with replaceable element in mounted to the outside of the cylinder block.

Cooling System

The fan and water pump are mounted on the cylinder head and driven at 1.3 times engine speed by belt drive from the crankshaft pulley. Cooling water from the pump passes to a rail cast into the top of the cylinder block for distribution to the tops of the cylinders and to the cylinder head.

Fuel Injection Equipment

The in-line injection pump supplies fuel from individual pumping elements to injectors mounted in the cylinder head spraying fuel into the combustion chambers. Two holes in each injector control spray direction to assist the combustion process and ensure easy starting. The CAV injection pump features a pneumatic governor controlled via a venturing in the induction manifold. Idling speed can be controlled from the driver's seat and accelerator pressure is light.

On the 6.357 and 6.3572 the injection pump was changed to the CAV DPA type.

Other Equipment

An exhauster can be fitted in tandem with the fuel pump, driven at half engine speed and providing vacuum for assisting braking systems.

Equipment to assist cold starting consists of a 'Thermostart' device burning fuel in the induction manifold, fitted with a reservoir and feed pipe and controlled in use for starting only through a key switch. Two such heaters can be specified for extreme temperature conditions.

24-volt dynamo, driven by the fan belt, and starter motor provided for vehicle applications.

TECHNICAL DETAILS

R6 and Six 340:

Bore:	4 inches
Stroke:	4.5 inches
Swept volume:	340 cu inches (5,56 litres)
Firing Order:	1, 5, 3, 6, 2, 4
Max Power:	108 BHP at 2,700 RPM
Max Torque:	240 lbf ft at 1600 RPM
Bare weight:	914 lbs.

The L4 engine was introduced in 1953 as a large, sturdy and cost-effective product, specifically aimed at the agricultural, industrial and marine market where a rugged and reliable unit was needed and high specific output was not a consideration. This engine had the proven Perkins patented 'Aeroflow' combustion system but in 1958 a revised version was introduced with direct-injection combustion and called the Four 270D. This was one of the first Perkins engines to feature the CAV DPA distributor-type fuel injection pump and was the first direct-injection product. In later years the engine capacity was increased to 300 and then 318 cubic inches, driven mainly by the requirement of Massey-Ferguson for more power and torque. For these later engines a Lanchester-type dynamic balancer could be specified to reduce the second order vibrations inherent in four-cylinder engines and accentuated by the large cylinder size.

Cylinder Block/Crankcase

A one-piece high duty alloy iron casting, fitted with centrifugally-cast wet cylinder liners, flanged at the top end and fitted with sealing rings at the lower end. The block is skirted to a level below the main bearing caps, improving rigidity and handling. The 4.300 and 4.318 cylinder blocks feature pressed-in dry liners, on some specifications these being chromium-plated for increased corrosion resistance.

Two cover plates are bolted to the right-hand side of the L4 and 4.270D, but the later block on the 4.300/4.318 has only one cover plate. The rear of the block on these later engines has an integral backplate for the flywheel housing, while the front end of the block incorporates extra forward facing lugs and fixing holes to suit tractor backbone frame and front axle attachment.

Crankshaft and Main Bearings

The massive forged alloy steel crankshaft runs in three main bearings on the L4 and 4.270D; the later versions have five main bearings. All feature hardened main and big end bearing surfaces for extended life. The shaft is statically and dynamically balanced, running in replaceable thin wall shell bearings of lead-bronze and white metal material on the early engines and aluminium-tin for the 4.300 and 4.318. The serrated crankshaft nose design allows an axial drive of up to 150 lbs ft torque.

Connecting Rods

Forged alloy steel connecting rods of 'H' cross-section carry replaceable bearings and a lead-bronze small end bush.

Piston Assemblies

Aluminium pistons are fitted with three compression rings and two oil control rings, and have fully-floating gudgeon pins. For the 4.270D and subsequent direct injection engines the piston crown features a toroidal combustion chamber with central pip.

Timing arrangement

The low-mounted camshaft and fuel injection pump are gear-driven from the crankshaft. The gear train, contained within a separate timing case and cover bolted to the front of the cylinder block, features an optional auxiliary drive for hydraulic pump or other low-power accessory mounted to the right side of the crankcase. Continuous maximum torque of 35 lbs ft is allowed.

Cylinder Head

This is an alloy iron casting secured to the cylinder block by well-spaced studs. The overhead valves are push-rod operated from flat-faced tappets mounted in the cylinder block, with rocker gear mounted on the cylinder head top face. The L4 features the Aeroflow combustion chamber machined in the head and closed by a bolted-on cap. On the other engines the injectors are mounted at an angle so that the injector tip protrudes into the piston crown combustion chamber almost centrally between the valves.

All the cylinder heads are of cross-flow design, with exhaust manifold on the left-hand (fuel pump) side and induction manifold on the right.

Lubrication

On the L4 and 4.270D a gear-type oil pump is secured to the cylinder block and driven by spiral gears from the camshaft, drawing oil from the sump through a strainer and delivering pressured oil via a full-flow filter to drilled passages in the cylinder block, and thence to main and big end bearings. Controlled flow to rocker gear ensures adequate lubrication.

On the 4.300 and 4.318 with the Lanchester balancer in the sump (bolted to the crankcase bottom face and driven at twice engine speed through an idler gear from the crankshaft front end) the oil pump is fitted to the rear face of the balancer and driven from the balancer drive shaft through a muff coupling.

Water Circulation

A centrifugal pump is mounted at the front end of the cylinder block and driven from the crankshaft by vee-belt. Internal water passages in head and block ensure vigorous water flow to combustion chamber and atomiser seating, plus adequate flow around the cylinders. Temperature control is via a thermostat mounted in the head. Cooling fan mounted on the water pump nose.

Fuel Injection Equipment

The fuel pump is flange mounted on to the rear face of the timing case. On the L4 the in-line CAV pump is fitted with either pneumatic or mechanical governor, while on the later engines the CAV DPA pump was mechanically governed. The fuel lift pump was mounted on the injection pump for the L4, on the upper flange of the timing case for the 4.270D and on the cylinder block driven by an eccentric on the camshaft for the other engines.

Decompressor

Provision is made for optional decompressor gear operating on the exhaust valves of the L4 and 4.270D so that with a suitable flywheel it is possible to hand-start the engine.

Electrical Equipment

12-volt starter motor and dynamo is fitted to the L4. On the later engines the dynamo is replaced by a 12 volt alternator. Cold-starting aids are available, usually 12-volt induction heater and fuel fed 'Thermostart' system.

TECHNICAL DETAILS

Number of Cylinders: 4

Firing order: 1, 3, 4, 2

	L4	4.270D	4.300	4.318
Bore (inches)	4.25	4.25	4.50	4.50
Stroke (inches)	4.75	4.75	4.75	5.00
Swept Volume Cu ins (litres)	269.5 (4,42)	269.5 (4,42)	302.2 (4,95)	318 (5,21)
Compression ratio	17.5 : 1	16 : 1	17.5: 1	16 : 1
Max power (BHP/rpm)	62 at 2000	62 at 2000	76 at 2200	86 at 2200
Max torque (lbs Ft/RPM)	182 at 1050	189 at 1000	228 at 1200	240 at 1300
Bare weight (Typical wt)	660 lbs dry (871 lbs)	680 lbs dry (891 lbs)	787lbs dry, (less f'wheel)	870 lbs (installed)

Applications

The L4 and 4.270D were originally intended for use in agricultural applications where the considerable weight and rugged construction suited tractors and combine harvesters. However, in line with typical Perkins practice for the time, the engines were also adapted for industrial and marine use – finding considerable favour in heavy-duty applications where weight and relatively low specific power output were not detrimental and could be an advantage. Consequently use in applications such as road rollers, loaders and workboats was common.

The 4.300 and 4.318 were used almost exclusively for agricultural applications, most being used by Massey-Ferguson for tractors and combines as the A4.300 and A4.318 (and later A4.3182).

This small engine, originally designated C99, became the 4.99 and was developed into the 4.107 and then the 4.108. Apart from small dimensional differences, and of course power output, the major change between the engines was that the 4.99 and 4.107 featured wet cylinder liners, while the 4.108 incorporated dry liners.

In later life the engine was developed to include turbocharged versions for some industrial uses: although it was field-tested in development light trucks and cars, the turbocharged specification was never released for vehicle use.

Cylinder Block/Crankcase

One-piece high duty cast iron alloy of monoblock construction, crankcase finishing at centre-line of crankshaft. Original versions with centrifugally-cast wet cylinder liners, flanged at the top and fitted with two synthetic rubber sealing rings to facilitate service replacement. Three main bearing caps each fastened to cylinder block with two high tensile setscrews, located to the block by ring dowels.

Cylinder Head and Valves

Cylinder head is a single alloy iron casting with two overhead valves per cylinder, pushrod operated through valve gear mounted on top of the head and enclosed by a pressed-steel cover. Single or twin valve springs fitted, depending upon engine rating and duty, retained by a hardened cap and split conical cotters. Springs seated upon hardened steel pressings. Inlet valve fitted with rubber ring seal, or fitted with oil deflectors depending upon duty. Un-shouldered cast iron valve guides pressed into head.

Combustion System

The Perkins 'Howard Chamber' patented combustion system is of the pre-combustion type, with the chamber formed by machining completely within the head casting and closed by an inserted plug containing the combustion throat connecting the chamber to the cylinder. The pintle-type fuel injectors are mounted vertically above the chamber and secured by two fixings.

Valve Gear

The valves are operated through mushroom type tappets, located in guides in the cylinder block, and pushrods actuating forged steel rocker levers. The rockers are mounted on a single shaft carried above the cylinder head and feature lead-bronze, steel-backed bushes. Tappet adjustment is carried out by a hardened ball-ended screw and locknut at the pushrod end of the rocker lever.

Crankshaft

Forged chrome molybdenum steel with four integral balance weights. Pin and main journals originally induction-hardened, but whole shaft 'tufftrided' on later and higher duty versions for improved wear resistance and improved strength. Rear of shaft machined for thrust location collar, oil thrower and flywheel location flange, with six fixings for flywheel retention. Front of crankshaft keyed for power take-off provision.

Crankshaft end float and thrust taken up by steel-backed copper-lead replaceable thrust washers fitted in cylinder block and rear main bearing cap. Main bearings themselves are aluminium-tin lining on thin-wall steel shells, pre-finished and replaceable.

Camshaft

Cast iron alloy with chill-hardened cams, mounted low down in the right-hand side of the cylinder block. The three bearings are pressure lubricated via internal drillings.

Connecting Rods and Bearings

Con rods are alloy steel stampings with 'H'-section shank, the big-end parting face being inclined at 45 degrees to the rod axis and serrated for cap location. Cap secured to rod by two high tensile setscrews. Big-end bearings are replaceable thin wall aluminium/tin lined, steel backed shells, with small end bearings steel-backed lead bronze lined wrapped bushes.

Timing Gear

The camshaft and fuel injection pump are driven through helical gears from the front end of the crankshaft, one idler gear being included. Provision included for valve and pump timing adjustment, and timing marks incorporated.

The timing gears are enclosed by a pressed steel cover bolted to a steel backplate.

Piston Assemblies

Pistons are of high silicon cast aluminium alloy, fitted with three compression rings and two oil control scraper rings, one below the gudgeon pin. These pins are hollow, being fully floating between retaining circlips. Piston ring designs varied with engine type and duty.

Lubrication System

System pressure fed by a rotor-type pump, driven by spiral gears from the camshaft. An oil strainer is fitted to the pump intake in the sump, the pump feeding through a full-flow filter bolted to the left-hand side of the engine. The oil supply pressure is metered at the camshaft for the rocker gear. A plunger-type relief valve limits maximum oil pressure.

Cooling System

A centrifugal-type circulating pump is fitted to the front of the cylinder block and is belt-driven from the crankshaft. The water outlet is taken through a thermostat housing, cast integrally in the front of the cylinder head. For marine engines, the sea-water pump is of rubber impellor type, mounted on the timing case front cover and driven from the forward end of the fuel injection pump drive.

Lubricating Oil Pan

A pressed steel, cast aluminium or cast iron sump is fitted depending upon customer and duty requirements.

Fuel Injection Equipment

A distributor-type fuel injection pump is flange-mounted on the rear of a cast iron housing on the left-hand side of the cylinder block and driven through a serrated shaft.

Hydraulic or mechanical governing, integral in the pump is specified, dependent upon engine duty and rating. An automatic advance/retard mechanism is incorporated in the injection pump for hydraulically-governed variable speed applications. The diaphragm type fuel lift pump is operated by an eccentric on the engine camshaft via a short pushrod, and is fitted with a hand-priming lever. The atomisers are fitted accessibly on the left-hand side of the engine, whilst provision is made for various positions of paper element fuel filters to suit application needs.

Manifolds

The induction manifold is of die-cast aluminium alloy, fitted to the right-hand side of the cylinder head. Provision is made for air cleaner fitment. The exhaust manifold is of cast iron, fitted on the left-hand side of the engine and upswept away from the fuel pump. For marine applications a water-cooled, jacketed, manifold is specified. For both manifolds options exist to suit customer installations.

Electrical Equipment

Twelve-volt generator and starter motor are specified. The generator is driven from the crankshaft nose and mounted on the right-hand side of the engine. The starter motor can be fitted to either side, flange mounted to the flywheel housing or adaptor plate.

Crankcase Ventilation

A large diameter open breather pipe is attached to the cylinder head cover. Air movement assists in draing fumes form the crankcase and a baffle plate inside the cover prevents oil mist being drawn into the pipe.

Starting Aids

For normal conditions a 'Thermostart' heater is fitted to the induction manifold. For severe conditions alternative systems such as heater plugs or ether atomisers can be fitted.

Technical Details

Parameter	4.99	4.107	4.108
Bore (inches/mm)	3.00/76,2	3.125/79,4	3.125/79,4
Stroke (inches/mm)	3.50/88,9	3.50/88,9	3.50/88,9
Cubic capacity (cu ins/litres)	99/1,621	107.4/1,760	107.4/1,760
Compression Ratio	20:1	22:1	22:1
Firing order	1-3-4-2	1-3-4-2	1-3-4-2
Basic weight (lbs/Kg)	320/145 *	330/150 #	330/150 *
Typical installed weight (lbs/Kg)	440/200 *	456/207 #	450/204 *
Maximum Gross Rating (bhp/rpm)	43/4000 *	41/3000 #	52/4000 *
Maximum Torque (lbf ft/rpm)	73/2250 *	79/1900 #	79/2000 *
Maximum BMEP (psi)	111.2	111	111

* assuming car/light van specification. Other applications heavier

industrial application with steel sump

1.8 6.354 ENGINE FAMILY

This engine was designed in the late 1950s and became the most important 6-cylinder development for Perkins post-war. It was adaptable for use in every market sector and was a mainstay of production from 1961 to the late 1990s.

The original 6.354 design went through many detail changes during its life, including the basic 'mark' changes designated by the .1, .2, .3 and .4 suffices, other models such as the T6 (turbocharged) and C6 (altitude compensated) versions as well as the bore size changes resulting in the 306 and 372 cubic inch capacities. A 335 cubic inch indirect injection version with reduced stroke was developed at Peterborough and produced only in Japan by Toyo Kogyo – it is therefore ignored here. The changes involved in the mark variants are given in brief only.

Over a long production span the power ratings of the 6.354 in its many guises varied widely, up to 300bhp for the 'boat race' turbocharged versions produced in the 60s and 70s.

Cylinder Block

A one-piece alloy iron casting with fully-skirted crankcase extending below the main bearing caps. The original block design featured two inspection covers on the right-hand side, fitted with pressed-steel covers; on the .3 and .4 versions the casting was changed to a 'crenulated' form similar to the 4.236, eliminating the covers. The most distinctive feature of the engine however is the unique drive arrangement on the left side of the block, where a 'turret' is cast to allow the DPA fuel pump to be mounted vertically, driven through a worm and wormwheel from the timing gears.

On all versions the engine features pressed-in cylinder liners with flanged tops on later versions. The .4 engines are fitted with 4-bolt fixings for oil filter and lift pump fixings, improving the sealing compared to the initial 2-bolt arrangements.

Seven main bearing caps are located into the cylinder block using thimbles and setscrews: on turbocharged engines these caps are in spheroidal graphite cast iron material.

The lube oil pump is spigoted to the underside of the auxiliary drive housing, but on .4 versions this is changed to a flanged fixing for improved sealing and alignment.

Cylinder Head

A one-piece alloy iron casting clamped to the cylinder block through 32 studs and nuts (originally 7/16" but later ½" UNF, in later versions replaced by setscrews). On the .4 version an additional 6 fixings were added to improve gasket sealing.

The injectors are fitted to the left-hand side of the head, clamped by two studs and nuts. Two valves are used in each cylinder, with cast inlet and exhaust ports to the right-hand side of the engine; on the .4 types the inlet ports are changed to fully machined to improve consistency of air flow. Valve seat inserts are fitted to all turbocharged versions. The cylinder head gasket varied through the life of the engine, starting as a copper/asbestos design but graduating to more modern and sophisticated materials. A one-piece pressed steel top cover features on all early engines, later versions being changed to iron or aluminium castings: the cover fixing arrangements started with peripheral screws, but moved to a centre post design on the .4 derivatives.

Manifolding

Aluminium induction manifolds of various configurations could be specified, in conjunction with cast iron exhaust manifolds giving a variety of outlet positions, used with induction and exhaust elbows as appropriate. For turbocharged and compensated engines the turbocharger can be fitted on top, to the side or at the rear of the engine, to suit applications requirements: both front- and rear-facing exhaust outlets are available. For vehicle engines air-to-air charge cooling, while on marine specifications water-cooled systems of various types are combined with the closed circuit marine packages, with a raw water pump driven of the auxiliary drive shaft.

Valve Gear

Through the life of the engine double valve springs are used, although the vehicle specification engines uses higher performance, shorter, springs. The original engines use unbushed rockers levers in cast iron; on later versions there is a change to bushed levers, in SG iron and later (.4) in steel levers.

Piston and Rings

The original engine uses an aluminium alloy piston with five rings – three compression and two slotted oil control. There are many variations of ring pack and of piston specification across the engine life and marks, culminating in the use of expansion-controlled pistons on the .4, with three rings only. Armoured top groove pistons are specified on some .2 engines, and on turbocharged engines a larger (1.5") diameter gudgeon pin and oil cooling to the piston underside are specified. The pistons featured a 'pipped' combustion bowl offset to the injector side of the engine.

Connecting Rods

Basic design shared with 4.236 engine. Big end cap located to rod by serrations. Parallel-sided small end bushed used on naturally-aspirated engines with 1.375" diameter gudgeon pin, with wedge-end and 1.5" diameter pin used for turbocharged engines. Drilled shank on conn. rod used on T6.354 engine for piston cooling; this is replaced by cooling jets mounted in cylinder block for later engines.

Crankshaft

Alloy steel forging used for every engine, with seven main bearings. Variations include 'mirror-drilling' for .4 versions (to improve load-carrying capacity of the centre main bearing), non-cold straightened, change of heat treatment from induction hardening of bearing surfaces through tufftriding or 20- and 60-hour nitriding of the shafts to increase strength for higher ratings.

Early engines have 6-bolt fixings for flywheels, later versions have 12-bolt flanges. The rear crankshaft oil seal was changed from a rope seal to lip seal to reduce oil leakage on all engines, while at the front end of the crankshaft the fixing arrangement for the pulley changes from serrations to a 'ringfeder' design to increase front-end drive capability on higher-rated .4 engines.

Timing Gears

The gear train has helical gear teeth, with twin idlers carrying the drive to camshaft and auxiliary drive gears. The standard material for the camshaft gear varies from cast iron to SG iron or steel depending upon duty requirements. A twin stud idler gear hub fixing arrangement for the .4 engines eliminates fretting.

The wormwheel is of phosphor-bronze, mated to a hardened steel wormshaft. The original design used a simple ball bearing arrangement; this was upgraded to a pressure-fed hydraulically-loaded sintered bearing plate to combat early wear problems.

Fuel System

The design of the engine depends upon the CAV DPA fuel pump and its ability to run with the driveshaft vertical. Many developments of the pump were used over the life of the engine: both hydraulically and mechanically governed pumps were used, depending upon the engine speed and the governing characteristics needed. Multi-hole injectors were used, fitted in the cylinder head at an angle to the vertical and spraying fuel directly into the combustion bowl in the piston.

A mechanical fuel lift pump was driven from a lobe on the camshaft, feeding fuel through full flow filters with paper elements: various configurations and types of filter were specified.

Water System

Modifications of water circuit through the cylinder head and block were made on the various 'marks' of engine. All feature a belt-driven water pump in either high or low position, with thermostat control. Higher capacity twin volute pumps are used on turbocharged engines and on all .4 versions.

Oil System

The lube oil pump is driven from the fuel pump drive shaft through a spline shaft. The original pump was replaced by a 16% increased capacity version from the .1 onwards, with a 67% increased capacity unit specified for all turbocharged engines. Full flow filters are fitted, with pressure flow feeding the crankshaft and camshaft bearings and metered flows to the timing gears, rocker shaft and fuel pump drive. On turbocharged engines oil cooling jets spray oil to the underside of the pistons to reduce ring-belt temperatures.

An open breather system is standard on all engines, with a closed breather optional on industrial applications. An oil cooler is standard on turbocharged engines and optional on others, depending upon application needs.

Auxiliaries

The wormdrive shaft extends rearwards allowing an engine speed drive for exhauster, compressor or hydraulic pump, driven through a flexible coupling. A cast pad on the cylinder block allows such auxiliaries to be mounted on a bracket to close axial alignment. A tachometer or hourmeter drive can be fitted to the cover plate on the auxiliary drive, whilst an optional axial drive from the front of the crankshaft can provide up to full engine torque for marine, industrial or vehicle power take-off.

Ratings and Dimensions

Original specification 6.354 vehicle specification:

Overall length (fan to crankshaft flange):	37.53 inches (953mm)
Width:	25.00 inches (635mm)
Height above crank centreline:	21.59 inches (548mm)
Height below crank centreline:	12.06 inches (306mm)
Typical basic weight:	836 lbs (380kg)
Typical installed weight:	1,020 lbs (464kg)

Typical ratings:

Vehicle Power	120 bhp at 2,800 rpm
Torque	260 lbf ft at 1,250 rpm
Agricultural and Industrial Power	104 bhp at 2,400 rpm
Torque	270 lbf ft at 1,200 rpm
Marine Intermittent Power	115 bhp at 2,800 rpm

In view of the very wide range of specifications it is impractical to give complete details. Turbocharged engines reached ratings of 150bhp at 2,600rpm for vehicle and up to 300shp for marine raceboat versions.

The original 4.236 engine was designed to have two configurations of cylinder block to suit the vehicle/industrial and tractor specifications respectively. Although originated in 236 cubic inch swept volume initially, the engine gradually spawned a series of derivatives with alternative capacities, namely the 4.248, 4.224, 4.212 and 4.204.

The 248, 212 and 204 cubic inch versions were originated for Massey-Ferguson, the differentiation of engine swept volume being a way of limiting engine output to suit tractor models, rather than use derated engines capable of being 'tweeked' to increase power. Later the 4.248 in particular was used by other customers needing increased power compared to the 4.236.

The 4.224 was a variant produced only by Japanese licensee Toyo Kogyo, being a higher speed indirect-injection version solely for the Japanese market. (A similar capacity engine but with high-speed direct injection configuration was developed in the late 1970s and identified as the 4.22X. Although it was tested in vehicles in the UK and Brazil it did not reach production but gave valuable initial experience in high-speed DI concepts.)

Derivatives of the 4.236 with spark ignition and carburetion provided gasoline and LPG production engines for MF tractors and various industrial users, predominantly for forklift trucks.

Turbocharged variants were developed for all applications of the 4.236 except marine: the ratings offered included 'altitude-compensated' and mildly-blown versions to suit customers' requirements. There were many different ratings for these engine variants, impossible to detail here: therefore the ratings given in the table are representative of the typical maximum powers.

Cylinder Block/Crankcase

Monobloc construction, made from high duty cast iron. The sides of the crankcase extend below the centre-line of the crankshaft to form a stiffening skirt and mounting flange for the oil sump. In the case of the tractor cylinder block design the rear of the block forms an integral housing flange for direct connection to the transmission housing: the front face also being modified to attach to the tractor front axle carrier. On the 'vehicle' block the rear face is simple and bolts to suitable flywheel housings, whilst the lower front corners of the side faces have machined and tapped flanges for mounting attachment.

Both blocks are fitted with centrifugally-cast dry liners, initially straight but later with a flange locating in a recess at the top of the block. The cast water jacket extends the full length of the liners and carries water round the whole periphery of each cylinder.

Five main bearing caps are located into the cylinder block, each using locating thimbles and two high tensile steel setscrews.

Cylinder Head and Valves

The one-piece cylinder head casting of alloy iron is secured to the block by studs and nuts (later setscrews) clamping a wire-mesh-reinforced asbestos gasket. The inlet ports are fully machined to provide consistent air flow and swirl. One inlet and one exhaust valve are provided per cylinder, with valve guides integral with the head casting. The valves are operated through overhead rocker levers fitted on a single shaft, the whole assembly being enclosed within a pressed steel cover. The valve seats are machined directly into the cylinder head casting.

Single or twin valve springs are fitted depending upon engine duty, with valve stem seals or oil deflectors as applicable. The valve springs are retained by hardened caps and split conical cotters.

Valve Gear

The cast-iron rocker levers are actuated via steel pushrods and mushroom tappets from the camshaft mounted low down on the right-hand side of the cylinder block.

Lubrication for the rocker gear is supplied via a pressure-reducing slot in one camshaft journal to the hollow rocker shaft. Tappet adjustment is by adjusting screws with hardened ball end and lock-nut, on the pushrod end of the rocker lever.

Combustion System

Direct injection is used, with the combustion chamber formed in the piston crown. Fuel is injected directly into each cylinder via multi-hole injector assemblies mounted on the left-hand side of the engine at an angle to the vertical.

Crankshaft

This is forged from chrome molybdenum steel, with integral balance weights on the vehicle (high-speed) version and a large flange at the rear end for flywheel securing. Main and big end bearing surfaces induction hardened for wear resistance. The crankshaft end-float and thrust are taken up by two split 360 degree thrust washers, located on the centre main bearing cap and cylinder block.

A cast-iron pulley is driven from the front end of the crankshaft through serrations and secured by a setscrew. (Later versions use a three-bolt fixing arrangement, often with 'Ringfeder' clamping for front-end drive capability.)

Main Bearings

The five main bearings are replaceable steel-backed thin wall shells, with aluminium-tin lining pre-finished to size.

Camshaft

High duty cast iron with chill-hardened cams, mounted low on the right-hand side of the block and supported by three bearings, each pressure lubricated. Cams and tappets are splash lubricated.

Timing Drive

The camshaft and fuel pump are driven from the front end of the crankshaft through helical gears with one idler gear. The timing gears are enclosed by a one-piece timing case, with cast cover. Most engines use aluminium die-castings for these components although cast-iron alternatives are used on heavy duty versions, with a special heavy duty idler gear and hub to accept auxiliary drives to one or two hydraulic pumps. A pressed steel cover plate allows access to the fuel pump gear for timing adjustment.

Connecting Rods

'H' section molybdenum steel stampings with replaceable, thin-wall, pre-finished steel backed big end bearings with aluminium/tin linings. Small end bushes are wrapped, steel-backed with lead bronze material, machined to size. The bearing caps are located to the caps by serrations, mating faces at right angles to the rod centre-line, and secured by two high tensile bolts and locknuts.

Pistons and Rings

Pistons are cast from high silicon aluminium alloy, each fitted with three compression rings and either one or two oil control rings, dependent upon the engine duty or specification. Fully floating gudgeon pins located in the piston by circlips. The combustion chamber is of toroidal form with a flat bottom rather than a 'pipped' shape. The spark-ignition variants also used an in-piston combustion chamber of wider and deeper profile to give the requisite lower compression ratio.

Lubrication System

Full pressure feed provided by a rotor type oil pump, mounted on the front bearing cap and driven by the crankshaft gear in the case of the 'vehicle' specification engine. On tractor specification engines the oil pump forms part of the secondary balancer assembly (q.v.).

An oil strainer is fitted to the suction pipe, the pump delivering oil through a full-flow filter on the left-hand side of the engine and thence to a drilled pressure rail running the full length of the block. A spring-loaded plunger type relief valve controls maximum oil pressure. Various application variations are provided for oil filter type and positioning: in later engines the paper element filter in a steel bowl was replaced by a 'spin-on' element filter. Additional options for turbocharged engines and variants with hydraulic pumps are available, on the vehicle block the filter can be fitted on the right-hand side as an alternative.

Lubricating Oil Sump

A variety of aluminium alloy or cast iron sumps are available dependent upon application, these allowing for different working angularities, axle clearance, etc. In the case of the tractor specification, the cast iron sump forms part of the stressed tractor frame, carrying mountings to front and rear for axle carrier and transmission respectively. Oil dipstick positions on either side of the engine are provided, and on some specifications a sump-mounted oil filler may be fitted.

Secondary Balancer

For applications where the engine is solidly mounted into the machine, such as agricultural tractors, the engine can be fitted with a second-order, Lanchester-type balancer. This is mounted to the underside of the cylinder block and driven from the crankshaft gear at twice engine-speed. The unit consists of two contra-rotating shafts carrying balance weights, timed to provide counterbalance to the second order out-of-balance forces exerted by a four-cylinder engine. During the life of the engine type a number of different balancer designs were used, each type incorporating a lubricating oil pump fitted to the balancer assembly.

Cooling System

Water is circulated through the cylinder block and head by a centrifugal water pump mounted on the front of the engine and driven by belt from the crankshaft pulley. A water rail is cast on the front left-hand side of the block and water exits via a thermostat housing and outlet on the front of the cylinder head. A steel-bladed cooling fan can be mounted on the water pump pulley when required.

For marine engines a 'raw water' circulating pump and heat-exchanger arrangement provide cooling for the closed engine water system: over the life of the engine family a number of variants of the marine engine featured different cooling system designs.

Fuel Injection Equipment

The rotary distributor-type fuel injection pump is flange-mounted horizontally at the rear of the timing case on the left-hand side of the engine. The fuel pump incorporates either a hydraulic or mechanical governor and may also feature an automatic timing advance/retard mechanism. During the life of the engine many specifications of injection pump were used, most being from CAV but others from Bosch. Paper element fuel filters are fitted on brackets conveniently placed to suit installation and servicing needs: again various specifications were used during the life of the engine type.

A fuel lift pump with hand primer lever is fitted to the right-hand side of the cylinder block, driven from an eccentric on the engine camshaft. The injectors are mounted very accessibly on the left-hand side of the cylinder head at an angle to the vertical, spraying through multi holes directly into the piston combustion chamber.

Crankcase Ventilation

An open breather pipe extends from the cylinder head top cover down the left side of the engine. Baffling within the cover prevents oil mist carry-over and on some engines an expansion box is fitted.

Induction and Exhaust Manifolding

An induction manifold cast from aluminium alloy is fitted to the right side of the cylinder head, with connections suitable for a variety of air cleaners. A variety of manifolds allow for installation variation, including variations of turbocharger fitment. A cast-iron exhaust manifold is also fitted to the right side of the cylinder head and allows again for a number of variants in shape, able to carry also outlet adaptors.

On marine engines a water-cooled exhaust manifold is fitted.

Electrical Equipment

12-volt equipment is standard, the generator being fitted to the right-hand side of the engine and belt-driven from the crankshaft and water pump pulleys. The early engines used dynamos, these being superseded by alternators in later versions.

The starter motor is fitted to either left of right side of the vehicle engine, depending upon the housing or backplate specified. For the tractor block version the starter motor position is predetermined by the cast adaptor, which has a position on the left-hand side.

Power Take-off

Provision is made for driving an exhauster, compressor or hydraulic pump at the rear of the timing case on the left side of the engine below the fuel injection pump. Special timing case and idler gear provision may apply for higher power take-off requirements. For the marine engine a stub shaft extension is fitted to the crankshaft nose to drive auxiliaries.

Other Options

Drive arrangements are available for tachometer and hourmeter options. Standard cold-starting aid is via 'Thermostart' heater fitted to the induction manifold, but optional ether start equipment is available for cold climate territories.

1.9 4.236 ENGINE FAMILY (Continued)

Technical Details

Engine type	4.236	4.204	4.212	4.248
Bore (inches/mm)	3.875/98,4	3.60/91,4	3.875/98,4	3.975/100,9
Stroke (inches/mm)	5.00/127,0	5.00/127,0	4.5/114,3	5.00/127,0
Cubic capacity (cu ins/litres)	235.9/3.86	203.58/3.336	212.3/3.48	248.2/4.06
Compression ratio	16:1	16:1	16:1	16:1
Firing order	1-3-4-2	1-3-4-2	1-3-4-2	1-3-4-2
Basic weight (lbs/Kgs)	580/263 *	720/326 #	595/270	595/270
Typical installed weight	700/318 *	?		
Maximum gross rating (bhp/rpm)	80/2800 *	56,5/2000 #	62/2200#	81/2500#
Maximum torque (lbf ft/rpm)	193/1400 *	161/1250 #		
Maximum BMEP (p.s.i.)	123.5 *	119 #		

* vehicle engine (other applications: ratings lower and weights heavier)

\# tractor engine

1.10 V8.510, V8.540 , V8.605 & V8.640

The first production engine was of 510 cubic inches (8.36 litres) displacement, followed by later versions of 540 cu in, 605 cu in and finally 640 cu in. All engines are V8 configuration, with 90 degree angle between banks. Turbocharged versions were produced for some variants.

Cylinder Block and Crankcase

Integrally cast in high duty cast iron with a skirt extending below the crankshaft centre-line. Left bank offset 1.34 inches forward to allow opposing connecting rods to fit side by side on crank pins. Dry cylinder liners with top flanges locating flush in the block.

Cylinder Heads

Two identical heads secured to block by setscrews with steel gasket interposed. Machined inlet ports provide consistent air flow from the induction manifold running down the inside of the vee, with exhaust manifolds fed by ports on the outside of the engine.

The two-valve design features rocker shafts and aluminium covers for pairs of cylinders on each bank. The valves run in cast iron guides pressed into the heads, with inserts for the exhaust valve seats and twin springs for each valve.

Valve Gear

The chilled iron camshaft runs centrally in five bearings in the block, operating the valves through steel pushrods and mushroom headed tappets mounted in pairs in carriers bolted into the block. Steel rocker levers are fitted with bushes and carry adjusting screws at the tappet end. Lubrication is by intermittent feed from the camshaft bearings.

Crankshaft

A chrome molybdenum steel forging with hollow crankpins set at 90 degrees, with balance weights bolted to webs 1, 2, 3, 6, 7 and 8. All pins and journals induction hardened with rear oil seal mounted on the rear flange, which has a 12-bolt fixing pattern for the flywheel. The serrated nose of the crankshaft carries a combined pulley/torsional vibration damper. The end float and thrust from the crankshaft is taken up by thrust washer fitted at the centre main bearing.

Main bearing and caps

Five cast iron bearing caps are secured to the cylinder block by vertical bolts and horizontal cross bolts to absorb operating loads. The main bearings of thin-wall type are fitted into the caps and are slotted and grooved for lubrication distribution.

Timing drive

The helical gear train at the front of the engine drives camshaft and air compressor through one main idler: the fuel pump drive being taken from the rear of the compressor. (Later engines feature a side-by-side drive for pump and auxiliaries.) The lubricating oil pump is driven from a small idler below the crankshaft gear. The timing case is in two pieces, the upper of aluminium and the lower cast iron.

Pistons and Rings

Pistons of high silicon aluminium alloy carry four piston rings above the gudgeon pin and feature an offset toroidal combustion chamber and recesses for valve clearance. (Later engines used 'Alfin' insert for the top ring groove.)

Connecting Rods

Hgh tensile steel stampings with big end parting line inclined at 37.5 degrees to rod axis to allow removal through the cylinder bores. The cap location is by a 'dog tooth' serration and each cap is secured by two high tensile bolts. The big end bearings are thin wall shells with a lead bronze bush for the small end.

Lubrication System

The gear type pump mounted below the front main bearing cap feeds oil to a separate relief valve and via internal drillings to a block mounted oil cooler and full flow filter. Oil is fed to the main bearing housings and thence to the big ends, with separate feed to camshaft and timing train.

Fuel Injection Equipment

Simms in-line fuel pump located between the banks, feeding injectors in each cylinder located on the outside of the cylinder heads. Pump fitted with an all-speed mechanical governor, a mechanical advance mechanism and excess fuel device for cold starting. A diaphragm type fuel lift pump is driven form the fuel pump camshaft and feeds fuel through paper element filters fitted at the rear of the engine. The V8.605 used a Sigma rotary fuel pump and injectors fitted into copper sleeves in the cylinder head.

Cooling System

A centrifugal type water pump is belt-driven from the front of the engine from the crankshaft pulley, feeding water to the front of each cylinder bank. Water returns via twin thermostat housings on the front of each cylinder head.

Auxiliaries

The compressor driven in-line with the fuel pump can be deleted and a drive housing fitted. The 24-volt alternator is belt-driven with the water pump while provision is made to drive a power steering pump from the timing gears. If required an impulse-type or mechanical tachometer drive can be fitted.

Dimensions and Ratings

V8.510 . . . . bore and stroke
4.25 inches by 4.50 inches. . . . . (108mm by 114.3mm)
V8.540 . . . . bore and stroke
4.25 inches by 4.75 inches. . . . . (108mm by 120,7mm)
V8.605 . . . . bore and stroke
4.50 inches by 4.75 inches. . . . .(114.3mm by 120.7mm)
V8.640 . . . . bore and stroke
4.63 inches by 4.75 inches. . . . .(117.6mm by 120.7mm)

Basic dimensions for a typical V8.510:

Overall length – water pump pulley to crank flange . . . . 36.55 inches (922mm)

Overall width – across exhaust manifolds . . . . 32.50 inches (826mm)

Height above crank centreline . . . . 23.06 inches (585.8mm)

Height below crank centreline . . . . 14.81 inches (376mm)

Basic weight, typical vehicle engine . . . . 1340 lbs
(607kg)

Installed weight, typical vehicle engine . . . . 1550 lbs
(703kg)

V8.510 vehicle rating

Power	170 bhp at 2,800 rpm
Torque	378 lbf ft at 1,600 rpm

V8.540 vehicle rating

Power	180 bhp at 2,600 rpm
Torque	412 lbf ft at 1,600 rpm

V8.605 vehicle rating

Power	205 bhp at 2,600 rpm
Torque	460 lbf ft at 1,600 rpm

V8.640 vehicle rating

Power	215 bhp at 2,600 rpm
Torque	488 lbf ft at 1,600 rpm

TV8.640 vehicle rating

Power	250 bhp at 2,600 rpm
Torque	600 lbf ft at 1,600 rpm

In view of the wide variation of specifications, no other weights, dimensions and powers are useful in this summary.

1.11 4.154 & 6.247 ENGINES

These two engine types were developed in conjunction with Toyo Kogyo in Japan and are both indirect injection units fitted with the 'Howard' combustion system. The engines feature conventional Perkins design details with cast-iron cylinder head, cylinder block of shell moulded spheroidal-graphite cast iron and fully-balanced forged steel crankshaft. The timing train is all gears driving a low mounted camshaft and fuel pump mounted in the rear of the timing case. The two valves per cylinder are driven through push rods and forged steel rocker levers. A rotary oil pump is driven from the timing train and a conventional centrifugal water pump by belt from the crankshaft pulley. Both engines were intended for use on vehicle applications, although the 4.154 has been used in industrial equipment.

Dimensions:

6.247 6-cylinder in-line of 247.3 cu inches (4.05 litres) swept volume.

Bore and stroke	3.62 inches by 4 inches	(92 mm by 101.6 mm)
Typical bare weight	643 lbs	(292kg)
Overall length	32.8 inches	(834.1mm)
Overall width	23.1 inches	(588 mm)

4.154 4 cylinder in line of 153.9 cu ins (2.523 litres) swept volume.

Bore and stroke	3.5 inches by 4 inches	(88.9 mm by 101.6 mm)
Typical bare weight	430 lbs	(195kg)

Ratings:
6.247 vehicle

Power	101 bhp at 3600 rpm
Max Torque	163 lbf ft at 2500 rpm

4.154 vehicle

Power	70 bhp at 3600 rpm
Max Torque	113 lbs ft at 2000 rpm

The engine was developed as a joint venture between Perkins and the Austin Rover Group Limited, based upon the envelope of the 2-litre 'O' Series ARG engine and utilising some of the foundry and machining equipment of that engine. The design and development was carried out by Perkins, using experience and technology allowing the production of the world's first high-speed direct injection passenger car diesel.

Alongside the specific requirements for ARG, the engine was designed to be used for other automotive, industrial and marine applications for which 500 Series would be the designation. The name 'Prima' was chosen by Perkins employees in a competition, while in ARG the engine was designated as 'MDi'.

Two versions were produced, a naturally aspirated 'Prima 65', rated 62bhp at 4,500rpm, and the 'Prima 80T', turbocharged and giving 80bhp at 4,500rpm.

Engine Specification

Cylinder Block – cast iron, specially designed to accept diesel loadings.

Cylinder Head – gravity die-cast aluminium, with inserted high tensile iron valve guides and heat resisting valve seats.

Crankshaft – five-bearing forged steel with integral balance weights.

Valve Gear – overhead camshaft of chilled iron, operating directly on to the valves via steel tappets.

Timing Drive – heavy duty glass-fibre reinforced neoprene toothed belt, 30mm wide, driving camshaft and fuel pump.

Pistons – cast aluminium alloy with expansion control by steel inserts. Top ring groove with austenitic iron reinforcement. Three low friction piston rings above the gudgeon pin. Combustion chamber formed in the piston crown, of re-entrant shape and featuring bowl edge armouring.

Connecting Rods – forged steel.

Fuel Injection Equipment – Bosch EPVE rotary fuel injection pump with KSB modulating cold start control system. CAV multihole injectors with two stage injection.

Cold Starting Equipment – glow plugs giving 'instant heat' fitted in cylinder head and protruding directly into the combustion bowl.

Turbocharger – on Prima 80T only, Garrett T2 turbocharger with wastegate boost control.

Dimensions and Ratings (vehicle engines)

Overall length:	517 mm	(20.4 inches)
Overall width:	567 mm	(22.32 inches)
Overall height:	630 mm	(24.8 inches)
with standard sump	655 mm	(25.8 inches)
with deep well sump		
Weight:		
Naturally aspirated	125kg	
Turbocharged	132kg	
Engine power:		
Naturally aspirated		46kW (62 bhp) at 4,500 rpm
Turbocharged		59.8 kW (80 bhp) at 4,500 rpm
Maximum torque:		
Naturally aspirated		122 Nm (90 lbf ft) at 2,500 rpm
Turbocharged		154 Nm (114 lbf ft) at 2,500 rpm

The Phaser (vehicle versions) and 1000 Series (all other applications) were developed as the replacements for the 6.354 and 4.236 engine ranges, providing latest technology products meeting all legislative requirements in the 1980s and 90s. The true family of products includes naturally aspirated, turbocharged and turbocharged intercooled versions of 4- and 6-cylinder engines covering a power range of 65 to 134kW (87 to 180bhp) at launch – later versions provided increased power.

Computer technology was used in producing cylinder block and head designs optimised for strength and rigidity, without excess weight. The combustion system was developed using laser-doppler anemometry and computer techniques to optimise performance and efficiency. Other engine components benefited from best practices and latest materials to increase reliability and durability.

Engine Specification

Cylinder block – rigid deep-skirted cast-iron block and crankcase, with dry cylinder liners silicon carbide honed for long life and low oil consumption.

Cylinder head – one piece cast iron with pressed-in valve guides and valve seat inserts (turbo engines only).

Crankshaft – chrome molybdenum steel forging. Viton rubber front and rear oil seals.

Pistons – aluminium with expansion control struts and Alfin top groove insert. Combustion bowl of patented 'Quadram' form cast into piston crown.

Connecting rods- forged molybdenum steel.

Water pump – gear driven from helical timing gears.

Turbocharged engines feature integral oil cooler and oil spray cooling of the pistons.

Dimensions and Performance

Phaser Turbo engines	6 cylinder	4 cylinder
Overall length (typical)	945 mm (37.2 ins)	711 mm (28.0 ins)
Overall width (typical)	755 mm (29.7 ins)	696 mm (27.4 ins)
Overall height (typical)	854 mm (33.6 ins)	774 mm (30.5 ins)
Weight (bare)	419 kg (922 lbs)	279 kg (614 lbs)
Max power	134 kW (180 bhp)	89.5 kW (120 bhp)
Max torque	581 Nm (429 lbf ft)	387 Nm (285 lbf ft)
1000 series ratings vary widely with duty etc.		

THE ORIGIN OF THE PERKINS SYMBOL

In the early years of F. Perkins Ltd, the Company name was displayed simply and in block capitals. The typeface used seems to have varied on the surviving examples of the early brochures, the common phrase 'PERKINS DIESEL ENGINES' at least trying to put a basic message across when diesels were a novelty in light vehicles.

The first symbol to appear, in 1938, was of a shield bearing a stylised 'P' with a laurel wreath and the word DIESEL: there was some association of this with the speed records set at Brooklands and the award from Russia.

In the late 1930s there was apparently a competition for a symbol set to all employees by Captain Alan Richardson, one of the Directors. The winning symbol was a six-sided star, incorporating the 'P' in the centre and DIESEL beneath. However, it was pointed out that this had strong religious connotations as the Jewish 'Star of David', and its use in publicity was quickly abandoned, although some copies survive.

As a result a new symbol was proposed, apparently by Laurie Hancock (who was responsible for publicity and advertising), which took the form of the four circles and the diamond still used today. There have been various 'explanations' for this symbol over the years, to the point where a level of folklore has grown up.

The writer is loath to debunk these suggestions, for instance:

'A square deal all round'

'Service in every corner of the earth'

'The sign represents the four major application sectors – vehicle, agricultural, industrial and marine'

(There are other, less printable, interpretations too!)

Other explanations for its inspiration reside in the use of the quatrefoil as ornamentation in churches, famously the Duomo floor and the Baptistery doors in Florence, and in various windows in Peterborough and elsewhere. In fact, the quatrefoil was a common ornamentation in the Late Gothic and Early Renaissance periods, appearing in windows, tracery, as a frame for sculpture and on goldsmiths' work. It is possible with imagination to ascribe further religious significance to the quatrefoil.

The explanation offered by Laurie Hancock himself, by letter to Perkins in 1982, is simple and closely linked to the origins of the Company:

'I personally designed the present "sign" or "symbol", denoting the four men and a boy (who formed the original Company), namely Charles Wallace Chapman, George Derek Perks, Francis Arthur Perkins and Captain Alan Richardson. The boy in question was Edward Marvill.' Later in the letter he comments: 'My design of the present symbol had nothing to do with embellishments of these cathedrals. I learnt about them sometime afterwards.'

The symbol as originally used had a thin outline, with the stylised 'P' in the centre. It was used by itself and the Company name appeared in a heavy italic script for some years. Early radiator badges also carried the name across the centre. The use of the simple symbol with thicker outline and always with the 'Perkins' in set script and to set rules and procedures came in the 1970s.

Whichever explanation you prefer, the Perkins logotype now forms one of the most long-lived, well-known and respected identifications in engineering today.

INDEX

INDEX

INDEX

Aveling and Barford, *A Hundred Years of Road Rollers*

Barford, Edward, *Reminiscences of a Lance Corporal of Industry*

Chapman, Charles W, *The Story of Perkins Diesels* (unpublished)

Collins, W N and Van Emden, R, *Last Man Standing*

Cook, Peter, *Massey at the Brink*

Encyclopaedia Britannica Year Books

Hancock, L W J, *The Perkins Story*

J L International Publications, *Chronicle of the 20th Century*

Key, Michael, *The Blackstone Collection (3)*

Muthaih, S, *Getting India on the Move*

Neufeld, E P, A *Global Corporation*

Porteous, David, *The Perkins Story*

Preston, J M, *Aveling and Porter Limited*

Pugh, Peter, *The Magic of a Name (Vol 1)*

Whitehead, R A, *Garrett Diesel Tractors*

In addition I have drawn freely upon many publications from the Perkins group of companies,   especially the following:

Perkins News (1946 to 1962)

Perkins Diesel Echo

Perkins Echo

Help from other archives include those of:

Gosport Navy Museum

The Imperial War Museum. Duxford

The RAF Museum. Hendon.

Emailed memories from Rudy Jansa, Bill Winemaster, Jorge Silveira and Ary Favero have been important in tracing the history of the companies in the USA and Brazil.